INTERNATIONAL SERIES OF MONOGRAPHS IN

Earth Sciences

EDITOR: DEAN EARL INGERSON

(Department of Geology, University of Texas, Austin 12, Texas, U.S.A.)

Volume 22

RESEARCH ON THE NATURE
OF MINERAL-FORMING SOLUTIONS

Research on the Nature of Mineral-forming Solutions

with special reference
to Data from Fluid Inclusions

by

N. P. YERMAKOV and OTHERS

Translated by

V. P. SOKOLOFF

Edited by

EDWIN ROEDDER
U. S. Geological Survey

PERGAMON PRESS

OXFORD · LONDON · EDINBURGH · NEW YORK
PARIS · FRANKFURT

Pergamon Press Ltd., Headington Hill Hall, Oxford
4 & 5 Fitzroy Square, London W.1
Pergamon Press (Scotland) Ltd., 2 & 3 Teviot Place, Edinburgh 1
Pergamon Press Inc., 122 East 55th St., New York 10022
Pergamon Press GmbH, Kaiserstrasse 75, Frankfurt-am-Main

First edition 1965

Library of Congress Catalog Card No. 64-18437

Printed in Poland

1316

PART I

STUDIES OF MINERAL-FORMING SOLUTIONS

N. P. YERMAKOV

Executive Editor
V. S. SOBOLEV

Translated from

Temperatures and State of Aggregation

*Publishing House of the A. M. Gorkii Memorial
State University of Kharkov*

Contents of Part I

Editor's Preface

PROF. N. P. YERMAKOV is the leading student of fluid inclusions in the Soviet Union. This book, which is the first to be published on the subject in any language, is a summary of his own work, and that of his students, at L'vov State University. These studies aided in the exploration for ore deposits in the Soviet Union, and he received the coveted Stalin Prize, the highest Soviet scientific award, for this work. The book contains a large amount of observational data otherwise difficult to obtain, and although there may well be disagreement on some of Prof. Yermakov's interpretations,* it was felt that a translation would be of considerable value to English-speaking scientists. Particularly interesting are the numerous observations on the behavior of inclusions in the region of the critical temperature, indicating the existence of highly concentrated fluids in nature. Included here are such phenomena as the re-solution, on heating, of large amounts of "captive" minerals precipitated from the inclusion fluids after trapping; inclusion liquid-gas homogenization temperatures considerably above the critical temperature for pure water; and the formation of two immiscible liquids from the remaining liquid phase just before the critical temperature is reached during filling temperature determinations. Considerable evidence is given also for changes in the relative temperatures of deposition of individual zones in single zoned crystals, and in the deposition of the different stages in complex ores. The first 100 pages of the original Russian version of this book are mainly a review of the pertinent literature; as this material is well covered by several summaries in English, and as Prof. Yermakov himself suggested that the translation begin with page 101, the Chairman of the Translation Committee of the Geochemical Society, Prof. Earl Ingerson, asked that this be done. This is a translation, and not a *précis,* so no attempt has been made to reorganize or abbreviate the original text.

In most places where some measure of interpretation by the translator or the editor had to be used, or where numerical inconsistencies were apparent, these are pointed out by footnotes or by brackets in the text, but it is not possible to eliminate all ambiguity in such a translation without extensive conferences with the author.

Since the original Russian publication of this book, there has been a large amount of research on fluid inclusions in the Soviet Union. Several

---

* A few of these are indicated in the text.

volumes have been published that might well be considered to be supplements, bringing this work up to date. These are in a series entitled *Transactions of VNIIP* (Vsesoyuznyi nauchno-issledovatel'skii institut p'yezooptiocheskogo mineral'nogo syr'ya—the All-Union Research Institute of Piezo-optical Mineral Raw Materials) *Research on Mineral-Forming Solutions,* N. P. Yermakov, Chief Editor. They consist of shorter articles by a number of authors including Prof. Yermakov and some of his students, on a wide range of inclusion studies. Volume I, No. 2 (179 pp., Moscow, 1957), and volume II, No. 2 (134 pp., Moscow, 1958), have been translated as part of the same project, and are included as Parts II and III, respectively, of this monograph.

This translation is published on behalf of the Geochemical Society, with financial assistance provided by a grant from the National Science Foundation.

U.S. Geological Survey
Washington D. C. 20242

EDWIN ROEDDER

CHAPTER I

Description and Natural Classification of Inclusions in Minerals

CLASSIFICATION OF INCLUSIONS ACCORDING TO THEIR COMPOSITION AND STATE

Ideal and absolutely identical crystals are extremely rare in nature. Inclusions of mineral fragments and rocks, of gangue minerals, or, most commonly, of relics of the environment in which the formation of the given crystal was taking place are the most important disturbances in the homogeneity of crystals. The term "inclusions" is used generally in the sense of *any space isolated hermetically within the body of the mineral in the course of the crystallization, and forming a phase-boundary with the mineral.* Inclusions of the mineral-forming media are the most common ones. Depending on composition and the state of such media, and on the once effective temperatures and pressures varying within a wide range in the surface environments of the earth, the original homogeneous systems are not observed in the inclusions, as a rule, but rather heterogeneous systems, with a certain number of inter-phase boundaries. The structures of the host crystals appear to be practically impermeable in the vast majority of cases. Thus it became possible, by a reactivation of one of the factors by which the mineral-forming environment is controlled—the temperature—to reduce the inclusions to a homogeneous state and, on the basis of the temperature of the homogenization, to arrive at some definite indications of the lowest temperatures at which the formation of the minerals took place as well as to obtain objective data on the aggregate state of the included solutions, which was even more important.

Inclusions of mineral-forming media proved to be highly variable in the surface environments of the earth. It became necessary, therefore, to develop their natural classification and nomenclature. The first variant of the classification was published at an earlier time [36, 37]. This variant, based on the composition and the state of the inclusions, is probably still inadequate for the expression of all of the variations of the types. The original classification has been expanded and is presented here as Fig. 1. A genetic classification of the inclusions themselves is given below in connection with the discussion of the mechanisms of their formation.

We divide the inclusions into four different groups: *solid, solidified, gaseous, and liquid* (Fig. 1).

The first one of these groups does not represent relics of the mother liquor. Characteristically, this group consists of foreign "associate" minerals captured by the crystal, minerals which settled on the formerly grow-

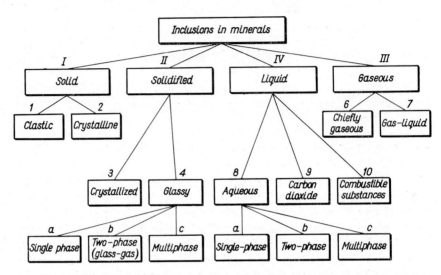

FIG. 1. Classification of inclusions in minerals by their composition and state.

ing crystal faces of their host crystal, or grew there, for a period of time prior to the sealing-off. Such inclusions of minerals preserve their individual structure and form which they had acquired either at an earlier time or concurrently with their host crystal, in contrast with inclusions belonging to the other three groups. Mechanically captured fragments of crystals and rocks are subjects only of small interest, for our purpose.*

A rigid subordination of the shape of inclusions to their host crystal is characteristic for the remaining three groups of inclusions which are especially interesting to us. The absolute dependence of the shape of such inclusions on their host crystal indicates that *the substance of the inclusions either was or is in its liquid or gaseous state* while their host crystal was already crystallized as a solid substance by the time when the inclusions were captured.

Two principal types may be distinguished in the group of inclusions which is characterized by the presence of associated captured minerals:

---

* Such inclusions are important only in ascertaining the position of a growing crystal in reference to the direction of the force of gravity.

(1) fragments and (2) inclusions containing faceted crystals—highly variable in their size, shape, and composition.

As it is shown below, types 3 through 8 of the three groups comprising solidified, gaseous and liquid inclusions serve to characterize a large variety of magmatic derivatives in the process of their evolution from the melt to the cooled solution. Among such inclusions of the parent substance, observed at the present in a very different physico-chemical environment of the surface of the earth, we recognize the following types in the second group: (3) "crystallized" inclusions and (4) inclusions of volcanic glass (amorphous). We recognize in the third group: (6)* essentially gaseous inclusions; (7) gas–liquid inclusions. The following types are distinguished in the fourth group: (8) inclusions of aqueous solutions or essentially liquid inclusions and (9) inclusions of foreign liquids and gases (carbon dioxide occasionally together with the solution (mixed inclusions); inclusions of combustible substances which have a considerable diagnostic value [35] outside the scope of the present study.

So far, possibilities of a further differentiation of inclusions within the types here enumerated were indicated only for types (4) and (8). Important differentiations within the other types will also be required undoubtedly in the future in ascertaining the mineral-forming processes by inclusions of the media [in which the minerals were formed—V.P.S.]. As regards the time of their formation, with respect to their host crystal, the inclusions may be primary, secondary, and pseudo-secondary ("primary–secondary"). This relationship is discussed briefly in the next chapter and it has been considered in some earlier publications [35, 37].

After the recognition of such a great variety of inclusions it became important to determine the relationship of the different groups to the environments in which their host minerals were formed.

It was established by examination of minerals from most highly variable geological environments that the Group I inclusions may be found in any mineral.

Solidified primary inclusions of Group II were observed only in minerals of magmatic rocks. Moreover, differences between the conditions of their solidification were reflected also in the character of the inclusions in pyrogenic minerals. Specifically, only primary inclusions of volcanic glass are identified in phenocrysts of effusive rocks. Globules of the magmatic solution captured by such inclusions remained amorphous in their rapidly cooling environment, while analogous globules of the magmatic solution, sealed in minerals of intrusive rocks and subjected to a slow cooling later on, were not solidified into a glass, but yielded instead different kinds of crystals inside the cavity. Composition of these crystals

---

* Type 5 is omitted in the text and in Fig. 1 [V.P.S.].

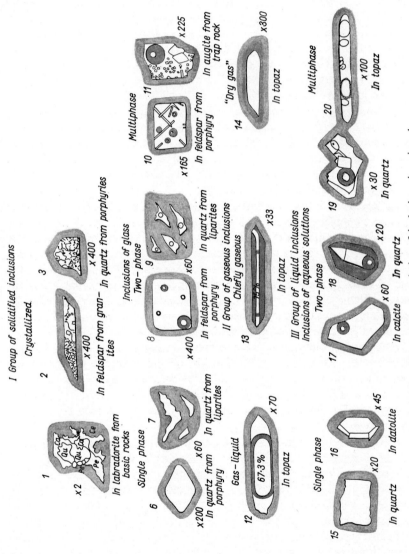

I Group of solidified inclusions

Crystallized

1
x 2
In labradorite from basic rocks

2
x 400

3
x 400
In feldspar from granites

In quartz from porphyries

Single phase

6
x 200
In quartz from porphyry

7
x 60
In quartz from liparites

Inclusions of glass

Two-phase

8
x 400
In feldspar from porphyry

9
x 60
In quartz from liparites

Multiphase

10
x 165
In feldspar from porphyry

11
x 225

II Group of gaseous inclusions

Chiefly gaseous

13
x 33
In topaz

"Dry gas"

14
x 300
In topaz

In augite from trap rock

III Group of liquid inclusions

Inclusions of aqueous solutions

Single phase

15
x 20
In quartz

16
x 45
In datolite

Two-phase

17
x 60
In calcite

18
x 20
In quartz

Gas-liquid

12
67·3%
x 70
In topaz

Multiphase

19
x 30
In quartz

20
x 100
In topaz

FIG. 2. Groups, types and varieties of inclusions in minerals.

represents composition of the melt. We designate such inclusions tentatively as "out-crystallized"* or, better, simply as "crystallized" inclusions.

Gaseous inclusions (Group III) were found by us first in topaz from the veins of the Sherlova Gora (Transbaykalia) and from the pegmatitic bodies of Volynia. The characteristic feature of this group of inclusions is the high proportion of the gas phase, over 50 per cent by volume, even at room temperature, while, on heating, the entire cavity may become filled by the gas phase in some instances. According to our findings, such inclusions are characteristic only for minerals from contact deposits or from vicinities of the primary ("parent") intrusions.

No gaseous or solidified inclusions could be found at any time in minerals from "alpine" veins or from hypogene veins of deposits at a distance from the intrusions. Minerals from these latter sources are characterized definitely by substantially aqueous liquid inclusions, commonly two-phase or multiphase (Group IV).

Minerals produced from cold aqueous solutions in surficial environments of the earth also contain substantially liquid inclusions, but only of the single-phase type.

In such manner a relationship between inclusions of the recognized groups and the supergene mineral-forming process was clearly indicated as the result of our studies of inclusions in minerals from certain definite geological environments. Of necessity, our results had to be harmonized with experiments involving artificial growth of minerals which could already be done easily.

Small solidified inclusions in slag minerals have been known for a long time, as representing the composition of the artificial melt from which the included minerals had crystallized. In artificial production of segnet† salts, alum, and other substances from solutions, one may easily convince oneself that the artificial crystals capture some of the mother liquor in the course of their rapid growth. If such crystals were formed in a gaseous environment, their pores are found to be filled with gas.

In the same manner exactly, various primary and pseudo-secondary inclusions in natural minerals serve to characterize the state of the medium wherein the crystallization was taking place. By this fact, they reveal objectively the true origin of their host minerals and function as reliable indicators of the state of aggregation of the mineral-forming environment. The last three groups of inclusions in our classification (Fig. 1), which is a systematization of data on inclusions in natural minerals, all three possible states of the mineral-forming medium are represented: the melt, the

---

* "Raskrystallizovannyye"—Such inclusions were formed as the results of a somewhat delayed crystallization of the globules of the magmatic solution and not as the results of a subsequent crystallization of the volcanic glass.

† $KNaC_4H_4O_6 \cdot 4H_2O$, potassium sodium tartrate.

gaseous solution, and the aqueous liquid solution. By such means it becomes possible to distinguish objectively the magmatic-proper, the pneumatolytic, and the hydrothermal stages of the formation of minerals.

The recognized types of inclusions, from the third to the eighth, enable us to gain a deeper insight into the conditions of the region and of the subsequent existence of minerals and, as is shown below, to indicate variations in the composition of the parent medium itself in the course of time.

Secondary inclusions are especially useful for this purpose, inasmuch as they are formed in the already existing minerals as the result of healing of small fissures during the subsequent alterations in the environment and during the coexistence of different stages and steps of the mineral-forming process in one deposit. For example, in the faceted crystals of topaz from Ukraine and from Transbaykalia it is possible to identify clearly the primary gaseous inclusions of either one of the two types as well as the secondary inclusions of aqueous solutions formed in small fissures in the crystals during the hydrothermal stage of the formation of the minerals.

The history of the mineral-forming process, in its later stages, may be read, on occasions, by means of the secondary inclusions in crystals which were formed at some earlier stage of the same process. As we have shown, in the case of the "transient" minerals from some fluorite deposits in Transbaykalia, and others, stages of the crystal growth, in every successive generation, are marked off by secondary inclusions in the corresponding minerals of the preceding generation. For example, as is shown below, *the temperature data on solutions, as indicated by studies of secondary inclusions in early minerals, agree with the temperature data obtained for primary inclusions in minerals of the later generations.* In exactly the same manner, secondary inclusions in minerals of the host rocks originating during a certain definite stage of the hydrothermal metamorphism of the rocks, judging by the homogenization temperatures, correspond either to the primary inclusions in the neomorphs* of the same stage or to the secondary inclusions in minerals of the next earlier stage of the mineral-forming process in the deposit in question.

SOLID INCLUSIONS IN MINERALS AND THEIR GENETIC SIGNIFICANCE

Both natural and synthetic minerals are able to capture and to preserve particles of the medium in which their formation or healing takes place. At the same time they may also take up some solid substances crystallizing concurrently with the minerals. Solid inclusions make it possible for us accordingly to form opinions regarding any earlier or contemporaneous

---

* "Novoobrazovaniye", presumably referring to currently forming minerals [Ed.].

minerals which were preserved only as inclusions in their host crystal. This is very important in ascertaining the complete paragenesis of minerals at the given deposit.

Clastic solid inclusions of fragments of minerals and rocks sometimes settle onto the faces of growing crystals by gravity [26], or are enclosed by their host crystals, very much like the calcite crystals in the "Fontainebleau sandstones" [35].

On the other hand, such minerals as mica, chlorite, hematite, and others, formed either before or contemporaneously with the host crystal, and present in the solution as suspensions, may settle on the faces of a growing crystal. Occasionally, such minerals, particularly the pyrite in some quartz crystals from a certain deposit we observed (p. 38 Fig. 4), and pyrite and chalcopyrite in fluorite from Kaznok, continued their growth for some time after their settling on the face of the crystal and, only later, were sealed off by their host crystal. Inclusions of this type show the zonal structures of the crystals, and the paragenesis of the minerals. Some highly conspicuous examples of such relationships have been very well described by Grigor'ev [26, Fig. 7a] in the instance of quartz and anatase from some veins in the Arctic Ural and by Grushkin [28, Fig. 13] for quartz and pyrite from the Aurakhmat deposit. In these cases, the arrangement of crystalline inclusions in the host shows an orderly relationship to the form as well as to the process of growth of the host crystal.* Complete inclusion of minerals such as rutile by overgrowth of younger minerals is exemplified by rutilated quartz.

The phenomenon of inclusion of small solid crystals is observed also in minerals crystallized from magmatic solutions. For example, accessory minerals in magmatic rocks are often captured by larger crystals. Inclusions of crystals in a crystal, in the forms of finest crystalline grains, needles, platelets, or "dust", may be so numerous, on occasions, that the optical characteristics of the host crystal, such as color, iridescence, and others may be affected by them. Determinations of included minerals of this sort are extremely difficult at times, but still not impossible. Crystalline inclusions, for example, of green augites, brown garnets, colorless nephelines, magnetite, etc., in leucite of lavas have been known for a long time. They are situated commonly parallel to the faces of the former growth of their host crystals and are expressions of its zonal structure.

It is evident from all these examples that minerals capture solid particles of substances that were either already present or were being formed concurrently with the growing crystal in question as particles in the crystallogenic solution. The range of our possibilities here is limited accord-

---

* This phenomenon of the orderly growth of crystals on top of their host mineral is known as "epitaxy" in the literature.

ingly to some extent, in ascertaining conditions under which the captured mineral was formed, *inasmuch as the captured minerals themselves need be "de-coded" in regards to the conditions of their origins.*

We shall relegate all solid inclusions (the "accessor" and the "predecessor" minerals) to a position of secondary importance in the present study, without trying to minimize the importance of solid inclusions in minerals, as, for example, in morphological studies of crystals, in determinations of paragenetic relationships, in ascertaining the crystallographic form of the host crystal, etc. Let us merely remark that *the most characteristic feature of primary solid inclusions, as a group, is their preservation of the crystalline form of the substance from which they were formed.* We paused briefly to consider the characteristics of solid inclusions, by their contrast with inclusions solidified after they were captured by the crystal, as they help us to understand the origin of these latter inclusions which are important indicators of the mineral-forming solutions in their fluid state.

SOLIDIFIED INCLUSIONS IN MINERALS

Inclusions in minerals belonging to the endo-magmatic stage of the mineral genesis must become important objects of studies by the Soviet petrographers in the future.

S. D. Belyankin, in his appraisal of the value of chemical analyses of magmatic rocks, is correct in saying that they represent merely the "denatured" ("obeskrovlennyye") composition of the magma, while its real and exact composition remains unknown [4]. One may foresee theoretically that only inclusions of the silicate melt, sealed off reliably in minerals, may provide the required data on the composition of the magma that would be more representative of the true one than is given by analyses of the rocks themselves, especially of the effusives from which the volatile constituents are rapidly lost. Moreover, some varieties of the inclusions (*b* and *c,* Fig. 1) in materials imbedded in minerals may indicate to us in the future the relative minima of the temperatures of the magmatic solutions, by means of homogenization studies.

Among the solidified inclusions, as a group, the following two types are characteristic: (a) *crystallized inclusions* and (b) *inclusions of volcanic glass.* Comparisons between these two types give us no indications of the natural evolution of the magma. They merely illustrate the marked differences in the conditions under which the magma has become solid. There are also intermediate types due to the fact that the imbedded minerals of effusive rocks and minerals of intrusive rocks may be formed occasionally under similar conditions. The imbedded minerals of such rocks are crystallized in depths along the course of the ascending magma. For that reason, inclusions of glass may become partially, but never completely, crystalline.

The fully crystalline form is characteristic only for the inclusions of the first type.

Crystallized Inclusions

Sorby [152],* at the dawn of mineralogy and petrography, had already noticed the presence of such inclusions in imbedded minerals of some igneous rocks, chiefly in porphyroid granites. We must note here that, in the latter case, these poorly visible crystallized inclusions of a very small size are generally overlooked and their presence is passed over in silence in descriptions of thin sections.

We were able to find only one article in which crystallized inclusions were described in detail, among contributions by modern petrographers, namely, A. P. Lebedev's "On the Subject of Inclusion of Quartz-calcite in Labradorites from Golovino, Northwestern Ukraine" [63]. These coarsely-crystalline labradorites are developed extensively in the south-eastern part of the Volynian anorthosite massif where practically every lump of the rock contains macro-inclusions up to 1 cm in diameter, and larger, on account of the large size of the labradorite crystals themselves. On the outside, they look like dark glass-like silicified areas with white calcite indicating their presence against the general dark background of the rock. The grains of quartz in these inclusions are irregularly rounded, as a rule, conspicuous by their homogeneity and by their orderly structure.

Such primary inclusions are essentially globules of a liquid magmatic melt. That is the reason why their shape is irregular, subordinate to their host mineral, or else repeating its form (a negative crystal).† However, it appears that there was an appreciable interval of time between the solidification of the inclusions, specifically, between the crystallization of quartz therein, and the crystallization of the rock-forming minerals. The solidification took place concurrently with the crystallization of the host minerals and continued after the plagioclase and the entire rock [63] had become solid.‡ Possibly some of the inclusions in question may represent the melt in the terminal stage of the formation of the rock.

Crystallized inclusions in quartz from ordinary coarse-grained granites are poorly defined and imperfect in their facets. Parts of feldspathic substance are visible in the inclusions. The inclusions are still more difficult to detect in feldspars of common granites and of diorites. Their form may

---

* Sorby is not listed in the bibliography under this number (probably 128) [V.P.S.].

† Solidified inclusions may show signs of a reworking occasionally and may contain mineral neomorphs inside.

‡ In my view, judging by the mineralogical composition of the inclusions, there is much doubt in regard to such origin of the inclusion, described by A. P. Lebedev (V. S. Sobolev, Ed.).

be tied to the crystal planes of the host mineral. Quartz and dark minerals may be identified at times in such inclusions.

A substance, related to the substance of the host crystal, from a globule of the melt, was being deposited on the pore walls of the inclusion. We may recognize traces of this substance occasionally at the original boundary of the vacuole. An inclusion of such type in feldspar from hypabyssal granites of the Tyrny–Auz District is represented in Plate XVII, 1. The relatively large size of the dark gaseous bubble in the central part of the inclusion is an indication of a considerable difference between volumes of the magmatic melt and of the solid phases which had crystallized from that melt. The globular shape of the gaseous bubble may be explained only as a contraction in the volume of the original globule of the melt accompanied by a differentiation of the gaseous phase which was apparently more abundant in the deep magmatic solutions than it is customary to believe. In this inclusion, the gaseous bubble is surrounded by crystalline silica having clearly defined boundaries with the feldspar which had settled on the periphery of the vacuole, in the given space, from the globule of the melt. Because of a certain difference between the indices of refraction of this feldspar and the feldspar of the host, the original boundary of the vacuole proved to be easily identifiable in the photomicrograph, Plate XVII, 1. The next one, Plate XVII, 2, shows inclusions in feldspar from the same granites.

Thus volatile constituents of the magma are preserved in crystalline inclusions which are captured securely by the mineral while they are still liquid. This is indicated further, indirectly, by the presence of extremely fine prisms of black tourmaline, identifiable, on occasions, among the inner minerals of such inclusions [152].

Crystallized inclusions are especially clearly seen in quartz, nepheline, leucite, and labradorite. They are much more difficult to ascertain in minerals of normal granites where their size is minute and their outlines are insufficiently clear, on account of the deposition of a substance, similar to the substance of the host mineral, on the inner walls of the inclusions.

Representatives of the crystallized type of inclusions in labradorites, feldspars from granites, and quartz crystals imbedded in porphyries were shown as *1, 2* and *3* in Fig. 2. By way of a conclusion, we must remark here that a search for this kind of inclusion may prove to be highly advantageous to science in ascertaining certain particular moments in the formation of endo-magmatic deposits, especially the ones that are associated with ultrabasic rocks.

Inclusions of Volcanic Glass (Amorphous Inclusions)

Inclusions of glass in minerals within effusive rocks occur extensively and have been known for a long time. Representatives may be seen, for example, in the well-known Cohen's Atlas, in the plagioclasses of liparitic and basaltic obsidians (Table 8), in olivine, and in other minerals (Table 10), [120].* In fairness, however, it must be stated that, so far, very little attention has been given to such inclusions. The inclusions in question are representatives of the medium wherein the growth of the phenocrysts was taking place. On account of the geological environments, however (a rapid cooling of the rock and of the host crystals), the captured magmatic solution was preserved in the state of an arrested crystallization or else has remained entirely uncrystallized.

Inclusions of glass are characteristic of rapidly solidified magmatic rocks. The parent medium is more fully represented in such inclusions than it is in the bulk of the rock itself which lost its mineralizers during the rapid drop in temperature and pressure. Single-phase, two-phase (glass-gas), and multiphase inclusions may be found among the glassy inclusions distributed parallel to the growth lines (former crystal faces) of the imbedded minerals.

Single-phase inclusions of glass filling entire vacuoles in the imbedded minerals are not particularly interesting, in our experimentation (6 and 7, Fig. 2, p. 12). The two-phase inclusions contain one or several gaseous bubbles that had originated because of a contraction in the volume and of the presence of gas in the included substance (8 and 9, Fig. 2).

Inclusions of glass with globular gaseous bubbles, resembling, in every respect, the inclusions of glass in effusive rocks, were known for a long time in crystals of a basic ferrous silicate found in slags. The first artificial inclusions of glass in olivine, crystallized from a molten mass, were obtained by Becker (1881). There are many reports on the formation of such inclusions in the more recent literature.

The inclusions of glass may be colorless or else they may be colored yellow, reddish, greenish or buff. Such colorations are observed chiefly in minerals of basic rocks. The inclusions' color coincides, on the whole, with the color of the bulk of the effusive rock.

The form of the glassy inclusions is highly variable. Unless their form is a miniature replica of their host crystal (Plate XVIII, 1), it may be drop-like, sharply angular, or shred-like with wedge-like points. The two-phase inclusions containing numerous immobilized gaseous bubbles look like sieves. The bubbles are generally spherical; the oval and the sack-like shapes are relatively rare. Boundaries of the inclusions look fuzzy, on occasions, because the indices of refraction of the glass and of the host mineral are so nearly alike (Plate XVII, 3). Because of the viscosity of the melt and of its rapid cooling on many occasions, the gaseous bubbles had no opportunity to coalesce into a single bubble which is so character-

---

* This reference is to Shcherbina who cites the Atlas, it appears [V.P.S.].

istic of liquid inclusions. Such coalescence may be brought about artificially at times, by heating and melting the inclusion's glass with its several small bubbles of gas, whereupon, after cooling, a single gas bubble may be produced. The temperature of the homogenization of this sort of inclusion represents apparently the temperature limit of the lava in which the imbedded minerals were crystallizing, inasmuch as the volatile substance was conserved by the glassy inclusions. Of course, our statement must be tested with the artificial minerals in slags formed from a melted charge of a furnace at a known temperature. It has been proved by us that the gaseous bubble begins to contract appreciably on heating to 680–650°C, while the subsequent cooling serves to make the glass-gas boundaries relatively indistinct.

Three-phase and multiphase glassy inclusions are especially interesting, because they contain an overgrowth of "captive" minerals on their walls derived from one or from several mineral substances formerly dissolved in the melt which had yielded the glass. Occasionally, such crystals grow as suspensions in the viscous melt within the inclusion. As already observed by Sorby [128], prismatic green "captive" crystals (probably pyroxene) protrude into the gaseous bubble; this serves as evidence that they were formed before the conversion of the melt into the glass.

Small anisotropic crystals of feldspars (with irregular facets), small green prismatic crystals of pyroxene, and minerals of rhombohedral habit were seen within the isotropic mass of the glass, in multiphase inclusions, with liquid glass functioning as a solvent for a number of substances present in the magmatic melt (*11*, Fig. 2, p. 12). In such inclusions, the vacuole filling is an imitation of a porphyritic rock. The "captive" minerals had grown only on the pore walls of the inclusions in many instances (*10*, Fig. 2). Substances related to the substance of the host crystal do not form independent crystals in inclusions of droplets of the melt but are deposited on the walls of the inclusions.

On homogenization of multiphase inclusions (*10* and *11*, Fig. 2), it is not only the gaseous bubble that disappears, but also the solid phases which may become dissolved completely in the melted glass, on occasions. The solid phases may be restored to their original state only by a very gradual cooling which is often impossible under laboratory conditions. The proof of the liquefaction of glassy inclusions is in the contraction, movements, and disappearance of gaseous bubbles inside the inclusions as well as in the melting of the inner crystals in multiphase inclusions.

The presence of mineralizers within the included glass is expressed, on occasions, by the better defined crystallization of such inclusions than the crystallization of the bulk of the extrusive rock matrix for the mineral substance in which these inclusions are contained, as observed (Plates XVII, 4, and XVIII, 2).*

The accumulated experience with our studies of the inclusions of volcanic glass allows us to maintain that the presence of such inclusions in minerals obtained by panning alluvium or in sedimentary rocks provides definite indications regarding the manner in which their host minerals were produced from magmatic solutions in the rapidly cooling environments of the surface of the earth.

GASEOUS INCLUSIONS

As already indicated, the presence of gaseous inclusions is a characteristic feature of minerals in contact zones and in pegmatitic deposits as well as of minerals produced by sublimation. On these premises and on the basis of our experiments, we have every reason to believe that such inclusions are characteristic of the group of minerals from partially pegmatitic and entirely pneumatolytic sources.

Gaseous inclusions are most common in topazes, tourmalines, quartzes, and garnets in the appropriate geological environments (close to the parent intrusives). Typical inclusions of this kind are shown in Fig. *2, 12, 13* and *14* (p. 12), as observed in the topazes from Volynia. Similar inclusions in topazes are represented also in Plates I, II, IX, X.

These inclusions are characterized externally by the very large size of their gaseous bubble, which occupies more than 50 per cent of the inclusion's volume at room temperature. *Gaseous inclusions* consisting almost entirely and even entirely of the gaseous phase† may be found occasionally, particularly in the early stage of the pegmatitic mineralogenesis. Inclusions containing less than 10 per cent liquid at room temperature were called by us, tentatively, inclusions of "dry" gases (*14*, Fig. 2). Inclusions of dry gases in a calcite from the pegmatites of the Vilyuy and in a topaz from Volynia are illustrated in Plate XII, 2 and 3 respectively.

Inclusions containing 76 to 90 per cent gas and becoming uniformly filled by the gaseous phase on heating were called by us *essentially gaseous.*

Inclusions containing 50 to 76 per cent gas at room temperature were called *gas–liquid.* Solid phases ("captive minerals") representing substances alien to the host mineral may be found very often in such inclusions, alongside the gaseous and the liquid phases.

Substances of the same type as the host mineral's substance are deposited, in very small quantites, on the walls of the pores wherein the inclusions are contained, in the course of the cooling of the inclusions.

---

* These photographs are of garnet, i.e. not extrusive rocks? [Ed.].

† Such inclusions are apparently also characteristic of minerals produced by sublimation.

This substance is rarely seen as a very *thin rim* ("bordure"—V.P.S.) on the periphery of the inclusions or, still more rarely, as a *wide band* which is formed in the process of formation of the inclusion up to the moment of the hermetic sealing-off of the inclusion.

The composition of gaseous inclusions has almost never been studied. One may presume that their gaseous phase consists of both strong and weak acids, such as HF, HCl, H_2S, CO_2, and H_2O, as well as of volatile substances, such as SiF_4, $SiCl_4$, BF_3, $FeCl_3$, etc. It is only by their presence that we may account for the observed and very intensive action of gaseous solutions on rocks as well as the very important fact that the "bordures" of the inclusions are non-uniformly dissolved on slow heating (non-sequitur? Ed.), even in the case of such a seemingly poorly soluble mineral as topaz.

The presence of carbon dioxide in gaseous and liquid inclusions is relatively easily demonstrated, because carbon dioxide develops a supplementary interphase boundary in the inclusion at room temperatures. This boundary is plainly visible in Plate XV, 4 (to the left of the gaseous bubble). An inclusion of this type, in crystal quartz, is shown in Plate XVIII, 3 where the liquid CO_2 disappears at 25°C (Plate XVIII, 4).

The shape of gaseous inclusions is highly variable, depending on the host mineral in which they are found. For example, in beryls, tubular rounded primary inclusions are the most typical ones. Such inclusions are also common in topaz. In the instance of pneumatolytic quartz, the most common shape of the inclusions is rounded, and faceted shapes are also common.

There is a tremendous number of such inclusions in gray quartz, with the aggregate volume of at least 10 per cent of the total volume of the crystal.

LIQUID INCLUSIONS

Among liquids locked in the pores of hydrothermal minerals, *aqueous mother liquors* are generally found; carbon dioxide alone, or together with the mother liquor, is found more rarely; inclusions of *alien liquids*, of combustible substances resembling petroleum, are very rare. Thus, there is a variation in the composition of liquid inclusions in minerals.

Inclusions of mother liquors have a basic importance, from the point of view of ascertaining temperatures of the environments in which the inclusions were formed. These inclusions are diagnostic for hydrothermal and cold-water minerals. However, in pneumatolytic minerals and in minerals crystallized from magmatic melts, it is generally easy to recognize certain indications of their secondary formation, in relation to the action of hydrothermal and "metamorphogenic" solutions on the minerals. Single-phase, two-phase, three-phase, and multiphase varieties of the inclusions, shown as *15–20,* Fig. 2 (p. 12) in drawings made from photomicrographs, may be recognized at room temperatures among the included liquid solutions in crystals.

The solid cavity walls of any type of inclusion do not remain inert during the homogenization but function in the capacity of a *supplementary phase*. It would be awkward, in our terminology, to take cognizance of the supplementary phase, although its presence must be taken for granted in any and all inclusions.

Single-phase inclusions in the pores of crystals which were formed in cold or tepid solutions consist entirely of these solutions. Inclusions of this kind in some late calcites from Tetyukhe are shown in Plate XIX, 1 and 2,* and inclusions in natrolites from Yukspor are shown in Plate XIX, 3. It is curious that in one and the same specimen of natrolite we found some essentially-liquid inclusions without any gaseous bubble (vapor) but with two small crystals grown on the inclusion's walls. These "captive" minerals would dissolve easily on heating to 50°C (Plate XIX, 4).

In two-phase inclusions the solutions, as observed at room temperature, do not completely fill the crystals' cavities, because they (each) contain a mobile spherical bubble of gas (vapor). The warm aqueous solution completely filled the inclusion's cavity while it was being captured by the growing crystal. The free space within the cavity has developed only after the cooling of the inclusion to room temperature, as the result of a contraction of the hermetically sealed liquid. This free space was immediately filled by gas (vapor).

On the whole, the relative size of the gas bubble, with respect to the size of the liquid phase, will be larger for inclusions where the solution was hotter at the time of the growth or regeneration of the crystal [31]. Such primary and secondary inclusions are shown at the end of the book in the following photomicrographs of quartz (Plates III, 1 and 2; and XX, 1), calcite (Plate XX, 2), fluorite (Plate XX, 3), sphalerite (Plate XX, 4), tourmalines (Plate XXI, 1 and 2), adularia (Plate XXI, 3).

Three-phase and multiphase inclusions of concentrated solutions were formed in the same way. As the result of cooling of the droplets isolated in the crystals' cavities, not only a gas bubble is developed (in the droplets) but also one or several solid phases, in consequence of the supersaturation, by which the "captive" minerals are formed. Isotropic cubical small crystals of chlorides are most common in the inclusions of this kind; carbonates and ore minerals are more rare. The inclusions may be seen in the photomicrographs of topazes (Plates V, 1; VI, 1; VII, 1, 2, 3 and 4), beryls (Plate XV, 2, 3 and 4, and XVI), and quartzes (Plate VIII).

An overgrowth of a "captive" mineral on top of another one may be seen occasionally in multiphase inclusions enabling us to form an opinion

---

* Plate XIX, 1 and 2, are of single-phase *Solid* inclusions, not liquid [Ed.].

in regards to the "internal paragenetic relationships" (Plate VIII, 1 and 2). A more complete answer to the problem of the sequence of such minerals, however, is provided by the sequence in which they are "melted" on applications of heat to the inclusions.

Naturally, the substance analogous to the crystal's substance is deposited only on the inclusion's walls (the supplementary solid phase), even as in the case of the solidified and of the gas–liquid inclusions, and the characteristic "bordure" of this substance along the present boundaries of the inclusion may be seen occasionally.

Inclusion of carbon dioxide in hypogene minerals is a fairly common phenomenon. Such inclusions were interesting for many investigators and their descriptions and experimental behavior were given a great deal of attention in the foreign literature.* Because of its very low critical temperature (31.1°C), in hypogene environments, carbonic acid was subject to capture by inclusions whose critical density is below 0.46, provided the pressure was not excessively high [sic]. Consequently, when the mineral is cooled to room temperature, the inclusion's pore proves to be filled chiefly by gaseous carbon dioxide, while the volume occupied by liquid carbon dioxide becomes relatively small. The gas bubble, in inclusions of liquid carbon dioxide, resembles closely the gas bubble of ordinary liquid inclusions. Heating the inclusion above 31.1°C leads to a disappearance of the liquid and to the conversion of the inclusion back to its super-critical (gaseous) state.

Cooling the inclusion below 31.1°C again causes the appearance of the liquid phase accompanied by a very turbulent effervescence of the entire contents of the included carbon dioxide. Density of the segregated carbon dioxide is greater than 0.46.

For a development of inclusions in which liquid carbon dioxide would occupy a larger volume than the volume of the gas phase, the natural environments need be characterized by an appreciable pressure and by a very low temperature (lower than 31°C). Such environments are very rare. Consequently, inclusions of carbon dioxide should be grouped more appropriately with the gaseous, and not with the liquid inclusions, in the overwhelming majority of the cases.

In complex inclusions of two immiscible liquids (aqueous solution–carbon dioxide), the commonly large gas bubble consists of water vapor and carbon dioxide gas. The liquid carbon dioxide disappears very rapidly when the temperature is made to increase only by 10 to 15°C (Plate XI 2, 3 and 4). Complex multiphase inclusions are formed after the separation of one or of several solid phases from the included solution of this type.

---

* Having had very little first-hand experience with such inclusions, we omit their detailed description.

Liquid inclusions of hydrocarbons, brown kerosene-like substances in crystals of quartz from Dauphiné, Ural, and other places were already reported in the last century. They were demonstrated in fluorite from Illinois by Bastin at a much later date (1931). As a rule, such inclusions are two-phase; single-phase ones are rarer. They luminesce in ultraviolet light. In recent times, numerous inclusions of bituminous substances were proved and described by K. K. Matveyev in grayish-brown scheelites, in morions from Murzinka, in amazonites from the Il'men' Mountains, and in anthraconites from Vereyn.

The classification pattern for liquid inclusions in minerals, according to their composition and physical state, may be represented as follows:

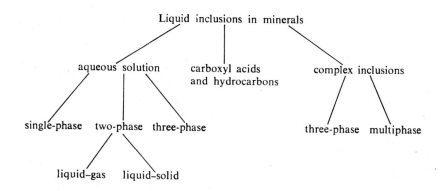

We must give our particular attention to the possibility of formation of anomalous two-phase liquid inclusions under certain conditions. We recognize two possible origins.

In the first one, the anomalous inclusion may be formed if the gas bubble within the liquid inclusion is of *primary* origin. The gas bubble, in such case, is related not to the contraction of the formerly heated liquid, but to the fact that the growing crystal had captured and preserved a bubble of some gas (CO_2, for example) which was stuck onto one of its faces. Cases of this sort are rare, for all practical purposes, and they may be indicated, in large populations of inclusions, by a conspicuously irregular ratio between the phases, in some particular inclusion, in comparison with the phase ratio in the rest of the population.

In the second case, the gas bubble has a *secondary origin*. The gas bubble develops in certain easily soluble minerals because the walls do not permit hermetic sealing. Under such conditions it is possible for single-phase liquid inclusions to acquire a gas bubble, in time, since some of their liquid may escape from the pore and the vacant space may become occupied by vapor of the liquid solution. Secondary gas bubbles of this kind are common within inclusions in halite, sylvite, inyoite, and other similarly soluble minerals. A single-phase essentially-liquid inclusion in inyoite is visible in Plate XXII, 3, on the left of the grid; in the upper right-hand corner of the picture there is a two-phase inclusion with a large gas bubble. Naturally, such inclusions with anomalous gas bubbles cannot be used for thermometry, but this fact escapes the attention of some American geologists [178].

Before we pass on to the topics related to the possible use of inclusions of aqueous solutions in solving thermometric problems, let us consider briefly the morphological characteristics of inclusions in minerals, together with their size and numbers.

In studies of minerals containing inclusions of aqueous solutions, it is easy to establish microscopically that the number of detectable inclusions increases at increasing magnifications This relationship holds chiefly for turbid crystals in which primary, pseudo-secondary, and secondary inclusions are abundant. Water-clear and unfissured crystals contain very few inclusions of mother liquor which may be located only after a painstaking search.

Inclusions may be divided conveniently, according to size, into three groups: macroscopic, microscopic, and submicroscopic. The first group is plainly visible to the naked eye, with inclusions ranging from one half millimeter to several millimeters and even centimeters. Inclusions in the second group are from tenth to hundredths of a millimeter in size; inclusions in the third group are measured in microns and in fractions of one micron.

Some macroscopic liquid inclusions in crystals may be exceptionally large. Thus Hidden [146] described liquid-filled cavities in quartz crystals from Carolina up to 6 cm long and up to 0.64 cm broad. Davy [124] found cavities in quartz crystals from Dauphiné, with liquid, up to 1 cm in diameter. Brewster [125] showed the presence of regularly shaped cavities up to 8.6 mm long containing multiphase inclusions in blue topaz.

Karpinskii [47] studied inclusions of carbonic acid in amethysts from Ural whose length was up to 2.55 mm. We showed the presence of rounded two-phase inclusions up to 2 mm in diameter in crystals of fluorite from Kulikolon and in crystals of quartz from Volynia. When such crystals were rotated, one could see the gas bubbles changing their position, even with the unaided eye. Zakharchenko [44] found exceptionally large primary inclusions in crystals of quartz from Pamir whose volume was up to 1.5 cm³. One of these inclusions occupied about 40 per cent of the volume of the skeletal crystal so that the crystal seemed to be empty inside. Gas bubbles in such inclusions were up to 4 mm in diameter. Macroscopic inclusions merit our special attention, in studies of the chemical composition of liquid inclusions.

In mineral-thermometric investigations one often comes across liquid inclusions from microns to tens of microns in size. Even then, the gas bubble is clearly visible under the microscope, in inclusions 0.003×0.001 mm. Such inclusions may be seen, at times, in prodigious numbers. The white color of vein and milky faceted quartz is caused chiefly by submicroscopic inclusion whose numbers, according to Sorby, may be as great as 5 or 6 million per mm^3 of the mineral. Zirkel [132] counted 250 isolated and plainly visible inclusions per mm^2 of the prepared section of quartz from Cornwall granites. A vast number of submicroscopic inclusions, showing as points, could be distinguished at 2000 magnification. Vogelsang [134] counted more than one hundred thousand inclusions in one cubic millimeter of a mineral. The shape of such minute droplets of liquid is highly varied, although the gas bubbles of two-phase inclusions of definite shape are spherical. The gaseous bubbles are compressed in flattened inclusions so that they transmit light practically without any scattering. The liquid phase and the gas bubble in such cases are recognizable only by the direction of the curvature of the interphase boundary.

According to their shape, the pores containing liquid inclusions may be divided into three large groups: *faceted* (negative crystals), *semifaceted*, and the *non-faceted*.

The faceted forms are negative crystals whose shape corresponds fairly closely to the external habit of the host mineral. Variations of their shape depend on the symmetry of the host (Plates VIII, 1 and 2; XVII, 3; XVIII, 1 and 3; XIX, 1 and 2, and XX, 2).

The semi-faceted inclusions originate chiefly in areas of inadequate supply to the growing crystal. For example, during skeletal growth of a quartz crystal, primary inclusions may form with an intricate configuration representing combinations of the normal crystal-faces with some vicinal figures and with areas without any trace of crystal-faces. The inclusions are highly varied in morphology for that reason; and negative crystals are but one of their many possible shapes. As already stated, the present shape of inclusions "is not the original one but is the final result of processes that had led to the equilibrium between the included solution and the host mineral" [37, p. 36]. The faceted and the semi-faceted shapes of the inclusions owe their origins, in most cases, to that particular process involving deposition and redeposition if the substance related to the substance [i.e., the same substance? Ed.] of the host crystal on the walls of their cavities.

Wherever this process has been less effective the inclusions are generally *ellipsoidal, rounded-flattened, droplet-shaped, tubular, irregularly shaped* or *amoeboid* and filled with the mother liquor or, after the crystal was formed, with the solution causing the healing of the fissure. Such non-faceted shapes are most characteristic of secondary inclusions.

TABLE 1

Groups and types of inclusions / Characteristic and genetic significance of inclusions	Phases observed in inclusions and their ratios*	Homogeneous phase after heating	State of the captured mother liquor	Origin of host minerals
I. Solidified				
1. Crystallized	K; $K+G$;	Liquid solution	Magmatic solutions	Igneous
			Solution solidified in depths	Intrusive
2. Amorphous	V; $V+G$; $V+G+K$;	Liquid solution	Solutions solidified at the earth's surface	Extrusive
II. Gaseous				
1. Essentially-gaseous	G; $G_{\frac{3}{4}}+L_{\frac{1}{4}}$;	Gas	Supercritical gaseous solutions	Pneumatolytic
2. Gas-liquid	$G_{\frac{1}{2}}$ to $\frac{3}{4}+L_{\frac{1}{2}}$ to $\frac{1}{4}$; $G_{\frac{1}{2}}+L_{\frac{1}{2}}+K$	Gas (vapor)	Gaseous solutions	Strictly pneumatolytic
			Solutions of water vapor	"Pneumatolytic-hydrothermal"
III. Liquid inclusions of aqueous solutions	$L_{\frac{1}{2}}+G_{\frac{1}{2}}+K$; $L>\frac{1}{2}+G<\frac{1}{2}$; $L+K$; L	Liquid solution	Aqueous solutions at different concentrations and temperatures	Hydrothermal
				Cold-water

* K—crystals; V—volcanic glass; G—gas (vapor); L—liquid. The numbers refer to the fraction of the volume of the inclusion at room temperature.

However, negative crystal cavities may occasionally be secondary inclusions, associated with healing of fissures as the result of the multinucleated growth of the crystal.*

Primary, pseudo-secondary, and secondary inclusions were observed by us and by other investigators in quartz crystal, igneous and vein quartz, fluorspar, aragonite, calcite, ankerite, siderite, barite, optical fluorite, Iceland spar, topaz, celestite, analcime, ruby, sapphire, almandite, grossularite, datolite, apophyllite, sodalite, nepheline, axinite, danburite, tourmaline, spinel, gypsum, anhydrite, halite, sylvite, carnallite, inyoite, natrolite, dolomite, native sulfur, albite, adularia, diopside, cassiterite, sphalerite, galena, pyrite, realgar, muscovite, vesuvianite, andradite, desmine, and others, i.e. in more than 50 minerals and varieties of minerals. There can be no doubt whatsoever that this list of inclusion-bearing minerals is far from complete. We have reasons to believe that all crystalline minerals contain some inclusions belonging to one or another group.

Table 1 presents descriptions and classifications of inclusions of mineral-forming media, as well as a correlation between inclusion type and the physico-chemical environments of formation.

---

* Negative crystal inclusions are often regarded as primary in the foreign literature.

CHAPTER 2

Origin and Genetic Classification of Liquid and Gaseous Inclusions in Minerals

LIQUID and gaseous inclusions are abundant in minerals in a very large number of hypogene ore deposits. It is essential for every investigator to understand clearly the highly varied character of these inclusions and the mechanisms of their formation, in his evaluation of the physico-chemical environments in which the minerals formed and in his interpretations of the inclusion data. The first objective is attained by the means of studies of the composition and state of the inclusions; the second by ascertaining their morphology and spatial distribution in the crystal.

Inclusions vary widely in origin, time of formation, and manner of distribution within their host crystal. The time factor is of particular importance in any geologic interpretation of experimental data from inclusions; it may be evaluated only in reference to the time of the formation of the host crystal.*

Because the investigators in the last century neglected to take into account the variety of origins and times of formation of inclusions, they obtained contradictory results. It was chiefly for this reason that interest in inclusions lagged for a long time. By way of an illustration, it is sufficient to remember the old controversy between Neptunists and Plutonists regarding the origin of granite. In this controversy, the Neptunists proved the aqueous origin of granites by the means of the aqueous liquid inclusions in the quartz of the granite. The fact that such inclusions are definitely younger than the igneous minerals was made clear at a much later date. These inclusions were formed much later than the granite, as the result of the healing of fractures in the course of the hydrothermal metamorphism.

In the earlier chapters, we said practically nothing concerning the mechanism of origin of inclusions. We stated only that such inclusions may be *primary* in their origin, i.e. contemporaneous with the host mineral, or *secondary*, i.e. of a later origin, resulting from later stages of

---

* Only certain types of solid radioactive inclusions in minerals are able to develop "pleochroic haloes" in their immediate vicinity which may be used for age determination.

mineral formation or hydrothermal metamorphism of the rocks. The correct understanding of the primary or the secondary origin of the inclusions is a very important matter in the history of applications of their studies to basic scientific problems. Possibilities of secondary origin of the inclusions were disregarded completely in the early work when the inclusions were treated as if they were automatic recording thermometers. Thus Phillips, Zirkel, and some others, having obtained a variety of homogenization temperatures for inclusions in one and the same crystal, concluded that it is impossible to determine the temperature at which the minerals are formed by this method. Later on some workers suggested that secondary inclusions, formed along fractures, are present in minerals.

In 1929, Lemmlein [163] definitely succeeded in decoding the mechanism responsible for the formation of secondary inclusions, by means of experiments with artificial crystals. His work, nevertheless, has led to the tendency to ignore inclusions in general, because an impression was created that all or nearly all inclusions are secondary in origin. The excellent demonstrations by Shubnikov [117], as early as 1923, of the normal formation of primary inclusions based on studies of the crystal growth of alum, were forgotten almost entirely. Only Newhouse [167], in the 1930's, used temperature measurements on inclusions, although his criteria for proving primary character were incorrect. The main criterion, advanced by Newhouse and used by other foreign scientists in recent years (Ingerson, 1947), was the erroneous assumption that inclusions in minerals from *vugs and from other open cavities are primary because of this fact.*

It is evident that correct identification of primary or secondary character of the relics of the mother liquor captured by minerals is absolutely essential for geologic interpretations. It was for that very reason that the Soviet scientists who became interested in making use of inclusions had directed their attention at once to the differentiation between the primary and the secondary ones. The recent papers of Grigor'ev and Grushkin deal with this problem. Specifically, they have demonstrated the existence of a new variety of primary inclusions in quartz, in the planes of the crystal's growth faces [25]. Grushkin ascertained the arrangement of primary inclusions in quartz, on the step-like surfaces formed by alternating growth of two adjoining prism faces or of a prism and a rhombohedron [28]. Zakharchenko [44] showed the existence of a fan-like distribution of large primary inclusions elongated toward the periphery of the core of the base of the crystal, in the direction of the pyramidal growth (Fig. 3). The genetic significance of inclusions situated along fractures in crystals, *so very abundant in the mineral kingdom,* was still depreciated, however, as a result of tradition. All such inclusions were believed to be of no use, until recently, for determining temperatures of formation of minerals by the homogenization method. Instead, the need for using only primary inclusion for this purpose was being emphasized continuously. Thus, the range of usefulness of the method was restricted by the prevailing opinion, inasmuch as strictly primary inclusions are not very common in minerals.

Up to the present, the best evidence of a primary origin for inclusions was their association with former crystal growth faces (Fig. 5, p. 39). The absence of such association was deemed to be the most diagnostic sign of secondary origin of the inclusions, with inclusions being situated along healed fissures of the crystal cutting across the crystal's growth zones and, locally, traversing each other. These criteria became *the rule* in the world literature, as well as in research work, and this interpretation is still widely used by geologists. A more detailed investigation of this problem, however, accompanied by examination of many hundreds of crystals, has led us to conclude the existence and very common occurrence of *primary–secondary* or *pseudo-secondary* inclusions in which the features of both primary and secondary types are combined [38].

Thus three types of inclusions are now established, *the primary, the pseudo-secondary, and the secondary*, each of which is further subdivided into varieties, depending on the origin and position in the crystal.

We should emphasize here that these detailed genetic subdivisions were made possible entirely on the basis of studies by Soviet scientists: A. V. Shubnikov, G. G. Lemmlein, N. N. Sheftal', D. P. Grigor'ev, I. I. Shafranovskii, O. M. Ansheles, G. G. Grushkin, P. S. Vadilo, A. I. Zakharchenko and others. Not every one of these investigators was concerned with inclusions, by any means, yet every one of them has contributed to our understanding of the mechanism of crystal growth. The work of Lemmlein was particularly fruitful in ascertaining origins of secondary inclusions.

PRIMARY INCLUSIONS

It is possible to recognize two most important processes resulting in the formation of primary inclusions of mineral-forming solutions in single crystals: *skeletal growth* and *multinucleated* growth of the host crystal. Ansheles* showed that in normal crystal growth every successive new layer begins its growth at the point and on the edges of the crystal and spreads eventually to cover the entire face. It may happen that the deposition of material in the central part of a crystal face may be retarded as a result of local stagnation of the solution from which the crystal is growing or as the result of an accumulation of unassimilated impurities at the crystal's face. Under such circumstances, further growth of the crystal takes place only in bands along the edges, with the consequent development of trough-like depressions in the faces. Skeletal crystals may be thus formed by this type and by still more complicated types of starvation growth. This

---

* *Uchen. zap. Leningrad. Univers., ser. geolog. pochv.* 5, 1933.

skeletal result is eliminated if the environment responsible for it is followed by the normal environment in which the trough-like depressions in the crystal faces become covered by growth of the substance from the "bands" along the edges toward the center of the crystal faces. This overgrowth causes capture and isolation of small samples of the mineral-forming solutions which is conducive to the formation of relatively large inclusions in central parts of the crystal faces. "Open" troughs may be encountered occasionally that remained unsealed because the crystal growth was arrested. They preserved their contact with the surface of the outer faces of the crystal and were therefore unable to retain their fillings to the present time. Inclusions of these types may be seen in Fig. 3, in the two quartz crystals on the right. Repeated alternations of the skeletal and of the normal growth result in the formation of a series of primary inclusion, of various ages situated on different planes of the crystal (Fig. 5, p. 39).

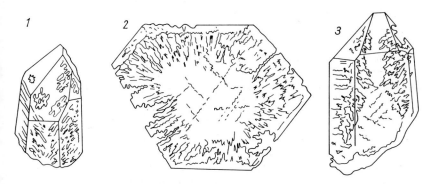

FIG. 3. Sketches of crystals of quartz from Odudi
(According to A. I. Zakharchenko.)

Zakharchenko [44] demonstrated these phenomena clearly in several zoned quartz crystals, from Pamir, containing large inclusions. Figure 3 shows a transverse section through one of these three-zoned crystals. The core is practically flawless and its few fissures were healed during the initial stage of the second zone. The second zone is represented by a turbid skeletal quartz overflowingly full of large primary inclusions, elongated radially or rather fanning out from the center of the crystal. This orientation of the inclusions coincides with the direction of the pyramidal growth. The outer zone of the crystal is transparent quartz enveloping most of the inclusions of the second zone but leaving some open.

The homogenization of inclusions in different zones of the crystal occurred over a range of temperatures. Inclusions in any one of the crystal's zones, however, would homogenize within a definite range of the temperature.

Shubnikov, in his experiment with artifically grown crystals of potassium aluminum alum, had already shown that certain (octahedral) faces of the crystal are able to grow normally while other (cubical) faces are growing skeletally, so that some points on the crystal may contain a large number of inclusions while others may contain none. In zoned crystals, the turbid zones, abundant in inclusions, are formed in consequence of rapid growth, while the transparent zones result from slower normal deposition of the substance from true solutions over the crystal.

Tubular inclusions in some quartz and, more commonly, in topaz and beryl were studied intensively by us, in connection with the development of the visual method of temperature determination and a study of the different types of the homogenization. Judging from studies of Vadilo [22], tubular inclusions develop originally as rut-like depressions along the crystal's edges and are sealed eventually by the rapid growth spreading out over the faces of the crystals. In such manner tube-shaped inclusions of the mother liquor are preserved in the crystal. (A crystalline magnesium heptahydrate was employed in ascertaining the mechanism of the formation of tubular inclusions.)

It appears that when two concentration currents meet each other over a crystal edge, the result is a zone of stagnation conducive to a blunting of the crystal's edge by a lack of growth there, while the advancing overgrowth of the crystal's regular faces, according to its habit, results in the formation of an elongated inclusion parallel to the crystal's edge. A series of elongated inclusions of the mother liquor parallel to the crystal's edge may be developed by repetitions of the sequence. Origin of the *inclusions along the path of growth of the crystal's termination* is almost analogous to the origin of tubular inclusions. Primary inclusions *on the step-like surfaces resulting from alternating growth of two adjoining faces of the crystal,* as described by Grushkin [28, Figs. 7 and 9], are but a special case of the inclusions developing on the outer elements of the original structure of the crystal.

Inclusions in multinucleated growth are formed when the crystallization is resumed after an interruption (which is often accompanied by a change of the crystal habit), during a regeneration of parts of the crystal which were damaged mechanically, chemically, or physically (by annealing). A multitude of nuclei on which the crystal's multinucleated growth depends, are formed by the solution on the crystal surfaces. Small amounts of the mother liquor in the depressions between the minute heads of the growing nuclei eventually become faceted primary inclusions. Such layers of inclusion-bearing crystal may completely envelop the crystal forming a "shirt" (as in some quartz crystals from Tetyukhe). Less commonly the inclusions are abundant only in the crystal termination, with the formation of the white porcelain-like cap or of the "stallion's teeth" at the Sherlova Gora.

Crystallites, between which particles of the mother liquor may be also preserved, may be formed when different parts of the crystal's faces are growing at different rates. The crystallites may disappear later, when the solution becomes less super-saturated, but the droplets of the mother liquor will remain inside the crystal [22].

Inclusions of the regeneration type are accumulated at the surface of *generally uneven* fractures, on etched surfaces, or, more rarely at the annealed surface of the crystal, making such boundaries much more distinct. Primary inclusions from multinucleated growth are formed also along this boundary, naturally, in the enveloping layer belonging to the new generation. Inclusions associated with the fracture surfaces and with etched surfaces belong rather to the pseudo-secondary type by virtue of their position in the crystal.

PSEUDO-SECONDARY INCLUSIONS

This type of inclusion shows indications of both its primary and secondary origin. The type is common especially in small fissures cutting across some of the inner zones of the crystal that do not reach the outer zones. Such small fissures develop because of internal stress in the crystal or because of external factors at different stages of growth of the crystal. The small fissures are healed eventually, either concurrently with the formation of a new zone of crystal growth or after an interval, as the result of an overgrowth of the crystal by material of a later generation. Pseudo-secondary inclusions in small fissures traversing the core of the crystal but not penetrating the crystal's outer zones were discovered by us for the first time in phantom crystals of fluorite. It was clear, in that particular case, that the healing of fissures in the core coincided in time with the start of growth of the outer zone and that, consequently, the homogenization temperature of pseudo-secondary inclusions in fissures in the core corresponds to homogenization temperatures in primary inclusions in the outer zones. This was indeed the case.

Spontaneously originating small fissures in growing crystals caused by internal stress in crystals at different stages of their growth were discovered both in natural and in artificially grown crystals. These generalizations are sustained further, even under ideal laboratory conditions, in the experience with the mass production of sodium potassium tartrate crystals.

Shternberg [121] performed certain important studies of the development of fissures in groups of crystals grown in entirely identical physico-chemical environments but developing asymmetric forms of various kinds. He proved that, in the process of crystal growth, fissures do develop in different parts of the crystals and that inclusions are formed in these fissures. In a growing crystal, "the fissures begin in the regeneration zone whereupon they spread out in the direction of the crystal's growth, but they never penetrate the core of the crystal. The more rapid is the regeneration, the greater is the number of the fissured crystals. There is no fissuring during a slow regeneration and the crystals so obtained are symmetrical" [121]. Such fissures do not extend to the crystal's surface. Their extension takes place intermittently and follows behind the continuous growth of the crystal's face. The fissures begin to develop branches, in certain directions where the rate of growth is markedly accelerated, with respect to the rate of growth of the other faces of the crystal.

We have seen such branching "sparkling" fissures, never healed, in natural crystals of fluorite and of other minerals [35]. We called them "dry" fissures and vacuoles. More often, however, fissures in natural crystals have become healed, although it is by no means always possible to prove that they originally came through to the crystal's present surface.

On the contrary, one sees often that the fissures terminate somewhere inside the crystal or else at a short distance from its present surface. In all such cases, we must assume that, at different times during the crystal's growth the tension-fractures were growing outward, from the crystal's core, as far as the surface of the crystal's growing face. This was caused probably by the natural mineral-forming environments which are markedly different from the ideal environments in the laboratory. The differences involve both the uniform cooling rates, under the laboratory conditions, and the protection of the crystallizer and the crystal from shock. In the complex processes of natural mineral formation, in which formation of ideal crystals is an exception, there are more or less abrupt fluctuations of temperature, there are earthquakes of unknown intensities, and certain other phenomena functioning as supplementary stimuli that may enable the tension-fractures to emerge on what was then the surface of the crystal.

It has already been remarked that the layers of new growth on crystal faces take place in steps and not simultaneously over the entire surface of the face. The new growth starts at the crystal edges and advances from either side across the entire surface of the crystal face. The formation of the new growth coincided with the healing of the inner fissures, in this particular case. The temperature of the solutions growing the crystal and healing its fissures was the same at that time. Thus the corresponding inclusions show evidence of their secondary origin, inasmuch as they occur in groups situated on planes cutting across the crystal's growth zones, while they are essentially primary, inasmuch as the healing of the fissures took place during the continuing growth of the crystal. We used the term *primary–secondary* [38], in order to emphasize the dual nature of such inclusions. It is clear from the present discussion that pseudo-secondary inclusions are just as important as the primary ones for our understanding of the formation of minerals. This was shown by us in the concrete example of the quartz crystal from Briestenstock [41, pp. 51–53] in which both groups of inclusions were present. In addition to the most common pseudo-secondary inclusions already described, we must classify also some other varieties as belonging to the same group.

Grigor'ev [25] had identified a new variety of inclusions which develops on the *induction surfaces* at the contact boundaries between concurrently growing crystals in druses ["compromise growth surfaces", Ed.]. Insofar as crystals in druses are generally oriented in different directions, the *inductional inclusions* may be formed in the plane of juncture of crystal faces with unlike indices. Consequently the character of the distribution of such inclusions differs from that of the strictly primary inclusions. It would be more appropriate therefore to relegate the inductional inclusions to the pseudo-secondary group. Since the sutures between adjacent crystals belong also to the forms of crystal growth, the inductional inclusions, on their homogenization, indicate the lower temperature limit of the formation of the surrounding crystals. Inclusions forming along *rejection paths of particles foreign to the crystal's substance*, identified as such for the first time by Shubnikov, must be also classed together with the pseudo-secondary inclusions, by virtue of their positions within the body of the mineral. Fine particles of foreign substance mechanically deposited on a growing face cause a local starvation of the face of the crystal. During additional growth, the foreign substance is often lifted and, as it is moving outwards, the trail of its migration becomes a chain-like series of drop-like and tubular vacuoles containing included solutions. This trail is perpendicular to the outer face of the crystal and, consequently, appears as though it were cutting across the different zones of the crystal's growth. Occasionally, only one single inclusion may be formed, e.g. in the case where a relatively large particle, having arrived at the crystal's face, stops its further migration in the direction of the growth, and becomes enclosed by its host.

Plate XXII, 4, is a record of an interesting example of the formation of inclusions, in connection with the presence of included solid halite in some quartz crystals from Pamir. The outer face of the quartz crystal is to the right from the halite cube. During the crystal's growth, when the former face of the quartz came up to the level of the upper face of the halite, there was no deposition of silica on the halite, because of the difference between the structures of these two minerals.

The advancing face of the quartz crystal was joined finally at a fairly long distance from the upper face of the quartz* and formed a roof over the irregularly shaped cavity containing the mother liquor. A substance

---

* "Halite" rather than "quartz"? [V.P.S.].

akin to halite was deposited from the droplet of the solution, it appears, on the exposed face of the halite, while potassium chloride, also a common constituent of hydrothermal solutions from which quartz is crystallized, was separated as an independent crystal which may be seen in the photo-micrograph above the gas bubble. Application of heat to this highly educational inclusion causes a rapid solution of the sylvite, but the crystal of halite which was formed earlier than the inclusion is not able to become dissolved in the very small portion of the solution which it has helped to preserve in the crystal in the form of a liquid inclusion.

The most characteristic feature of the pseudo-secondary type of inclusions here identified is the fact that such inclusions are secondary only with respect to certain inner portions of the crystal and were formed either contemporaneously with the outer parts of the crystal or at a still earlier time. Thus, on the whole, with respect to the total mineral, the pseudo-secondary inclusions are *syngenetic*.

SECONDARY INCLUSIONS

Secondary inclusions are *epigenetic* with respect to the entire body of their host mineral, in contrast with the two other types previously described. They are situated in fissures cutting through all of the growth

FIG. 4. Solid inclusions of pyrite (dark areas on the right) in crystal of quartz from Pamir.

zones of the crystal and through other boundaries, such as the boundaries of the pyramidal growth, twin planes, regeneration surfaces, inductional crystal boundaries, and the intra-mineral fissures wherein pseudo-secondary inclusions are situated. Fissures of various age in a crystal may cut

through each other frequently, while traversing a whole series of crystals
[35]. The most characteristic feature of secondary inclusions is the *absence
of any relationship between them and the process of the growth of their
host crystal*. They are formed in fissures outcropping on the surface of the
crystal's faces which were healed during the latest period of mineral formation and metamorphism, when there was no further growth of their host
crystal. The zones of secondary inclusions cutting across each other are
plainly visible in Figs. 4 and 6.

Fissures in minerals have different origins. Most commonly, they are
due to the *mechanical action* of tectonic stresses on the crystal or else to
polymorphic transformations resulting in drastic changes in the specific
volume of the mineral. Fersman* was the first one to explain this fissure-
forming process in crystals using the $\alpha \to \beta$ transformations of quartz as
the example. *Temperature effects* are probably among the main causes of

FIG. 5. Zones of primary inclusions in quartz from Pamir.

the fissuring of minerals. At the surface of the earth, fissures may be
developed in minerals chiefly as the result of actions on the part of various
agents of erosion, although there is practically no healing of the fissures,
under such conditions, and the secondary liquid inclusions have the character of "in-flows"†, in such environments [35].

Secondary inclusions that are sealed securely within crystals are formed
in hypogene environments by healing of fissures of varied origin in the
crystals. This healing of the already fully grown crystals is brought about

---

* *In: Izv. Ross. Acad. Nauk,* ser. 6, t. 7, (1913).

† "Zatyoki", i.e. some extraneous fluids enter the originally "dry" fissures or
cavities. [V.P.S.].

by *solutions representing some other phase or stage of the mineral formation.* Thus fissures in igneous quartz are healed generally by the pneumatolytic β quartz or by quartz of hydrothermal origin. Fissures in quartz of the earlier generations are often healed by some later quartz by

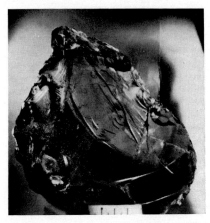

FIG. 6. Intersections of zones of secondary inclusions in quartz from Volynia.

which isolated crystallites of quartz of a different generation and habit are produced in the same deposit. Lemmlein [163] showed that capillary fissures begin to be healed at their inner wedging-out tips, as the result of an overgrowth of the dendritic type.

In the absence of connection and where diffusion is slow, renewal of the fissure-healing solutions becomes difficult. It is for that particular reason that the new growth becomes skeletal or dendritic. At the same time, joining of the dendrites assures a reliable isolation of the minutest droplets of the solution *depleted* with respect to the cognate substance of the inclusions. Healing of the relatively wide fissures depends on multinucleated overgrowth by which droplets of the solution are sealed in faceted vacuoles in the interstices between the terminations of the micro-crystals. An example of such overgrowth of a wide fissure in a crystal of quartz is presented in Figs. 23 and 24.

The foregoing discussion is important fundamentally, inasmuch as it shows the ways in which mineral-forming solutions may be captured by crystals and give rise to inclusions of different genetic species and types.

The shapes of these inclusions are unimportant for the purposes of the present work. In passing, one may remark that, in many instances, their shape is not the original one but the end-result of the process by which the equilibrium between the included solution and the host crystal was established. Specifically, as shown by Lemmlein, some fantastic shapes of inclusions, having a large specific surface, are unstable and the tendency of the inclusions is to attain the form having the smallest surface energy, while keeping the volume constant. The included substance migrates from projections to re-entrant corners; the inclusion becomes rounded and may even become a negative crystal after coming to complete equilibrium.

Studies of inclusions and applications of the results so obtained are not possible without a clear understanding of the various origins and the time of their formation with respect to that of the host crystal.

The principal ways in which inclusions are formed alongside the genetic classification of liquid and gaseous inclusions have been given by us schematically ([37], pp. 34–35). We have summarized the genetic classification of inclusions in the form of a more definitive Table 2.

TABLE 2

Types and sub-types of inclusions	Species of inclusions and their position in crystals
A. Syngenetic inclusions	
I. Primary inclusions	On elements of the initial crystal boundaries
1. Inclusions of skeletal growth	On planes of faces On the path of growing edges On the path of growing formations of crystals In zones of pyramidal growth In tubular crystals
2. Inclusions of multinucleated growth	In planes of overgrowing crystal faces, between crystallites
	In the envelope of the crystal; a new generation (after interrupted growth)
II. Pseudo-secondary inclusions	In fissures of different growth zones of the crystal
	At boundaries of the uneven surfaces of regeneration or of solution
	In the induction planes of druses
	On paths of the rejection of foreign substance by the crystal
	In vicinities of included "accessory" minerals
B. Epigenetic inclusions	
III. Secondary inclusions	In fissures of mechanical origin
	In fissures of stress and slippage, in the polymorphic transformation of minerals
	In fissures caused by erosion

CHAPTER 3

Theory and Practice of Homogenization of Liquid Inclusions by Heat

BASIC PRINCIPLE OF THE METHOD

The liquid in aqueous inclusion functions like mercury in a thermometer in inclusion thermometry, since application of heat causes an expansion of the mercury, which is then measured against a calibrated thermometric scale. One may easily imagine an analogous water thermometer in a hermetically sealed tube with the water filling all of the tube at 100°C. On cooling to room temperature, the water contracts so that only a part of the tube remains filled with water. A vacuum develops therefore in the tube and it becomes filled by water vapor, and is thus a gas (vapor) bubble. A hermetically sealed aqueous system of this kind may be graduated so as to make it function the way mercury functions in a thermometer. If so, the entire volume of the tube must be filled with water at the original temperature (100°C, in this particular case). A substantially greater thermal coefficient of expansion for mercury makes it convenient in practice to use mercury in thermometers that depend on expansion and contraction of liquids.

The same basic principle is employed in thermometry studies of two-phase inclusions of aqueous solutions common in hydrothermal minerals. At the time of their sealing off, the hot hydrothermal solutions completely filled their cavities in the minerals, forming hermetically sealed homogeneous systems. On cooling of the mineral, the included liquid must contract more than the pore in which it was confined. This is due to the greater expansion and contraction coefficients of liquids on warming and cooling (specifically of water and of aqueous solutions), than of the solid substance. The difference between the contraction in volume of the droplet of liquid and the pore itself causes a vacuum in the inclusion. This vacuum is filled rapidly by vapor from the inclusion liquid, resulting in the formation of a second phase, the gas bubble. Naturally, the hotter the liquid was, the more it will contract on cooling, relative to the contraction of the pore, and the larger will be the gas (vapor) bubble, generally speaking.

Theoretical calculations show that the size of the gas bubble depends on the original temperature of the resulting cooled solution, in the absence

[42]

of appreciable effects due to the concentration of solutes and to high external pressures. This conclusion is sustained by numerous observations on the size of gas bubbles in crystals of quartz, calcite, and fluorite formed at different temperatures in deposits at shallow depths. The greater the temperature of the included mother liquor, the greater the volume of the gas bubbles in relation to the volume of the pore, in a given mineral, although no direct proportionality could be observed.

Heating the crystal causes an increase in its volume and in the volume of the cavities. The mother liquor in the pores, however, undergoes a greater increase in volume. This causes a gradual diminution in the size of the gas bubble, an increasing pressure in the bubble, and the ultimate disappearance of the gas phase. At the moment when the volume of the heated liquid coincides exactly with the volume of the cavity, the bubble of gas (vapor) disappears entirely and this represents the closest approximation of the temperature of the unsaturated mother liquor trapped in the inclusions at a relatively low external pressure.

Formation of bubbles as described here, was produced experimentally by us [32], using heated liquids (water and aqueous solution) in cavities in a transparent plastic. Heating the plastic containing these artificial inclusions resulted in disappearance of the gas bubbles when the temperature was equal to the temperature of the liquid at the time of the filling. Later on, the same type of experiment was performed, with the same results, on inclusions produced in artificial crystals grown in hot solutions.

Experiments and numerous observations on natural inclusions in low-temperature minerals thus verify the foregoing explanation of the origin of the gas bubbles and the cause of their disappearance. Gas bubbles in the inclusions, after homogenization at a certain temperature, reappear upon cooling a few degrees or tens of degrees below the homogenization temperature. The moment of the reappearance of the gas bubbles is fixed definitely by observation. The liquid in the cavity boils, on occasions, with the resulting formation of many small bubbles that coalesce instantaneously into a single one. As a rule, however, only a single small gas bubble reappears first and continues to grow, depending on the rate of the cooling. We have also observed an abrupt appearance of a relatively large gas bubble out of some corner of the inclusion which may be associated, it appears, with the presence of included carbon dioxide.

Experiments with bubbles produced in artificial inclusions in plastic duplicate the phenomena observed in their reappearance in natural minerals on cooling. The boiling of the liquid at the moment of formation of the vacuum in the pore is understandable. The formation of a single gas bubble, by coalescence of small ones, takes place probably in inclusions where the solution is confined under an appreciable pressure. If the original external pressure was much higher than the internal vapor pressure, the gas bubble is formed only when the temperature falls much below the temperature at which the inclusion was formed.

The pressure also decreases on cooling and the gas phase appears soon after the pressure is reduced to the vapor pressure of the liquid in the inclusion. It happens occasionally that gas bubbles do not reappear on cooling of inclusions (those not destroyed by the heating), whose homogenization temperatures are below 70 to 80°C. If so, artificial cooling of the slide below room temperatures is required to form a gas phase.

If the solution at a high temperature contains a certain quantity of dissolved gaseous compounds, these will go into the gas phase. However, such additions are relatively unimportant in the formation of the gas bubble. Carbon dioxide and water vapor are the main constituents of the gas bubble only in the case of the complex liquid inclusions (aqueous solution—carbon dioxide). The newly formed gas bubble increases gradually in size with cooling of the slide, after homogenization of the inclusion, and attains its original size at room temperature.

Our previous explanation of two-phase inclusions in minerals is supported further by the uniform homogenization temperatures and by restoration of the original volume ratios of the phases in groups of inclusions of the same type.

If the solution was saturated with respect to various solutes, its cooling may result not only in the development of a gas bubble (the *compression-bubble*), but also in super-saturation, whereupon the various solutes may precipitate as solid phases. In such cases solutes that are similar to the substance of the host crystal may precipitate as a "film" on the walls (due to the crystal structure of the host), while other materials will come out of the solution as independent "captive" minerals.

In this case, during the cooling to room temperature, there is a development of a multiphase complex that can generally be reduced to its original homogeneous state by heat. However, utilization of inclusions of this sort in determining the true minimum temperature is possible only if we can ascertain the effects of composition and concentration on the exact homogenization temperature. Moreover, we must make sure that all of the precipitated film on the pore walls redissolves.

The homogenization temperature of primary and pseudo-secondary two-phase inclusions of aqueous solutions is taken as *the minimum temperature* of the crystallization of the corresponding growth zone of the mineral in question, unless the original external pressure was appreciably greater than the vapor pressure of the solution. The same qualification applies also to minerals originating at shallow or intermediate depths. The observed homogenization temperature for minerals from greater depths must be corrected for pressure and concentration, in order to approximate the true temperature of formation, as shown below.

Several other aspects of the problem also require clarification, along with the basic principle involved in the utlilization of aqueous inclusions as self-recording thermometers, to give us a general theoretical background for the method.

THE PROBLEM OF HERMETIC SEALING OF INCLUSIONS

There has been practically no discussion of this problem in any of the earlier contributions to the subject, yet the use of aqueous inclusions for thermometry depends on a satisfactory answer to this problem. If the inclusions lose some of their contents, during the very long history of the mineral, their system cannot be restored to their original state and, consequently, we have no reason for arriving at the temperatures of formation from the temperatures of homogenization. The results of our measurements will be in error also in case there are leaks from the inclusions during the measurement itself, no matter how small, when there is a drastic increase in the pressure within the inclusion.

The experimentor must be sure therefore that the inclusions are hermetically sealed in the mineral. Some minerals are not suited for such studies, according to our experimental evidence.

Halite, sylvite, carnallite, and other easily soluble minerals are most unsuitable. Formation of the gas bubble in liquid inclusions in these minerals is caused by leakage of liquid through the walls and not by contraction in the volume of the originally hot liquid. For this reason, single-phase inclusions in halite and alum crystallized from cold solutions are transformed into two-phase inclusions within a relatively short time.

We must recognize, however, the absence of such possibilities in the vast majority of other natural minerals such as quartz, calcite, barite, fluorite, etc. This assumption is sustained by the very fact of the *present-day occurrence of single-phase inclusions* in quartz crystals from Marmarosh, in calcite, datolite, and apophyllite from Tetyukhe, in the last generation of fluorite from Transbaikal, in celestite from Pinega, in analcime from Arkhangel'sk, and in other minerals. There can be no doubt whatsoever that these minerals were formed *many tens of millions of years ago* and were able to maintain homogeneous liquid inclusions hermetically sealed during all of that time. Were it not so, "anomalous" gas bubbles would have developed in their liquid inclusions.

Crystals of halite, sylvite, and alum, for example, cannot provide a reliable isolation for their inclusions, to the point that single-phase liquid inclusions in the peripheral zones of these crystals acquire their gas bubbles even on the second or the third day after crystallization, while inclusions in the inner zones of the crystals do so somewhat later. Our studies of a large faceted macro-inclusion (7 mm long, 5 mm wide, 3.7 mm high) in a natural crystal of halite from Velichka, during recent years, showed a slow but noticeable increase in the size of its gas bubble, over the years, caused by permeability of the crystal (the diameter of the gas bubble increased from 3.8 to 4.0 mm in four years).

In the article by Dreyer, Garrels, and Howland [178] which appeared in 1949, the authors tried to determine the former temperatures of salt-depositing Permian brines of the Kansas salt beds by the homogenization method applied to inclusions in halite. They arrived at serious misconceptions because they paid no attention to the reasons for the anomalous heterogeneity of inclusions and to the consequent impossibility of making use of such "anomalous" inclusions in mineralogical thermometry. Their example shows how important it is to solve the problem of hermetic sealing of the inclusions if they are to be employed as self-recording thermometers.

In addition to the negative evidence above, we must refer also to the fact that liquid carbon dioxide, so common in the inclusions in quartz, topaz, calcite, and other minerals, exists there undoubtedly under a high pressure. Inclusions of liquid carbon dioxide are preserved for tens and hundreds of millions of years nevertheless, because inclusion walls of these minerals are impermeable.

This imperviousness may be argued also from the evidence of studies of primary inclusions in different zones of the crystal. Painstaking measurements of the size of the gas bubble, in relation to the volume of the liquid in the inclusion, indicate that inclusions grouped on the periphery of the crystal and separated from the crystal surface by a thin layer (fractions of a mm) of substance (quartz, topaz) carry relatively small gas bubbles (as the solution temperature was lower at the end of the crystallization), smaller than is found in the inclusions situated in the inner zones of the crystal. Were there any leaks, we would expect the reverse relationship between the phases in inclusions on the periphery and in the core of the crystals. Moreover, the equal degrees of filling of the inclusions and of the healed fissures in the same zone of the crystal is an indirect indication of the hermetic character of the sealing.

As previously stated, heating of the inclusions to their original temperature leads to progressively increasing pressures in the inclusions. Heating above the homogenization temperature results generally in rupture even of the most resistant minerals. If, however, the overheating is not allowed to occur (as it is not needed for the homogenization), the initial phase ratios of the inclusions are restored on subsequent cooling.

The investigator always has the opportunity to ascertain these facts if he makes careful measurements of the degree of filling at exactly the same temperature before and after the experiment. Thus, it is proved that there is no leakage from the inclusions, it appears, even at very high internal pressures, except in some special cases. In working with minerals having a perfect cleavage (barite, calcite, etc.), one may occasionally see how a minute fissure forms next to an inclusion. Some of the inclusion's fluid then leaks into this fissure and the gas bubble increases rapidly in size. If the liquid is squeezed out quantitatively, the gas bubble will fill the entire pore, the inclusion will become darker, and, of course it will not return to its original state after cooling (Plate III, 1). Homogeneity of a cooled inclusion which was heterogeneous before the experiment is an abnormal phenomenon and, more often than not, is an indication of a leakage. Partial leakage may be easily recognized also if the liquid inclusion in question contains an uncommonly large gas bubble in comparison with other inclusions of the same type in its immediate vicinity. Obviously, such inclusions are homogenized at anomalously high temperatures and their homogenization temperatures must be disregarded.

We have not discussed general studies of permeability of minerals to aqueous solutions and gas, because our experience with inclusions in the vast majority of minerals demonstrates the imperviousness of their crystal structures. This is indicated, first of all, by the fact that the volume ratios of phases generally remain unchanged, even after many repeated homogenizations of one and the same inclusions, provided, of course, that the volumes are always measured at the same temperature.

VARIATIONS IN VOLUME OF VACUOLES CONTAINING INCLUSIONS

There is generally a slight reduction in the volume of vacuoles at room temperature, as against their original volume. This reduction is caused by a general *contraction* of the host crystal by cooling and by a *deposition* of the cognate substance on the walls of the vacuoles which may be both syngenetic and epigenetic, i.e. may take place both at the time of the formation of the vacuoles and after their sealing.

Decrease in Volume Caused by Contraction of Crystal on Cooling

The development of a gas bubble inside a vacuole filled by a hot aqueous solution is associated with cooling of the crystal and inclusions, as has already been indicated. This cooling results in a greater contraction of the liquid than of the vacuole. The difference between these two contractions results in a free space inside the vacuole occupied by the bubble of gas (vapor). This is the normal sequence of volume changes in a two-phase aqueous inclusion. Such changes due to the difference between the contraction of water and quartz may be illustrated by the following values $\times 10^{-6}$ [172].

TABLE 3

Temperatures (°C)	$P = V \times P_1$ H_2O	$P = 1$ atm	$P = 2000$ atm	
	water	quartz	water	quartz
30	45.2	2.76	34.9	2.65
75	48.4	2.78	34.3	2.67
150	67.9	—	—	—
225	136.5	—	—	—

These empirical data of Dorsey and Sosman make it evident that water is more than 13 times as compressible as quartz even at 2000 atm. This difference in the contraction will be presumably still greater at higher temperatures.

We have proved that different homogenization temperatures of inclusions having identical gas–aqueous solution ratios in different minerals depend, to a degree, on the expansion coefficients of the minerals [32, Fig. 5]. However, the original volumes of both the inclusion and the liquid are more or less restored by the homogenization. Only in the case of multiphase inclusions in which the solid phases either remain undissolved or on rapid heating dissolve long after the disappearance of the gas bubble is the restoration of the original volumes unattainable. Such solid phases are relatively rare in multiphase inclusions and, naturally, do cause a decrease in the original volume and distort the phase ratios.

Contraction of Volume of Inclusions Caused by Deposition of Cognate Substance on Their Walls

It is natural that the observed volume of an inclusion will become somewhat smaller at room temperature (although generally by an insignificant amount), because of the deposition of a substance cognate to the host crystal *from the sealed droplet* onto the cavity walls.

The question regarding the particular quantity of the substance so deposited, after the inclusion has been sealed, is of interest, as is the magnitude of the difference between the vacuole's original volume and its volume at room temperature. These questions need be answered separately for primary inclusions and for inclusions produced by healing of fissures, i.e. pseudo-secondary and secondary ones.

As has been already pointed out, we have made careful microscopic studies involving many thousands of genetically variable inclusions, but found only tens of cases, among the high-temperature minerals, in which the presence of a thin selvage of the cognate substance could be demonstrated. The selvage was sufficiently wide, in some isolated cases (Plate XVII, 1 and 2*), to suggest an erroneous conclusion, namely, that there

---

* Plate XVI, 4, in original [Ed.].

has been a significant change from the inclusion's original volume to its observed volume at room temperature.

The facts here reported have their explanations in the very mechanism of formation of inclusions. It is often forgotten or ignored that the development of a primary inclusion is *a process the duration of which is not known to us.* From the beginning of this process to its termination, at the moment when a droplet of the solution becomes effectively sealed in the pore, a change in the chemical composition of the droplet undoubtedly must have taken place. The very development of the vacuoles of primary inclusions is related to stagnant areas of solution *impoverished with respect to the crystal's cognate substance.* It is for this reason that blunted edges and terminations of crystals are the places where inclusions are formed, as was discussed in the preceding chapter. The ease of skeletal growth of the crystal is obvious.

The droplet of solution, already impoverished with respect to the crystal's cognate substance, laid down its original excess of this substance while it was stagnant and semi-confined. The deposition could have and undoubtedly did cause, even at that time, *a withdrawal of the corresponding amount of exhausted solution from the still partially open pore.* Thus the isolation of that particular droplet from the rest of the mineral-forming solution and its retarded contact with the solution does not mean that a *typical* portion of the super-saturated solution was captured by the mineral. *Only the temperature, but certainly not the composition, of the captured droplet could have been the same as that of the mother liquor.* They may have been identical with respect to substances *alien* to the mineral, inasmuch as natural solutions have a complex composition.

There is no resemblance, however, and there could not be any, between the concentrations of the cognate substance in the *stagnant* drop of exhausted mother liquor, on the verge of becoming an inclusion, and in the *free* mineral-forming solution. This is especially characteristic of low-temperature and medium-temperature hydrothermal solutions, in contrast with high-temperature liquid and particularly gaseous solutions in which the diffusion of substances is less intensive. We were not able to detect even a thin layer of cognate substance deposited on the inclusion's walls as the result of cooling of the solution after sealing (see photomicrographs) in any inclusions in low- and medium-temperature minerals, by any special procedures (the diaphragm method, the photo-filters, the apparatus for studies of contrasting phase) [i.e. phase microscope? — Ed.].

We believe that a certain portion of the cognate substance still must have been deposited on the walls of two-phase inclusions. This portion, however, for reasons here discussed, *has no appreciable effect on the volume of the cavity, as observed at room temperature, in reference to its original volume at the time when inclusion was sealed.*

If we consider the undoubtedly low concentrations of substances in two-phase inclusions, any changes in the vacuole's volume will appear insignificant, having little or no effect on the homogenization temperature, as determined on slow heating.

We must remember here, in order to explain the extent of such changes in quartz, that 1 liter of water dissolves 450 milligrams of silica at 100°C, at ordinary pressure; twice as much silica is dissolved at 200°C and nearly four times as much at 300°C, while at 340°C the solubility is five times as great, and yet the total dissolved silica is insignificant at that; not over 0.25 per cent. Even if we assume that 1 per cent dissolved silica could be present in a two-phase aqueous inclusion at a high pressure in quartz and that all of this silica would be precipitated on cooling down to room temperature, still the total decrease in the vacuole's volume would constitute only 0.033 per cent of its original volume [*sic*].

As previously stated, all or practically all of the solid phases ("captive" minerals) pass into solution when multiphase inclusions are homogenized by heat. Some of the solid phases do not dissolve rapidly at the temperature at which the gas bubble disappears and require the maintenance of that high temperature for a more or less long period of time.

Naturally, the cognate substance that crystallizes on the walls ought to return entirely or almost entirely to the included solution at the homogenization temperature, on slow heating, thereby restoring the original volume of the inclusion. If this does not take place on rapid heating of *two-phase* inclusions, the change in the volume of the vacuole is so small, as we have shown, that it has no effect on estimations of the temperatures by the homogenization method.

It would be premature, however, to expand this conclusion to involve also multiphase inclusions that are found generally in high-temperature minerals. It was in such minerals that we and Lemmlein have observed the "bordures" and the "selvages" of cognate substance on the walls of the vacuoles. They were described in the earlier part of the book and are shown on Plates XVII, 1, and XXII, 1 and 2. These "bordures" made of cognate substance are sufficiently wide, in some cases, to suggest a significant decrease in the original volume of the vacuole (as much as 20 to 25 per cent). In none of the cases we have observed, however, did the cognate substance encircle the entire contour of the inclusions, but a very thin ringlet ("obodok") would outline the inclusion's boundary, in a circle.

Of course, supercritical solutions in incompletely sealed inclusions assure an easier exchange of substances than is accorded by hydrothermal solutions, particularly of substances cognate to the host crystal. On the other hand, as we know experimentally, concentrations of solutes in supercritical solutions are *appreciably lower* than they are in aqueous solutions.

Consequently, the wide "bordures" of the cognate substance that occupy as much as 20 to 25 per cent of the inclusion's volume cannot be regarded as being epigenetic with respect to the moment when the inclusion was fully sealed. They are products of a syngenetic deposition of the cognate substance diffusing into the droplet undergoing the inclusion process. The cognate substance is separated from specifically *stagnant* zones of inclusion-forming solutions and not from freely circulating solutions. This feature of the deposition, in relatively quiet environments, is responsible for a difference between the cognate substance and the substance of the host crystal in regards to physical properties (index of refraction). It becomes possible accordingly to ascertain the very delicate boundary between the normally crystallized substance of the host and the "bordure" or the "ring" of cognate substance in the inclusion, with the aid of certain special devices.

After the complete sealing of the inclusion and cooling to room temperature, a certain very small quantity of the cognate substance, easily redissolved on slow heating, inevitably must be deposited on the walls from the type of the solution here discussed. This extremely narrow *inner* "*ring*" may be detected, in practice, at very high magnifications under the microscope. On occasions, the *ring* is deposited on the surface of the peripheral "bordure" which could not be redissolved by us even on prolonged heating at a temperature close to the point of the homogenization.

These observations and experiments justify our assertion to the effect that *deposition of a substance, cognate to the host mineral's substance, is continuous up to the very moment of complete sealing of the inclusion, in the form of a discontinuous "bordure" on the inclusion's walls*, especially in pneumatolytic minerals. Only *insignificant quantities of the cognate substance* are deposited after the sealing of the inclusion and after its subsequent cooling to room temperature. *This deposition of the cognate substance* from aqueous and especially from gaseous solutions, already sealed, *is seen occasionally as a very thin ring*, on the inclusion's walls, which may be *redissolved on slow heating*.

The original volume of the sealed inclusion may be decreased significantly by a deposition of such substance, in the case of multiphase inclusions in high-temperature minerals. Consequently, in order to obtain satisfactory results with the homogenization of multiphase inclusions of this type, it is necessary to heat them at a certain definite rate—generally a very slow rate—in order to bring them back to their original volume. The most exact data on multiphase inclusions are to be obtained later, after a long storage in a thermostat at a temperature somewhat below their homogenization temperature. Only after this preliminary heat treatment are the materials ready for the microthermal chamber, for the repeated and definitive measurement of the homogenization temperature.

As previously discussed, pseudo-secondary and secondary inclusions of mother liquor are also very important in thermometric studies. The mechanisms of their development differ from those of the primary inclusions in several respects. The principal distinction here is due to the origin of the inclusions, which are products of the syngenetic and epigenetic healing of fissures in minerals. Even the finest fissures in crystals are easily penetrated by hydrothermal solutions in more or less hot environments and at considerable pressures. Such solutions are *self-sealing* as their healing effects are contingent on substances cognate to substances of the host crystals. Since the fissures are generally of capillary dimensions, renewal of the injected solutions is naturally slow. Inasmuch as we can see that such healing always took place, we must infer that the healing solutions were sufficiently concentrated with respect to the substance cognate to the host to permit its diffusion, at least in the outer parts of the fissures.

As shown by Lemmlein, and by us in the preceding section of this book, fissures in crystals are healed during dendritic and multinucleated crystal growth. Solutions that enter the fissures *are bound to exhaust their reserve of the cognate substance* due to the severely impeded diffusion in the absence of convection and additions of growth material. *The bulk of the dissolved cognate substance is expended undoubtedly in sealing the solution in the fissure.* Composition and concentration of such self-sealed inclusions hence are the same as that the free solution, in reference to the accessory substances which do not participate in the crystallization of the host; the temperatures are also the same. *However, the concentration of the cognate substance is not the same.* Some small part of this substance is undoubtedly preserved in the solution within the pseudo-secondary and the secondary inclusions at the temperature of their final sealing.

While the host crystal is cooling down to room temperature, there is also a development of an equilibrium between the included solution and its walls. While the inclusion may be changing its shape, *there is very little change in its volume,* because the included solution was *already depleted of its reserve of cognate substance to a greater degree than the free solution.*

As we have already indicated, the very thin but occasionally visible ring of cognate substance, precipitated epigenetically on the walls after complete sealing, may be formed around an inclusion, as it appears to us now, only in high-temperature environments where the "hydrothermal brine," a concentrated solution, is captured and isolated. Upon sufficiently slow heating up to the homogenization point, some of the cognate substance that has been precipitated after the sealing may redissolve and the vacuole return to its original volume. The vast bulk of the cognate substance that was precipitated as the "selvage", prior to the complete sealing of the inclusion, cannot possibly be redissolved, as we have verified in every case.

Very wide "bordures" of the cognate substance were observed by us occasionally in some healed cracks containing secondary inclusions, in topaz, for example. Their presence tells us that the substance deposited in these fissures was derived from solutions that were very similar, but more important, that the depositional environment was different, and quiescent, so that diffusion of the cognate substance into the fissures was relatively impeded. The index of refraction and probably some other physical properties of the newly-crystallized substance were affected by such circumstances. It is for this particular reason that the fine boundaries between this substance and the major portion of the crystal may be distinguished microscopically, with the aid of certain special techniques of observation.

Let us now summarize the problem of the extent of the differences between the present-day volume of inclusions, as observed at room temperature, and their original volume.

First of all, we recognize three successive stages in the development of the vacuole and only two terminal stages. The three development stages correspond to certain stages in the development and existence of the inclusion and have three different volumes.

The first one, the aboriginal volume, corresponds to the time during the formation of the inclusion when, for various reasons, the existence of the inclusion and its position in the crystal became entirely definite.

The second one, the original volume, as used in thermometric research, may differ markedly from the aboriginal, especially in minerals which crystallized from or were healed by *supercritical solutions,* as correctly observed by Lemmlein. During the formation of an inclusion, which may be a long process, and depending on the rate of diffusion of the cognate substance, this substance will be deposited in the relatively calm environment on the walls of the vacuole until the very last moment of sealing, and the excess aqueous fluid will be forced out of the vacuole. It is evident that *the quantity of the solution so displaced, up to the moment of the sealing, will represent the difference between the aboriginal and the original volumes of the vacuole.*

The third, *the observed* volume at room temperature, differs very little from *the original* volume, as a rule. It is inevitable, however, that the observed volume is somewhat smaller than the original one, representing the moment of the sealing of the inclusion, by a generally insignificant amount. This difference is indeed small, in the case of (gaseous) fluids, because, *as a rule, concentrations of dissolved substances are much lower in gaseous than in liquid solutions.* This conclusion is based both on the exact findings in the laboratory and on observations of the inclusions. The quantity of substance tied-up in the form of "captive" minerals is vastly different in these two kinds of solutions and "captive" minerals are either undetectable or are present in infinitesimal quantities in essentially-gaseous inclusions.

The range of falling temperature, from that at the moment of sealing of an inclusion to the surficial environment of the earth, is not particularly wide, for low-temperature and medium-temperature hydrothermal minerals, such as we have generally been dealing with in our thermometric research. Moreover, within this temperature range, the aqueous solutions cannot dissolve much of the cognate substance, *whose thermal solubility coefficient is generally small,* regardless of their self-depletion (as we have shown to be the case for silica). It is scarcely possible under such circumstances that hermetically sealed two-phase inclusions could have become supersaturated with respect to the dissolved substances. That is the very reason why we could not find even one "ring" of cognate substance in inclusions in low- and medium-temperature minerals, and why we were able to observe only rarely the separation of "captive" minerals, whose relative volume was small.

In high-temperature minerals crystallizing from hydrothermal brines at temperatures as high as 450 to 500°C there is an appreciable deposition of cognate substance in the sealed inclusions, to the point that their observed volume differs appreciably from their *original* volume. This phenomenon also has its expression, of course, in the volume of the gas bubble, which functions as a "buffer" for the practically incompressible liquid of the inclusion. The volume ratios of the gas and liquid phases in such inclusions are distorted for that very reason. We have avoided using them even in the preliminary appraisals of temperatures over 250°C by the "visual" method (see below). A very slow rate of heating is essential for the homogenization of such multiphase inclusions, in order to restore the original equilibrium between the included solution and the walls of the vacuole. The equilibrium may be attained only when the observed volume equals the original volume by the dissolution of the cognate substance precipitated on the walls. If not, the homogenization temperature of the inclusion will appear lower than the true one, because of its smaller volume.

The largest difference seen between the observed and the original volumes is in the case of droplets of magmatic solution captured by igneous minerals (see above). The cognate substance may be precipitated occasionally as a wide "ring," as shown in Plate XVII, 1. Utilization of such inclusions in thermometry, however, is probably a matter for the distant future.

Studies and measurements of *the original* or the *primary* volume of inclusions in minerals offer some interest chiefly from the morphological point of view.

Measurements of the *initial* and the *observed* inclusion volumes* show very little difference between them, in thermometric studies of two-phase inclusions of essentially liquid and the essentially gaseous types. An ordinary slow heating leads invariably to an equalization of these volumes and hence is conducive to satisfactory results.

A very slow heating at different rates for different minerals, with a long pause at the homogenization, is essential in dealing with multiphase inclusions in high-temperature minerals. Only then may one rely on the measurements of the *relative* temperatures. The true temperatures are not as reliable, however, because the exact effects of the high concentrations on the homogenization temperatures are still insufficiently clear, in the present state of our knowledge.

COMPOSITION AND CONCENTRATION OF SUBSTANCES IN LIQUID INCLUSIONS AND METHODS OF THEIR STUDY

We can hardly overestimate the value of qualitative and quantitative analyses of the original mother liquor included in minerals. Practically futile controversies are continuing even now among theorists of mineralization as to whether the changing environments of mineral genesis (gaseous and liquid solutions) were acid, alkaline, or neutral. As to the composition and the concentration of the mineral-forming solutions, all that was offered by the science so far were conjectures.

Without going too deeply into the discussion of the composition of vein solutions and its implications in mineralogical thermometry, we shall attempt here a summary of all of the scanty data available from the results of studies of liquid inclusions in minerals. We will also describe the most satisfactory methods and procedures. This part of our work is also essential for ascertaining the significance of the concentration of solutes in measurements of the temperatures of mineral genesis by the homogenization method.

Qualitative investigations of included aqueous solutions may be made by the analytical, the physico-chemical, and the mineralogical method.

The Analytical Method

There are several variants of this method as applied to the problem at hand:

(a) Qualitative and quantitative chemical analyses of aqueous solutions obtained by opening of large macro-inclusions in hydrothermal minerals and crystals from veins of the Alpine type. This direct analytical approach yields the most reliable data, under certain conditions. Its applications are very limited, however, because inclusions of the required large size are extremely rare.

---

* I.e., before and after homogenization. [V.P.S.]

(b) Chemical analyses of aqueous extracts of representative aliquots of a finely ground or of an ignited mineral containing an abundance of micro-inclusions. At best, the analysis of this type may represent only an average composition of the (primary) solutions from which the mineral was crystallized and the (secondary) solutions causing healing after its crystallization. One must consider also, in this connection, that multiphase inclusions in the mineral may contain some water-insoluble captive minerals.

(c) Microchemical analyses of droplets of the solutions obtained by opening inclusions in a cleavage plane.

(d) Microanalyses of volatile constituents of the inclusions. The apparatus for this type of work is well known and is in general use. The inclusions are exploded *in vacuo* by heating them above their homogenization temperature.

(e) Comparisons between spectrographic analyses of a mineral with abundant inclusions and of the same mineral without any inclusions. In this case, the mineral is fragmented, as a rule, and the test material best suited for the purpose is selected under the microscope. This is easily done with the aid of an immersion liquid having an index of refraction near that of the mineral in question.

(f) Determinations of volatile constituents in inclusions required for the calculation of their concentration may be done by the following procedure.

A definite aliquot of the mineral with liquid inclusions is ignited to 500–600°C in a platinum crucible so as to explode the inclusions completely. The loss on ignition curve is determined at 50 to 100°C intervals, representing loss of volatile constituents (water, carbonic acid, etc.). The water content may be determined also by igniting the aliquot of the mineral in a silica flask attached to an "elbow" condenser. The water content of inclusions may be determined also by its absorbtion in a calcium chloride tube connected to the silica flask. Carbon dioxide may be trapped and weighed in Liebig's KOH absorber.

Next, the ignited mineral is pulverized, its soluble salts are extracted, and the extract is filtered. The total soluble salts are determined by difference between the weight of the ignited sample and the weight of the extracted sample, after drying, and the mean concentration of the solution is calculated.* The filtrate is evaporated sufficiently to produce a concentrated extract, whereupon it is analyzed qualitatively and quantitatively, by the conventional procedures. Concentrations of individual solutes in the liquid of the inclusions may be calculated accordingly.

---

* These calculations and the data beyond derived in this manner are based on a series of critical assumptions that do not appear in the text. [Ed.]

Composition and concentration of substances dissolved in the mineral-forming solution may be obtained by comparisons between carefully performed chemical, microchemical, and spectrographic analyses. However, the analyses *will not reveal the true concentration of the substance from which the mineral was formed*, most or all of which has precipitated on the walls of the inclusion, during cooling. As the result, any concentration of the mother liquor, as indicated by the methods here described, will be somewhat lower than the true concentration, with respect to substances cognate to the crystal.

In order to approach the true composition of the mother liquor in such studies, it seems reasonable to recommend a *gradual and prolonged thorough heating of the inclusion at temperatures somewhat below their homogenization temperatures*. After such heating *the inclusions may be exploded, with the liberation of their contents*. The general potentialities of the analysis of inclusions have already been described. The problem is highly involved and the necessary methods for this important research still need refinements. Work done so far should be considered preliminary.

The Physico-Chemical Method

The homogenization procedures used and reported by us [37] may contribute significantly in the future to research on the composition and concentration of included solutions. Specifically, the homogenization temperatures of the essentially-liquid inclusions that are significantly higher than the critical point of water are direct indications of relatively high concentrations of solutes in some sources of mother liquor.

In the course of homogenization of multiphase liquid inclusions, one may determine the relative solubility temperatures of the captive minerals. These, in turn, may serve as supplementary indications of their probable composition. For example, in the solid phase in the inclusions in topaz from Volynia, No. 1, Plates V and VI, it is halite and not sylvite that is last to disappear, just at homogenization, since we know that, unlike sylvite, the thermal coefficient of solubility for halite is practically zero.

Our recently started experiments with freezing of the included aqueous solutions and with liquefaction of gaseous inclusions in a special micro-freezer serve to increase the possibilities of the physico-chemical method in the low-temperature range. A body of data so accumulated will prove to be useful in evaluations of the concentrations of dissolved substance in such inclusions. The freezing point of included solutions is very important to us, as the lowering of the freezing point, in °C, is proportional to the solution's concentration. Moreover, determinations of freezing points, in addition to the other measurements on the inclusions, will serve to complete our view of the phase relationships in the inclusions. Our diagrams of the types of homogenization [37] may be extended accordingly into the temperature range below 0°C. However, all these possibilities belong chiefly in the future.

The Mineralogical Method

This method is applicable mainly to three-phase and to multiphase liquid inclusions. The method is based on microscopic identifications of captive minerals, which also helps in estimating the composition of the mother liquor.

Identification of minerals in the inclusions involves considerable difficulties, on account of the extremely small size of the minerals. Captive minerals may be removed from their host crystals only occasionally, if the host has a well developed cleavage and if the inclusions are relatively large. Under such conditions it is not particularly difficult to identify them by the immersion method. Most commonly, however, attempts at isolating the captive minerals are unsuccessful. Our attempts to do so mechanically (by breaking the host) and then locating the "captive" in the powder in immersion liquids proved unreliable. The captive minerals are much more easily pulverized than the host and hence they lose their crystalline shape. Moreover, the hosts for multiphase inclusions often contain also minute hard "accessory" mineral inclusions interfering with identifications of the captive minerals. Nevertheless the method of the mechanical isolation may occasionally yield satisfactory results.

We now prefer to use in our laboratory V. A. Kalyuzhnyi's procedure for the identification of captive minerals as follows:

(a) A preliminary microscopic study of form, color, relief, and isotropism or anisotropism of the captive minerals.

(b) Extraction of the mother liquor by the means of two holes in the inclusion, and injection of immersion liquid in its place.

(c) Determination of the refractive index of the captive mineral by the usual procedures. For this purpose one should make use of the dispersion of the injected liquid with a monochromator or monochromator plates.

By this procedure refractive indices of 1.549 ± 0.001 and 1.490 ± 0.001 were determined for the isotropic cubical captive crystals in multiphase inclusions in the Volynian topaz and in the quartz from Pamir, corresponding to the indices of halite and sylvite respectively.

In the case of the regularly shaped three-phase tubular inclusions with a cubical solid phase (generally either halite or sylvite) we measured the phase–volume ratios directly under the microscope, in order to estimate the concentration of this substance in the solution. For example, in a regularly shaped inclusion in the Odudi quartz (Pamir), 13 per cent of the volume was occupied by the gas bubble, 40 per cent by the halite crystal, and 47 per cent by the aqueous solution. Assuming that the aqueous solution would be saturated at room temperature, i.e. would contain 26 per cent NaCl, the total concentration of sodium chloride in the inclusion should be at least 52 to 53 per cent*. Thus we are nearer to ascertaining the composition of the mother liquor, with the aid of microscopic identifications of captive minerals, and we may reconstruct the concentration of the solution by determining the phase ratios microscopically.

A body of data on indices of refraction of aqueous solutions, which increase with increasing concentrations, is now being accumulated. It is known that the index of refraction (yellow light) of 20 per cent aqueous sodium chloride is 1.36446 at 17.5°C and is 1.37710 for a 24.6 per cent solution at the same temperature. The index is 1.35885 for 18.5 per cent solution of potassium chloride and 1.63348 [sic] for 25 per cent potassium chloride, etc. Insofar as we know the indices of refraction of the host mineral, we may estimate also the index of refraction of the mother liquor from the angle of total internal reflection at a liquid–solid interface, using a refractometer or even a universal stage.

There is no doubt that we can expect considerable progress in the near future in our understanding of the composition of mineral-forming solutions, and greater accuracy of our measurements of liquid inclusions as self-registering thermometers, as the result of an integration of all of the methods and procedures very briefly described here dealing with composition and concentration of included mother liquor.

The data available to science at this time, however, are still very modest. Despite the fact that composition of liquid inclusions began to be studied as early as Davy's time [124], as may be seen from our review of the history of the subject, this very important problem is still in its initial stage. This is explained by the absence of systematic studies and by sporadic interest in the problem, on the part of various workers, reporting disorganized and not always reliable findings on the composition of inclusions.

Principal Results of Studies of Composition
of Inclusions

As early as the first half of the last century, two clearly defined groups of liquid inclusions were recognized: inclusions of aqueous solutions and inclusions of carbon dioxide.

Presence of Na and K chlorides and of about 15 per cent of the sulfates of K, Na, and Ca in aqueous inclusions in quartz was recognized already by Sorby [128]. Zirkel [132] demonstrated the presence of halite in quartz,

---

* This is apparently *volume* per cent of pure phases; the data given indicate 71 *weight* per cent sodium chloride [Ed.].

in three-phase aqueous inclusions, both chemically and spectrographically. Lasaulx [148] determined Na_2SO_4, $CaCl_2$, traces of potassium, barium, and strontium, in addition to sodium chloride in the included solutions. Sjögren [151] reported the total salt content of the included solutions as 4.023 per cent, of which 66.2 per cent was NaCl, 11.4 per cent Na_2SO_4, 9.7 per cent $CaSO_4$, 9.0 per cent $MgCl_2$, and 3.7 per cent K_2SO_4, in single-phase liquid inclusions in Sicilian gypsum.

Lindgren and Steigl [151a] studied the composition of liquid inclusions in quartz from California. Having extracted the powdered quartz, with abundant inclusions, they analyzed both the filtrate and the residue, with the following results:

TABLE 4

Constituent	Residue	Filtrate
SiO_2	3	28
Al_2O_3 and Fe_2O_3	2	2
CaO	13	44
MgO	—	1
$(K,Na)_2O$	—	29
SO_3	—	78
Cl	—	5
Sum	18	187

This analysis showed the presence of appreciable quantities of the sulfates of calcium and the alkalies, together with noticeable quantities of sodium and potassium chlorides. The presence of the alkali chlorides in inclusions in quartz was generally reported in the investigations of the last century as the most common occurrence.

Königsberger and Müller [153] had performed some very careful qualitative and quantitative analyses of liquid inclusions in quartz from Alpine

TABLE 5. INCLUSIONS OF AQUEOUS SOLUTIONS IN QUARTZ

Constituent	Bechistock veins	Veins in Aar Massif
	per cent	
H_2O	83.4	85.0
CO_2	9.5	5.0
Na	2.0	2.5
K and Li	0.7 (Li–0.2%?)	1.5
Ca	0.3	0.3
Cl	1.6	1.5
SO_4	0.5	0.7
CO_3	1.8	3.5

veins of the Bechistock and the Aar Massif. They found that the volatile constituents (H_2O and CO_2) account for 90 to 93 per cent of the contents of aqueous inclusions. Their analytical data could be summarized in Table 5 [34].

The content of Na, K, Li, and Ca, in the case of the Bechistock quartz, was checked spectrographically and the results of the chemical analysis were confirmed by the relative densities of the lines (lithium and calcium were indicated by weak lines). The Na : K ratio was found to be about 3 : 1 by the control microchemical analysis using the chlorplatinate method. The analysis showed also that dissolved silica was almost quantitatively precipitated on the inclusions' walls. It should be desirable, in our view, to analyze the liquid inclusions after prolonged heating at the homogenization temperature. This would give us the true composition of the mineral-forming solution. The presence of certain quantities of the alkali salts appears to be a very important factor in the crystallization of quartz.

Lindgren and Whitehead [155], on the assumption that small cubic crystals in three-phase inclusions in quartz from Mexico are halite, determined the average solid–liquid volume ratio as 37 : 63 at 20°C, by the means of microscopic measurements of the volumetric relationships between the crystals and the solution. This corresponds to 53.6 per cent sodium chloride in the included solution at its original temperature.*

Inclusions in galena and sphalerite were investigated during recent decades, in studies of composition of vein solutions. Newhouse's work [166] is very interesting in this connection.

When crystals of galena are cleaved, the liquid inclusions become exposed and easily detectable under oblique light. The brine escaping from the inclusions spreads over the surface of the cleavage plane and, on its evaporation, deposits crystals of halite oriented parallel to the galena. At the end of this crystallization, there is a deposition of *calcium chloride* around every one of the *sodium chloride crystals*. Microchemical tests for sodium, by the uranyl acetate method, yielded the characteristic crystalline precipitate; the sulfuric acid test for calcium yielded fine crystals of gypsum; the chloride was indentified as silver chloride, after its precipitation by silver nitrate. The chloroplatinate tests for potassium, the sodium phosphate tests for magnesium, and the silver nitrate tests for S and SO_4 gave negative results. However, we should recognize that small quantities of potassium and magnesium may not be detectable microchemically, in the presence of large quantities of sodium in the solution.

Sodium and calcium chlorides were found to be present in the inclusions in every crystal of galena and sphalerite from 17 different sources.

---

* According to the more exact data of Bowen.

The concentrations of NaCl were estimated at 12 to 25 g per 100 cm³ of water, by comparisons with residues from evaporated droplets of standard sodium chloride solutions placed on the galena's cleavage plane. Newhouse concludes, on the basis of his experiments, that saturated solutions of chlorides may be the ore carriers [166].

Ivantishin [45] used aqueous extracts of finely pulverized galena, in his studies of inclusions in this mineral from Mogilev-Podulia, and found 9.33 per cent $Na_2O + K_2O$, and 8.66 per cent Cl in the filtrate. Recalculations of his analysis on the basis of the entire aliquot used (Table 6) showed the following:

TABLE 6

Constituents	Per cent of aqueous extract	Residues as per cent of galena
Na_2O+K_2O	0.014	0.060
CaO	0.060	0.408
MgO	none	none
Cl	0.043	0.044
SO_3	0.062	0.449

These results give us a much clearer quantitative characterization of the liquid inclusions than the results of Newhouse, although here too the analyses should be made after a prolonged heating of the inclusions at temperatures just below the temperatures of their explosion.

Zakharchenko [44], most recently, carried out some very interesting analyses of macro-inclusions in quartz involving determinations of the reaction of the included mineral-forming solution. These most complete and modern studies deserve a more detailed discussion.

The mother liquor was extracted from the large macro-inclusions (up to 1.5 cm³) through artificial punctures. Since the inclusions generally exist under a high pressure, the liquid effervesces strongly on emerging. Unfortunately the gas in the liquid was not caught. The liquid showed a definitely alkaline reaction to litmus paper. Cations in the solution were determined spectrographically. The carbons were saturated in the liquid at room temperature, prior to the analysis. The results obtained are shown in Table 7.

According to the analysts, sodium amounts to tens of per cent* and seems to be somewhat higher than calcium. The proportions of magnesium and silicon are variable and are subordinate to those of the two major constituents (i.e., a few per cent). As we see, small but fairly constant quantities of iron and aluminum are present in the included solutions.

---

* Per cent of the sum of the constituents listed in Table? [V.P.S.].

TABLE 7

Sample No. \ Constituents	Si	Al	Mg	Ca	Fe	Na
1	trace	medium	medium	very high	trace	very high
2	high	medium	high	very high	trace	very high

The silver nitrate tests for chloride resulted in an instantaneous precipitation of a thick white flock of silver chloride.

In addition, 100 g of finely pulverized quartz were extracted with 200 g distilled water at 60°C; the extract was evaporated to 2 or 3 cm³ volume afterwards. Cubes of halite were produced from the concentrated filtrate by further slow evaporation.

Rhombic and platy crystals taken out of the large inclusions were identified as *calcite* or as *magnesian calcite* by the immersion method.

A mineral appearing red in transmitted light was identified as *specularite*.

Presence of liquid and gaseous CO_2 was definitely proved, in some inclusions.

The correctness of our identifications of the captive minerals in quartz from Pamir was confirmed entirely by the investigations of Zakharchenko, with the exception of *sylvite*, about which we have no doubts, however [37].

N. L. Lopatina, analyst at the Laboratory of the All-Union Geologic Institute, had performed the following analysis: 100 g quartz containing 5 to 6 per cent inclusions by volume was extracted with water. The filtrate was weakly opalescent. The salt content of the filtrate was 54.8 mg, including 18.1 mg Cl, 6.1 mg HCO_3, 0.7 mg SO_4 (corresponding to 0.51, 0.1, and 0.01* milliequivalents respectively). Sodium, as calculated [by difference?] from the anion content amounted to 14.3 mg or 0.62 m-equiv. The soluble silica was 13.8 mg.

Electrometric measurements of the pH were done by the hydrogen-calomel electrodes. The pH was proved to be 8.6, a clear indication of the alkaline reaction.

Composition of the dissolved salts (dry residue on evaporation of the filtrate) was determined by quantitative spectrographic analysis. The results (as percentages†) were as in Table 8.

In discussing these analyses, Zakharchenko noted that sodium is markedly preponderant, chiefly as chloride and possibly also to some

---

* 0.015 m-equiv. would be closer, in the conversion [V.P.S.].

† The basis of these percentages is obscure in the original [V.P.S.].

TABLE 8

Constituent	Dry residue of filtrate	Ash of filter
Si	1–10	very high
Al	0.01–0.1	0.01
Mg	0.01–0.1	0.001–0.01
Ca	1	0.01
Fe	0.01–0.1	0.001–0.01
Mn	0.001–0.01	0.001
Ti	0.001	0.001
Cu	0.001–0.01	0.001
Sr	0.01–0.1	--
Ba	0.1	—
Na	very high	—
K	0.1–1	—

extent as Na_2CO_3, in the vein solutions from which the quartz of Pamir has been crystallized. Potassium chloride, as compared with sodium chloride, is present in small quantities. Calcium and magnesium are present as carbonates and barium and strontium as sulfates. Iron and manganese appear to be in the carbonates and iron may also form the specularite. Aluminum is present possibly in sericite-like captive minerals, while the forms of titanium and copper remain obscure.

The presence of dissolved silica is characteristic of the solutions here examined. This quantity would have been greater still, were the inclusions subjected to the preliminary treatment with heat and were they exploded above their homogenization temperature.

The absence of carbonate in the filtrate may be due to the failure of the carbonates to dissolve and to the escape of gaseous CO_2 during the pulverization of the quartz and during the heating of the filtrate.

Zakharchenko's studies showed conclusively that the quartz-forming vein solutions are *alkaline* and that they carry appreciable quantities of chlorides, carbonates, and bicarbonates. Their sulfate content and free carbonic acid is insignificant and tends to be characteristic only of low-temperature solutions. Thus alkaline solutions of salts assume the aspects of the principal carriers of silica (in the molecular state) in the hydrothermal process whose solubility in these solutions is apparently very high.

These conclusions may be expanded to include the ordinary solutions by which the hydrothermal ore deposits are formed.

As already shown, qualitative studies of essentially liquid inclusions by Soviet geologists (Ivantishin and especially by Zakharchenko) give us a far more exact characterization of the composition of liquid inclusions, qualitatively and quantitatively, than is given by Newhouse and by other foreign geologists.

Inclusions in minerals offer definite possibilities for our specific study of the chemical composition and concentration of the solutions. Thus we believe that the solute concentrations in the liquid phase of two-phase inclusions is not too high and is generally between 10 and 15 per cent. This may serve to explain the fact that no solid phase is developed in such inclusions even when their temperature has fallen by several hundred degrees, despite the corresponding marked decrease in the solubility of the dissolved substances.

On the other hand, there can be no doubt that concentrations of solutes may be high in the aqueous phase of multiphase inclusions examined by Zakharchenko. The effect of such high concentrations on estimation of the temperatures, by the homogenization method, may also be appreciable.

Effect of Concentration of Included Solutions on Homogenization Temperature

The homogenization of two-phase liquid inclusions with the gas-liquid ratio of $1 : 9$ is generally below 150°C, as we have shown, while the homogenization of three-phase and multiphase inclusions with the gas–solid–liquid ratio of $1 : 1 : 8$ takes place generally at 190°C and somewhat higher. Thus due to other factors, the disappearance of the gas bubble takes place at different temperatures notwithstanding its uniform size, depending on other factors. These differences are due to significant variations in the concentration of the included solutions and to contraction of the gas bubble from precipitation on the walls of the inclusion and crystallization of the captive minerals.

Experiments with solutions at low concentrations show, on the other hand, that their critical densities are only slightly different from the critical density of water and, for that reason, are without any significant effect in the temperature estimations by the homogenization method.

Sorby [128 (1)] determined experimentally the expansion of 10 per cent KCl in the temperature range from 25 to 200°C. He also derived the equations for calculation of the temperature at which the vapor phase disappears at a given degree of filling of the inclusion.

Ingerson [172], proceeding from the foregoing data and from the critical temperature data on solutions of certain alkali halides reported by Schröer, had drawn a curve (Fig. 7) showing the increase in the critical temperature of the solution, depending on the weight per cent of NaCl or KCl, over the critical temperature of water.

Figure 8, by Ingerson, represents the ratio between the degree of filling and the homogenization temperature for pure water and for 10 per cent solution of the chlorides. From 100°C on, the two curves part from each other gradually, since progressively higher temperatures are required for the disappearance of the vapor phase in the confined saline solutions. For example, with the vapor phase occupying 20 per cent of the volume

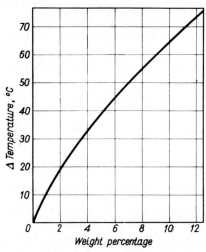

FIG. 7. Critical temperatures of solutions of NaCl and KCl.

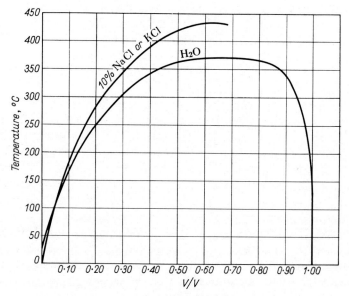

FIG. 8. Relationship between degree of filling of inclusions and temperature, for water and for 10 per cent solution of halides.

of the confined system complete filling with pure water will take place at 250°C, while a 10 per cent aqueous saline solution with the same degree of filling will require 274°C.

The critical homogenization temperatures are raised still higher, of course, at increasing concentrations of the salts, as we have already demonstrated. As a result, there are serious difficulties in any broad comparisons of the homogenization temperatures of two-phase inclusions with the homogenization temperatures of three-phase and multiphase inclusions in minerals from different sources, even if the concentrations of the solutes are known in every case. Experimental and theoretical premises of such comparisons are still lagging behind the evidence and require additional research.

Comparisons of the homogenization data on two-phase inclusions, in minerals from one or from several sources is permissible since, as shown above, the concentrations of the included solutions of this type are generally low and the range of their variation is narrow, to the point of having practically no effect on estimations of the temperatures by the homogenization method. Variations in the coefficients of thermal expansion, for solutions at different concentrations, do have a certain small effect, undoubtedly, on homogenization temperatures even of two-phase inclusions, but such factors are already outside the limits of accuracy of our present measurements of two-phase inclusions as self-registering thermometers.

EFFECTS OF PRESSURE ON ESTIMATION
OF TEMPERATURES AND POSSIBILITIES OF TAKING
SUCH EFFECTS INTO ACCOUNT

Crystallization of minerals and sealing-off of their liquid and gaseous inclusions took place at quite appreciable external hydrostatic pressures. Indeed, the hydrostatic pressure is defined generally with respect to the depth of the deposit, although the possible effects of a uni-directional stress cannot be accounted for exactly, in the present state of our knowledge. According to D. S. Korzhinskii, this stress is not an idependent factor in mineralogic equilibria, so it may be omitted tentatively from our present consideration. From here on, the external pressure is to be understood only as a direct hydrostatic pressure (P_1) acting against the internal pressure of the gas phase of the solutions (P_2), i.e. against the vapor pressure of the solutions.

The solutions could be sealed off at different magnitudes of P_1 and P_2. If P_1 was much higher than P_2, the sealed solution could be more or less compressed and, if so, there is no guarantee that the homogenization temperature of a two-phase inclusion could be particularly close to the true temperature of the solution. Under such conditions, the homogenization temperature would show merely the minimum temperature of the captured droplet of the solution and, in order to approximate its true temperature, we must take into account the effect of the external pressure. *The presence of large fissures and cavities may decrease P_1 significantly* and, as we know, hydrothermal solutions move upwards relatively freely, as in a properly functioning water main. P_1 may equal P_2, under such conditions (and even $P_1 < P_2$ is possible) and the homogenization temperature of an included aqueous solution may coincide with the true temperature, in case the concentration effects are unimportant. The same relationships between the pressures may be expected also if the minerals formed at moderate depths, not deeper than one kilometer.

Presence of open cavities, even at appreciable depths, leads us to the opinion that the effects of external pressures on the homogenization temperatures are less important than they are believed to be at the present time. In the case of low temperature minerals from shallow hydrothermal deposits, the relative sizes of the entire inclusions and of the gas bubble formed on decrease in temperature are indications of the temperature difference between that of the solution on sealing and the much lower room temperature at which we observe the inclusion. As to the inclusion's homogenization temperature, in this case, it coincides entirely or practically with the true temperature at which the inclusion-bearing zone of the crystal formed.

Determinations of the true temperature of the mineral genesis are apparently more complicated, when the experimentator is dealing with minerals from great depths.

Long-term geologic and mineralogic investigations of mineral deposits have given us so far practically no reliable foundation for ascertaining the possible magnitudes of the hydrostatic pressures existing during their formation. The science of geology has even fewer objective data on this subject than on the subject of the temperature.

We must recognize that the problem of geologic and mineralogic manometers has been very poorly developed, so far. The conventional geologic manometer, in the field of our interest, is the thickness of the overburden that existed at the time of the formation of the given mineral deposit. The pressure of the overburden may be given as the conventional 250 atm/km depth. Unfortunately, it is not always possible to reconstruct the geologic profile, in order to determine the depth of the mineral formation. However, even a mere order of magnitude of the depth may help us to approximate the true temperatures of formation, with the aid of the appropriate corrections for hydrostatic pressures.

A series of experiments were performed for ascertaining the depths of the mineral genesis and the corresponding pressures of the overburden. Thus Adams [180]experimened with specimens of limestone in which longitudinal and transverse channels had been drilled. Crushing of the limestone and closure of the channels took place at 2320 kg/cm² pressure, corresponding to about 9 km depth. However, if the specimens were encased in a steel tube, there was no deformation of the channels even at 4500 kg/cm² and 450°C. The deformation could be brought about only at 490 to 513°C and at 6750 kg/cm² pressure. Proceeding from these findings, the experimenter concluded that small cavities in the earth's crust may exist even at 17 km depths.

Bridgeman [181], in his studies of deformation of rocks and minerals at high hydrostatic pressures, proved that cavities drilled in granite, limestone, barite, calcite, and quartz become filled with an extremely fine "sand" without any accompanying plastic deformation. Specifically, in the case of granite, it has been established that artificially drilled cavities become full of the "sand" within one hour at 500 kg/cm² hydrostatic pressure applied to the specimen. As one may see, these findings are at variance with the Adams' findings and, consequently, the existence of open cavities in the host rocks of a deposit is of no aid to us in determinations of the depth of formation of the deposit.

The character of fissuring and deformation of the rocks gives us also very little concerning geologic barometry. The available data on this subject were summarized by Farmin [182] and are given here as Table 9.

The indications summarized in this table are useful in appraisals of pressures and depths at which the deposits were formed, although they are too general to afford numerical expressions of these variables of acceptable reliability.

Attempts at estimations of the depths of the mineral genesis, based on studies of structures and mineralogy of deposits, do not attain a degree of accuracy comparable with that of the temperature measurements by the homogenization method applied to inclusions of aqueous mother liquor.

Mineralogical barometers employed in research on the geological environments of hypogene mineral genesis are more useful in ascertaining the origins of rocks than in determining the environmental variables. In this connection we must first call attention to the "abyssal" mineralogic facies, as defined by Korzhinskii [51]. This series of silicate associations opens some important vistas of science, in regards to depths of origin and metamorphism of rocks. Specifically, his grossularite-free facies may be accepted as diagnostic of the abyssal zones and of high hydrostatic pressures.

Many investigators are looking for evidence, to use in estimating the depths and the pressures of mineral genesis, in the composition and the textural–structural criteria of mineral associations. Such indications may indeed be suited for characterizations of some relatively shallow depths. Presence of fine-grained and "comb-like" quartz, the common presence of prismatic, needle-like, and finely radiated crystals, as well as of datolite, chalcedony, antimonite, cinnabar, realgar, and other so-called low-temperature minerals, and of colloform minerals, etc., are generally regarded as such indicators.

These structures, textures, and mineral associations may evidently have a bearing on our problems, but, when it comes to finding numerical expressions for depths and pressures, the investigator is faced again with a rather wide choice.

TABLE 9

Zones of static loading	Types of deformation	Character of structures	Types of movement, proportions
Low	Splintered rupture cavities	Open fissures Fissures with peeling walls Tile-like rubble developed from fissures	99% stretching 1% break 50% stretchnig 50% break
	Brecciation	Coarse uncemented breccia; mixed compact breccia	
		Sandy granulation; mixed breccia and clay flour	
Medium	Brecciation	Compacted breccia and clay flour	
	Fragmentation and attrition	Zones of tectonic clay flour (without breccia)	
		Clay flour different thickness associated with schistosity	
		Compressed rolled-out tectonic clay flour	1% stretching 99% compression
High	Slipping	Slip–slide and drag folds without clay flour	
		Ditto, without drag-folding	
		Cleavage fissures	
		Cleavage flow and gneissoid deformation	
"Over-loading"	Plastic flow	Flow without discrete structural features	No stretching

According to the Leypunskii's approximations, diamond, if it develops in nature as an equilibrium phase, represents the stable form of carbon at 60,000 atm pressures, i.e. it is a mineralogical manometer for high pressures [98]. However, the scarcity of this mineral in nature imposes a limitation on its usefulness as a manometer.

The present state of our knowledge of mineral genesis is thus farther from the solution of the pressure problem than of the temperature problem. The interdependence of pressure and temperature demands new approaches toward the solution of the problem. These new paths are barely visible at this time and much effort will be required in obtaining acceptable data.

Examination of the possibilities of estimations of the hydrostatic pressure shows that some of the data required for mineralogical thermometry may be obtained only by reconstructions of geologic profiles.

The problems involved in a coordination of such data with the homogenization temperatures were taken up recently by Ingerson [172]. He presented a scale of corrections for pressures (depths) to be applied to liquid inclusion thermometry of specimens from different sources and different depths. His corrections serve to bridge the gap between the observed and the true temperatures of mineral genesis and render the former that much more valid in the general case. If a uniform scale of pressure corrections is adopted, tentative as it may be, the accuracy of the temperature estimations (with an adherence to all of the rules for these measurements and attention to the concentrations of the solutions) will be dependent only on the accuracy of the estimations of the depth of the mineral genesis.

Aqueous solutions in two-phase inclusions, if dilute, resemble pure water in their properties, as discussed in the preceding chapter. For that reason, we may employ for our purposes the temperature–pressure–volume relationships of water, as established by physicists, in ascertaining the effects of pressure. The most recent data on specific volumes of water at high temperatures and pressures are summarized in Fig. 18, where the abscissa is temperature and the ordinate is pressure and depth, as kg/cm^2 and the corresponding kilometers respectively. However, this relationship is more conveniently shown by Tuttle's diagram, refined by Ingerson [172]. The abscissa of this diagram (Fig. 9) shows the ratio of the total volume to the volume of the liquid (i.e. the degree of filling of the inclusion at room temperature [actually the reciprocal of the degree of filling—Ed.]) and the ordinate shows the temperature, as degrees centigrade. The isobars and the "dome" are represented by solid lines. This diagram makes it possible for us to visualize variations in pressure at different degrees of filling and at different temperatures. Specifically, the dotted line represents the progressively increasing pressure in an inclusion two-thirds full at room temperature. As water expands on heating, the gas bubble contracts and the pressure increases up to the point when the gas phase disappears entirely at 320°C (at the point of the intersection of the dotted line and the "dome"). The pressure at this point equals 120 atm, but the subsequent rate of increase is very rapid; 500 atm at 350°C and 2500 atm at 400°C.

This example shows that pressure is determined by the degree of filling and by the temperature and that if we know any two of these variables, the third one may be found. Specifically, the true temperature may be

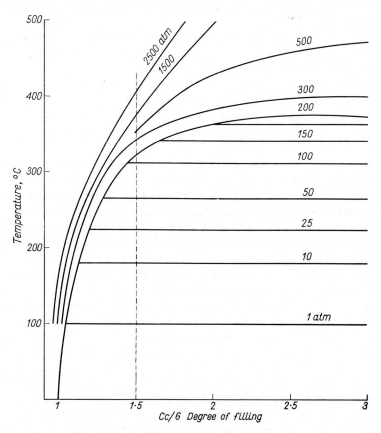

FIG. 9. Relationship between pressure, temperature and volume of water.

generally determined if the degree of filling and the pressure are known. The degree of filling is difficult to measure, in practice, and the required accuracy is not attainable in most cases. Moreover, the expansion and contraction coefficients are not the same for different host crystals and these differences affect the phase ratios, as we have already pointed out [39]. Consequently, it should be more appropriate, for our purposes, to measure the temperature at which the vapor phase disappears, with the highest accuracy and exactitude, since this temperature is a function of the degree of filling and since the differences in the expansion coefficients of different minerals are accordingly equalized, inasmuch as *the heating serves to reduce the volume of the vacuole wherein the inclusion is confined to its original condition.*

Ingerson's diagram (Fig. 10) shows the relationships between the temperature at which the vapor phase disappears, the pressure (or depth) at the time of mineral genesis, and the temperature at which the inclusion was sealed. The left termini of the calculated curves for different temperatures of disappearance of the gas phase correspond to the observed homogenization temperatures. Every other point on the curve shows the actual temperature, in relation to the depth at which the host mineral was formed, as established by geologic data. As we see, theoretical corrections for pressure may attain substantial magnitudes, so that *they may be disregarded only for deposits and minerals that have originated at relatively shallow depths.**

The diagram, based originally on the hydrostatic principle, was modified by Ingerson for the sake of convenience in determining the temperature corrections (Fig. 11)*. The modified diagram has the homogenization temperatures on its abscissa and the pressure-corrections, in °C, on its ordinate. The curves were drawn for kilometers of depth. The application of this diagram for comparison of the observed temperatures for minerals from different depths requires no special explanations and the diagram is acceptable tentatively, at least the left part, pending new possibilities for determinations of the pressures.

Ingerson [172] believes it is possible to determine the temperatures of mineral genesis even from supercritical solutions by the homogenization method with the aid of his diagram. He says that, "if the inclusions were filled by the liquid exactly at 360°C and were formed at 2100 atm pressure, the temperature of the crystallization was 500°C." This "exceeds appreciably not only the critical temperature of water but also the critical temperature of a 10 per cent solution of alkali chlorides".

In our opinion, however, homogenization temperatures of such inclusions may be far from temperatures of the mineral genesis, on account of the unknown and variable concentrations of the solutes in the included supercritical solutions and of the variations in the types and sub-types of the homogenization (see Chapter 7).

Inclusions of aqueous solutions belonging to the right half of the diagram (Fig. 11) are the highly concentrated three-phase and multiphase inclusions, in the vast majority of cases in our work, rather than two-phase

---

* It is not reasonable to assume high pressures also for minerals crystallizing in large fissures or in other open cavities even at great depths.

inclusions. This fact introduces large corrections into the interpretations of the homogenization data, larger than the corrections for the pressure, and invalidates the diagram for the solutions in question. We found it

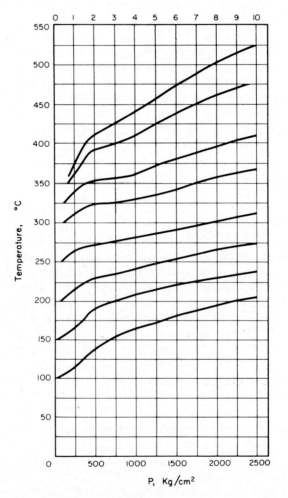

FIG. 10. Curves showing relationships between temperatures of disappearance of gas (vapor) and pressure (depth) at the time of the formation of a two-phase inclusion.

possible accordingly to employ only the left part of the diagram, for temperatures from 250 to 275°C. Moreover, in the higher temperature range, for minerals crystallizing truly from supercritical solutions, as we have already pointed out, the filling of the inclusion with liquid, on heating of the mineral, is observed only in the secondary inclusions, while the primary and the pseudo-secondary inclusions display some new and different types of homogenization [37].

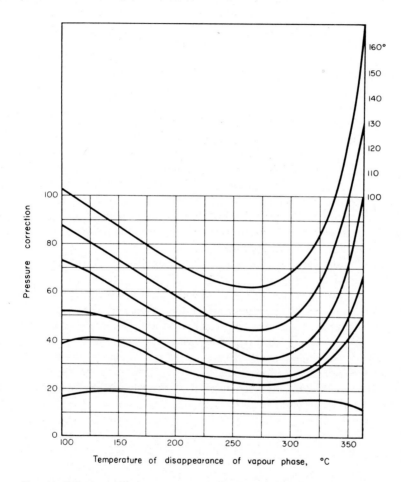

Fig. 11. Diagram of temperature corrections for pressure at temperature obtained by homogenization of a two-phase inclusion.

Summarizing our discussion on correcting for pressure in estimations of the temperatures, and on the determinations of the pressures themselves, we should emphasize the following aspects of the problem:

(a) The action of a high external hydrostatic pressure results in a lowering of the observed temperature (as determined by the homogenization of two-phase liquid inclusions) with respect to the true temperature of the mineral genesis.

(b) In order to obtain comparable results for minerals from sources at different depths, we must introduce corrections for the external pressure which, so far, may be ascertained satisfactorily only by a reconstruction of the geologic profile.

(c) Ingerson's diagram, offered for this purpose, so far, is acceptable only in its left part, as a tentative standard for correcting the temperatures for the pressures, to approximate the true temperatures of the crystallization.

(d) Minerals from sources whose depths cannot be determined geologically can and must be investigated by the homogenization method. *The true temperatures may not be obtainable*, under such circumstances, but the minerals may still be classified on the basis of experimental homogenization of their inclusions, with reference to stages and phases of their origin. Moreover, as shown below, relative homogenization temperatures of inclusions in hydrothermal minerals may serve in ascertaining the temperature range and the crystallization sequence for different generations and nucleations of the minerals.

(e) We must intensify our quest for new and more reliable geologic and mineralogical manometers.

(f) The pressure factor is still an unknown in the formation of endogenetic deposits and minerals, and in the science of the origin of ores. External pressures may be appreciably lower than that apparent from hydrostatic pressures as direct functions of the depth, even in abyssal deposits developing in major fissures or in open cavities. It should therefore be reasonable, so far, simply to omit the pressure factor in our appraisals of the temperatures of most of the deposits of such type.

It is far more important to focus our attention on determinations of composition and concentration of the included substances and on corrections for these much more important variables in our determinations of the true temperatures of the mineral genesis by the homogenization method.

DETERMINATION OF THE NATURE OF INCLUSIONS AND THE MEANS OF THEIR RECOGNITION

Correct recognition of the nature of inclusions in minerals under examination is an absolute prerequisite to their analysis by the homogenization method and is indeed decisive in the geologic interpretation of the results.

There are many examples in the history of the subject, down to the most recent time, when painstaking studies of liquid inclusions not merely failed to yield positive results but had led to errors, as, for example, in determinations of the formation temperatures of quartz in granites [179] or of the temperature of crystallization of halite in a sedimentary deposit [178]. There was an outright misunderstanding of the range of possibilities of the formation of liquid inclusions in granites as well as of *the secondary origin* of the gas bubble in the included aqueous solutions in halite, in these particular instances ([37], pp. 51–52).

One may also be reminded here of how the 80 years' neglect of Sorby's findings [128] concerning the possible secondary origin of inclusions was detrimental to applications of inclusions as autographic thermometers. The true significance of pseudo-secondary inclusions, originating during the crystal's growth but bearing earmarks of their secondary origin, was entirely neglected in the temperature measurements, even in the last 20 years. The most thorough investigations may prove to be worthless in science, unless one knows what kind of inclusions he is studying.

It was for these very reasons that we endeavored to give the first classification of inclusions on the basis of their composition and state and to generalize the findings of our scientists, in regard to the modes of formation of inclusions, in the form of a genetic classification [37]. The resulting scheme, based on studies of minerals of highly diverse origins, leads to the following generalizations:

(a) Minerals crystallizing from magmatic solutions contain only solidified inclusions as the primary type. In case any aqueous inclusions are to be found in such minerals, they must inevitably show evidence of their secondary origin. The temperature measurements in such inclusions may be indicative only of the temperatures of late hydrothermal metamorphism or epimorphism, of the kind to which veins of the Alpine type owe their origin.

(b) Minerals crystallizing from gaseous solutions contain inclusions of various gases containing, at room temperature, less than 50 per cent liquid by volume, in the form of primary and pseudo-secondary inclusions. As a rule, the preponderantly liquid inclusions in such minerals are secondary, as they formed by healing of fissures outcropping on the crystal's surface. Primary and pseudo-secondary liquid inclusions may be encountered only in the outer zone of crystals of various pneumatolytic minerals whose growth continued through the hydrothermal stage. Investigations of gaseous and liquid inclusions are particularly valuable in such cases as the means of ascertaining the composition and the state of aggregation as well as the reaction of the mineral-forming environment. Determination of the true temperatures is still impossible, but a determination *of the relative homogenization temperatures* of gaseous and liquid inclusions is definitely useful in the eventual solution of the problem and in ascertaining the position of the host mineral in a given stage of the process.

(c) Hydrothermal minerals and minerals of "Alpine" veins carry both primary and pseudo-secondary inclusions of mother solutions, whose studies contribute significantly in ascertaining the true temperatures of crystalization, the temperature range for individual crystals, refinements in the sequence of different generations and nucleations, the dependence of the evolving crystal form and color on the temperature of formation, and several other aspects of the subject having a high scientific and practical significance.

In contrast with previously current opinion to the effect that primary inclusions in a given crystal must show one and the same homogenization temperature,* it needs to be emphasized here that such results may be obtained only in dealing with the same growth zones of the mineral but never for the crystal as a whole. The crystal is formed generally within a certain range of falling solution temperature, and liquid inclusions as sensitive autographic thermometers register these temperature variations in the course of growth as different homogenization temperatures for different growth zones and healed fissures in these zones.

We must give our particular attention now to the need of a painstaking recognition of primary, pseudo-secondary, and secondary inclusions in every crystal. The different methods of formation of inclusions and their positions in crystals were already described. We should emphasize here the necessity of cross-comparisons between the homogenization data on all these inclusions and the results for inclusions in crystals of earlier as well as of later generations at the same deposit, and not merely of comparisons of results obtained for crystals of some single generation or some single nucleation. This practice enables us to reconstruct the temperature regime and its variations in a given deposit in its entirety. Homogenization temperatures of primary and pseudo-secondary inclusions in crystals of a later generation coincide, as a rule, with those of secondary inclusions of the earlier generations. Homogenization temperatures of secondary inclusions in minerals of the host rocks of a deposit coincide with homogenization temperatures of primary inclusions in minerals of the same composition present in veins of the Alpine type.

The unfolding of possibilities of the use of inclusions in the geologic and mineralogical sciences has barely begun, and an intelligent approach is required in any application of the homogenization procedures in scientific and practical studies of test materials from mineral deposits, pending development of more universally applicable methods.

A new student of inclusions faces difficulties at times in distinguishing between two-phase inclusions of glass and inclusions of aqueous solutions, or between the latter and inclusions of carbon dioxide or of two immiscible liquids. It appears to us desirable, for that reason, to call atten-

---

* So that the homogenization method would be deemed questionable inasmuch as no such agreement could be observed in practice.

tion to certain indications and procedures for the recognition of such inclusions, based on personal experience and on data from the literature.

Most glass in solidified inclusions has functioned as a solvent for a number of mineral constituents, with its role as a droplet of magmatic solution being analogous to that of water in liquid inclusions. As previously stated, there may be a possibility, at times, for some of the solutes to separate from the cooling drop of a magmatic solution in the form of isolated solid phases, "the captive minerals", i.e. a possibility of the formation of multiphase inclusions analogous to those developed on cooling of saturated aqueous solutions. Spherical bubbles of gas are also found in the majority of glass inclusions, while the glass itself looks just as homogeneous as an aqueous solution and is perfectly transparent under the microscope. Thus there is a good deal of resemblance between inclusions of glass and inclusions of aqueous solutions.

Obviously every investigator must first make it clear to himself just what kind of primary inclusions may be expected in the given mineral. If the mineral comes from a pneumatolytic or a hydrothermal source, it would be unreasonable to expect any glass inclusions and, on the contrary, if the mineral is a phenocryst from an effusive rock, primary inclusions of volcanic glass would be expected and would be found, as a rule. In the latter case, however, if the rock has been subjected to hydrothermal metamorphism, the phenocryst may also contain secondary liquid inclusions of aqueous solutions alongside the primary inclusions of volcanic glass.

Prognosis for the expected inclusions, as justified by the investigator's experience, is not appropriate if the test mineral occurs as detrital grains in a sedimentary rock, or is a constituent of the light-weight fraction of a panned sample. The correct recognition of inclusions, in such instances, would amount to a final decision regarding the origin of the host mineral and there can be no room therefore for any prognosis.

Table 10 is a summary of the characteristic indications by which inclusions of aqueous solutions may be distinguished from inclusions of volcanic glass under the microscope.

The diagnostic signs enumerated in Table 10 allow us to distinguish easily between inclusions of aqueous solutions and volcanic glass.

Two-phase inclusions of gases contain a large dark gas bubble (more than 50 per cent of the inclusion's volume) and are easily distinguished from liquid inclusions of aqueous solutions containing, as a rule, a small spherical gas bubble (appreciably less than 50 per cent of the inclusion's volume), showing as a light area or indicated by a point-like reflection of light from its center.

In case two-phase inclusions of gas are flattened out appreciably, they transmit light like liquid, without scattering. Under the microscope the gas bubble in such circumstances differs from a liquid only by the concavity

TABLE 10

No. in sequence	Inclusions of aqueous solutions	Inclusions of volcanic glass
1	Characteristically rounded or polyhedral shape	Irregular zigzag-like contours with wedge-like acute corners are more commonly characteristic
2	Boundary margins of inclusions are generally broad and dark in transmitted light, on account of a large difference between the indices of refraction of the mineral and the fluid. The broad margin of "full-volume" inclusions resembles the margin of the gas bubble	Host mineral-inclusion boundaries are generally narrow and delicate, because of the small difference between the indices of refraction of the mineral and the glass. Such fineness of the boundaries is not in accord with the appreciable darkening of the gas bubble, its broad dark margins, and the small spot of light in its center
3	There is only one gas bubble; its contours are generally sharp and its shape is rounded. The bubble sits in the center or at least in the central section of the inclusion	There are several and even very many gas bubbles in one and the same inclusion; their outlines are not as sharply defined. Some of them look as if they were pressed against the inclusion's wall by the glass (i.e., are on the sides of the inclusion)
4	There is a spontaneous movement of the gas bubble, unless the bubble is squeezed between the inclusion's walls. Turning or jolting the slide causes the bubble to change its position in the inclusion	Gas bubbles are immobile and look as if they were rigid; their positions are not changed by turning of the slide
5	Heating of the slide causes an appreciable decrease in the size of the gas bubble, down to a complete disappearance	There is no observable change in the size of the gas bubbles even on an intensive heating of the slides (up to 600°C)
6	The included aqueous solution is colorless and transparent	Color of the included volcanic glass resembles, on the whole, the color of the bulk of the rock containing the phenocryst; it may be yellowish, greenish, or dark
7	Truncation or abrasion of the thin section through the inclusion results in leakage of the fluid and in disappearance of the gas bubble. The inclusion grows dark or, if it was only half-opened, it becomes almost invisible	Truncation of the thin section across the inclusion does not cause the gas bubble to disappear; the cavity in its former location, on filling with the Canada balsam, assumes the appearance of gently outlined disc without any light reflection (a bright spot in the central part of the bubble)

of the phase boundary (see Plate I, 2, and the lower inclusion in Plate I, 3). Single-phase "full-volume" inclusions of "dry" gases look either entirely dark *in transmitted* light, under the microscope (Plate XII, 2) or in case of a flattening of the cavity containing the inclusion (Plate XII, 3) appear to have a wide dark contour with a bright spot inside, without showing the curved dark interphase boundary. Because of the low index of refraction of the gas, as compared with that of the host crystal, gas inclusions shine brightly in *reflected light*.

Difficulties may be encountered occasionally in distinguishing such inclusions from inclusions of aqueous solutions. In aqueous inclusions in negative crystals, the planes may be so inclined to the line of the observation that they reflect the passing light more or less completely. As the result, the inclusions look either completely dark or strongly shadowed, like the "dry gas" inclusions. Their gas bubble becomes unrecognizable and their true character may be unveiled only at the correct inclination of the apparatus. Examinations in reflected light are also useful as the means of detecting the gas–liquid interface.

It was essential for us to distinguish two-phase inclusions of carbon dioxide from two-phase inclusions of aqueous solutions. This is particularly important since both of these types, looking very much alike, may be found in one and the same crystal. Inclusions of carbon dioxide are most reliably identified in groups containing both types by heating up to 30–31°C. Even a touch of the slide by a finger or heat from a desk lamp may cause a rapid decrease or a disappearance of the liquid phase in carbon dioxide inclusions. The liquid phase and the associated gas bubble, practically a duplicate of the gas bubble in included aqueous solutions, reappear instantaneously after a slight but rapid cooling of the system. Their reappearance is accompanied by a violent boiling. On the other hand, inclusions of aqueous solutions remain unaffected but such slight warming and cooling and their original appearance is preserved unchanged.

Complex inclusions of immiscible liquids (aqueous solution–liquid carbon dioxide) appear to have a *binary* gas bubble (see Plates XI, 1 and 2, and XVIII, 3). The aqueous solution generally occupies the peripheral part of the inclusion, while the liquid and the gaseous carbon dioxide occupy the central part (see Plate XI, 1 and 2). There are definite and clearcut interphase boundaries between the liquid carbon dioxide, the gaseous carbon dioxide and water vapor. The gaseous carbon dioxide preserves its spherical shape in the "full-volume" inclusions. It thus appears as though the two bubbles were set inside each other (Plates XI, 4, and XVIII, 3). Occasionally one may see also the fourth phase in such inclusions, a solid in the form of a small crystal inside the aqueous solution.

Volume ratios of the phases in the general association of such complex inclusions are generally highly variable.

Two-phase inclusions of combustible petroleum-like substances (hydrocarbons) found occasionally together with inclusions of aqueous solutions and carbon dioxide in crystals are easily distinguished from the latter by their yellow colors in transmitted light.

EXPERIMENTAL METHODS AND TECHNIQUES. HISTORY OF THE DEVELOPMENT OF RESEARCH TECHNIQUES

On occount of the small size of the inclusions of mother liquor in minerals, the microscope has been employed for their study since the second half of the last century. However, the need for applying heat to minerals containing inclusions of microscopic size has led to construction of special attachments to the microscope for this purpose. The slides were heated on a steam bath placed on the microscope's stage. This was sufficient only for the homogenization of carbon dioxide inclusions, but was not suited for the other, and most important, categories of inclusions.

Sorby's single experiment in homogenization of aqueous solutions [128] was already cited. However, the first technical solution of the problem belongs to Phillips [137]. Phillips built a rectangular bath of brass, with glass windows on either side. The test mineral containing liquid inclusions was placed between these two windows. The bath was filled with melted paraffin. A mercury thermometer's tip was set in the paraffin, in order to measure the temperature of the bath. The bath and the paraffin were heated by a gas or an alcohol burner. The inclusions were watched through one of the windows in the bath, through a microscope fixed horizontally on the side. The illumination of the slide was through the opposite window of the bath. The relatively narrow temperature range possible with paraffin did not permit Phillips to extend his observations beyond 180–185°C, in homogenization temperature measurements of inclusions in quartz.

Königsberger [153] made alterations in the apparatus design and succeeded in measuring the homogenization temperature of inclusions in quartz from Alpine veins, in the range of up to 260°C. It appears that he kept his test material in an electrically heated air chamber. The vents in the chamber were closed by platelets of fused silica which served also as windows for the microscopic observations. The slide was set on a perforated slab of copper inside the chamber. A mercury thermometer was inserted through a special orifice in the apparatus, in order to measure the temperature. It was assumed that the temperature rise of the copper slab will be the same as of the test material, within 0.5°C. The entire rather bulky apparatus was set on the stage of the microscope which was protected from the heat by asbestos, wood, and air. The objective of the microscope was cooled by water. It was proved that gas bubbles within the inclusions in quartz vanish within a temperature interval of 3 to 12°C. The apparatus was a step forward for the simple reason that it could withstand temperatures up to 400°C. For some inexplicable reason, however, its use was confined to a few measurements of homogenization temperatures by Königsberger himself.

British and American geologists persisted in their use of the paraffin bath up to 1949. The bath was improved by Newhouse in 1933 [167]. His bath was made of Pyrex glass and looked like an evaporating dish. Asbestos paper was used in insulating the bath and in protecting the microscope from the heat. The heating device was a resistance element of carbon inside a glass tube which was set in the paraffin bath. The test slide was in the paraffin, whose temperature was measured by a mercury thermometer with an accuracy of 1–3°C. An attachment of this sort to the polarizing microscope appeared to have suited Newhouse very well, together with the other investigators, during the next two decades, since no one made any attempts at studies of minerals crystallizing within a wider range of the temperature.

Having begun, in 1941, our studies of included aqueous solutions in optical-grade materials from central Asia, we became convinced directly that baths filled with some liquid are both troublesome and messy. The main point was the impossibility of obtaining the required temperature for the homogenization of inclusions in a variety of minerals by the means of heating liquids in baths. We were obliged therefore, jointly with Tsybyshev, engineer-geologist, to design and build a new apparatus that could produce the required temperatures of 300 to 400°C.

The following specifications for the mineralothermometric apparatus were formulated at that time, on the basis of relatively small experience:

(a) The instrument must be adapted for observation of small bubbles of gas in liquid inclusions of microscopic size under the microscope or a binocular.

(b) There must be provision for a slow and uniform heating of crystals to high temperatures, as required.

(c) There must be a provision for a definitive reading of the temperature of crystals with inclusions within the accuracy of one to a few °C.

It was essential moreover to eliminate the sources of injury to the objectives, during the heating, to assure simplicity in setting the test crystals inside the apparatus, and in changing their position.

A fairly simple solution was found after several unsuccessful trial constructions. It developed that all of the foregoing specifications would be met by a slow heating of thin platelets of the test mineral in an insulated air-space with an inserted thermometer. A GOST 215–41 laboratory mercury thermometer guaranteed the following accuracies at the following temperatures: up to $100\pm1°C$; up to $200\pm2°C$; up to $300\pm3°C$. The temperature difference between the air and the adjacent thin platelet of the crystal in the confined air-space was kept to the minimum by slow heating (about 1°C) and there was a certain slight error in the use of large inclusions, contingent on the microscopic or binocular limits of visibility even at low magnifications (40 to 60 times), but the combined error in the temperature measurements, with careful work, was not over 3 to 5°C.

The attachment to the binocular was built in the form of a thermo-shelf [32, Fig. 3]. The outer walls of the shelf were made of a reliable thermo-insulating material (asbestos–cement). A cylindrical porcelain tube coiled with nichrome wire was the resistance heater set inside the shelf. The bottom of the tube was insulated by a thick glass and its top had a plug with an eccentrically located small glass window for observing the inclusions and with another small opening for the tip of the mercury thermometer set right next to the surface of the test slide. Resilient metallic rings inside the tube served as supports for a thin cover slip or a mica platelet on top of which the test crystal was placed.

A beam of light from the microscope (or binocular) mirror was directed through the lower glass inside the tube, and then through the test crystal which was observed through the upper window. The heating was conducted extremely slowly, in view of the necessity of maintaining a close correspondence between the temperatures of the confined air surrounding the test slide and the thin section of crystal on the slide.

This apparatus was described in one of our earlier publications [32]. In the further development of our studies and in the expansion of their scope, we constructed a more refined instrument that came to be known as the "Yermakov Chamber" among the Soviet investigators.

Construction of the Microthermochamber, its Installation, and Integration with Other Instruments

The standard installation of the microthermochamber on the Soviet-made MIN-2 microscope, in combination with the minimum of required apparatus, was shown in Fig. 1 ([37] p. 38). We began to use this new apparatus in our studies in 1946. Improvements over the original model of the microthermochamber were made in reducing its bulk while increasing the temperature range up to 650°C. It was important also to obtain simplicity in the placement of the test material inside the chamber and ease in vertical transpositions in the working space.* Appearance and construction of the chamber are shown in Figs. 12 and 13 (pp. 86 and 89).

---

* Horizontal movement of the test slide under the microscope objective was easily done by moving the microthermochamber itself, if the latter was mounted on slides.

This relatively simple apparatus has been in production at the experimental shops of the University of L'vov since 1948, because of the many requests by different organizations.

The microthermochamber (Fig. 12) has the total height of 30 to 39 mm and consists of cylindrical body *1*, made of polished cast metal, covered by lid *2*. The chamber as a whole looks like a cylindrical box with the outer and the inner diameters of 69 and 66 mm respectively. The floor of the chamber has a hole *3*, in the middle, 27 mm in diameter, for a window *4*, made of mica. Two 4 mm apertures are drilled through the chamber's side wall, for clamps to connect to the electrical circuit *6*. The floor of the chamber *7* is lined with dense asbestos *8*, 12 mm thick, on top of which a thin-walled cylinder *9* is placed, made of refractory quartz glass or of some metal (steel, copper). This cylinder, with the inner diameter of 27 mm, is coiled with nichrome wire *10* functioning as a resistance-heater the ends of which, *11*, are joined to the outer clamps by screws. The clamps themselves are screwed into the apertures in the body of the chamber and are insulated from the body by special gaskets ("shayby") made of fiber or micanite, *12*.

The resistance-heating unit is insulated from the inner cylinder by mica *13* and is encased in an envelope of asbestos cardboard *14*. This inner part of the apparatus is fixed firmly in the chamber by the means of three horizontal spikes ("rosporki") of dense asbestos board and the space between the inner and the outer cylinders is packed with asbestos cotton *15* and overlain by asbestos paper *16*. The inner margin of the body of the chamber at the top is made somewhat wider (inner diameter 67 mm) by polishing flush with the fitted lid, and has a small notch to help in raising the lid. This polished steel lid *2* is the surface on which the rest of the working attachments are mounted. The top part of the lid coincides exactly with the outer diameter of the chamber's body but its lower part, fitting the cylinder, has the outer diameter of 67 mm. The height of the lid is 7 mm, 5 of which fit inside the microthermochamber.

As shown in Fig. 12, the lid has three eccentric small openings and one large upper one, *17*, intended for the window. This large opening has a diameter of 20 mm and coincides with the inner cylinder (but not with its axis) and is covered by the window plate through which the inclusions are observed. The first small orifice, *18* (4.5 to 5 mm diameter), is drilled next to window for the insertion of a small porcelain tube, *34*, with two grooves for the thermocouples. The second orifice, *19*, 10 mm from the first one and likewise at the rim of the upper window, is 2.2 mm in diameter. This second orifice is adapted for the insertion of the mica-coated rod of the "slide-holder" on which the test mineral is placed. The third small orifice, *20*, has the same diameter and is situated near the margin of

General view
(Pt.1)

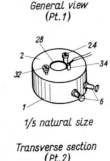

1/5 natural size

Transverse section
(Pt.2)

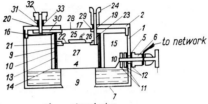

to network

1/2·5 natural size

View from top
(Pt.3)

View from bottom
(Pt.4)

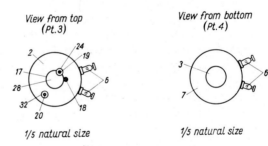

1/5 natural size   1/5 natural size

FIG. 12. Yermakov's microthermochamber construction.

1. Body of cast metal
2. Lid of the thermochamber
3. The lower body aperture
4. The lower mica window
5. Aperture in the wall of the body
6. Clamps for connection
6a. Clamp screw
7. Floor of chamber
8. Layers of asbestos
9. The inner cylinder
10. Resistance heating unit
11. Bolts
12. Fiber discs
13. A thin layer of mica insulation
14. Asbestos board
15. Asbestos cotton
16. Asbestos paper
17. Upper aperture for mica window
18. Aperture for setting of thermocouple

19. Aperture for slide-holding rod
20. Aperture for turning handle of the upper window of mica
21. Slide-holding ring
22. Mica of the central window
23. Slide-holding rod
24. Knob of the slide-holding rod
25. The slide (the object of study)
26. End of the thermocouple
27. Working space in the thermochamber
28. The upper window of mica
29. Ring of the upper window
30. Lever for the ring of the upper window
31. Lever of the turning handle
32. Knob of the turning handle
33. Spring of the turning handle
34. Porcelain tube with the thermocouple

the lid, where it serves as the recess for the turning-handle by which the upper window of mica may open or shut.

The polished metallic ring, *21*, of the slide-holder is fitted with mica, *22*, and has an outer diameter of 26 mm and an inner one of 18 mm. This ring is fastened on one side to a rod, *23* 21.5 mm long* and 2.1 mm in diameter. A screw thread is cut in the rod 12 mm below the top. This rod is inserted through the second orifice in the lid, *19*, from the bottom up, and the rounded copper knob, *24*, is screwed onto the rod. The ring of the slide-holder, together with the test slide, may be moved up and down on the screw by rotating the knob. This is essential for bringing the test slide closer to the upper window, depending on the focus of the objective used in the examination, and for better contact of the test slide, *25*, with the inserted thermocouple, *26*.

The vertical movements of the ring of the slide-holder take place within the working space, *27*, of the inner cylinder. The upper mica window, *28*, is very easily opened or shut, so that there is no need to dismantle the top of the apparatus for replacing one test slide by another one. The window consists of a flattened metallic ring, *29*, with the inner orifice of 20 mm diameter with the inset mica slip, *28*. The lever, *30*, slides horizontally together with the ring under the lid of the thermochamber. As the lever's tip is sealed onto the vertical shaft of the turning handle, *31*, inserted through the third orifice of the lid, *20*, and as it extends 8 mm above the orifice, the ring of the upper window can be manipulated from the outside, by a simple rotation of the handle knob, *32*. A spring, *33*, placed between the knob and the surface of the lid on the rotary shaft assures a tight contact between the upper mica window ring and the surface of the lid. There is a notch on the sidewall of the lid in which the upper window metallic ring is caught when the window is open. This notch must coincide with the notch on the chamber's body when the lid is shut.† At the same time, the ring of the test-slide holder is lowered into the working space of the thermochamber's inner cylinder and the thermochamber is ready for use.

A brand-new thermochamber must first of all be ignited thoroughly, while open, because the asbestos board and the asbestos cotton may contain combustible impurities the soot from which may settle on the upper mica window. As a rule, the ignition is done during the trial run of the apparatus.

The microthermochamber is designed to work at 24 V and is connected to the circuit through a reducing transformer. Since such transformers are rarely found on sale, each set of the microthermochambers (two pieces)

---

* 2.15 mm in original [Ed.].

† This makes it easy to remove the lid, in case any repairs are to be done in the thermochamber.

made at the shops includes one transformer. An easily operated adjustable rheostat, 25 to 30 Ω, 4 to 5 amp, is included in the low-voltage circuit, to facilitate smooth and gradual variation of the temperature during the heating or a temporary stabilization of the temperature inside the thermo-chamber.* If the transformer is not available, the microthermochamber may be connected with a 110 or 220 V circuit through a single 300 Ω, 4 to 5 amp rheostat. (Much power is wasted by this rheostat.) The current tolerance of the heating unit is 4 to 4.5 amp. If the current exceeds this limit, the heating unit will burn out. For that reason, in case the rheostat only is used (no transformer), an exact ammeter must be included in the circuit with the scale up to 5 to 6 amp. The ammeter is desirable also if both the rheostat and the transformer are employed, in order to keep track of the current entering the heating unit, while regulating the rate of heating by the means of the rheostat.

The thermochamber is connected with the electrical circuit when the rheostat is set at its highest resistance, whereupon the resistance is adjusted *gradually* until the desired temperature is obtained. An autotransformer is a highly desirable piece of equipment to have on hand, among the others, as it may be needed, on occasions, for maintenance of the microthermo-chamber's temperature at a certain level. Thus the operational set-up for the microthermochamber requires presence of three additional pieces of apparatus; a reducing transformer, a rheostat, and an ammeter. Moreover, a thermocouple is also required, with some kind of an attachment for measuring the temperature. Thermocouples of various metals may be em-ployed successfully, with their relatively high electromotive force changing significantly at different temperatures.

The platinum–platinum-rhodium thermocouple, with its small electro-motive force, requires the use of a highly sensitive galvanometer, millivolt-meter, or potentiometer, or the automatic temperature recorder "Kent". This thermocouple has the advantage that it is suited for a wide range of temperatures (100 to 1500°C). The copper–constantan thermocouple is very convenient for intermediate and low temperatures, but its measure-ments are exact only up to 300°C. The silver–constantan thermocouple is suited for measurements within the generally indispensable temperature range up to 650°C. The other thermocouples are not so desirable for use with the microthermochamber. One must know the characteristics of thermocouples when they are used together with a given temperature measuring device. The cold ends of thermocouples must have equal tem-peratures at the place where they are joined to copper wires leading to the

---

* It became apparent that we could get along without a special thermoregula-tor and with the aid only of the rheostat and the autotransformer, to avoid further complication of the thermochamber and of the entire apparatus.

measuring instrument, to assure exact determinations. This requirement may be obtained by keeping them in a box packed with cotton. The working thermocouples must be checked periodically, with the aid of the critical points of certain substances or by comparisons with a standard thermocouple.

There is no need here to describe the pyrometers. It is simply desirable to assemble the set with the most exactly graduated scale that would assure reliability of the measurements within 1 to 3°C.

An ordinary illuminator with a powerful lamp is generally used as the source of light for the microscope.

The microthermochamber may be set on the stage of an ordinary Soviet polarizing microscope. If so, of course, the thermochamber's lower window must be set against the hole in the stage and its upper window must be in line with the microscope tube. One or two asbestos rings are

Fig. 13. At work with microthermochamber.

placed under the chamber, in order to protect the stage and the body of the microscope from the heat.

Objectives with long focal distances ought to be used in the work, to avoid deterioration of the optical pieces caused by the heat. When the thermochamber is used continuously at high temperatures and over long periods of time, it is recommended to employ a fan, of the type used for drying hair (but without pre-heating the air). The main stream of cold air is blown from the side at the objective of the microscope. Inasmuch as a continuous observation of inclusions is not invariably required, the microscope tube and objective should be raised preferably at every interval in the operations, for radiant heat is produced just the same, in spite of the perfect thermo-insulation of the chamber.

Best of all, however, a single simplified microscope, the MIN-2 or the M-9 type, should be used in these investigations. The stage and the condenser are taken off, in such a case, and the microthermochamber is set in place of the condenser. An asbestos ring is placed under the bottom of the thermochamber, as before. The screw by which the condenser could be raised or lowered may be used in moving the microthermochamber up and down (see Fig. 13).*

For taking photomicrographs of the thermal homogenization process, the microscope with the microthermochamber is placed on the stage of the Soviet-made RU-1 apparatus, whose photographic attachments can be raised to the desired height, on the rod, and can be easily coupled sideways with the microscope's eye-piece at the desired moment (see Fig. 14).

Thus the ordinary standard installation for thermometric studies of inclusions in minerals consists of the following combinations of apparatus and equipment: (a) microthermochamber installed on a given type of microscope; (b) adjustable rheostat; (c) reducing transformer, to lower the voltage to 24 V; (d) ammeter; (e) thermocouple; (f) pyrometer (galvanometer, millivoltmeter, etc.); (g) illuminator. A general view of the microthermometric installation, in operating position, and the instrumental circuits, is shown in Figs. 13 and 14.

A mineral-thermometric laboratory must be equipped with a section-polishing lathe and a lathe for crystal cutting is desirable. The required test sections may be obtained by a simple splitting of the cleavage planes only in the case of minerals with a very good cleavage (topaz, calcite, fluorite, barite, etc.). Most minerals require preparation of sections with two very smooth fine-polished surfaces or else preparation of common thin sections somewhat thicker than usual.

The Author's Method and Experimental Procedure†

Crystals from various sources are subjected first to the customary examination and description. Forms of crystal growth, their generations

---

* In case one has to work with high magnifications, it is convenient to use a binocular polarizing microscope with a long focal distance, even at magnifications of 600×.

† Although the procedure for homogenization of inclusions was known, the method and the experimental technique were developed, for the first time, by the author.

and epochs, their syngenetic and epigenetic defects, both internal and external, etc., must be ascertained microscopically. The sequence of these operations was discussed by us in detail, with fluorite crystals as examples

FIG. 14. Microphotographing of inclusions in the processes of homogenization.

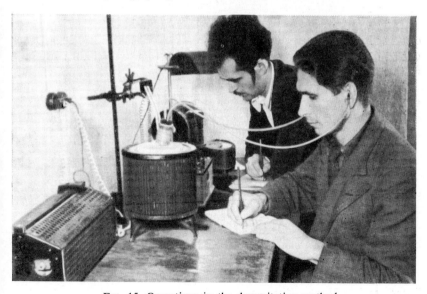

FIG. 15. Operations in the decrepitation method.

[36], and in the papers by Grigor'ev and Shafranovskii [24, 26, 116, etc.] and by Grushkin [29].

Detailed microscopic examinations (generally with the aid of a lens [*sic*]), and thorough studies of peculiarities of individual minerals and of their contacts with other minerals, are essential prerequisites to any intelligent studies in mineralogical thermometry. Internal structures of crystals must generally be examined with particular care. This operation is made easier by rubbing the crystal faces with kerosene or some other liquid with a suitable index of refraction and by examining the crystal in a strong transmitted light beam. Only after completion of these studies and after the tentative sketching or photographing of crystals, may there be the selection of areas in crystals (identified appropriately by numbers) from which the test sections are to be cut separately for thermometric studies of their inclusions.

For the sake of a better identification of primary, pseudo-secondary, and secondary inclusions, it is recommended that one or two doubly polished sections are cut at right angles to the long axis of the crystal and others parallel to this axis. After that, the sections may be cut into individual test preparations for studies of their inclusions in the microthermochamber.

These preparations are made either by cutting out from the broken fragments or by the ordinary procedure on the polishing lathe. The subsequent polishing of the surface is done by hand, on a smooth board and cloth, with the aid of chromium oxide. A very thorough polishing of the preparations is essential (a frosted surface is of no use) for minerals with high indices of refraction to make the inclusions and other defects clearly visible in any part of the polished section. There can be no standard thickness for minerals of different transparency. It is desirable to maintain the above specifications for preparations a few millimeters thick. Thickness in excess of 5 mm is not recommended, since it would interfere with the uniformity of heating of the preparation in the microthermochamber. Semi-transparent minerals require the making of doubly polished sections 0.5 mm thick, and thinner (0.2 to 0.4 mm). Most of the inclusions are destroyed in the process, of course, either by cutting them open or by explosions caused by the heat generated by the polishing. Preparations containing carbon dioxide must be polished with particular care. For these reasons, inclusions are found very rarely or not at all in standard thin sections.* The optimum mean thickness of the preparations is generally 2 to 3 mm. This thickness is sufficient as a sample of the volume of the crystalline substance wherein the inclusions best suited in terms of shape

---

* A possible reason why so little attention was given to inclusions of mother liquor by mineralogists and petrographers

and size may be sought and found. The surface area of test pieces of a polished section must not exceed 1.5 to 2.0 cm², in conformity to the working space of the microthermochamber.

After the preparation of the thin sections from different parts of the crystal of interest, the thin sections are examined, in the search for the most suitable primary, pseudo-secondary, and secondary inclusions (of an appreciable size, regular shape, and, in the case of elongated or flattened inclusions, their perpendicular position, with respect to the axis of the microscope, etc.).

At low magnifications under the microscope or when the inclusions are extremely small, the inclusions look like nebulous spots; these spots are resolved into isolated inclusions only at the appropriately high magnifications.

Individuals and groups of inclusions that are best suited for investigation are marked by two dots on the section's surface or are circled with India ink of different colors. The markings employed for this purpose may be of various kinds.

Unless the section is made of an ideally transparent perfectly "pure" part of the crystal, there is no difficulty in locating inclusions that are well suited for the experiments, if sufficiently high magnifications are employed.

Of course, one must have a trained eye in looking for inclusions in ordinary materials. Gas bubbles appearing as black spheres or dots in inclusions are often the first things to attract the investigator's attention.

The identification of primary inclusions is contingent on their correlation with the forms of the mineral's growth. In the case of pseudo-secondary inclusions, we must endeavor to determine to what particular zone of the crystal does the outer end of the healed zone extend, where groups of such inclusions are present. As to secondary inclusions, we must examine thoroughly the site where their host fissure outcrops at the face of the crystal, prior to making a decision regarding their secondary origin. A microscopic view of a thin section perpendicular to the crystal's face may show convincingly that such fissures are separated from the crystal's surface only by a very thin layer of substance that was laid down at the very last moment. If so, the groups of the inclusions in question represent the end-stage of the mineral's growth, i.e. the inclusions are pseudo-secondary and not secondary.

The most typical inclusions seen in the polished sections must be either sketched or photographed. This is absolutely essential for multiphase inclusions of aqueous solutions, which are not restored to their original appearance after heating because of the rapid and often disorderly redeposition of the substance of the "captive" minerals (a mush of fine intermixed crystals).

Both linear and planar ratios of different phases in inclusions must be measured carefully by the micrometer scale or grid before as well as after their homogenization. This is essential as a check on the measurements (absence of leakage caused by development of extremely fine fissures, and the general hermetic sealing of inclusions in a given crystal).

The preparations may be studied in the microthermochamber after the preliminary examination and authentication of the inclusions here described.

The preparation is set onto the mica of the test-slide holder, through the open upper window of the chamber, with the aid of special forceps. If the inclusions are very small, the thin section of the mineral must be set close to the upper window at once, by rotating the knob on the slide-holder rod. By such vertical transposition the end of the thermocouple is pressed firmly against the mineral. A firm contact between the preparation and the thermocouple is an absolute prerequisite to reliability of the measurements. The upper window of the thermochamber is shut, by the means of the special handle, and the preparation is placed as near this window as is consistent with focusing of the high-power objective on any one of the inclusions. One must make sure at the same time that the thermocouple is not touching any part of the apparatus except the porcelain tube.

After these operations, the previously code-marked inclusions are located, using a low-power magnification and a uniform illumination from below, by a systematic horizontal movement of the microthermochamber either manually or by moving the slides.

Secondary and pseudo-secondary inclusions, with smallest gas bubbles, must be examined first. The last ones to be examined are the inclusions whose gaseous phase occupies the greatest volume. This sequence is obligatory, because most of the former group of inclusions is exploded during a thermal analysis whose temperatures exceed their homogenization temperatures. This explosion is accompanied by fissuring of the thin section. The fissures may destroy some of the inclusions marked for analysis or else may make them invisible. One must provide in advance for such contingencies either by having the marked inclusions in different parts of the thin section or by preparing duplicate thin sections beforehand.

Having located the inclusions marked for the early analysis, by the means of the low-power magnification (it is desirable to have several inclusions of the same family within the same field of vision), the highest-power objective and eye-piece are focused on the group. The most common magnifications used are $180-200\times$; $300\times$, $400\times$, and $600\times$ are used more rarely. The thermochamber is connected with the electrical circuit when the circuit's rheostat is set at its highest resistance, whereupon its resistance is adjusted *gradually,* so as to assure a slow uniform heating of the test material until the desired temperature is reached. When the gas bubble volume has markedly decreased, the rheostat resistance must be increased abruptly, just before the bubble disappears completely, so as to retard further increase of the temperature and even, if possible, to keep the temperature at the same level, for a while. This is necessary in order not only to assure reliability in the measurement of the homogenization temperature by the pyrometer, but also in order to allow the included solution to come to an equilibrium with the inclusion's walls, which are not inert. One and the same *rate of heating* must be established for the homogenization of inclusions of the same type in a given mineral from a given source. The average duration of an experiment with two-phase inclusions may be assumed to be 1 hr. It is preferable, however, to determine the rate of heating empirically, for the sake of economy of time, for a given mineral from a given source.

Two-phase inclusions of the same general association and even single inclusions must be homogenized over progressively increasing spans of time (5–10 min. increments). Under normal conditions when a certain quantity of the cognate substance has been laid down on the walls of the vacuole, a retardation of the rate of heating will cause a certain small increase in the homogenization temperature.

When any further increase in the time-span of the heating has no appreciable effect on the homogenization temperature, consistent with the accuracy of the determination, the minimum rate of the heating has been found. In such circumstances, the included solution will be indeed saturated with the cognate substance, at the temperature of the homogenization, and the walls of the vacuole will remain inert even if the homogenization process is to require an appreciable lenght of time.

Naturally, the rates of heating will be more rapid for two-phase inclusions in low-temperature minerals than for multiphase inclusions in high-temperature minerals. In the latter case, one homogenization experiment may last as long as 4–5 hr, because satisfactory results are obtainable only in this time.

The microthermochamber is cut off from circut after the temperature measurement has been made, and the restoration of the gas bubbles is observed. The temperature at which the gas bubbles make their first reappearance must be recorded alongside the homogenization temperature. Next, the end point of the experiment is repeated once or several times, for the sake of verification of the observed homogenization temperature. In case of doubt, a second analyst needs to be engaged in the replicate experiments, so as to ascertain the correctness of the original determination. After ascertaining the correct measurement, one proceeds with the analysis of the earlier general associations of inclusions (or of one single inclusion). Replicate analyses of the same test material are highly desirable, if the material can stand it.

We must always have in mind the possibility of finding *intermediate* homogenization temperatures, in the range between the homogenization extremes of pseudo-secondary and primary inclusions in one and the same crystal, since crystal growth takes place at progressively falling temperatures of the crystal-forming solutions. A single temperature may characterize only one single moment in the growth or in the healing of a given zone of the crystal. One should endeavor to find the extremes of the homogenization temperatures of primary and pseudo-secondary inclusions, in every particular case, so as to characterize the crystallization of the entire mineral. Naturally, more measurements of the intermediate homogenization temperatures for inclusions in different zones of the crystal yield a more complete characterization of the crystal's growth. A single datum for the crystallization temperature of a given crystal may be deduced merely as an average or may be assumed only because of a scarcity of inclusions in a given crystal, as for example, when the crystal is very small.

We have outlined here the general experimental procedure which, of course, becomes complicated in dealing with minerals containing multiphase inclusions or inclusions of gas; the latter requires combinations of heating with very careful micrometric scale measurements of the phase ratios during the homogenization, and representation of the results in the form of curves on special diagrams. This latter method is discussed in the sixth section of the book and is applicable in ascertaining the types of homogenization and, from there on, of the state of aggregation of the mineral-forming solutions.

We should now report on the reliability of the measurements by the procedures just described, and indicate the sources of errors in the proposed method and in the operational techniques.

Sources of Error in Thermometric Analyses

We can evaluate the mean homogenization temperature of several carefully performed thermal analyses with an accuracy of ± 2 to $3°C$, on the basis of reproducibility of the results for a given inclusion examined by different analysts and by the means of different reliable temperature-recording devices, with allowances for all possible errors. Any deviation from the mean toward a higher figure are related to the following factors:

(a) An inexactly graduated scale on the temperature recorder, so that temperature has to be estimated "at sight," within a certain range.

(b) *The limit of visibility* of the gas bubble plays a certain role, at a given magnification. It has been observed even by the earlier investigators that gas bubbles of different size in small inclusions become invisible to the eye a few degrees earlier than gas bubbles in large inclusions of the same kind, despite the identical phase ratios in both large and small inclusions and at one and the same magnification.

Grushkin [27] had performed especially designed experiments with single types of inclusions in quartz from Aurakhmat. However, a verification of this sort requires an exact determination of the percentage ratio of the phases in tubular inclusions of different size rather than measurements of the area of the inclusions, approximate as they are, in any case, or measurements of the diameter of the bubble which may (or may not) be a flattened one. Our verifying experiments were conducted with inclusions of different size but identical phase ratios and showed a difference only of a few °C, while the difference was practically insignificant when the visibility was very good.

Gas bubbles in small but rounded inclusions, by the way, remain plainly visible during homogenization, up to the very last, while they are maintaining themselves in the center of the inclusion. On the other hand, gas bubbles in inclusions of the same family but angular and irregularly shaped squeeze themselves in some nook, as a rule, during the last moment of homogenization, becoming poorly visible even earlier than in the former case. Thus *the factor of visibility* of inclusions themselves, and of their gas bubbles, must be also taken into account in these cases.

While agreeing with other writers that only the largest inclusions must be selected for the analysis and only the highest microscopic magnifications must be employed, in order to assure satisfactory visibility of the phases, we still see no reason for ascribing any great significance to the size of inclusions in estimating homogenization temperatures.

(c) *Plain visibility of interphase boundaries* throughout the experiment is an important prerequisite to accuracy of the results. There are several factors in liquid inclusions interfering with this prerequisite, aside from the case of the inclusions of gas whose homogenization leads to a "melting" or "abrasion" of the interphase boundaries when the densities of liquid and gas become about the same [i.e., disappearance of the interphase boundary at the critical point—Ed.].

An excessively high magnification, for example, causes a general darkening of the field of vision which interferes with the clarity of interphase boundaries, particularly at high temperatures.

The gas bubble is generally more difficult to see, to the point of practical invisibility, in inclusions whose rims are broad and dark, on account of reflection of transmitted light from the inclusion's walls. When the gas bubble becomes really small, it hides entirely in the shadowed section of the inclusion. Under such conditions, as previously stated, in order to make sure that the gas bubble does exist, one has to resort to the use of reflected light or to the appropriate tilting of the apparatus, so as to change the orientation of the inclusion with respect to the axis of the microscope. Either way is very inconvenient and it is best to avoid experimenting with such inclusions, as far as possible.

(d) *High rate of the heating* leads to errors and is not permissible. Homogenization of the inclusion within the test material may take place at a temperature not at all the same as the concurrent temperature of the hot surface of the test material; it is the latter that is being registered by the thermocouple and by the measuring apparatus. An error of this kind cannot be very high, however, in minerals with high thermal conductivity.

Excessively high results due to rapid heating may be caused also by time-lag, inasmuch as the analyst must leave the microscope in order to read the measuring device and the reading itself also takes time. This error is minimized by a slow heating at a constant rate and by repetitions of the end-stage of the experiment.

Most important of all, when the heating is rapid, there is not enough time for the included solution to come to an equilibrium with the walls of its vacuole, so that the homogenization occurs in a somewhat smaller volume and not in the original volume of the inclusion.

(e) *Irregular rate of heating*, in the case of inclusions with identical phase ratios in the same crystal, or the same rate of heating for two-phase as for multiphase inclusions, are not permissible. The correct rate of heating is easily determined (see above) and its determination must precede the experimental operations. An extremely slow rate of heating, with a pause just before the instant of the homogenization, precludes the possibility of errors, but requires an unreasonable expenditure of time on every measurement.

(f) *Absence of firm contact* between the test material and the thermocouple may lead to serious errors, especially when the heating is rapid. If the thermocouple end is "hanging" in the air space of the chamber, if it is pressed against the mica of the central window of the chamber or, worst of all, if the thermocouple is touching any inner part of the apparatus, the temperature reading will be incorrect. As to the magnitude of the possible error in the measurements at different positions of the end of the thermocouple with respect to the test material, the point may be illustrated by the following experimental findings related to the homogenization of one and the same inclusion in quartz from Transbaikal:

End of thermocouple pressed against mica; temperature—160°C

End of thermocouple hangs in air; temperature—165°C

End of thermocouple barely touches the apparatus; temperature—175°C

End of thermocouple firmly pressed against the test material next to the inclusion (the true temperature)—180°C

In order to avoid such errors, our microthermochamber was equipped with a lifting device for the slide-holder, so as to assure a firm contact of the test material with the end of the thermocouple.

(g) Errors resulting from *selection of anomalous inclusions for analysis* may lead to completely erroneous conclusions. Anomalous inclusions, unsuited for the experiments, may be of the following three types:

(1) Inclusions with a primary bubble of gas sealed in the crystal together with an aqueous solution.

(2) Inclusions with a secondary bubble of gas (vapor) originating in the absence of the hermetic sealing of a liquid in an easily soluble mineral.

(3) Inclusions whose hermetic sealing was impaired during the experiment (by fissuring).

The first anomalous type is recognizable in a general association of inclusions by its abnormally large gas bubble, different from the rest. The second and the third anomalous types are easily identified by determining their phase ratios or by exact measurements of the diameter of the gas bubble at the same temperature, before and after the experiment. Inclusions in which the original phase ratios are not re-established cannot be regarded as reliable self-recording thermometers and they must not be considered in appraisals of crystallization temperatures of test minerals.

As shown, there is a great variety of the sources of error in experiments with homogenization of inclusions. Beginners in this field of study must adhere rigidly therefore to the procedures described in the preceding chapter. Any departure from the rules of the experimental procedure which was developed by us originally, as the result of a systematic and long investigation of inclusions, will undoubtedly lead to errors of various kinds, as observed very often in the works of foreign investigators.

CHAPTER 4

Supplementary Methods of Study of Inclusions

HOMOGENIZATION of inclusions by heating under the microscope, as here described, was and will remain the basic method of study of inclusions, in their capacity of self-recording thermometers. In addition to this method, however, several others have been proposed, suited for the advancement of mineralogical thermometry, either as simplifications of the measurements or adaptations expanding the range of minerals suited for thermometric studies of their included mineral-forming solutions. The calculation method of Sorby [128], the visual method of Yermakov [32], and the fissuring method of Scott [175] belong to the category of supplementary methods.

THE CALCULATION METHOD

The Sorby method, a subject of a purely historical interest at this time, as it will be shown later on, is based on the expansion of liquids by heat, very much like the homogenization method. Initially, cavities in minerals were completely filled by the included aqueous solutions. When we examine these inclusions under the microscope, at room temperature, we do not see such complete fillings, because the liquid has contracted in its volume to a greater extent than has the cavity it occupies in its host crystal, so that a bubble of gas (vapor) is now occupying the liberated space in the cavity. The relative size of this bubble is an expression of the extent of contraction of the liquid, as against contraction of its crystalline host, within a certain definite interval of falling temperature. As shown in the discussion of the homogenization method, it is possible, by means of heat, to equalize the volumes of the inclusion and of the more expandable liquid, i.e. to transform a heterogeneous inclusion into a homogeneous one.

Sorby had calculated the probable homogenization temperature from the relative sizes of the gas bubble and of the liquid, as seen in inclusions. Taking the liquid volume as unity and determining the relative size of the gas bubble microscopically, Sorby succeeded experimentally in ascertaining the laws of expansion and contraction of water and of solutions of salts. In his experiments, liquids were heated to different temperatures and sealed hermetically while hot in sturdy glass tubes 5 cm long and 8.5 mm in diameter. After cooling, he measured the phase ratios in his ampules of glass and proceeded to reheat his confined systems on a paraffin bath, measuring at the same time variations in the phase ratios under the microscope. Sorby found, by these procedures, that the increase in volume may be represented as $V = Bt + Ct^2$, where t is the temperature, in °C, and B and C are constants dependent on properties of the aqueous solution.

Sorby's experiments were conducted within the temperature range 25 to 200°C and showed a good agreement between the calculations and the experiments. *This agreement was impaired at the higher temperatures by the sufficiently strong solvent action of hot water on glass.* Sorby believed, however, that his equations (see below) may serve to yield sufficiently reliable approximations to the true values up to 300°C.

Sorby gave the following numerical expressions for the effective values of his constants B and C for water and for solutions of salts, taking the volume of the latter at 0°C as a unity:

(1) Water $B = 0.0001344$ $C = 0.000003245$
(2) 10% aqueous potassium chloride $B = 0.0001868$ $C = 0.000002524$
(3) 25% aqueous potassium chloride $B = 0.0003006$ $C = 0.000001410$
(4) Water with 12.5% KCl and
  12.5% NaCl* $B = 0.0003580$ $C = 0.000001422$
(5) 25% aqueous sodium chloride $B = 0.0003520$ $C = 0.000001370$
(6) 25% aqueous sodium sulfate $B = 0.0003077$ $C = 0.000001644$
(7) 25% aqueous solution of mixed salts $B = 0.0003221$ $C = 0.000001461$
  (average of 3, 4, 5, and 6)

As one may see in this table, additions of salts to water serve to increase the B coefficient while decreasing the C coefficient. Sorby's experiments showed that the product of these two coefficients is practically a constant and that the C coefficient is a simple function of the dissolved salts while the quantity of water remains unchanged.

The foregoing data take into account the effect of concentration of the solutes on the temperature measurements, if the external pressure on the liquid equals its vapor pressure. This condition does not always exist in nature and, for that reason, the calculation must take into account contraction of the liquid itself, if the liquid is under an increased pressure. The contraction of volume of pure water when the pressure is increased by 1 atmosphere equals 0.0000502, but this magnitude decreases at increasing temperatures. This contraction is smaller for a saline solution than for pure water (0.0000379 for NaCl), but it increases at higher temperatures.

The volume-contraction is a simple direct function of the pressure, for pure water as well as for saline solutions. This contraction should probably be reduced to a certain mean level at high temperature, both

---

* 12.15% in original [Ed.].

for the water and the solutions, especially at intermediate concentrations of the solutes. We must consider also contraction of the crystal itself (and hence of the volume of the cavities). The contraction of glass is 0.0000358 per every added atmosphere of pressure. This corresponds to 0.00000897* per 1 meter of overlying rocks at a density of 2.5.

The volume of a liquid expanded by heat up to $1 + V$ per 1 meter pressure of rock will be $(1 + V) \times 0.00000897$. At high temperature and pressure (P meters of rock) the actual volume of a hot but compressed liquid will be $(1 + V) - 0.00000897\,P\,(1 + V)$ at the time of the formation of aqueous inclusions. After the inclusions are cooled to room temperature and the external pressure is no longer effective, the volume of the resulting gas (vapor) bubble will be expressed by the difference between the effective volume of the hot compressed liquid and the volume here taken as unity, i.e. $V - (1 + V) \times 0.00000897\,P$ (see eqn. II below).

The pressure of water vapor, expressed in terms of meters of rock, according to the empirical formulae of Dulong and Arago, per degree Centigrade above 0°C, is calculated by Sorby with the aid of the following equations:

$$e = 4 \times [1 + 0.007153\,(t - 100)]^5.$$

Sorby derives a series of equations, using all of the foregoing data, that enable him, according to his view, to calculate the temperatures from the measured relative volumes of gas bubbles in inclusions and from the pressures derived from geologic data. In Sorby's equations:

t—temperature

P—pressure, in excess of the vapor pressure at t

V—the relative volume of gas bubble at 0°C, as of $t°$, when $P = 0$

v—observed volume of gas bubble at P pressure

e—saturated vapor pressure at t

B and C—empirically determined coefficients whose magnitudes depend on properties and concentration of saline solutions in inclusion cavities.

The dimensions are: t in °C; P in meters of rock at 2.5 density. The volumes of gas bubbles take into account the volumes of the included liquid at 0°C. The equations proposed by Sorby have the following appearance (after conversions to meters):

$$V = Bt + Ct^2 \tag{I}$$

$$V = \frac{v + 0.00000897P}{1 - 0.00000897P} \tag{II}†$$

---

* We convert British feet to meters here and later in the text (1 atmosphere corresponds to 4 meters pressure or to 13.2 British feet, since 1 meter = 3.3 British feet).

† V at left omitted in original [V.P.S.].

$$t = \frac{\sqrt{4C + B^2 - B}}{2C} \tag{III}$$

$$t = \frac{\sqrt{\dfrac{4C^V + 0.00000897P}{1 - 0.00000897} + B^2 - B}}{2C} \tag{IV}$$

$$v = (Bt + Ct^2) \times (1 - 0.00000897P) - 0.00000897P \tag{V}$$

$$P = 369.000 \frac{V - v}{1 + V} \tag{VI}$$

$$e = 4[1 + 0.00715(t + 100)]^5 \tag{VII}$$

If $P = 0$, $v = V$.

Sorby believes these equations to be fully exact only for the intermediate magnitudes of t and P. However, he does not indicate the permissible limits of their application. In his discussion of these equations, Sorby [128 (1)] says:

"Equation V shows that the true relative volume of the bubble depends both on the temperature and the pressure at which the bubble was formed. We are dealing therefore with equations containing two unknowns, so that neither one of them can be determined unless the other one is known. Were the pressure known, the temperature could be calculated from IV—and liquid inclusions would serve then as self-recording thermometers; if either V or the temperature were known, the pressure could be calculated from VI—and we could use liquid inclusions as barometers. Indeed, liquid inclusions are analogous to air thermometers which can be used either as thermometers or as barometers, depending on whether the true temperature or the true pressure is known. *If the effective* pressure is known, however approximately, as long as it remains the same for any two crystals, or more, whose V is not the same, the corresponding difference in the temperature may be calculated from IV. Or, if the temperature were the same and if the value of V were known, by an approximation, the pressure-difference could be determined from VI.

"I believe that we may also rely entirely on *the ratios,* as determined for the minuscule tubules of inclusions in solid crystals, if we proceed on the basis of data obtained from the larger tubes employed in our experiments." [128].

Sorby used his equations for determining the temperatures for different minerals. In the instance of the Ponce quartz veins, he showed that the relative size of gas bubbles constitutes 14.3 per cent of the volume of the pores containing included aqueous solutions of sodium chloride, sulfate, and carbonate and that the calculated corresponding temperature is about 220°C. He obtained approximately the same temperatures for the quartz veins of Cornwall. The mean relative volume of gas bubbles in quartz from the granites of Saint Michaels and Mousehall was found to be 14.8 per cent, corresponding to the temperature of about 230°C. The calculated temperature for quartz veins from granites of the latter district, with the mean relative volume of gas bubbles at 13.3 per cent, proved to be 16°C below the former figure. Identical temperatures were obtained for quartz from the granites of Camborn and for quartz veins from the same granites. The relative size of gas bubbles in quartz from the Trewalgen granites indicated the temperature of 230°C. The relative volume of gas bubbles was 12.5 per cent and the calculated corresponding temperature was 200°C for quartz from the schists of Cornwall at a considerable distance from the granites.

Gas bubbles in quartz from mica schists in the southern part of the mountains of Scotland proved to be so small (5 per cent of the volume) that the temperature indicated by Sorby's equations was only 105°C (assuming the pressure was not excessive). On the other hand, gas bubbles in quartz of the Ponce trachytes were found to be so large (about 30 per cent of the volume) that the calculated temperature was indicated at 356°C. The same temperature was established by Sorby for the hornblende from rocks thrown out by Vesuvius. Vesuvianite and feldspar in these rocks were found to contain multiphase inclusions of aqueous solutions with about one-third gas, indicative of a temperature of 380°C by Sorby's calculations. The relative volume of gas bubbles in nepheline from the same rocks was 28 per cent and the corresponding calculated temperature was 340°C. Gas bubbles in aragonite and zeolite from vugs in lavas of the Vesuvius had the relative volume of one-tenth of the total (and the calculated temperature of 160°C).

We undertook a special study in 1948, with the aid of R. F. Sukhorskii, student-candidate, University of L'vov (now engineer), for the sake of comparison between the calculation method of Sorby and the homogenization method, using inclusions in quartz as test materials. Our findings were as follows:

TABLE 11

Measured volume of gas bubble per cent of total	Temperature calculated by Sorby's method (°C)	Temperature determined by homogenization of inclusions (°C)
5.0	105	104
12.5	200	160
13.3	214	170
14.3	220	172
14.8	230	174

One may see in the foregoing comparison that, the lower the temperature and the smaller the gas bubble, the closer is the agreement between the results obtained by the different methods. The difference between the calculated and the determined homogenization temperature is nearly 60°C when the included gas occupies 15 per cent of the total volume. These results were reported by us in the form of a plain curve, using the temperature and the volume of the gas bubble as coordinates (Fig. 16, p. 112). The relative volume of the gas bubble in quartz from Arctic Ural (*1, 2, 4, 6, 9, 11*), Central Ural (*7, 15, 18*), Aldan (*3, 8, 13, 14, 16, 17, 19*), Salayir (*5*), Volynia (*10*), and Altay (*12*) and homogenization temperatures of the inclusions were determined with extraordinary care [39].

These determined homogenization temperatures were substituted into the Sorby's equations, whereupon the relative volumes of gas bubbles were calculated for pure water, 10 per cent potassium chloride, and 25 per cent mixed salts, at pressures of 1, 250, 500, and 750 atm.*

The results of our measurements and calculations were as shown in Table 12.

The foregoing results indicate, first of all, that the calculated curves, at different pressures, lie very close to each other and, next, that curves representing 25 per cent solutions of mixed salts have steeper slopes than the pure water curves. The curve for the 10 per cent potassium chloride occupies an intermediate position.

If the data reported in Table 12 were represented as curves, one would easily see the striking discrepancy between the calculated and the determined homogenization curves for temperatures above 100°C (see Fig. 16, p. 112).

Uncorrected for the pressure, *the homogenization method yields substantially lower results for the (homogenization) temperatures, as compared with Sorby's calculation method.* As evident from the curves, this large discrepancy cannot be explained entirely by the pressures. The more important reason for this discord between the results is in the fact that our measurements of the phase ratios were made at room temperature and not at 0°C, as required by Sorby's equations, and that there appears to be a substantial difference between glass and natural minerals in regards to their coefficients of linear and volume expansion.

As we had already stated, the coefficients in Sorby's equations were derived from his experiments with glass tubes and, it appears, they may not be applicable to minerals. Sorby's calculations and equations may yield satisfactory results and may agree with the results of the homogenization method possibly only in the instance of secondary inclusions in obsidian.

---

* It should be possible, of course, to calculate the expected temperature from the measured volumes.

TABLE 12

Point No. and homogenization temperatures of inclusions of aqueous solutions of low strength	Calculated volume of gas bubbles, as per cent of total volume of inclusion, on basis of homogenization temperature				Determined volume of gas bubbles
	1 atm	$p = 1000$ m	$p = 2000$ m	$p = 3000$ m	
1. Water	0.69	0.67	0.66	0.64	
T = 55°C 10% KCl	0.79	0.77	0.76	0.74	0.70
25% mixed salts	0.10	1.08	1.06	1.04	
2. Water	1.53	1.51	1.48	1.46	
T = 76°C 10% KCl	1.61	1.59	1.56	1.54	1.85
25% mixed salts	2.02	1.99	1.97	1.94	
3. Water	1.72	1.70	1.67	1.65	
T = 80°C 10% KCl	1.79	1.77	1.74	1.72	2.52
25% mixed salts	2.21	2.18	2.15	2.12	
4. Water	2.24	2.21	2.18	2.15	
T = 90°C 10% KCl	2.28	2.25	2.22	2.19	2.86
25% mixed salts	2.71	2.67	2.64	2.61	
5. Water	3.15	3.11	3.04	3.04	
T = 105°C 10% KCl	3.11	3.07	3.03	3.00	4.80
25% mixed salts	3.51	3.47	3.43	3.39	
6. Water	3.56	3.52	3.48	3.44	
T = 111°C 10% KCl	3.47	3.43	3.39	3.35	5.06
25% mixed salts	3.85	3.81	3.76	3.72	
7. Water	4.99	4.94	4.88	4.83	
T = 130°C 10% KCl	4.74	4.70	4.65	4.61	6.67
25% mixed salts	4.99	4.94	4.88	4.83	
8. Same figures as for point 7.					7.34
9. Water	5.58	5.52	5.46	5.40	
T = 137°C 10% KCl	5.26	5.20	5.15	5.09	8.36
25% mixed salts	5.44	5.38	5.32	5.27	
10. Water	6.10	6.04	5.97	5.91	
T = 143°C 10% KCl	5.72	5.66	5.60	5.54	10.20
25% mixed salts	5.84	5.78	5.72	5.76	

TABLE 12 — continued

Point No. and homogenization temperatures of inclusions of aqueous solutions of low strength	Calculated volume of gas bubbles, as per cent of total volume of inclusion, on basis of homogenization temperature				Determined volume of gas bubbles
	1 atm	$p = 1000$ m	$p = 2000$ m	$p = 3000$ m	
11. Water	6.75	6.68	6.61	6.54	
T = 150°C 10%					
KCl	6.28	6.22	6.15	6.09	12.16
25% mixed salts	6.31	6.24	6.18	6.11	
12. Water	6.94	6.37	6.80	6.73	
T = 152°C 10%					
KCl	6.44	6.37	6.30	6.24	12.21
25% mixed salts	6.45	6.38	6.31	6.25	
13. Water	8.24	8.16	8.07	7.99	
T = 165°C 10%					
KCl	7.56	7.48	7.40	7.33	13.51
25% mixed salts	7.37	7.30	7.22	7.15	
14. Water	8.88	8.79	8.70	8.62	
T = 171°C 10%					
KCl	8.11	8.03	7.95	7.87	14.64
25% mixed salts	7.82	7.74	7.66	7.58	
15. Water	10.46	10.36	10.25	10.15	
T = 185°C 10%					
KCl	9.45	9.35	9.26	9.17	17.30
25% mixed salts	8.89	8.81	8.72	8.63	
16. Water	11.05	10.94	10.84	10.73	
T = 190°C 10%					
KCl	9.95	9.85	9.75	9.66	17.00
25% mixed salts	9.29	9.20	9.11	9.02	
17. Water	12.04	11.92	11.81	11.69	
T = 198°C 10%					
KCl	10.79	10.68	10.58	10.48	20.61
25% mixed salts	9.95	9.85	9.75	9.66	
18. Water	13.06	12.93	12.80	12.68	
T = 206°C 10%					
KCl	11.65	11.54	11.42	11.31	22.65
25% mixed salts	10.62	10.51	10.41	10.31	
19. Water	14.68	14.54	14.40	14.26	
T = 218°C 10%					
KCl	13.00	12.87	12.75	12.63	25.65
25% mixed salts	11.66	11.55	11.43	11.32	

We showed definitely in 1942 [32, p. 36, Fig. 5], that inclusions in different minerals (fluorite and barite), with identical phase ratios, are homogenized at different temperatures, depending chiefly on the expansion and contraction coefficients of the minerals. In this connection, differences in the expansion coefficients of the solutions themselves play a certain role, depending on the concentrations, as do differences in the quantities of the cognate substance laid down on the inclusion walls, in different minerals, in the case of excessively rapid heating (which is not permissible).

It appears to us, therefore, that the calculation method of Sorby has no scientific and practical future, as the means of determining the temperatures of crystallization of different minerals by their inclusions. As shown, the point here is not in the complexity of exact measurements of the relative volumes of phases, with the required reduction to 0°C, or in the intricacy of the calculations involved in the use of the Sorby's equations, but in the fact that his standard equations fail to take into account the case of inclusions in *different* specific minerals.

These equations are evidence of a fundamental break between the laboratory experiments with artificial systems and systems as they are in nature, to the point where the experimental data proved to be unsuited for the investigation of the latter.

We give considerable attention to Sorby's method here, because certain investigators [167, 172] continue to treat it as if it were adapted for practical use, and because the original description of this method is very difficult to procure for a wide geologic audience, since the journal where it was published [128] has become a bibliographical rarity. The "visual" method of determining the temperatures, based empirically on the studies of natural systems themselves, proposed by us [32, pp. 34–36], is much better suited for the approximate determination of homogenization temperatures of two-phase inclusions by means of measurements of the percentage ratio of gas bubble volume to inclusion volume.

THE "VISUAL METHOD" (METHOD OF EMPIRICAL CURVES)

Significance and Principles of the Method

As shown, the homogenization method requires a special apparatus for heating minerals to high temperatures under the microscope. This is not always possible at any given place or time. We attempted therefore to produce empirical curves for the most common vein minerals that would help an investigator, equipped with any kind of a microscope, in drawing tentative conclusions in regards to the temperature minima at which a given hydrothermal mineral may have been formed. In contrast with Sorby's method, we used the data obtained by measurements of the phase ratios in hermetically sealed and confined natural systems of inclusions in low-temperature minerals, after they were subjected to homogenization, rather than laboratory findings, in experiments more or less unrelated to natural environments.

In developing our method, we proceeded from the established fact of the evident dependence of the size of gas bubbles in two-phase liquid inclusions on the temperature at which the mother liquor was sealed off. Theoretical calculations based on the expansion (contraction) coefficients of minerals and water on heating (and cooling) emphasize the physical essence of this relationship which was first surmised by direct observations of the size of gas bubbles in the same mineral formed at different temperatures.

The gas bubbles were of a size varying over a wide range, from barely perceptible at high magnifications to plainly visible to the unaided eye, depending on the volume of the pore. The ratio of the bubble volume to the total volume of the inclusion remained practically constant, however. Inasmuch as measurements of solution-filled pore volumes and of gas (vapor) bubble volumes in the inclusions proved to be a highly complicated operation, we attempted from the start to substitute planar for the volumetric measurements because it is easier to measure areas under a microscope or under a binocular with the aid of a micrometric scale or grid.

Gas bubbles are rounded, as a rule, and it is always possible to find tens of pores among the many liquid inclusions whose planar projection is either a circle or a regular ellipsoid. The projected areas can be measured easily, in either case, by determining their diameters with a micrometric scale. As the first approximation of the phase volume ratios, we used the apparent ratios between the projected areas of the gas bubble and of the cavity. It seemed sufficient for this purpose to determine either the ratio of the squares of the radii or of product of the half-axes of the ellipse to the square of the radius of the gas bubble. The probable error of these measurements, caused by the fact that a globular gas bubble is projected, under the microscope, as a smaller circular area than is given by the projection of a circle or an ellipse of a flattened inclusion, was disregarded in the early stages of the investigation. More or less significant deviations from the true volume-ratios were only natural as the result of such conversions from the two-dimensional to the three-dimensional estimations [32].

The gas bubbles were too small in comparison with the size of liquid-filled cavities in many crystals. In some others, the gas bubble volume would constitute an appreciable percentage of the inclusion volume. With the aid of a large number of measurements of the areal ratios in inclusions in fluorite and barite crystals formed at different temperatures, whose homogenization temperatures were previously determined by the heating method, it was possible as early as 1943 to obtain the first curves showing the areal ratios between gas and liquid-filled inclusions as functions of the temperature. These early curves for fluorite and barite [32, Fig. 5, p. 36] still do not come up to the degree of accuracy attainable, for the reasons previously indicated. In estimations of the probable minimum temperature of crystallization, it is sufficient to take the arithmetical mean of several tens of areal measurements in the test crystals of fluorite or barite, and find the temperature by interpolation on the corresponding curve.

Satisfactory results with the estimation of probable homogenization temperatures of inclusions, as shown by actual measurement, could be obtained by using the arithmetical mean of at least ten measurements in ten different inclusions in the crystal. A larger number of measurements serves merely to increase the accuracy of the estimation and takes very little additional time, on the whole. One or two hours may be enough for 100 such measurements of the relative areas in different pores of the crystal, after some practice. It appears that such estimations of the probable homogenization temperature by the "visual" method of areal measurements are accurate within ±4 to 5°C, for fluorite and barite. Extraordinary coincidences, within 1°C, were occasionally observed, in a series of crystals, between the results obtained by *the heating* and by *the visual methods.* The agreement between these two methods had led us, as early as 1942, to the possibility of a practical application of the "visual" method to inclusions in low-temperature minerals and, first of all, to inclusions in fluorite and barite.

The non-coincidence of the empirical curves derived for these two minerals was an indication of different homogenization temperatures of their inclusions despite the identical areal and volumetric phase ratios. Different minerals have different coefficients of linear or three-dimensional expansion and contraction. They do not fit into the standard equations of Sorby and require separate curves for the estimations of their temperatures. Such curves, as expressions of the orderly relationship between the phase ratios and the homogenization temperatures of inclusions, facilitate substantially the preliminary appraisals of the minimum temperatures of that particular stage of mineralogenesis. The relative sizes of the inclusion and of the gas bubble contained therein indicate the extent to which the temperature of the solution, at the moment of the sealing of the inclusion, was above the ordinary room temperature at which our studies of the inclusion were made.

The visual method definitely loses its reliability, in the instance of medium-temperature and particularly high-temperature hydrothermal minerals, where striking differences in concentration of included solutions are reflected in the thermal expansion coefficients of the liquids, while the volume of the inclusions, as observed at room temperature, becomes that much more different from the initial volume, because of an appreciable deposition of cognate substance on the walls of the pores.

Empirical Curves for Quartz and Calcite

It became possible in recent years to derive empirical curves for the visual method for inclusions in quartz and calcite, the two most common vein minerals in hypogene deposits. However, we had met with enormous difficulties. The point was that it was extremely difficult to form the correct idea of the gas bubble's relative size simply by measuring its single planar projection. A multitude of inclusions have irregular shapes that are not susceptible to exact measurements. Such measurements are indeed possible, provided that the outer boundaries of a flattened inclusion are regular and its upper and lower planes are equidistant (i.e. the depth of the inclusion is uniform). The gas bubble is compressed, in such conditions, and, for that reason, its contour is dark only on its margins. The area measurements may represent the volume ratios only if the foregoing requirements are satisfied. In measurements of phase ratios in inclusions, the ideal is a regularly tubular form of fine inclusions whose linear phase ratios are easily determined by the eye-piece micrometer and are indeed directly proportional to their volumes. Inclusions of this sort are fairly rare, however, in both quartz and in calcite.

It became necessary therefore to assemble a very large body of test materials for these two minerals, from deposits formed at different temperatures, in view of the many sources of possible error in the measurements. We succeeded in finding the most desirable regularly tubular inclusions with different phase ratios among the test materials we had assembled. The selection was continuing during the last seven years, whereupon, with Sukhorskii's aid, the most careful and time-consuming measurements were carried out, using quartz from Ural, Aldan, Altay, Volyn', Salayir, and other sources.

Despite the wide variety of sources, the fixed points whose parameters were cited in the preceding chapter showed an orderly distribution on a plot of temperature vs. volume of gas, so that a smooth curve could be drawn showing the relationship between the temperature (the ordinate) and the volume percentage of gas phase (the abscissa) (see Fig. 16). It was essential to test the suitability of this curve for the "visual" and approximate estimation of possible homogenization temperatures. This verification of the curve was done by two analysts. One of them, having measured exactly the phase ratios in an inclusion (or in a group of inclusions) would estimate the homogenization temperatures with the aid of the already drawn curve, while the other one would determine the homogenization temperature independently, by a direct measurement of the very instant of the homogenization in the thermochamber.

The results of such tests proved to be specifically as shown (Table 13, p. 113).

Thus the series of tests of the curve yielded satisfactory results for the low–temperature stage of the formation of hydrothermal quartz (up to 200°C).

We were not able to show a comparable agreement between the results for high-temperature quartz because of the effects of high pressures

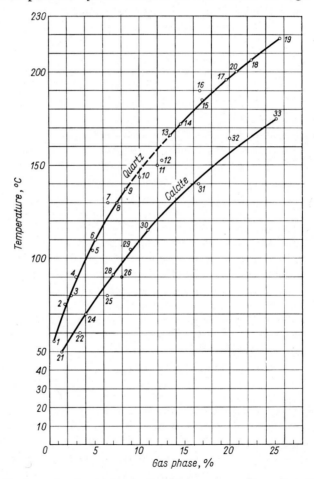

FIG. 16. Curves for visual determination of temperatures of formation of hydrothermal quartz and calcite.

and concentrations of the solutions. The close interdependence of the phase ratios and the temperatures also does not obtain because the gas bubble is compressed on *contraction of the volume* of the inclusions due to the deposition of the cognate substance on their walls. Under such circumstances, the required studies become complicated by the necessity of determining composition and concentration of the included solutions, with attention to the volume ratios not only of the liquid and the gas, but also of various solid phases.

We may cite here only a few figures on measurements of volume and tests of quartz in the microthermochamber. Secondary inclusions in quartz from Volyn'—temperature: 238, 245, 251, 290°C; volume of gas, respectively: 34.7, 37.33, 40, 48.96 per cent. The increasing homogenization temperature here, as one may see, lags behind the increasing volume of

TABLE 13

No. in sequence	Sample No. and source of quartz	Gas (vapor) %	Temperature from curve (°C)	Homogenization temperature of the same inclusion (°C)	Difference (°C)	Remarks
1	6, Volyn'	2.50	80	80	0	Secondary inclusions
2	1, Barnavadj (Pamir)	6.20	120	118	2	
3	5, Parnuk (Arctic Ural)	6.45	122	120	2	Secondary inclusions
4	27, Oyon (Aldan)	14.63	171	170	1	
5	5, Parnuk (Arctic Ural)	15.80	175	180	5	Primary inclusions
6	Transbaykalia	21.00	200	200	0	Primary inclusions
7	20, Kochkar' (Middle Ural)	21.50	202	206	4	Primary inclusions
8	5, Parnuk (Arctic Ural)	26.70	224	233	9	Primary inclusions

the gas. The lag may be due, to same extent, to an insufficiently slow rate of heating. A boiling of the liquid and the subsequent elimination of the interphase boundaries* were observed in the last inclusion of the series when the size of the gas bubble decreased to a third of the

* Critical phenomena in aqueous solutions containing carbon dioxide may have been taking place, in this case.

total volume of the inclusion. Primary inclusions in quartz from the Kochkar' deposit contained 37 per cent gas and homogenized at 248°C, while quartz from Oyon, with 37.87 per cent gas, showed a homogenization temperature of only 240°C. Such inconsistent results had led us to abandon the derivation of the empirical curve for inclusions containing large gas bubbles (more than 26 per cent of the volume) and having high homogenization temperatures.

For calcite, the next most common one among vein minerals, the mean empirical curve was derived from the data on a deposit of Iceland spar in Central Asia, on lead–zinc deposits in DVK,* and on some relatively high-temperature specimens of Iceland spar from the Yakutian trap rocks. The calcite curve seems to be less reliable to us than the quartz curve, because the volume ratios in calcite are even more difficult to determine than in quartz, on account of the generally irregular shape of the inclusions. We measured the following percentages of gas and the corresponding homogenization temperatures, as reported in Table 14, in the best-suited inclusions, with the aid of V. F. Lesnyak, Assistant.

TABLE 14

No. of points on curve	Source of specimen	Volume of gas (%)	Homogenization temperature (°C)
21	Central Asia	1.5	50
22	Central Asia	3.3(?)	60
24	Central Asia	3.67	70
25	Yakutia	6.3	80
26	DVK	8.0	90
28	Central Asia	7.2	92
29	Yakutia	9.0	105
30	Yakutia	11.0	115
31	DVK	16.6	140
32	Yakutia	20.0	165
33	Yakutia	27.0	185

As we see, the determined points are somewhat scattered on the temperature–gas volume diagram (Fig. 16, lower curve), but, just the same, their distribution is generally orderly. This enabled us to obtain the first approximation of the mean curve for calcite.

Deviations of the determined points from the mean, for quartz and calcite, is due not merely to certain inaccuracies in the microscopic measurements. The causes may involve also differences between the ex-

* Dal'nevostochnyi Krai'—the Soviet Far East [V.P.S.].

pansion and contraction coefficients of the minerals themselves as against those of the included solutions. Moreover, difference in concentrations of the solutions and in their pressures may have had effects. We attempted to eliminate the pressure variable, at least for calcite, by using specimens from sources at depths known to be shallow. However, exact determinations of concentrations of the included solutions are still outside our reach. We may be able to assume that two-phase inclusions homogenizing at low temperatures contain relatively dilute solutions, although there still must be some variation in the quantity of their solutes. It was for that reason perhaps that we had come across the cases where two-phase inclusions in one and the same mineral showed variations in their homogenization temperatures despite their identical phase ratios.

The differences in the thermal expansion (and contraction) of these minerals are among the important factors responsible for the discrepancies between homogenization temperatures of inclusions with identical phase ratios but situated in different minerals, as we had already emphasized. The following table shows the volume-expansion differences for certain minerals, including quartz and calcite.

TABLE 15

No. in sequence	Mineral	Temperature (°C)								
		50	100	150	200	250	300	350	400	600
1	Quartz	0.17	0.36	0.56	0.78	1.03	1.27	1.56	1.87	4.50
2	Fluorite	—	0.16	—	—	—	—	—	—	—
3	Calcite	—	0.08	—	0.21	—	—	—	0.60	1.14
4	Beryl	—	0.061	—	0.079	—	—	—	—	—
5	Topaz	—	0.03	—	0.09	—	—	—	0.20	0.35
6	Orthoclase	—	0.12	—	0.34	—	—	—	0.76	1.23

Note: The numbers in the table are percentages.

The foregoing data indicate that, if a solution at the same concentration were sealed in quartz and calcite at the same temperature, the gas bubble in calcite will be bigger than in quartz, on cooling to room temperature, in the inverse proportion to the ratio of their expansion (contraction) coefficients. The homogenization of these inclusions will occur at the same temperature in both minerals, however.

One may plainly see therefore that identical volumes of gas bubbles in quartz and calcite are indicative of different homogenization temperatures and that these temperatures are higher for quartz. If, for the sake of comparison, we plot three rather exact determinations of the size of the gas bubble and of the homogenization temperature for inclusions in fluorite from Kulikolon (points *34, 35, 36*; volume of gas 7.3, 8.7, 9.6 per cent, homogenization temperature 105, 118, 125°C, respectively) on our diagram of the relationship between the degree of filling and the homogenization temperature for quartz and calcite (Fig. 16, p. 112), we see that the indicated curve for fluorite appears to be situated somewhere between the empirical curves derived for quartz and calcite (closer to the calcite curve). This corresponds to the intermediate position of fluorite between quartz and calcite, in regards to the parameter in question.

Highly incomplete as they are, the data show a dependence of the gas bubble size in inclusions in minerals not only on the temperatures of the included solutions but also on the thermal coefficients of the volume-expansion (and contraction) of different minerals. Insofar as this fact is neglected abroad, foreign scientists (Ingerson [172] and others) are continuing to believe that the method of Sorby is suited for mineralogical thermometry. As one may see, the empirical curves here derived for different minerals are better adapted for the purpose. However, we do not consider our method satifactory even for the low temperatures (up to 200°C) for which the curves were derived, despite the satisfactory agreement between the results obtained by these curves and the determined homogenization temperatures.

Deviations from the true temperatures of formation of minerals are caused by differences in concentrations of the included solutions affecting the expansion coefficients, and by variations in quantities of the cognate substance deposited on the walls of the vacuoles. These deviations increase in parallel to the increasing difference between the low concentration (here taken as the mean) of the included solutions, used as the reference points in our curves, and the test inclusions whose homogenization temperatures had to be measured for the first time. When we know how to determine concentrations of included solutions easily and relatively simply, we shall accumulate a body of data sufficient for proof and will finally arrive at the means of *determining the concentrations of the solutions from the differences in their homogenization temperatures* (in the given mineral).

The curves we have derived are suited only for approximate determinations of the anticipated homogenization temperatures of inclusions. One may resort to them only in the absence of the microthermochamber. In case the curves are not at hand, we recommend the use of certain simple formulas for tentative estimations of homogenization temperatures of inclusions in quartz and calcite—formulas that were derived from our curves and not divorced, like Sorby's, from inclusions in the corresponding natural minerals.

Empirical Equations for Calculation of Probable Homogenization Temperatures of Inclusions in Quartz and Calcite

Our equations for calculation of probable homogenization temperatures for quartz and calcite are based on a simple mathematical analysis of the experimental curves.

We used logarithms of the per cent gas (g) and temperature (t). We plotted on the X axis the logarithms of the percentages of gas, log g, and, on the Y axis the logarithms of the corresponding temperatures, log t. As shown in Fig. 17 the lines through the plotted points are straight lines, for quartz as well as for calcite.

As we know, if the equation of a straight line is $y = Ax + B$, the "curves" have a general equation $y = Bx^A$.

By substituting values in place of our variables (t) and (g), the homogenization temperature and the per cent of filling with gas respectively, and by replacing the constants B and t by k and α, we obtain $t = kg^\alpha$. The logarithmic form of this equation is $\log t = \alpha \log g + \log k$. If $\log g = x$, $\log k = \beta$, and $\log t = y$, $y = \alpha x + \beta$, i.e. the curve becomes a straight line, $\alpha x + B - y \neq 0$, for the experimental points and the corresponding square of the mean error is $\delta = \sum(\alpha xk + \beta - yk)^2$. The theoretical curve may be represented appropriately by

$$\sum Xx(\alpha xk + \beta - yk) = 0 \, ; \qquad \sum (\alpha xk + \beta - yk) = 0.$$

By removing the parentheses (cross-multiplying), the two equations with two unknowns lead to the following system

$$\alpha \sum xk^2 + \beta \sum xk = yk = \sum xk \cdot yk \qquad \text{(I)}$$

$$\alpha \sum xk + \beta \cdot n = \sum yk \qquad \text{(II)}$$

where n is the number of points on the curve.

By multiplying eqn. I by $\sum xk$ and eqn. II by $\sum xk^2$ and by subtracting the second product from the first one, we obtain, after the cancellations

$$\beta = \frac{\sum xk^2 \sum yk - \sum xk \sum xk \cdot yk}{n \sum xk^2 - (\sum xk)^2} \, .$$

By multiplying eqn. I by n and eqn. II by $\sum xk$ and by the same type of mathematical operations, we obtain

$$\alpha = \frac{n \sum xk \cdot yk - \sum xk \cdot \sum yk}{n \sum xk^2 - (\sum xk)^2} \, .$$

In order to find the numerical values of α and β from the numerical parameters of the points on our experimental curve, we determine $\sum xk^2$; $\sum yk$; $\sum kx$; $\sum xk \cdot yk$. This is contingent on our knowledge of the following magnitudes:

(1) For the quartz curve: xk, yk and $n = 20$;
(2) For the calcite curve: xk, yk and $n = 11$.

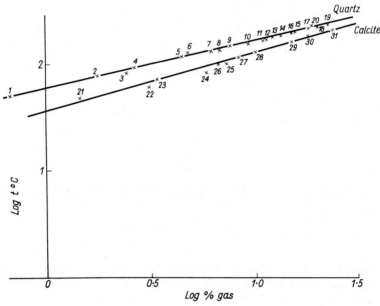

FIG. 17. Log-diagram of empirical curves for quartz and calcite. Empirical equations: for quartz $t° = 58.69g^{0.39}$; for calcite $t° = 37.25g^{0.47}$.

The values of α and β are determined for each curve after taking the logarithms, summation of the data for points 20 and 11, and their placement in the equations. As shown, the equation for our curve is:

$$t = kg^{\alpha} \text{ and } \log t = \alpha \log g + \log k \text{ where } \log k = \beta, \text{ i. e.}$$

$\log t = \alpha \log g + \beta$, or, in numbers, *for the quartz curve*,
$\log t = 0.39 \log g + 1.7686$, which is the same as

$$t° = 58.69g^{0.39},$$ or, in round numbers, $t° = 58.69g^{2/5}$.

The following equation *for the calcite curve* is similarly obtained

$$t° = 37.25g^{0.47}.$$

The value of g, in per cent, is obtained by microscopic measurements of the relative volume of the gas bubble with the aid of a micrometric scale or a grid. By substituting this numerical value into the appropriate equation we obtain the probable homogenization temperature by a simple calculation. The required parameters* for the empirical points on our curves, together with the calculated temperatures, are presented in Table 16.

As shown in Table 16, the calculated temperatures agree closely with the determined homogenization temperatures for the inclusions whose points lie in proximity to the curve. The points off the empirical curve represent serious discrepancies, generally within 9–10°C. The probable error in our calculated temperatures, by the formulas, is appraised by us at ±5%. However, the accuracy of the calculated temperatures or of temperatures estimated from the curves depends very much on the accuracy of the measured percentage of the gaseous phase in the inclusions.

The crystallization temperatures, as determined by the visual method, are nearer the true ones progressively at progressively decreasing pressures and concentrations of solutes in the included solutions. The method is entirely unsuited for multiphase inclusions of aqueous solutions and for complex inclusions of two immiscible liquids. The main value of the method here described is not as much in ease of the tentative estimations of the temperatures as in its usefulness in a series of theoretical problems involved in the utilization of inclusions as self-recording thermometers. Moreover, the method serves as the basis of a new methodology in ascertaining the state of aggregation of mineral-forming solutions by the determination of phase ratios not in their static condition at room temperature but in their mobile state produced by the restoration of the original temperatures of the included solutions.

Such methods served to demonstrate new types of homogenization of included mineral-forming solutions. They were already discussed in brief [37, pp. 37–51] and they will be considered in some detail in the sixth part of this book.

Methods of Determining Phase Ratios in Heterogeneous Inclusions of Solutions

The need of determining phase ratios in heterogeneous inclusions at room temperature as well as in the course of their homogenization, in order to ascertain the state of aggregation of solutions sealed in minerals,

---

* We are indebted to B. V. Gnidenko, active member of the Ukrainian Academy of Sciences, for his consultation in these calculations.

TABLE 1

Table for calculation of parameters for equations of quartz and calci

No. in sequence	g	t	$Xk = \log G$	$Yk = \log t$	$\log Xk$	$2 \log Xk$	Xk^2	$\log Yk$
	Quartz							
1	0.70	55	0.1549	1.74036	1.19005	2.38010	0.02399	0.24065
2	1.85	76	0.26717	1.88081	1.42684	2.85368	0.07139	0.27434
3	2.52	80	0.40140	1.90309	1.60358	1.20716	0.16112	0.27946
4	2.86	90	0.45637	1.95424	1.65935	1.31870	0.20830	0.29099
5	4.80	105	0.68124	2.02119	1.83327	1.66654	0.46402	0.30561
6	5.06	111	0.70415	2.04532	1.84763	1.69526	0.49572	0.31075
7	6.67	130	0.82413	2.11394	1.91598	1.83196	0.67914	0.32508
8	7.34	130	0.86570	2.11394	1.93737	1.87574	0.75117	0.32508
9	8.36	137	0.92221	2.13672	1.96483	1.92966	0.85050	0.32974
10	10.20	143	1.00860	2.15534	0.00360	0.00720	1.01672	0.33351
11	12.10	150	1.08279	2.17609	0.03429	0.06846	1.17070	0.33768
12	12.21	152	1.08672	2.18184	0.03611	0.07222	1.18090	0.33881
13	13.51	165	1.13066	2.21748	0.05330	0.10660	1.27820	0.34586
14	14.64	171	1.16554	2.23300	0.06655	0.13310	1.3586	0.34889
15	17.30	185	1.23805	2.26717	0.09272	0.18544	1.5326	0.35547
16	17.00	190	1.23045	2.27875	0.09006	0.18012	1.514	0.35768
17	20.61	198	1.31408	2.29667	0.11863	0.23726	1.7269	0.36109
18	22.65	206	1.35507	2.31387	0.13197	0.26394	1.8363	0.36433
19	25.65	218	1.40909	2.33846	0.14894	0.29788	1.9855·	0.36893
20	21.00	200	1.32222	2.30103	0.12129	0.24258	1.748	0.36192
			18.31474	42.66941			20.05377	
			$\left(\sum Xk\right)$	$\left(\sum Yk\right)$			$\left(\sum Xk^2\right)$	
	Calcite							
21	1.5	50	0.1761	1.6990	1.2458	2.4916	0.0310	0.2302
22	3.3	60	0.5185	1.7782	1.7148	1.4296	0.2688	0.2499
23	3.67	70	0.5647	1.8451	1.7518	1.5036	0.3189	0.2660
24	6.3	80	0.7993	1.9031	1.9027	1.8054	0.6389	0.2795
25	8.0	90	0.9031	1.9542	1.9557	1.9114	0.8154	0.2909
26	7.2	92	0.8573	1.9638	1.9331	1.8662	0.7348	0.2932
27	9.0	105	0.9542	2.0212	1.9796	1.9592	0.9103	0.3056
28	11.0	115	1.0414	2.0607	0.0174	0.0348	1.0830	0.3141
29	16.6	140	1.2201	2.1461	0.0864	0.1728	1.4880	0.3316
30	20.0	165	1.3010	2.2175	0.1143	0.2286	1.6920	0.3460
31	27.0	185	1.4314	2.2672	0.1556	0.3112	2.0470	0.3554
			9.7671	21.8561			10.0281	
			$\left(\sum Xk\right)$	$\left(\sum Yk\right)$			$\left(\sum Xk^2\right)$	

ırves and calculation of theoretical temperature by equations

$\log Xk + \log Yk$	$Xk \cdot Yk$	$\log(\alpha Xk)$ (theoretical)	αXk (theoretical)	$\log t = (\alpha Xk + \beta)$ (theoretical)	t (theoretical)	Difference between $t°$ of homogenization and $t°$ theoretical, °C (in rounded numbers)
1.43070	−0.26959	2.78625	−0.06113	1.70747	50.988	− 4.0
1.70118	0.50255	1.02304	0.10545	1.87405	74.826	− 1.2
1.88304	0.7639	1.19978	0.15841	1.92701	84.53	+ 4.5
1.95034	0.89205	1.25555	0.18011	1.94871	88.86	− 1.1
0.13888	1.3768	1.42947	0.26882	2.03742	109.0	+ 4.0
0.15838	1.4401	1.44383	0.27786	2.04646	111.29	−
0.24106	1.742	1.51218	0.32522	2.09382	124.11	− 6.0
0.26245	1.830	1.53357	0.34164	2.11024	128.9	− 1.1
0.29457	1.9705	1.56103	0.36394	2.13254	135.69	− 1.3
0.33711	2.1733	1.59980	0.39791	2.16651	146.72	+ 3.7
0.37191	2.3546	1.63043	0.42700	2.19560	156.89	+ 6.9
0.37492	2.371	1.63231	0.42886	2.19746	157.57	+ 5.5
0.39916	2.507	1.64950	0.44617	2.21477	163.97	− 1.0
0.41544	2.6028	1.66275	0.45999	2.22859	169.27	− 1.7
0.44919	2.8132	1.68892	0.48857	2.25717	180.79	− 4.2
0.44774	2.8038	1.68626	0.48558	2.25418	179.55	−11.5
0.47972	3.018	1.71483	0.51860	2.28720	193.73	− 4.3
0.49630	3.1354	1.72817	0.53478	2.30338	201.09	− 5.0
0.51787	3.2951	1.74514	0.55609	2.32469	211.2	− 6.8
0.48321	3 0424	1.71749	0.52179	2.29039	195.16	− 4.8
	40.365 $\left(\sum Xk\,Yk\right)$					
1.4760	0.2992	2.9178	0.0828	1.6539	45.07	− 5.0
1.9647	0.9219	1.3868	0.2437	1.8148	65.28	+ 5.3
0.0178	1.0420	1.4238	0.2654	1.8365	68.63	− 1.4
0.1822	1.5220	1.5747	0.3755	1.9466	88.43	+ 8.4
0.2466	1.7640	1.6277	0.4243	1.9954	98.90	+ 8.9
0.2263	1.6840	1.6051	0.4028	1.9739	94.17	+ 2.2
0.2852	1.9290	1.6516	0.4483	2.0194	104.6	− 0.4
0.3315	2.1460	1.6894	0.4892	2.0603	114.9	− 0.1
0.4180	2.6180	1.7584	0.5733	2.1444	139.4	− 0.6
0.4603	2.8860	1.7863	0.6114	2.1825	152.3	− 7.7
0.5110	3.2430	1.8276	0.6724	2.2435	175.2	− 9.8
	20.0551 $\left(\sum Xk\,Yk\right)$					

requires a discussion also of the ways of determining the phase ratios in inclusions of different forms.

Three types of measurements and calculations may be applied in practice. The most reliable is the *linear* one, applicable to the regular tubular inclusions; the *areal* one is used for flattened inclusions and flattened gas bubbles; the *volumetric,* the least exact one, is used for disc-shaped, globular, and faceted inclusions.

Regularly elongated tubular inclusions, either circular or flattened in their cross-section, are suited for the *linear* method. In the latter case, the interphase boundaries and the outlines of the inclusions themselves are very fine, so that it is difficult at times to distinguish the gas bubble from the liquid. We should remember here that, in such cases, one must be guided by the meniscus of the interphase boundary, convex toward the liquid and concave toward the gas.

The ends of tubular inclusions are rounded, as a rule, and it is these rounded ends that coincide with rounded interphase boundaries. It is essential to measure both the total length of an inclusion and the length of the section occupied by the gas phase, by employing an eyepiece-micrometer (and the highest possible power of objective), whereupon one proceeds with the ordinary calculation of the percentages. The measurements must be made in a uniform fashion and it is best to make divisions of the micrometric scale coincide with one-half of the rounded end of the inclusion and also with one-half of the meniscus' arc. The longer the inclusion, the more accurate the measurements. The error of such measurements is generally within ± 1 per cent.

Regularly rectangular or triangular inclusions with finely defined boundaries, as well as circular or ellipsoidal inclusions, are suited for the *areal* measurements. A conspicuously flat gas bubble, between the upper and the lower boundaries of the pore, is also an important prerequisite of such measurements. The flatness of the bubble is indicated by its fine boundaries, so that the core of the bubble transmits light and appears to be just as lightly colored as the liquid of the inclusion. The flatter the gas bubble, the larger is the circle of light inside the bubble; on the contrary, if this circle becomes a shining point, the gas bubble is definitely a spherical one. In the latter case, it is completely *impossible* to determine the phase ratio by the areal method, even if the inclusion itself is a flat ellipsoid or a disc.

Techniques of areal measurements require a calculation of the total area of the inclusion (defined either as a simple geometrical figure or a combination of figures) and of the area of a circle (more rarely of an ellipse) representing a projection of the flattened gas bubble. There are no difficulties with calculations of the percentage of gas under such circumstances. The limit of error is within ± 1 per cent, in the case of flat inclusions well suited for the purpose. The error increases in parallel with the increasing width of the dark border of the gas bubble and may rise to ± 1.5 to ± 3 per cent.

In quartz and calcite suitable flat inclusions are more common than suitable tubular inclusions. Measurements on both flat and tubular inclusions were used in the construction of our curves.

One may resort to using the curves with irregularly shaped inclusions, resembling a sphere or an ellipsoid only in extreme cases, where none of the better kinds are available. It is extremely difficult to calculate the volume of negative crystals, so common in quartz.

Reliability of the volumetric measurements may be increased only by a study of an inclusion in two or three mutually perpendicular projection planes. For that reason, the test material must be cut in the form of a cube or of a square prism. The gas bubble has a spherical shape in regularly shaped inclusions. The bubble's volume may be calculated from the volume formulas for a sphere or an ellipsoid of rotation. As already stated, these inclusions are difficult to handle also by the homogenization method. The problem is that light, while passing through an inclusion of this sort, is scattered not only in the spherical gas bubble but in the inclusion as a whole, so that the entire inclusion looks dark. There is a play of the reflections of light in the inclusion, so that even small changes in the focus are sufficient to alter the inclusion's general outlines and to "transpose" the phase boundaries. Naturally, all these phenomena serve further to complicate measurements of the phase volume ratios. The optimum results may be obtained only after a long experience in observing inclusions of different kinds, whereupon the relative percentage of gas may be calculated by the well-known stereometric formulae, with a fair degree of accuracy.

The direction and the magnitude of probable errors were ascertained using a crystal of quartz from Middle Ural one zone of which contained both the flattened-ellipsoid (three-dimensional) and the typically flat families of inclusions, genetically contemporaneous. Exact measurements on the latter group showed fluctuations in the per cent of the gas bubble from 6.36 to 6.84 per cent of the inclusion's total volume, with the arithmetical mean of 6.67 per cent (point 7 on the curve).

Two inclusions, nearly perfect in form, were selected among inclusions of the three-dimensional type; an ellpsoid and a sphere. A check by the heating method showed that all of the inclusions, flat and three-dimensional, homogenize at 130°C. However, there were striking differences between these two inclusions, as indicated by the areal and the volumetric measurements, with the following results:

(1) Areal measurements of the ellipsoid, in relative figures (divisions of the micrometer) were: $R_1 = 3.75$; $R_2 = 3.0$; $P_{common} = 35.36$ (0.002253

mm², in absolute numbers); V of the spherical gas bubble $= 1.15$; the bubble's area $P = 4.1548$; *per cent gas* $= 11.77$. Volumetric measurements on this inclusion, with its shape closely resembling an ellipsoid of rotation, were: $R_1 = 3.75$; $R_2 = R_3 = 3.0$; total volume, $V_0 = 116.25$ $(0.00005952$ mm³, in absolute numbers); $V = 1.15$; $V_2 = 6.3569$; *per cent gas* $= 5.47$.

(2) Areal measurements of the spherical inclusion gave the total area $P_0 = 36$ $(0.0023$ mm²$)$ and P of gas $= 3.8013$; *per cent gas* $= 10.56$. Volumetric measurements at $R_1 = R_2 = R_3 = 3.0$ gave $V_0 = 113.10$ $(0.0000579$ mm³$)$ and $V_2 = 5.5763$; *per cent gas* $= 4.93$.

Thus the areal measurements on the three-dimensional inclusions showed 10.56 to 11.77 per cent of gas while the volumetric measurements showed 4.93 to 5.47 per cent. At the same time, the true relative volume of the gaseous phase was found to be 6.67 per cent, by reliable measurements in the favorable flat inclusions.

These figures show the impossibility of taking into account the small departures from the ideal shapes of the ellipsoid and the sphere. The determined per cent gas is somewhat too low, while the areal measurements of the volume-type inclusions yield strikingly high results and are definitely not suited for the purpose.

Similar comparisons involving much more test material indicated an appreciable mean error (up to ± 5 per cent) in the volumetric measurements, so that their application may be justified only by an extreme need.

We must call attention also to the high delicacy of all such measurements, on the whole, and to the fact that it takes time for the observer's eye to acquire the necessary experience. We recommend *microphotographing of inclusions against a scale*: tubular ones against a ruler and flat ones against an eyepiece micrometer grid. Magnified reproductions of the pictures will help to increase the accuracy of the measurements and of the calculations.

DECREPITATION METHOD

It has been known since the first half of the last century that inclusions of carbon dioxide, homogenizing below the temperature of the human body, cause a fissuring of their host mineral even on warming by hand. Anyone who has had even a small experience with homogenization of included aqueous solutions, by heat, had the opportunity to see how easy is the rupture of such inclusions above the temperature of their filling.

These observations were utilized recently by Scott [175] as the basis for a procedure and technique of determining the probable temperature

method and its technique; the optical method, requiring no complicated apparatus, was suggested by us [41a].

The Acoustic Method

About 1 cm^3 of a certain definite size fraction of a fragmented mineral (the charge) is placed in a tube made of refractory glass. The end of a thermocouple is set inside the charge; the thermocouple is connected with a temperature recorder and the end of the tube is connected with a stethoscope. The refractory tube containing the test material is placed in a muffle furnace, so as to assure a slow and uniform heating of the element to the desired temperature. The course of decrepitation is followed by ear and is recorded by hand, as notes. A simplified set-up of this sort was used in 1949 at the mineralogical laboratory of the Government University of L'vov. The operations are shown in Fig. 15.

A more recent improved apparatus was described by Peach [177]. It consists of the already mentioned element, set in a muffle furnace, plus a crystal microphone (with an amplifier) protected from outside noise, an electronic relay converting the sounds of explosions into vibrations of a constant amplitude, a special circuit integrating resistance with power, and a recording milliammeter producing a frequency curve of the decrepitation vs. time, with a synchronized record of the temperature on the previously prepared base.

The decrepitation curves so obtained ("decrepigrams") intercept definitely the decrepitation peak and the corresponding temperature is accepted as the homogenization temperature, with certain allowances for time-lag and other errors. By employing this apparatus, Peach [177] obtained highly encouraging results with a specimen of synthetic quartz. This specimen was grown in a dilute solution of sodium carbonate, with the specific volume of 1.53 at the temperature of crystallization, so that the homogenization temperature of its primary inclusions ought to have been close to 340°C. As determined by the decrepitation diagram, the homogenization temperature of inclusions in this quartz was 355°C. Thus the determined temperature was only 15°C above the expected one.

Scott, using his simpler apparatus [175], examined eight natural minerals from different sources. He measured acoustically the frequency and the intensity of decrepitation vs. the temperature. He recorded the results as curves whose density indicated intensity of the explosions (Fig. 19). The abscissae of these curves represent temperatures to which the minerals were heated and their ordinates represent the frequencies of decrepitation, which were the main criteria in appraisals of the homogenization temperature by this method.

We must point out here the high degree of subjectivity in the appraisal of the rate of decrepitation estimated by Scott on a seven-degree scale—rare, occasional, slow, moderate, rapid, "sizzling", extreme. Scott admits himself, in his paper, that "the frequency and the intensity are subject to a personal judgment, to a certain degree. Consequently, different observers may obtain different curves for one and the same mineral".* The "flags" on the decrepitation diagrams (Fig. 19) here cited show his evaluations of the temperatures assigned by him to quartz, calcite, siderite, cryolite, beryl, and pyrite from five different sources. Also, the different levels at which the "flags" are placed indicate the degree of the decrepitation frequency in the choice of which, from the "occasional" to the "extreme" explosions, Scott felt rather free. Much work is still to be done, in refinements and proofs of the decrepitation method, and it appears, that the acoustic method, with *autographic record of the results,* will prove to be more objective and more feasible.

The Optical Method

This variant in obtaining results by the decrepitation method has a greater objectivity. It requires no apparatus in addition to the one employed in the homogenization method. The accuracy of the measurements is increased due to the facilities for slow heating, in keeping with the basic rule of the homogenization procedure.

A test-slide holder of a new design, equipped with a double window made of mica, was adapted for use with our microthermochamber. A single layer of the "charge" (fragmented mineral) was spread over the lower window and then the upper window was set in its place. The upper window was 2 to 2.5 mm from the lower one, so that it did not touch the powdered test mineral. After charging, the test-slide holder was set in the working space of the microthermochamber. The microscope objective, with a low or an intermediate magnification, was focused so as to bring the entire field occupied by the mineral grains within uniform visibility. Outlines of every individual grain were made clearly visible by strong light from below. One end of the thermocouple was inserted through the upper window and pressed against the lower one. The ordinary procedures were followed, in slow heating and in determining the temperatures of explosions of the particles. For the sake of a more precise fixation of temperatures of the explosions and of the included solutions to reach equilibria with their pore walls, we recommend the average rate of heating not to exceed 5°C per minute.

When inclusions or groups of inclusions explode, the grains of their host mineral shudder or move into conspicuously different positions. Even a slight transposition of a grain is positively indentified, at a low

---

* After confessions of this sort, this investigator's rather condescending attitude to the previously described and objective method of homogenization is very peculiar indeed.

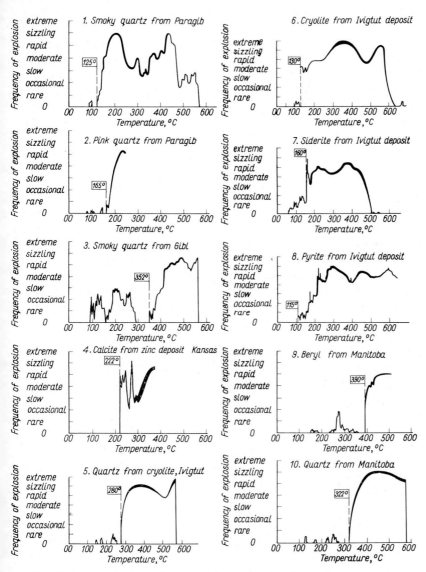

FIG. 19. Curves of relative frequency of decrepitation. (According to Scott.) Thickness of curves indicates intensity of explosions.

magnification, and, when the rate of heating is slow, it is possible also to count the number of the granules whose explosions take place early. As to the peak of the rupturing, its moment is easily recognized by the eye and even by the ear.

In our view, the fissuring is purely an auxiliary method, poorly developed at that, whose wide application may become feasible only by laborious and systematic comparison with the homogenization method.

We had this particular purpose in mind in setting up some small-scale experiments. Their aim was to establish the optimum particle size for every mineral and the optimum quantity of "charge", for obtaining results that would be comparable to the results of the standard homogenization method for primary, pseudo-secondary, and secondary inclusions. Studies of this kind will enable us in the future, in the case of opaque minerals, to introduce certain corrective temperature coefficients for the time-lag in the explosion of the corresponding inclusions in various minerals, as well as to ascertain the dependence of the explosion on the degree of filling of the inclusions and on their type of homogenization. We are presenting here only some incomplete results of our experiments with the use of the optical method of establishing explosions.

EXAMPLE 1. Our test material was quartz from Oyon (Aldan). Its careful analysis by the homogenization and by the visual methods revealed the following characteristic phase ratios in primary and secondary inclusions of liquid solutions and the following homogenization temperatures:

(1) Gas 7.34 per cent; homogenization temperature 130°C
(2) Gas 14.64 per cent; homogenization temperature 171°C
(3) Gas high; homogenization temperature 240°C.

This inclusion-bearing quartz was fragmented and about 100 pieces of the 0.7–0.25 mm fraction were taken for the analysis. Fissuring of the inclusions proceeded as follows

(1) Weak explosions of isolated inclusions	60–70°C
Pause in decrepitation	70–120°C
(2) Decrepitation (the first solitary explosions took place at 120°C)	130–140°C
Pause in decrepitation	140–165°C
(3) Decrepitation (the first solitary explosions at 165°C)	170–190°C
Pause in decrepitation	190–250°C
(4) Decrepitation	250–260°C
(5) The last solitary explosions	about 300°C
No decrepitation whatsoever	300–440°C.

The earliest weak explosions occurred in inclusions situated very near the surface of the fragments or else from some secondary inclusions we had not noticed. The intensive decrepitation at 130–140°C represents very well the secondary inclusions containing 7.34 per cent gas. The second incidence of decrepitation, from 170 to 190°C, represents the primary inclusions containing 14.64 per cent gas, and the last period of decrepitation, from 250 to 260°C, represents primary inclusions whose gas bubble is relatively large. The last explosions, at about 300°C, it appears, also belong to the latter category but their positions lie closer to the core of the fragments. The check over the next wide temperature interval (300–440°C) showed that every one of the inclusions has been exploded below 300°C. This result seems to be encouraging to us, since the ruptures of the typical inclusion groups took place within 10–20°C temperature range above their homogenization temperatures.

EXAMPLE 2. The test material was the first generation quartz from a deposit in Transbaykalia. The ore veins of this deposit were formed in a complex environment and within a wide temperature range. The typical primary inclusions in the quartz had homogenization temperatures at 280–295°C and looked as if they were formed either somewhat earlier than cassiterite or at about the same time as cassiterite whose inclusions had homogenization temperatures fluctuating in vicinity of 280°C. A series of secondary inclusions was also present in the quartz, with homogenization temperatures of 160–180–200°C. We identified also the latest group of included aqueous solutions whose mean homogenization temperature was 100°C. The quartz was fragmented to the size of 0.7–0.25 mm; 100 fragments were taken for the analysis.

The thermoanalysis, by decrepitation of liquid inclusions and optical determination of the results, proceeded as follows:

(1) A weak cracking of the fragments   100–120°C

(2) Intensive decrepitation   130°C
    Pause in decrepitation   130–170°C

(3) Intensive decrepitation   170–180°C

(4) Weak decrepitation   200°C and slightly over;
    Pause in decrepitation   210–267°C

(5) Weak decrepitation   267°C

(6) Intensive decrepitation   330°C
    Complete cessation of decrepitation at 330 to 390°C and higher.

As shown by the results, the three temperature intervals, 100–130°C, 170–210°C, and 267–330°C, in which a weak or an intensive decrepitation of the inclusions was taking place, are separated by two intervals in which there was no decrepitation. In this particular case, the second period of decrepitation coincides very well with the findings by the homogenization method, while the first one and the last one differ from homogenization temperatures by 30 and 45°C, respectively.

EXAMPLE 3. The results obtained for a high-temperature quartz from pegmatites of Volyn' seemed to be unsatisfactory. The gas bubbles occupied 34–40 per cent and 48 per cent of the inclusions' volumes and the corresponding homogenization temperatures were 238–251°C and about 290°C. The explosions of these inclusions were practically continuous at 245–270–280–290–300–310–320–330°C and were accompanied by a strong crackling above 280°C. Intensity of the explosions was weakened at 340–360°C but was increased again at 370–380°C. There were several powerful explosions at 390–400°C, coming from individual inclusions, and there was a new peak of frequency and intensity of explosions at 410–420°C.

Subjectivity cannot be avoided in our coordination of these results with the characteristic homogenization temperatures of the inclusions. If the first frequency–intensity peak at 280–330°C is to be referred to the first group of the inclusions, with the homogenization temperatures of 238–251°C, and the second peak, at 390–420°C, is to be referred to the second group of the inclusions, with the homogenization temperatures at 290°C, and somewhat higher, the mean excess of the decrepitation temperatures over the homogenization temperatures will be 60°C, in the first case, and at least 100°C in the second case.

We may conclude, it appears, that the decrepitation method becomes progressively less acceptable at increasing percentages of gas in liquid inclusions and at increasing homogenization temperatures, as the means of determining the temperatures of host minerals. *The interval between the homogenization temperature and the decrepitation temperature increases proportionally to decreasing density of the included solutions.*

The decrepitation method here described was not among our working methods, in our studies of the temperatures of mineral genesis, and we shall limit ourselves here to the brief comments on this method, as already given.

DEFECTS AND LIMITATIONS OF THE METHODS OF THERMOMETRIC STUDIES OF INCLUSIONS

We considered here four methods of thermometric studies of inclusions of mineral-forming aqueous solutions. The calculation method of Sorby was found to be unsuited for any practical use. Our main attention was given to the *homogenization of inclusions by heat*, the fundamental method, the method we had employed in solutions of a series of problems in mineral genesis, as will be shown below.

Notwithstanding the fact that the homogenization method has met so far with only a fleeting interest in the practice of the geologic–mineralogical research and that its methodological and technical progress and development were retarded appreciably, the method has already become an important tool in the hands of geologists. The method has already yielded such an abundance of precise data on the origin of minerals, despite its certain limitations as here noted, that it will enter, within a short time, the common arsenal of research in endogenetic deposits of mineral raw materials by geologists, geochemists, and mineralogists. The utilization of the mainly liquid inclusions in the capacity of autographic thermometers for determining temperatures of natural mineral genesis by the homogenization method has become liberated, by this time, from most of its theoretical, technical, and methodological difficulties that used to be formidable obstacles on the paths of the earlier students of inclusions.

These difficulties are now largely overcome, in the case of two-phase liquid inclusions in low-temperature and medium-temperature hydrothermal minerals, on the basis of our very slowly acquired experience and with the aid of modern scientific techniques. Much work is still to be done on multiphase liquid inclusions until the results of their thermometric studies may be used with confidence in geologic interpretations in relation to determinations of the true temperatures of hypogene mineral genesis. The scope of possibilities of the homogenization method is revealed by us in Chapter 5 of this book, by means of specific examples including studies of individual minerals as well as of certain mineral deposits.

The principal limitation of the homogenization method is its restriction to transparent and semi-transparent minerals. This limitation is not too formidable, however, if we consider the fact that the overwhelming majority of vein minerals accompanying ore minerals are able to transmit light, at least in thin sections.

We endeavored to develop the simplest possible method and technique suited for experiments even in the field, provided an electrical current is available. It was under conditions of this sort that we were employing the homogenization method for five years, in our studies of minerals and mineral deposits of different kinds.

The *"visual" method* was proposed for contingencies where the required apparatus cannot be made or acquired, as an aid in the evaluation of approximate temperatures. One of the shortcomings of this auxiliary method is that the empirical curves for minerals crystallizing below 200°C could be derived, so far, only for the most common vein minerals. The precision of its temperature measurements is inferior, of course, to the precision of the homogenization method. The probable homogenization temperatures for inclusions in quartz and calcite may be determined with the accuracy of $\pm 10°C$, by the equations based on the empirical data, as here proposed. Difficulties in exact measurements of phase ratios in inclusions should be added to the list of defects of the "visual" method.

Inclusions of submicroscopic size are not suited either for the "visual" or for the homogenization method. Precision of the measurements increases with the size of inclusions.

The *decrepitation method* is applicable to all transparent or non-transparent hydrothermal minerals and minerals containing sub-microscopic inclusions. This method will probably become, in the future, an important supplement of the homogenization method. However, the decrepitation method is still "blind", wherein lies its main defects. Since it is not possible to distinguish primary, pseudo-secondary, and secondary inclusions and to ascertain their homogenization type in non-transparent minerals, it is very difficult to interpret the results objectively. It appears, moreover, to be difficult to recognize the frequency–decrepitation peak, if the test mineral had crystallized within wide temperature range. The rupture-resistance of minerals is highly variable, so that every particular mineral requires a correction of its own ("the coefficient of the excess"), in reference to the homogenization temperature. Deposition of the cognate substance on the inclusions' walls and the common occurrence of complex inclusions (carbon dioxide–aqueous solution), whose presence cannot be proved optically in minerals, cause series complications in the use of the method. At the same time, the thermal "expansiveness" of carbon dioxide is so great that it is able to mix with water vapor of the inclusion, in different proportions. Subjectivity in appraisals of the temperatures obtained by this method is still impermissibly high. Much experimentation is still in order before the decrepitation method may be passed on to geologists as a useful tool. The beginnings of this experimentation were already made.

While pointing out the relative imperfections of the "visual" and the decrepitation methods, we must admit nevertheless that the results obtainable by these methods are incomparably more precise than the ordinary mineralogical thermometers* based on minerals themselves as indicators of temperatures.

---

* Detailed in Part One of the original book, and not translated here [Ed.].

CHAPTER 5

Results by Ordinary Procedures Employed in the Homogenization Method for the Determination of the Temperatures

DESPITE the seemingly long period of time devoted to studies of liquid inclusions (more than one hundred years have passed since the first idea to use them as self-registering thermometers), if we make a tally of the concrete results so far obtained, we realize that these results are still quite insignificant. The multitude of problems that could have been solved by the homogenization method are still not only unsolved, but are not even touched by such investigations. It may seem, at the first glance, that the collective effort and energy of many scientists who dealt with inclusions in minerals had failed to yield any scientific or practical results. This is not the case, however. Many investigators cited here in the historical review have each contributed his bit to the soil prepared for future studies, for the creation of *practical methods* of the investigations that were put in shape and presented, for the first time, in the preceding part of the book.

There has been no systematic work with inclusions up to the present time. It was this fact that was the main cause of the incredibly slow development in this particular field of mineralogic knowledge, the field of our interest. This and only this was the reason why studies of relics of mineral-forming solutions, preserved by nature, are still outside the common research practices of investigators of minerals from endogenetic sources.

The first measurement of the temperature at which the gas bubble disappeared in an inclusion in quartz from a vein in Cornwall was done by Sorby [128] and was registered at 220°C. This single experiment was performed by him in order to serve as the basis of his calculation method for determining temperatures of mineral genesis.

Phillips [137], in 1875, applied the homogenization method to inclusions of aqueous solutions, using a highly imperfect apparatus, and showed that gas bubbles in some inclusions in quartz from veins in California disappear on heating up to 80°C, while some other gas bubbles, in some other inclusions in the same crystal remain plainly visible even at 180°C. It was found also that in inclusions in quartz from granites, porphyries, and veins of Cornwall, gas bubbles become much smaller on heating up to 185°C. It has become established accordingly that the homogenization temperatures of the inclusions are higher than the temperature that could be measured reliably in a melted paraffin bath. Even these early experiments showed, however, that gas bubbles in inclusions in one and the same crystal disappear *at different temperatures.* This result, in the mind of the last century's scholars who were not accustomed to think in terms of processes, was so devastating, in regards to the possibility of using inclusions as self-registering thermometers, that the subject was abandoned, for all practical purposes, in the studies of the temperatures of mineral genesis.

Not until the beginning of this century did Königsberger [152] perform a few measurements of homogenization temperatures of aqueous inclusions in quartz from Alpine veins and show that their gas bubbles vanish at temperatures ranging from 160 to 260°C. Later on, in 1906, working together with Müller [153], he made the following measurements of the homogenization temperatures of inclusions in crystal quartz from Alpine veins: from Bechistock 215–222°C; from the Alpinger Glacier 223–229°C; from the Watting Tunnel 199–210°C. They estimated the accuracy of their measurements of the crystallization temperatures of the quartz at ±15°C.

In 1925, Holden [161] heated some included aqueous solutions in two crystals of smoky quartz from veins of the Alpine type, in order to determine pressures with the aid of carbon dioxide in the inclusions, and found their homogenization temperature, to be 125 and 135°C. The same method indicated the temperature of 150°C for an amethyst from Schemnitz.

In 1933, Newhouse [167] performed, for the first time, a large number of measurements of the crystallization temperatures of *sphalerite,* from deposits of the Mississippi Valley and from some other districts, and—what is especially important—used the results of his study in ascertaining the origin of these deposits. It appears that he examined tens of samples containing liquid inclusions of the parent liquor. His findings were summarized in a table of the crystallization temperatures of sphalerite, as indicated by liquid inclusions (Table 17).

Newhouse concluded from his studies that the ores of the lead–zinc deposits in the Mississippi Valley district were deposited by low-temperature hydrothermal solutions (80–135°C) and not by surficial solutions, as was believed by many other investigators.

In 1941–1943, we conducted a research on inclusions of aqueous solutions in the most common vein minerals from 22 sources in Central Asia. We examined 140 specimens of quartz, calcite, fluorite, and barite.

TABLE 17

No. in sequence	Source of mineral	Description	Temperature °C
1	Joplin, Mo.	Dark brown crystals from vugs	125–135
2	Picher, Okla.	Same	125–130
3	Tuknagou (?)	Zinc blende	115–125
4	Granby	Massive coarsely crystalline dark brown sphalerite with barite	110–115
5	Joplin	"Dull ore"; well preserved sphalerite crystals in hornfels	90–105
6	Boston Mine, Ky.	Vein of barite–sphalerite–galena; massive dark yellowish brown zinc blende	70–95
7	Badger Mine	Dark brown massive sphalerite ore with pyrite and marcasite	80–100
8	Wisconsin	Banded ore; chiefly dark brown sphalerite with smaller quantities of galena	90–105
9	South-west Missouri	Massive yellow sphalerite with cleavage fissures	105–125
10	Picos, Santander (Spain)	A single crystal; not fully idiomorphic; transparent; yellow and light brown; apparently from a vug	145–160
11	Rabenstein, south Tyrol	Well formed yellow and brown crystals; entirely transparent	145–150
12	Schemnitz (Hungary)	Zonal well formed crystals with large inclusions in the greenish yellow outer zone	180–190
13	Echigo (Japan)	Well formed crystals; dark brown to black	more than 225*

* The paraffin bath technique would not permit Newhouse to measure the homogenization temperatures exactly. He estimated this temperature at 250–275°C from the size of the remaining gas bubbles.

The total number of measurements of homogenization temperatures in this study was several times as large as the combined total number of measurements by all of the earlier investigators. Some of our findings have been published already [30, 31, 32]. At about the same time, beginnings of the new methods took shape [41]; we made use of them in the following years.* Some of these earlier measurements are cited in the present study as illustrations of developments and applications of the methods. The more basic and important results of our studies have been commented upon in the historical review of the subject.

Twenhofel, in 1947 [173], measured the homogenization temperatures of 63 primary inclusions in a crystal of fluorite from New Mexico. His very interesting results are presently to be discussed.

Laz'ko, also in 1947 [61], while measuring variations in the homogenization temperatures of inclusions in some specimens of quartz from Aldan, had found these temperatures to exceed 250°.

Toward the end of 1947, Ingerson [172] reported the homogenization temperatures of liquid inclusions in quartz from pegmatitic veins of Brazil, Connecticut, and North Carolina, as summarized in the following table:

TABLE 18

Source of specimens	Homogenization temperature (°C)	Most probable homogenization temperature (°C)	Remarks ("c.p." means correction for pressure)
Paragiba	150	156	Pink quartz c.p.+62°C
Paragiba	101	101	Smoky quartz c.p.+73°C
Brazil	67–157	100	Included in topaz c.p. +73°C
Connecticut	167–245	180	Milky quartz c.p.+54°C
Connecticut	153–165	155	
Connecticut	156–158	157	
Connecticut	175	175	Inclusion in beryl
North Carolina	160	160	Close to a small cavity
North Carolina	182	182	Same specimen; inclusion farther away from the cavity

Ingerson concludes, on the basis of his thirteen measurements, that the observed temperatures were lower than the accepted temperatures for such minerals. It appears to us that the author has had too little experience in differentiating between primary and secondary inclusions. The temperatures he reports may represent a later stage of the crystal growth, in many instances, involving also healing of fissures in the test crystals of different generations. Moreover, the temperature characteristics of the formation of a given crystal may be expressed by a simple figure

---

* Some other Soviet and foreign investigators have begun to use our methods successfully since 1947: [29, 44, 173, and others].

only if the crystal was growing within a narrow temperature range. Deviation of average temperatures, as done for example by Ingerson for quartz from Brazil, appears to be impermissible to us, because crystals grow generally within a much wider range of decreasing temperature than is commonly believed and because crystals grown at some particular temperature are extremely rare in nature.

In 1948, Grushkin [28, 29] published the first results of his studies begun in 1947. For the sake of ascertaining the dependence of the observed homogenization temperature on the size of inclusions and on magnification under the microscope, he performed 40 measurements on inclusions in quartz, including determinations of the diameter of gas bubbles and of the approximate size of the inclusions [28]. In his second interesting study [29], Grushkin reports homogenization temperatures for inclusions in two crystals of quartz belonging to different generations. The temperature was found to be 219°C in the inner part of the quartz crystal of a columnar habit; the temperatures for the intermediate and the outer zones were found to be 196°C and 193–192°C, respectively. Moreover, Grushkin showed that secondary inclusions in healed fissures of various ages, in the same crystal, homogenize at 168, 144, 138, and 129°C. The typical homogenization temperatures in his short columnar comb-like quartz were 144–145°C.

Grushkin, proceeding from his measurements of secondary inclusions in quartz of an early generation, correctly concludes that such groups of inclusions, with definite temperatures, correspond to growth stages of other quartz crystals belonging to the later generations.* His researches, in our view, are an example of an intelligent approach to the study of inclusions in minerals, something that cannot be found, so far, in the works of the majority of American geologists and mineralogists.

For example, in 1949, Dreyer, Garrels, and Howland [178] made a singularly unsuccessful application of the homogenization method to inclusions of halite from a sedimentary deposit in Kansas. As we have stated, such inclusions inevitably acquire a gas bubble of *secondary* origin, and, as to the inclusions themselves, they too may have a secondary origin, to a certain extent associated with the circulation of young vadose waters in beds of rock salt.

Two out of seven sets of measurements (curves *2* and *3*, Fig. 20) by these three authors cannot be taken seriously at all, documented as they are by heating and cooling curves. As shown by the curves, the hermetic

---

* That is, the homogenization temperatures of primary inclusions in crystals of late generations are about the same as homogenization temperatures of secondary inclusions in crystals of early generations. The latter ones were being healed while the former ones were growing still, all other things being comparable [V.P.S.].

character of the sealing of the inclusions was so poor that liquid escaped from the inclusions during the experiment. The authors themselves discarded the results of these two experiments. Their experiments represented by curves *4, 5,* and *8* yielded homogenization temperatures of 100, 90, and 97°C, respectively, although the cooling curves failed to coincide with the heating curves in every single case. In brief, *the original condition of the inclusions was not reestablished after the experiments.* This fact alone is logical evidence of non-hermetic sealing of the inclusions, even if their gas bubbles were not necessarily of secondary origin. This did not prevent them, however, from deeming their results acceptable, by all appearances. In two other tests (curves *6* and *7*), the homogenization occurred at 85 and 73°C. By analogy with the three preceding ones, there is no doubt here too that the original condition of the inclusions was not re-established after the experiment, even though the authors made no record of the cooling curves. The series of homogenization temperatures they had obtained for different inclusions (100–97–90–85 and 73°C) by repeated determinations, using the same inclusions, could not be replicated without question. On the contrary, were they to repeat the series, they would have come out with different sets of figures every time. If the authors would risk even one such check, they would have refrained from extensive interpretations of their results.

Most recently, Bailey [179] published his thermometric results on liquid inclusions in quartz of granites from different sources: 1 and 2— Wisconsin; 3—Vermont; 4 and 5—Saxony; 6 (granite) and 7 (rhyolite)— Cripple Creek, Colorado; 8—Scotland; 9—Massachusetts. The results of his 135 experiments with the disappearance of gas bubbles in liquid inclusions are summarized in Table 19.

It is perfectly self-evident that this investigator was not able to draw any genetic conclusions from kaleidoscopic data of this sort. First of all, he failed to become aware of the fact that *there can be no primary liquid aqueous inclusions in granites.* Such inclusions in minerals of granite rocks are the result of a hydrothermal metamorphism or epimorphism in different stages of alteration of the rock. The inclusion studies, as applied to metamorphic processes, are still relegated to the future. There have been practically no systematic studies of this problem, so far, and the results of Bailey's investigations can scarcely be regarded as a start of such studies.

There are no important omissions, it appears, in our present review of the principal results of the ordinary applications of the homogenization method to inclusions of aqueous solutions in minerals. This review and the history of the subject show that it was only in the past decade that we had indications of radical shifts in the use of the homogenization

TABLE 19

1	2	3	4	5	6	7	8	9
170°C	222°C	208°C	192°C	195°C	195°C	205°C	234°C	216°C
240	248	216	200	215	220	231	262	233
300	260	232	208	221	235	252	283	250
	305	298	215	250			286	
226	300	300	241	278	218	160	330	228
243	235	338	260	280	235	200		241
267	276	340	310	292	250	220	195	262
	298	368		330	278	223	218	265
216	350	384	223	358	280	250	265	
225			251		335	298	278	
260	198	270	280	227				
270	230	291		243	180		240	
340	258	300	200	260	200		245	
	289	320	206	285	230		260	
200	310		215		280		275	
220	320	225	223	200				
240	360	230	225	242				
260		256	240	245				
		260	260	276				
216		267	304					
225		280	310					
248		300						
		317						
172								
196								
330								

method in the analysis of the process of mineral genesis. Some individual scientists laid the foundation for a purposeful approach to the problem. They took decisive steps on the road to revealing the possibilities of the method in ascertaining growth processes of primary minerals, their alterations and transformations into qualitatively different varieties and even into different minerals, the processes whose integrated whole reveals to us the evolution of the mineral kingdom. Our own studies are dedicated to this important philosophical and practical subject and to the development of the research methods and techniques.

Specific examples of study of individual crystals from certain deposits of minerals containing largely liquid inclusions, by the new methods of thermometric analysis, are presently to be reported as examples of the possibilities implied in the homogenization method. We adhere rigidly, in our research, to the previously formulated propositions, both with regard to the principles of the homogenization method and to the operations of the methods. We are confident therefore that the numerous sources of errors (pp. 96–99), leading to incorrect conclusions, were eliminated in our work.

Theoretical and practical difficulties as encountered in every step by a new student are not considered in our subsequent discussion of the results. We were able to surmount such difficulties because of our considerable experience in systematic work. The appropriate qualifications are stated only in cases where test materials or circumstances made it impossible to determine the true character of an inclusion or of a group of inclusions. For that particular reason we omitted from our report certain data on individual minerals and deposits, so that in the present state of our knowledge, we could be dealing not as much with ordinary materials as with "high-quality" data.

This refers, first of all, to the degree of transparency and the perfection of faces of our test crystals. Our "selective" approach to the test materials is the best one, perhaps in its relation to the problems of the present study. The reliably determined relationships in excellent test materials are not likely to be ascribed in the future to errors in observations and measurements in handling of any kind of an ordinary test material from any kind of a hydrothermal or a pneumatolytic source.

Our approach must not be construed as evidence of a stringent limitation of the method. The homogenization method is applicable to all transparent, semi-transparent, and even non-transparent (transmitting light only in thin sections) minerals. Our conviction is based on studies of test materials from certain tin and tungsten ore deposits in Transbaykalia. These results are omitted in the book, but they will be put to use in a series of contributions by our scientists who have studied these ore deposits in person.

CHAPTER 6

Methods of Thermometric Investigation of Minerals and of Mineral Deposits and Results of their Applications

GENERAL PRINCIPLES OF THE METHODS

As we know, so far, not a single one of the principal factors of mineral genesis (temperature, pressure, concentration), as well as the state of aggregation of the solutions, could be measured and evaluated with scientifically acceptable accuracy, in investigations of the origins of minerals and of mineral deposits. The factors here listed, on which the course of mineral genesis depends, had received neither qualitative nor quantitative characterization, so far, for all practical purposes. It is for that very reason that the evolution and change in the mineral kingdom could not be sensed sufficiently clearly and the inappropriate terms "dead" or "non-living" Nature came to be applied to minerals.

After a long period of study of inclusions in minerals, we became convinced that exact measurements of the homogenization temperatures serve to provide the background against which the processes of formation not only of hydrothermal deposits but even of individual crystals in such deposits may be viewed with precision.

The very first measurements of the homogenization temperatures of inclusions in different growth zones of fluorite and quartz crystals, in 1942, showed variations in the temperatures [32]. This was the foundation of thermometric studies of individual crystals to which we gave the name of the *mineralothermometric analysis*.

It was believed possible in former times to express the temperature of formation of a mineral, an ore vein, or even of a whole mineral deposit, by some single figure somehow produced, notwithstanding the resulting contradictions with the general theory of the phenomena. One of the main reasons why experimental work with liquid inclusions, as self-recording thermometers, was discontinued in the past was that very fact that inclusions in one and the same crystal homogenized at different temperatures [137, 138]. This same fact was established also by our early experiments but it was an encouragement and not an embarrassment to us. The method was recognized by us as the very means by which it is possible to detect changes in the temperature of the solutions, not only in dealing with the formation of mineral deposits but also with crystal-forming solutions from which a given mineral has formed. All that was needed then was an intelligent approach to the study of inclusions of different types in different growth zones and sections of crystals and in different healed fissures.

We were led to the necessity of differentiating our inclusion studies by growth zone and by crystal section, in view of the inevitability of variations in the temperature, in harmony with the theoretical concepts derived from the data of physics and chemistry, even the kind that only accompanies the cessation of mineral genesis. Comparisons of the results of such studies serve to ascertain definite relationships between the general and the specific, to provide a clear-cut characterization of the growth processes of every individual mineral of a definite generation or nucleation. This characterization, based on actual measurements of homogenization temperatures of inclusions in every discrete zone of the crystal, shows us the course of variations in the temperature regime of the mineral-forming solution, but in turn constitutes but a moment in our understanding of the entire process of formation of the deposit.

A general view of the process, against the background provided by the accompanying variations in temperature, is reconstructed by comparisons between the temperature data for different minerals and for different generations of one and the same mineral.

Thermometric analysis may help appreciably in determining the crystallization sequence of minerals. It enables us to answer certain questions involving relationships in the crystal-forming environment, in consideration of the homogenization temperatures of inclusions, and to determine alterations in the host rocks caused by crystal-forming solutions [20]. The mineralothermal analysis reveals to us certain intricate inter-dependences between these solutions and the geological environment expressed as a given mineral product of their interactions.

Of course, there exists a wide variety of crystal-forming environments in nature, even from one and the same solution. This variety is conditioned by the rate and the character of variations in the solution itself which depended, in turn, on variations in the geological environment, in places where it interacts with the solution.

There are radical variations in the geological environment within the range from the active section of a magmatic source to the earth's surface, even between closely lying transverse planes through sections of the earth's crust. In our appraisals of the geological environment, aided by natural outcrops or mining works within the boundaries of a given deposit, by reference to some of its well-defined features (composition and permeability of host rocks, extent and type of their tectonic disturbance, etc.), we recognize that the environment is not and was not the same, both in depth and in overburden, which has been stripped by erosion by this time.

The mineral genesis is more or less the same, as a whole, in hypothetical horizontal planes somewhat below and somewhat above the deposit, but is not the same in its details. There are points of resemblance and dissimilarities between any two such planes. The over-all orderly relationships governing these variations are still imperfectly understood and, for that reason, one often runs into difficulties in his estimate of the nature of the deposit in depth.

Possibilities of an easy recognition of variations in the geological environment of mineral genesis are limited for us to a given erosion plane of a mineral deposit. We may see for example, a metasomatism of rocks that was active in the early stages of the formation of a deposit, while observing simultaneously the conditions of the deposition of minerals in fissures or, rarer, in broad open cavities that functioned as natural crystallizing reservoirs. There are variations in the simultaneous deposition of minerals in these variable geological environments, even during one and the same stage of activity of the mineral-forming solutions, because the local conditions are never the same, in any specific case, even within a small area.

Identical solutions, injected into pores in rocks and ascending freely in fissures, do not contribute to the formation of minerals in exactly the same vay. Variations in the crystallization of minerals increase progressively, in case the solutions penetrate large cavities in rocks functioning as natural crystallization reservoirs. The free space of such cavities is generally conducive to quiescence, where crystallizing minerals are able to grow in the form of faceted regular individuals. In such quiet environments, typical of deposits of crystals of piezo- and optical grades, large crystals are able to grow even at a very slightly falling temperature of the solutions, since the solutions are maintained supersaturated in this natural crystallizer by quiet accessions of fresh portions of the solutions.

An example of such a situation is found in Tadzhikistan (see below), in a deposit of crystals of optical fluorite. In this case it can be shown definitely by the inclusion studies that the fluorine-bearing solutions, operating at about two kilometers' depth, crystallized their minerals within a narrow range of temperature, from 175 to 140°C (correction for pressure: +40°C). Within this range, however, crystals in some individual clusters grew to a large size within a very small drop in the temperature.

It was only in the end-stage of the crystallization, when accessions of fresh solutions had ceased, that the relatively rapid cooling of the natural reservoir became the only stimulus for a continuation of the crystal growth.

Every mineral in a genetically complex deposit is *a product of the crystal-growing medium and of the geological environment* and its origin occurs at a certain definite stage of their interaction. This stage may be defined objectively, in the light of our research, by the temperatures at the beginning and at the end of crystallization of the mineral of a given generation and nucleation.

While deciphering the origin of a mineral deposit, we regard the study of different growth zones of every individual crystal, typical of a given generation of the mineral formed within a certain definite stage of the process, to be of basic importance. It was for this particular reason that we begin our presentation of the results of the temperature studies of certain deposits and ore provinces by the discussion of the results obtained with individual crystals.

These data are not too abundant, so far, but their active accumulation will assure better understanding in the further development of the science of origin of ores.

RESULTS OF THERMOMETRIC ANALYSIS OF INDIVIDUAL CRYSTALS

Application of Methods in Determining Successive Lowering of Temperatures of Crystal Growth

Mineralothermometric analytical methods were first employed by us in 1942, in a study of conditions determining formation of optical and piezoelectric minerals. We examined a large crystal of transparent bluish optical fluorite from Cluster No. 36 of the Kulikolon Deposit [32]. This crystal had a large number of defects [36], particularly small primary inclusions, on its periphery, in its core, and in its middle sections.

Ten slides containing two-phase inclusions of aqueous solutions were prepared from different sections of a non-zoned crystal. Three of these slides represented the core, near its attachment to the matrix, and showed temperatures of 166 to 167°C. Four other slides from the central part of the crystal showed a temperature of 165°C and two slides from the periphery of the crystal showed 163°C. The areas from which these measurements were made are indicated on the crystal section (Fig. 21, left). Temperatures of slow homogenization of the inclusions were determined by a mercury thermometer, with particular care. Replicate determinations by different analysts gave identical results. Indications obtained in a different fluorite crystal from the same cluster were similar. The optical fluorite

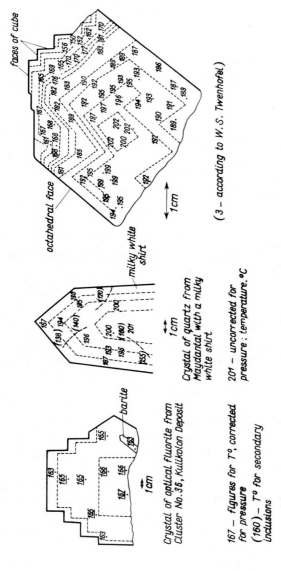

FIG. 21. Temperature range of crystallization of quartz and fluorite.

faces of cube

octahedral face

milky white shirt

barite

Crystal of optical fluorite from Cluster No. 36, Kulikolon Deposit

Crystal of quartz from Maydantal with a milky white shirt

167 – figures for T°, corrected for pressure

(160) – T° for secondary inclusions

201 – uncorrected for pressure; temperature. °C

(3 – according to W. S. Twenhofel)

here examined overgrew a crystal of optical barite formed at 177 to 183°C, as shown by the homogenization method, assuming a pressure correction of 40°C. The minimum temperature for the optical fluorite crystals was 153°C [*sic*] for this particular cluster. We suggest the designation of *monothermal* for mineral individuals whose crystallization was not accompanied by a drop in the temperature of the mother liquor in excess of 10°C. Only for such crystals do we have the right to express the crystallization temperature by a single average figure, as in the case in question, where this temperature is 165°C.

On the basis of this and of other studies of a series of other crystals, we concluded that the crystallization of optical fluorite in natural crystallizer-reservoirs (vugs), from its beginning to the end, takes place under extremely slowly and uniformly decreasing temperatures of the mother liquor [32, p. 39].

In another case, in 1943, we examined a tapered crystal of quartz from the Pskem River with a prism edge ranging from 5 to 6 cm. We cut a plate along the long axis of this crystal and cut 17 sections from this plate, from different growth zones of the mineral. The outer zone of the crystal was milky-white; its inner part was entirely transparent and had no zonal structures. The section through the crystal, showing places from which the test sections were taken, is represented in the center of Fig. 21.

Primary inclusions in the inner part of the crystal showed temperatures of 200–201°C (uncorrected for pressure), in three sections. Temperatures from 195 to 197°C were established, in four sections, closer to the periphery of the crystal. In the surficial layer of the transparent body of the crystal, under the milky-white layer, the temperatures were 193–194°C. The homogenization temperatures of liquid inclusions in the milky-white zone itself were also rather monotonous (187–190°C). As shown in the sketch, these measurements allowed us to draw three isotherms inside the crystal, at 200, 195, and 190°C. The last one of these isotherms coincides with the boundary between the transparent core and the white zone. It was thus proved [32, p. 42], that a crystal of rock crystal grows at a fairly uniformly decreasing temperature of the solutions, from 201 to 187°C (within a range of 14°).

Inclusions in healed fissures are objects of considerable interest in this type of crystal studies. Three homochronous groups of such inclusions were indentified by their homogenization temperatures in the crystal we had examined. As one may see in Fig 21, the first one of these groups has homogenization temperatures of 155–160°C. Inasmuch as the host fissure of these inclusions does not extend to the very surface of the crystal, as we could see on the subsequent microscopic examination of the section, there is a basis for the belief that we are dealing here with pseudo-secondary inclusions [38, 39]. It is possible that the temperatures here indicated represent solutions from which the very last portions of the substance were deposited on the crystal surface. If so, the temperature range of the growth of our crystal may be wider than we thought it to be in 1943, when all inclusions in fissures were still being classified by us as secondary. If this is the case, the temperature curve of the solutions should assume a steep downward slope, toward the end of the crystal-forming process, and the temperature range of the crystallization would extend over 41–46°C and not over 14°C.

The two other groups, with homogenization temperatures of 138, 140, and 120°C, belong undoubtedly to secondary inclusions. The time of their healing corresponds apparently to the growth of the amethyst crystals found in the same deposit, among the younger generations.

Twenhofel [173], in 1947, three years later, citing the results of our studies, carried out a similar piece of work with a crystal of ordinary fluorite, apparently of the vein type, grown in moving and not stagnant solutions. The temperature of the moving solutions changed appreciably with time. The results of his measurements of homogenization tempera-tures in different parts of the crystal (uncorrected for pressure) are re-presented in Fig. 21, on the right.

The bulk of the crystal grew in the octahedral form, from 202 to 170°C, and acquired an apple-green color at the same time. At about 170°C, the crystal began to change its shape into a cubic one and to acquire a lilac color. After this the fluorite continued to grow until 150°C, as indicated by the homogenization temperatures of inclusions in the peripheral zone of the crystal. This independence of color and shape is striking in the mineral and the change in both was caused apparently by the same variables, with temperature being among the major ones (if not the principal one).

We are dealing with polythermal environments of crystal growth in both of these examples, which are the most common ones in nature, as we shall presently see. We suggest the term *polythermal minerals* for minerals crystallizing over a wide temperature range.

The curves in Fig. 22 represent falling temperatures of crystal-forming solutions, as indicated by the crystals we examined. The ordinate shows the temperature, in °C; the abscissa shows the isotherms, at 5°C intervals, from the outer boundary to the center of the crystal. The abscissa coincides also with the coordinate of time. As illustrated by the curves, we are dealing with a most common case of progressive but non-uniform decrease of temperatures of the solutions. The great variety of natural phenomena, however, is by no means invariably in correspondence to the standards we have already established. As we shall see later on, the decreasing temperatures of the solutions, in the growth of zoned crystals and minerals involving two-, three- and multiphase formations, are subject to drastic disruptions in their gradual character, expressed in abrupt changes, both up and down, of the temperature of the mineral-forming solutions.

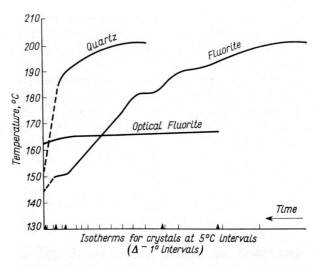

Fig. 22. Curves showing sequence of falling temperatures during crystal growth.

Before we pass on to the study of complex variations in the temperature regime of the solutions, in the course of formation of certain hypogene minerals, let us consider some examples of application of the mineralothermal analysis that have a very important bearing on our methods.

Temperature of Formation of a Quartz Crystal from Bristenstock and Significance of Pseudo-Secondary Inclusions

In bringing to light the results of mineralothermometric investigations, we shall begin with a concrete example that clarifies the most acute problem in the use of inclusions of aqueous mother liquors in the capacity of self-registering thermometers. This problem involves primary inclusions, associated with growth forms of crystals, and secondary inclusions, associated with healing of fissures in crystals. The incorrect understanding of the genetic significance of these two types has strongly hindered the advancement of research on the origin of minerals.

Figure 23 represents a rather large (13 cm long and 7 cm across) crystal of quartz from Bristenstock (the Alps) showing clearly a large fracture parallel to the rhombohedral face of the crystal. The main fissure and its lateral branches resulting from the break were found to be healed and overcrowded by two-phase inclusions. Inclusions in fissures of this sort

Fɪɢ. 23. Crystal of quartz from Bristenstock.

are regarded as secondary, as a rule, and data on such inclusions are regarded as unrelated to the formation of the mineral.

It is known that the largest number of inclusions in crystals is asso‐ ciated generally with fissures cutting the crystal growth forms and not with the growth forms themselves. This problem led to much apprehension, on our part, in the early stage of our work with inclusions. We first obtained encouraging results with phantom crystals of fluorite [38] and it became possible eventually to ascertain the true significance of such inclusions also in other minerals.

We choose here a quartz crystal as an example because quartz is one of the most common minerals and, moreover, very commonly has such "secondary" inclusions. We are using this crystal from Bristenstock also because the healing of its fissures proved to be entirely complete. If we turn the crystal around, we shall have the view shown in Fig. 24—a self-evident and an instructive picture. The fissure in the right part of the crystal looks now as if it were completely healed, while in the left and the broader part of the crystal, the fissure is still open and gaping. One may clearly see on the lower surface of the fissure that its healing was the result of a multinucleated growth.

If the accessions of silica-bearing solutions had continued at the site of crystal growth, the crystal would have been completely regenerated and every one of its prismatic faces would have assumed the appearance of the central prism face (Fig. 24) which shows so clearly the relics of completely

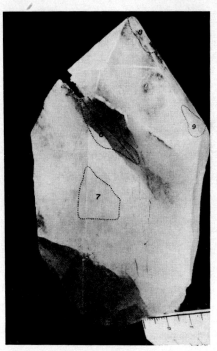

FIG. 24. The same crystal from Bristenstock seen from the other side.

healed fissures with their "secondary" inclusions. A question presents itself at once, as we examine the crystal; just what was the relationship of the "secondary" solutions, preserved in the inclusions in the healed fissures, and the crystal's growth? Are we justified in applying the data obtained on these inclusions to the entire quartz crystal here discussed?

In order to clear these points, we prepared three sections (1, 2 and 3, Fig. 23) from the surface of an incompletely sealed fissure supporting a multinucleated growth of quartz which had effectively healed the fissure. There other sections were taken from the opposite side of the crystal, where the healing of fissure has ended by their complete sealing off (*4, 5* and *6*, Fig. 24). Finally, three more sections were taken from the upper growth zone of the crystals: *7*th, from the prism face; *8*th, from the crystal's termination; *9*th, from the rhombohedral face. After that, all of the nine sections were investigated, as usual, by the method of the homogenization of their "secondary" and primary inclusions.

The results of these studies are summaried in Table 20.

They show that the fine crystals of multinucleated growth, which had no time to seal their fissures, were formed within the range of 120 to 142°C. The "secondary" inclusions in the healed fissures showed homogenization temperatures from 113 to 154°C, while the primary inclusions in the central part of the crystal were homogenized at 158 to 162°C. Primary inclusions in the crystal's outer zone, by which the present appearance of the crystal is defined, had homogenization temperatures from 115 to 152°C.

These data, obtained by painstakingly careful measurements, permit us to state that the outer faces of the crystal were growing concurrently with the healing of the fissures by multinucleated growth of quartz. The zone

TABLE 20

No. of test sections	Position of test section of crystal	Series of homogenization temperatures (°C)	Genetic types of inclusions according to the present classification
1	Surface of incompletely healed fissure	120–124–136	
2	Small crystals of multinucleated growth	120–123–132–142 (at base of crystals)	Primary (in crystals of multinucleated growth)
3	Small crystals of multinucleated growth	125–132–134	Same
4	Upper parts of incompletely healed fissures	113–126–142	Secondary
5	Middle parts of completely healed fissures	119–124–128 130–132–138 140–142–150 152–154	Same
6	Lower part of a completely healed fissure	132–154	Same
7	Prism face of crystal	121–138–152	Primary (for the entire crystal)
8	Termination of crystal	124–138	Same
9	A rhombohedral face	115–142	Same
10*	Central part of crystal	158–162	Same

* The 10th slide could not be shown in the photograph.

of extremely fine crystals, visible through a lens on the well-formed rhombohedral and prismatic faces, had developed at the very end of the crystal growth, at temperatures corresponding apparently to the very last moments of incompletely healed fissures, as in the zone represented by section *4* (113–115°C).

The most important aspect of our investigation, however, is the fact that the secondary inclusions in the crystal's fissures are, in reality, primary–secondary ones [38] or, as we called them later, *pseudo-secondary inclusions* associated directly with the growth of the "host" crystal. Fissures containing such inclusions are sealed in conjunction with the deposition of the later and last layers on the crystal's outer faces, the layers defining the present habit of the crystal. In order to avoid giving an impression that any inclusion in a crystal must be either primary or pseudo-secondary, we shall now consider the following case which also has general significance in shedding light on our approach to determinations of the temperature range wherein certain minerals and druses were formed, as indicated by slow homogenization of their inclusions on heating.

Studies of Temperatures of Formation of a Quartz Druse from Aldan and Identification of Secondary Inclusions

As we see now, an investigator employing the thermal analysis of minerals in ascertaining temperatures of the solutions in which crystals and druses were growing must understand clearly the type of the inclusion on which his measurements are made, in every single case. This is not an easy problem, unavoidable as it is, since inclusions of different origins may yield a whole gamut of homogenization temperatures.

In the instance of small crystals especially, it is not always possible to determine at what particular temperature a crystal, with its multitude of fissures, began and ended its growth. Healing of some of the fissures may coincide, in time, with the growth of the host crystal, as has been shown already. Inclusions in such fissures will be pseudo-secondary, inasmuch as the final sealing of fissures at the crystal's surface depends on the deposition of the very last layers of substance on the surface. If the outermost crystalline layer is very thin, the associated pseudo-secondary inclusions will register a temperature not too different from the temperature characterizing the end of the crystal growth. If, on the other hand, genuine primary inclusions are encountered in the outer zone of a crystal, as in the preceding example, their homogenization temperatures are going to be the same as that of the pseudo-secondary inclusions here indicated. The fissure wherein such inclusions are found is sealed by the outermost zone of the crystal substance.

It becomes possible therefore to determine *the lower limit of temperature* at which a given crystal's growth was terminated, with an accuracy of a few degrees. This limit may be determined with a still greater reliability for druses of crystals, provided the crystals formed compromise growth surfaces, one with the other, and the crystal growth is dense.

Inclusions associated with closely joined surfaces of crystals (the "compromise growth surfaces")* indicate temperatures of the solution from which the last of the contacting outer layers of substance were deposited. The lower limit of the temperature of mineral growth may be determined reliably by primary inclusions in the outermost zone of growth, by pseudo-secondary inclusions in fissures sealed by the substance of this zone, or by the compromise growth inclusions, which facilitate greatly the subsequent mineralothermal analysis of the crystals.

Having determined the lower temperature limit of the host mineral's growth, it is not too difficult to verify that inclusions showing temperatures below this threshold are secondary, with respect to the given generation of the mineral, and are also indicative of temperatures at which a succeeding generation of the mineral could be formed. If we follow the fissure containing such low-temperature inclusions outward, we shall find that the fissure *emerges at the surface of the crystal.*

A fissure of this sort *cuts across the compromise growth surfaces* of closely joined crystals in druses, as may readily be shown, and its secondary inclusions indicate identical temperatures for different crystals. Thus the excessively low homogenization temperatures, as determined, may be excluded at once from the set of characteristics of the temperature environments of the crystal's growth, as indicated by the inclusion studies.

All primary and pseudo-secondary inclusions will naturally register temperatures exceeding the temperature registered by inclusions in the compromise growth surfaces, for crystals grown normally in environments where temperatures of the mother liquor were falling progressively and slowly.

The upper limit of the temperature at which the crystal began to grow needs to be determined by primary inclusions that must be searched for in the central part of the crystal, near the crystal's base. The maximum temperature so ascertained will be either the true temperature at the beginning of crystal growth or, at any rate, will not be too distant from it.

We should bear in mind, in this connection, that pseudo-secondary inclusions may be found also in the central part of the crystal where their temperatures do not represent the temperature here sought. The tempera-

---

* The Russian for "induction surfaces" is here rendered "compromise growth surfaces" in accord with the English usage proposed by Haynes, *Am. Min.*, vol. 44, 1089, 1959 [Ed.].

ture of these inclusions represents some intermediate stage of the crystal's growth, including even some of the early zones.

The maximum temperature (or an approximation thereof) at the beginning of the crystal's growth is determined objectively, as a rule, by inclusions in a transverse section through the crystal, or as in the given case, through a group of crystals. By such means the temperature range of crystal growth may be defined with a reasonable accuracy.

Let us illustrate here the sequence of the operations, using a quartz druse from Aldan as the example. A transverse cut through this druse is the polished section shown in Fig. 25. Boundaries of individual members of the druse are visible in the picture. These boundaries are surfaces of compromise growth of the crystals reaching the surface of the polished section. Homogenization temperatures of inclusions associated with these surfaces are within the range of 130–138°C. Inclusions in the hair-like and relatively large fissures cutting through the compromise growth surfaces of the crystals are identified as secondary. They were homogenized at 80–124°C, within a temperature range unrelated, by our interpretation, to the main process of the crystal growth of the druse.

The following series of temperatures was found for the primary inclusions in the large crystal *1*, on the lower left (Fig. 25), from the periphery to the core: 151–154–192–198°C. The homogenization temperatures of inclusions in the small lower left crystal *2*, in the corner, were from 175 to 188°C.

Two large individuals (*3* and *4*), closely joined by an irregular growth, are visible in Fig. 25, above the crystals just described. Inclusion "a"* in the compromise growth surface between these two crystals registered the temperature of 130°C.† Inclusion "b" in the fissure cutting through the compromise growth surfaces was homogenized at 109°C. In crystal *3*, on the left, on the periphery of the polished section, primary and pseudo-secondary inclusions in the middle showed the following series of homogenization temperatures: "v"‡ 178; "d" 180; "l" 182; "e" and "g" 184; "i" and "k" 188; "n" 190°C. The temperatures of the middle section of the neighboring crystal *4* on the right were also determined and were found to be 200–204 and 217°C. Primary inclusions in the isolated crystal

---

* In our practice, inclusions are identified by letters after the number assigned to every individual section.

† In the fissure in the lower crystal (*8*, Fig. 25), we found inclusions with homogenization temperatures from 134 to 148°C. This relatively large fissure appeared to have originated during the course of crystal growth of the druse; the fissure was reformed afterwards and was healed at the very end of the druse-forming process.

‡ The low-case Russian italic letters in the original are transliterated as follows: *a* — a; *b* — v; *э* — e; *u* — i; *б* — b; *д* — d; *г* — g; *к* — k; *л* — l; *н* — h.

5, on the extreme right, showed homogenization temperatures of 140, 162, and 170°C. The crystal in the lower right corner of the druse, 7, was examined. The temperatures shown by primary inclusions were 210–214°C

FIG. 25. Polished section of quartz druse from Aldan.

in the central section, 145–148°C on the periphery, and 138°C on the compromise growth plane between crystals 6 and 7.

We came to the conclusion, as the result of the thermal analysis of the first generation of the druse crystals, that these crystals were formed between 220 and 130°C.

Crystallization of Minerals from Solutions in Which There Are Interruptions in the Normal Gradual Lowering of the Temperature

In the course of genetic investigations of mineral deposits including several generations of a given mineral and a crystallization sequence of different minerals, one may often be led to the conclusion, even on the basis of macroscopic studies alone, that there were interruptions in the mineral-forming process. These interruptions may be recognized and evaluated objectively thanks to the occasional evidence of solution phenomena at the base of crystals of a younger generation of the mineral. Thus two adjoining crystals of a different age may be separated from each other by a gel-like film or some other substance whose formation may be explained only by a temporary and abrupt change in the conditions of genesis.

In such a case, and in others, one may justify the conclusion that there was an interruption in the gradual and orderly sequence of the crystallization of the minerals. However, the duration of this interruption cannot be definitely ascertained. Also, the solution phenomena cannot always be satisfactorily explained.

Temperature conditions are one of the principal variables in the formation of minerals. Consequently, by regarding this process against the background of temperature variations, as indicated by fluid inclusions, we come into possession of a powerful weapon to measure and define the interruptions within the crystallization process. In addition, there is a pos-

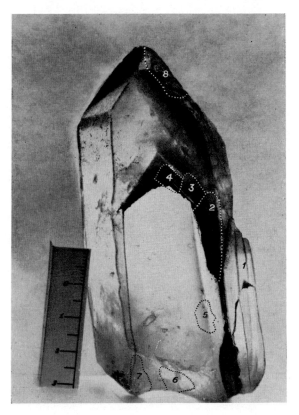

FIG. 26. A complex crystal of quartz from Kilerchi.

sibility of a quantitative expression of such interruptions on the customary time-scale.

It was with this particular yardstick, suited for both absolute and relative applications, that we measured discontinuities in the crystallization of a single crystal or of a deposit. Examination of phantom crystals is very important here, as these crystals are very common in nature and are representative of a complex mineral genesis.

A large crystal of quartz from Kilerchi (Aldan) is shown in Fig. 26. This crystal has a small neighboring crystal to the right, grown jointly with the large one. The large crystal measures 35 mm between outer prism faces; the distance between the corresponding faces of the inner crystal, plainly visible in the photograph, is 25–28 mm. The boundary between the two crystals is made visible by a coating of sericite.

Thermometric analysis of inclusions in the inner crystal indicated the following series of progressively decreasing temperatures: 212–201–200–198–186–184–183–182°C (the sections are identified as *5, 6* and *7* in the photograph). These data may justify the conclusion that the inner crystal

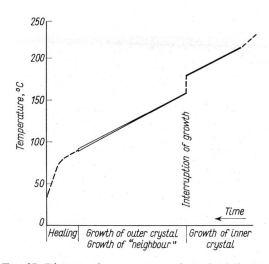

FIG. 27. Diagram of temperature regime of solutions.

grew from a progressively cooling liquid over a range of at least 30°C (212–182°C).

The typical homogenization temperatures of inclusions in the outer crystal fall within the following series of actually determined temperatures (sections *2, 3,* and *4,* in the photograph); 160–148–145–140–134°C.

Section *8*, from the termination of the outer crystal, gave temperatures of 134–120–114–92°C; the outer part of section *2* gave temperatures of 116–98–92°C. The following temperature series was established for the small "neighbor" (section *1*): 128–125–118–115–113–102–95°C.

Thus the temperature range of solutions involved in the formation of the outer crystal and of its "neighbor" was 160–92°C and 128–95°C respectively. A consideration of these figures leads us to the following generalized view of the analytical results.

While the inner crystal grew the temperature was falling from 212 to 182°C, then there was a pause in the crystallization until the temperature fell to 160°C. Only sericite precipitated during this 30°C pause. Growth of the outer crystal began at 160°C and the neighboring crystal began growth at 130–128°C. From then on, the outer crystal and the neighboring crystal grew concurrently, until the temperature fell to about 90°C. At that temperature the adjoining crystals assumed their final morphology

Healed fissures reaching the very surface of the crystal are evidence of a subsequent bathing and healing of the crystal by warm silica-bearing solutions. These solutions left behind some secondary two-phase inclusions with average homogenization temperatures of 80–60°C, as well as some single-phase inclusions indicative of temperatures below 50°C.

Figure 27 is a diagram representing the falling temperature during the growth of these quartz crystals from Aldan.

Crystal growth involving interruptions in the crystallization and the solution is occasionally observed in nature. Following are two examples of such growth. Figure 28 shows a small crystal of calcite from a deposit

Fig. 28. Phantom crystal of calcite showing solution.

in DVK.* The inner part of this crystal is entirely transparent but its outer part, the envelope, is semi-transparent and gray.

The boundary between the inner and outer parts proved to be clearly defined, but the surface of this boundary looked rough and showed evidence of solution. We decided on first examination of this crystal that the growth of the inner part had been subjected to an interruption. It appeared desirable to determine the length of this interruption (on the temperature scale) and its cause.

Seventeen sections from this phantom crystal, including nine from the gray envelope and eight from the inner transparent zone, were prepared for analysis. The following series of homogenization temperatures was found for the inner zone: 130–125–124–123 and 120°C. The typical mean temperature for this transparent zone was 123°C. The temperatures shown by inclusions in the gray zone immediately adjacent to the transparent zone, were 136–134–133–130 and 129°C. The arithmetical mean for the gray envelope, up to 5 mm thick, was 132°C i.e. 9°C above the mean temperature of the inner crystal. Inclusions in the outer 7 mm thick gray zone of the crystal showed homogenization temperatures of 122–119–92 and down to 65°C. An inclusion in a fissure in the inner crystal gave a temperature of 73°C.

The following view of the formation of the phantom crystal may now be developed, on the basis of our reported findings.

The inner part of the transparent calcite crystallized from bicarbonate solutions at 130–120°C. The crystallization was interrupted. A fresh pulse of hotter but not super-saturated solutions dissolved the faces of the previously formed crystals. Beginning at 136°C, these fresh bicarbonate solutions become super-saturated, whereupon there was a relatively rapid deposition of material composing the gray envelope. From then on, crystallization continued uninterrupted, down to low temperatures (65°C and possibly still lower). The late low-temperature solutions penetrated the inner transparent zone of the crystal along fissures forming secondary inclusions. The history of the phantom crystal of calcite is represented by a diagram showing the variations in temperature of the crystal-forming solutions (Fig. 29, p. 162).

A very interesting crystal of quartz from N.† Dzhauvasi (Pamir) was found and examined by Zakharchenko [44]. The crystal has four terminations; the outer termination has clearly defined faces; the termination in the middle shows evidence of solution and is coated with sericite, chlorite, calcite, and an ore mineral; the inner "dome-like" termination is a typical "solution cap" or "hood"; the second outer termination is of the regenera-

---

* Dal'nevostochnyi Krai—the Soviet Far East. [V.P.S.].

† "N." stands probably for "nizhni" ("lower") and not for "novyy" ("new") [V.P.S.].

tion type and was formed before the crystal had parted from its substratum.

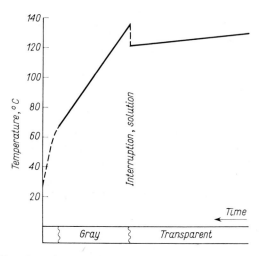

FIG. 29. Diagram of temperature regime of solutions.

Examination of a crystal of this sort naturally posed a series of important questions that could be only answered incompletely or not at all by the ordinary methods of mineralogy, such as length of the interruptions [in crystal growth—V.P.S.], the time when the crystal broke loose, the time when the fourth termination was formed, etc. (on the temperature scale). Some of these problems were very successfully solved by Zakharchenko, who undertook in 1949, on our advice, thermal studies of inclusions in quartz from Pamir.

Primary inclusions in the hooded inner zone of the crystal indicated temperatures of 270–260°C, although the highest temperature at which this zone was formed remained rather obscure.

Inclusions in the crystal's intermediate zone showed homogenization temperatures of 250–195°C. The range of temperatures in the peripheral part of this zone, which was contemporaneous with the precipitation of calcite and pyrite, was 210–195°C.

Temperatures from 215 to 190°C were obtained for the outer zone and for its outer upper termination. The same temperatures were found to be characteristic for the lower termination which was formed on the base of the crystal after breakage. Temperatures shown by pseudo-secondary inclusions of the regeneration type in a fissure between the lower termination and the base of the crystal were 190–210°C.

Temperature variations in the course of the three-stage formation of the crystal are shown as a diagram (Fig. 30).

The results here obtained justify our conclusion that there was a slight decrease in the temperatures of the crystal-forming liquors and an in-

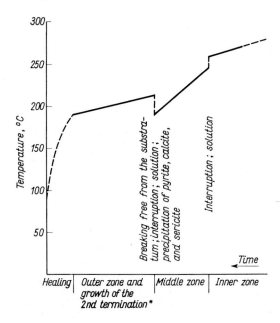

FIG. 30. Diagram of temperature regime of solutions.

tensive solution of a part of the complex phantom crystal already formed, prior to the formation of the middle zone. There was also a small break in the temperature of the liquor and a renewed pulse of crystal-forming solution in the natural reservoir-crystallizer before the beginning of growth of the outer zone.

The healing of the broken base, the regeneration of the crystal's lower termination, the growth of the crystal's upper termination, and the growth of the entire outer part of the crystal were concurrent processes that occurred as the temperature fell from 215 to 190°C. Every one of the primary and pseudo-secondary inclusions in the crystal belongs to the category of multiphase and three-phase essentially liquid inclusions. Since we do not yet know the required corrections for solution concentrations, we cannot speak here of exact determinations of *the true temperatures*. However, the suitability of such inclusions for determinations of *relative temperatures*, by the means of their slow homogenization, appears to be self-evident to us.

* I.e., the second one of the outer ones, the same one as "the 4th head" in the preceding text [V.P.S.].

Abrupt Changes in the Temperature
of Crystal-Forming Solutions

Figure 31 represents calcite whose inclusions were employed by us in ascertaining the temperature regime of solutions in which zoned crystals grew. This specimen was taken from a vug in a fissure zone in the Upper Silurian limestones of the Zeravshan Range.

As one may see in the photograph, the crystal contains two transparent complex zones and three semi-transparent dark zones with an admixture

FIG. 31. Calcite crystal with growth zones (Zeravshan).

of an extremely fine clay substance. The center and the base of the crystal were not examined.

Individual small sub-zones are conspicuous within the zones here identified. There are twenty seven such sub-zones, counting from the dissolved surface of the crystal (on the left) to its central part, whose inclusions were examined separately. Unfortunately, genuine primary inclusions could not be identified in every one of the sub-zones.

In all, 34 sections from 22 sub-zones of the crystal were prepared and examined. The results are presented in Table 21.

The thermometric studies were conducted with particular care, including repeated determinations in different inclusions in sections of one and the same sub-zone. Nevertheless, the results seem to be contradictory. First of all, of the six analyses of the dark central zone of the crystal

TABLE 21

No. in sequence	No of sub-zone	Temperature (°C)	Remarks	No. in sequence	No. of sub-zone	Temperature (°C)	Remarks
1	25–26	68		12	11	82	Inner dark zone
2	24–25	70⎫	Central	13	9	76	
3	24	71⎪	dark zone	14	8	70	
4	23	69⎰	of crystal	15	7	67⎫	Outer
5	22	73⎭		16	6	62⎪	transpa-
6	21	75		17	5	61⎪	rent zone
7	19	81		18	4	60⎭	of crystal
8	16	74⎫	Inner	19	3	72	
9	14	63⎬	transparent	20	1	81⎫	Outer
10	13	78⎭	zone	21	0	78⎬	dark
11	12	86	Inner dark zone	22	0	78⎭	zone

showed lower temperatures than other series of analyses of the outer zones. Second, highly diverse homogenization temperatures, ranging from 60 to 86°C, were registered by inclusions in different zones. Moreover, the *magnitude* of these fluctuations, reaching a span of 26°C at maximum, *varied* in different zones and, what is especially important, *varied in direction*. It was established definitely (see Fig. 31) that temperature maxima coincide with dark zones and that temperature minima (Fig. 32) are characteristic of the light-colored transparent zones. Even if we assume that the mean accuracy of the measured homogenization temperatures is only ±2 to 3°C, the general pattern will remain unchanged, because the temperature differences between the dark and the light zones amount to tens of degrees centigrade.

We feel that the growth of this particular zoned crystal occurred in a pulsating flow of bicarbonate solutions. Also, every fresh portion of fluid had a higher temperature than the solution already present in the natural reservoir-crystallizer, thus causing a stirring of clay particles in the reservoir. These particles settled on the faces of the growing crystal and the dark coloration of the corresponding growth zones, characterized by the temperature peaks, was the result. The subsequent clarification of the solution coincided with a decrease in reservoir temperature and its expression was the growth of the clear zones of the crystal.

Regardless of how we treat this problem, however, the example here discussed justifies the conclusion that abrupt fluctuations of temperature may occur during natural mineral genesis, not only in the course of development of a whole mineral deposit but even on occasions during the

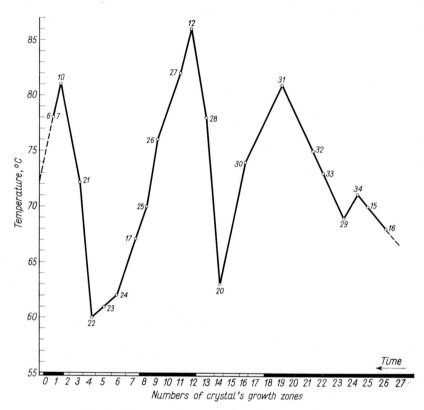

FIG. 32. Diagram of temperature regime of solutions.

relatively short time involved in the growth of a single crystal. The example represented in Fig. 32 is typical of still another possibility of a change in the temperature regime of pulsating solutions.

Thermometric Analysis of the Formation of Complex Crystals and Synchronization of Their Growth Zones

Di-pyramidal phantom crystals of quartz, with inner crystals of a prismatic habit, are widely known at one of the lead–zinc deposits in the DVK. The transparent outer crystal has the appearance of an almost regular hexagonal di-pyramid whose horizontal edges have a narrow bevel corresponding to the prism face. The less transparent inner crystal, as a rule, has well-formed prism faces and small rhombohedral faces on its termination.

The characteristic appearance of this crystal is shown in Fig. 33. The same crystal is shown on the right of the picture, in a cut parallel to the long axis of both the outer and the inner individuals.

Crystallographic and mineralogic description of similar crystals was published recently. Figure 1 of that publication [90, p. 267] is a diagrammatic representation of one crystal inside the other one showing that both crystals are doubly terminated. Such specimens have not been found in the deposit here discussed. It has always been possible to prove that the prismatic inner crystal grows out from its substratum and has only one termination.

The two crystals are generally separated from each other by a very thin film of a colloidal substance which, by this time, is partially crystallized. The faces of the outer di-pyramidal crystal have shiny surfaces, but the inner crystal's faces, on freeing them from the film by which they are coated, look frosted.

In this case we are dealing with a parallel orientation in the crystal of low-temperature di-pyramidal quartz of the so-called Cumberland Type (Type V), according to the literature, overgrowing a singly terminated crystal of prismatic quartz of Type III [according to Maucher—see footnote p. 171: Ed.]. As we know, quartz crystals of different habits are widely employed in geologic (or, to be exact, mineralogic) thermometry*. This method ascribes the temperature range of 365–250°C to Type III and the range of 200–180°C, and lower, to Type V. Thus the peculiar crystals in question have a double interest for us: as a means of checking on the accepted morphologic temperature scale and as test materials in determining the temperature span of the interruption between the crystalization of the two types of quartz.

Let us pause to consider the problem of the junction between the minerals in our specimens before we proceed with the discussion of the results of thermal investigations. Prismatic crystals of quartz overgrow gray unfaceted quartz with an oily luster. As shown in Fig. 33, the overgrowth is not always oriented parallel to some single individual of the di-pyramidal quartz. One may often observe various orientations of several small crystals of this sort growing on the faces of a larger prismatic crystal, without epitaxy. The colloidal film is present invariably between these different generations of crystals. Crystals of di-pyramidal quartz develop compromise growth surfaces with a crystallographically complex transparent calcite. An impression is given occasionally that such calcite grows on top of the di-pyramidal quartz and accordingly is younger than the quartz. It has been possible, however, in nearly every case, to prove that both of

---

* These habits are discussed on pp. 57–58 of the original Russian (untranslated) [Ed.].

these minerals were in fact crystallizing concurrently, as indicated by the presence of compromise growth surfaces between them.

The following series of homogenization temperatures were established, by thermometric investigations, for primary and pseudo-secondary inclusions in prismatic quartz: 280–258–254–202–178–156–153–150–147°C. The homogenization temperatures of secondary inclusions were 127–108–86°C.

Fig. 33. Di-pyramidal quartz: left—external appearance, right—section through crystal.

Several inclusions discovered in crystals of the di-pyramidal quartz, in the central part of the section through the crystal (see Fig. 33), showed by Analysis No. 7 a temperature of 120°C and inclusions situated near the crystal's periphery showed temperatures of 106–104°C, by Analyses 8 and 9. Moreover, there was a large number of single-phase secondary inclusions of warm aqueous silica-bearing solutions which healed fissures in the crystal.

Analogous studies of the calcite crystals, combinations of a rhombohedron with a prism and a scalenohedron, served to develop the following temperature series: 130–128–127–120–116–114–110–102°C. Single-phase inclusions were also found in the calcite.

The thermometric analysis demonstrated that the inner prismatic quartz grew over a relatively wide temperature range, from 280 to 150°C. The interruption in the growth of quartz, from 150 to 130–125°C, i.e. to the point when the di-pyramidal quartz and the calcite began to grow, was accompanied by the deposition of a colloidal substance on the crystal faces. The temperature range of crystallization of di-pyramidal quartz and of calcite was narrow: 130–100°C, whereupon calcite and other minerals were precipitated in other crystallographic forms.

We believe that the quartz without prism faces from the Donets Basin (Karakuba), described by Chirvinskii [114], also crystallized at some such low temperatures.

Odd quartz crystals with a "checkered" or a "feathery" structure, (Fig. 34), may be found also in the same DVK deposit. They are slightly

FIG. 34. Quartz crystal of multinucleated growth ("checkered" quartz).

olive-gray colored multinucleated crystals. Their structure, however, proved to be a complex one on detailed examination.

The axial section of these crystals consists of transparent prismatic crystals of quartz with well-defined faces, including a thin outer zone of a semi-transparent quartz showing a shade of yellow in transmitted light. The outer multinucleated "shirt" of this complex crystal consists of a grayish-green quartz with numerous inclusions of a gel-like substance which makes this quartz turbid and non-transparent.

The central "axial" crystal of this quartz gave the following typical series of temperatures: 300–295–285–280–278–275–260–250–240°C; the outer semi-transparent zone gave temperatures ranging from 190–180° to 152°C. Secondary inclusions in fissures in the same part of the crystal yielded the following homogenization temperatures: 130–120–115–110–105–90°C. Very fine fibers, possibly tremolite, were observed in the outer zone of the inner crystal, together with dark inclusions of rounded and rectangular shapes (apparently ilvaite). The indicated homogenization temperatures of secondary inclusions in the central crystal are characteristic of the temperature range of the multinucleated growth zone.

After considerable difficulties, it became possible to recognize several primary inclusions at the boundary between the multinucleated and the semi-transparent zones. The homogenization temperatures of these inclusions were in the range of 110–120°C. It is probable that the terminations of the quartz crystals, with their gel-like substance, completed their growth at temperatures below 100°C.

Comparisons of the thermometric results for crystals so different in appearance as the di-pyramidal and the "feathery" quartz, taken from different parts of the lead–zinc deposit, allows us to undertake a synchronization of different zones of these crystals on the basis of the temperatures of their formation. The "axial" quartz crystal of prismatic habit in both cases belongs to the same generation, formed between 300 and 150°C. There was a radical break in the deposition of the crystal substance below this temperature. In the first instance, there was a deposition of originally colloidal but now partially crystalline substance (spherulites, fine-micaceous minerals), from 150 to 130°C, forming a very thin layer on the surface of the inner crystal, after which, at 130–100°C, the transparent di-pyramidal quartz of the last generation began to grow concurrently with the crystals of calcite.

In the second case, the deposition of colloidal substance began at the same time but it continued also at lower temperatures, down to 100–90°C, during the entire period of growth of the "checkered" multinucleated quartz. The gel-like substance produced a vast number of globular inclusions in the quartz of this latter generation which made it greenish gray and non-transparent.

In the first case, the true hydrothermal solution of silica was rapidly cleared of its colloidal particles, possibly because of the electrolytic properties (ionization?) of the associated bicarbonate. The transparent di-pyramidal quartz and the calcite were crystallized from true solutions.

In the second case, there was no rapid coagulation of the colloidal particles in the solution of silica and the multinucleated growth of quartz in mixed solutions was accompanied by a continuous deposition, among others, of colloidal substance on the crystal faces.

Despite the marked external differences between the di-pyramidal and the "checkered" quartz, these minerals are "twins", formed at the same time, and synchronous also with calcite having a combination of a blunt rhombohedron with a scalenohedron and prism.

The range of the crystallization temperatures for the "long-columnar" quartz (Maucher's Type III*) and the "di-pyramidal" quartz (the "Cumberland Type") accepted in the literature are lower, in fact, than they are believed to be. Thus, instead of 360–250°C, in the first example (Type III), the homogenization of included solutions of mother liquor shows the temperatures of 300–150°C and, in the second example (Type V), the temperatures are shown as 130–100°C and not 200–180°C.

The range of the minimum crystallization temperatures of the quartz specimens we have examined will not be affected significantly by corrections for pressure, in view of the relatively shallow depth at which the deposit was formed (up to 1 km).

Examples of Studies in Paragenesis of Minerals by Inclusions of Mother Liquor

Some of the previously discussed applications of thermal analysis to the problem of the origin of complex crystals have shed some light on the paragenesis of minerals in mineral deposits. It appears possible to estimate objectively the relative age of individual minerals, in cases where minerals are found next to each other, growing on top of each other, or having compromise growth surfaces. Such relatively easy recognition of the relationships, however, is by no means always possible in nature.

---

* Maucher's classification (1914) elaborated by Virovlyanskiy in Kvartz kak Geologicheskiy Termometr (Quartz as a Geological Thermometer), Zap. VMO, 67(3), 1938, in brief:

Type I, eruptive: over 800°C; irregular grains or hexagonal di-pyramids crystallized from magmatic solution.

Type II, pneumatolytic: over 374°C; trigonal–prismatic, as a rule; twin crystals common; "flat", milky-white, pink quartz and smoky (morion).

Type III, hydrothermal: 365–250°C; columnar; isohedral uniformly shaped crystals. Sub-types (in the order of decreasing temperatures of crystallization): IIIa, Dauphinais: long-columnar; one of the rhombohedrons predominant; IIId, Pskem: 330–310°C; long-columnar, obelisk-like; main rhombohedra equally well developed; IIIb, Gottard: dense and repeatedly twinned crystals of white and smoky quartz; IIIc, Harz: dense druses of generally turbid crystals. Type IV: dense or finely fibrous quartz, chalcedony, agate, etc. Type V: 200–180°C, and lower; the Cumberland Type, with predominant di-pyramid and a short prism; the prism may be absent; also, pyramidal quartz and amethyst [Translator].

If two given minerals in a mineral deposit are never found in direct contact with each other and yet are found growing on one and the same substratum, it becomes very difficult to determine objectively the time of their formation. We cannot help agreeing with Fersman, under the circumstances, that "determinations of the sequence of crystallization of minerals constitute by no means an easy problem which is still methodologically unsolved" [108]. We do not pretend to have arrived at a definitive solution of this very important problem, although we do have a hope that the results we have already obtained in the research on inclusions of mother liquors has brought us nearer the goal.

Our early investigations along these lines were naturally concerned with test materials from sources where the mineral paragenesis was clearly defined. Specifically, at the Kulikolon, it is perfectly clear that barite formed first, that optical fluorite grows on top of barite, and calcite on top of optical fluorite.

Homogenization temperatures of primary and pseudo-secondary inclusions in these minerals, measured by us many times in 1943, correspond exactly to the established sequence of their crystallization at progressively decreasing temperatures, from barite through fluorite to calcite [32]. Figure 35 represents a summation of these variations. The upper part of the figure gives the results for the deposit as a whole; the lower part for one of the deposit's typical vugs of minerals (No. 47). The average homogenization temperatures of a large number of determinations are 138, 122, and 101°C* for barite fluorite, and calcite respectively. Not even once did we encounter a temperature that would counter-indicate the crystallization sequence of these minerals, as here defined [32, pp. 37–38].

The same report presented another example of the research on quartz, at the headwaters of the Pskem River, involving a well determined paragenesis of minerals with the orientation according to Fersman's geophase pattern [32]. Phase "E" of the pattern is represented, in this district, by milky-white semi-transparent quartz whose inclusions gave homogenization temperatures higher than 300°C. Phase "H" of the pattern was represented by transparent quartz crystals with rutile and chlorite; inclusions in the three crystals examined by us gave homogenization temperatures from 280 to 200°C. The milky white "shirt" of these crystals and the amethysts, classified under phase "I", gave average homogenization temperatures of 187–133°C respectively. As we see, these results are in a full agreement with the definite paragenetic relations of the minerals in the mineral deposits. This is a demonstration of the applicability of

---

* By way of an approximation to the true crystallization temperature of these minerals, we introduced the correction for pressure (depth) in the diagram (Fig. 35) corresponding to 40°C.

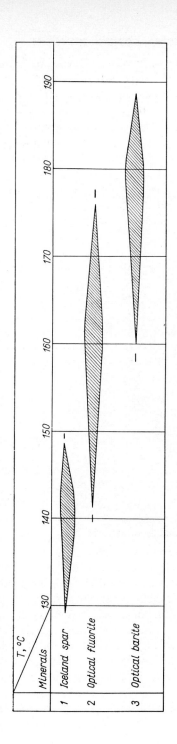

DIAGRAM
of the Course of Crystallization of Optical Minerals in Vug. No. 47

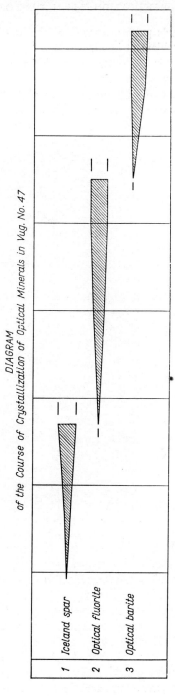

Fig. 35. Diagram of temperature intervals in crystallization of optical minerals from Kulikolon.

Ferman's pattern as well as the applicability of thermometric analysis to the problem at hand.

Figure 36 shows a small druse of prismatic quartz crystals from a lead–zinc deposit in DVK. The substratum of these crystals was a granular semi-transparent quartz with galena, sphalerite, and chalcopyrite. On top of the quartz crystals of prismatic habit (on the right of the photo-

FIG. 36. A druse of prismatic quartz crystals with sulfides.

graph), one may see the overgrowth of well-defined crystals of pyrite and chalcopyrite coated with a loose crystalline material consisting of di-pyramidal quartz. Disseminated fine grains of the sulfides may be seen also inside the prismatic quartz crystals. The other specimens show a clearly-defined overgrowth of quartz crystals by calcite, in various combinations of crystallographic forms (scalenohedron, low rhombohedron, prism). Disseminated sulfides are found also in the early calcites (basal and the low rhombohedron).

Thermometric analysis of primary inclusions in the gray granular quartz gave characteristic temperatures of 280–300°C; the temperatures of the prismatic quartz were 280–260–250–240°C; the temperatures of the sulfide-bearing calcite: 125–145°C; the temperatures of calcite without any disseminated sphalerite or galena: 115–80°C.

The homogenization temperatures of secondary inclusions in the granular and the prismatic quartz were as low as 100–90°C, and were even below 80°C in the sulfide-bearing calcite.

These temperatures of healing of fissures in the minerals here indicated correspond apparently to the stage in which the di-pyramidal

FIG. 37. Interfering growth of crystals from Vilyuy.

quartz was crystallized (see Chapter 5) and to the formation of the non-sulfide-bearing calcite of the youngest generation. This latter calcite may be found occasionally in the form of twinned scalenohedra with rhombohedral faces of a bi-pyramid, and as little beads.

The figures here cited show a correspondence of homogenization temperatures with the established crystallization sequence of the minerals and serve as the basis of our belief that the *principal sulfides of the deposit were laid down within a wide range of decreasing temperatures of the solutions,* from 300 to 125°C, and that the deposition of pyrite and marcasite was continued even later.

Interference of growth of three minerals, quartz, ankerite and zeolite (radiating crystals in the center of the specimen), were observed in a specimen from one of the Vilyuy deposits in a fissured zone within trap rock, as illustrated by Fig. 37. The zeolite, as we see, grows over both carbonate and quartz, so that there is no doubt that it is the youngest of the three. The faces of quartz are well defined and are overgrown by ankerite on all sides.

The quartz was formed earlier than the rest, but the end of its crystallization coincided with the growth of the ankerite, since both minerals are in contact along a compromise growth surface, on the left of the zeolite.

Investigations of primary inclusions in the quartz produced the following temperature series: 190–165–158–150 and 145°C. The typical mean homogenization temperature for inclusions in the ferruginous carbonate was 140–130°C.

Fig. 38. Quartzes from the Pisek deposit (Czechoslovakia).

There are reasons to believe, therefore, that the crystal of quartz continued to grow down to 150°C, that quartz and carbonate were growing together from 150 to 140°C, and that only ankerite continued to grow at the lower temperatures. The zeolite, which contains only single-phase inclusions of aqueous solutions, was formed much later; these inclusions were sealed in the mineral evidently at temperatures lower than 50°C.

Figure 38 shows a complex druse of crystal quartz from a "mesothermal" deposit at Pisek, Czechoslovakia. Transparent colorless crystals of comb quartz, 2, formed a dense overgrowth on the granular gray sulfide-bearing quartz, *1*, apparently inside a small cavity within a vein. Fine grains of sulfides are present also in the lower part of this zone. Well crystallized small terminations of amethyst, *3*, had grown over the crystal surfaces of the comb quartz that have only compromise growth surfaces. On top of the amethyst, in the center of the druse (showing white in the photograph), there are well crystallized transparent fine crystals of quartz, *4*, forming a small rosette-like druse of their own. Reliable identifications of primary and secondary inclusions were extremely difficult due to poor polishing of the crystals. We are reporting therefore only the overall series of homogenization temperatures, except in the case of the transparent quartz in which there was no doubt at all in regards to the primary nature of the inclusions:

(1) Comb quartz: 305–235*–260–200–185 –180–150–145°C
(2) Amethyst: 231–219–205–200–173 –170–150°C
(3) Transparent quartz: 190–187 and lower, down to 145°C.

In cases such as this, although it is virtually impossible to separate primary, pseudo-secondary, and secondary inclusions, it still seems to us permissible to form an opinion, by way of an orientation, on the temperature range wherein the minerals in question were formed, by a process of elimination using comparisons between the lowest temperatures. The transparent quartz was formed at 190–145°C (omitting the correction for pressure); the amethyst was formed probably between 231 and 200°C; the comb quartz, between 305 and 235°C. While the amethyst was being formed, the same solutions were healing fissures in the comb quartz, with the resulting formation of inclusions with homogenization temperatures from 230 to 200°C. The fissures in both comb quartz and amethyst were healed during the growth of the transparent quartz, at 185–180–170–150°C.

However, *the elimination method* of estimating the temperatures must be used only in very difficult cases and with extreme caution.

The examples of paragenesis of minerals here discussed coincide very well with all other similar examples, whose description is here omitted, in regards to thermometric data, and justify even now our hope for the future of the method as the means of deciphering the intricate interrelations of minerals in hydrothermal (and pneumatolytic) deposits.

On the Temperatures of Formation of Quartz Pseudomorphs after "Paper-Spar"

Figure 39 shows a crystal of quartz from a lead–zinc deposit in DVK with a very peculiar "cleavage" resembling the orientation of cleavage in the early calcite common throughout the deposit. The "cleavage" fractures

---

* A misprint for 285? [V.P.S.].

are filled with a ferruginous colloidal substance and their planes have a consistent orientation in their intersections at 60°. Some of these planes slant through and cut practically all of the quartz at a 45° angle to the long axis, while the second orientation of the "cleavage" departs from this

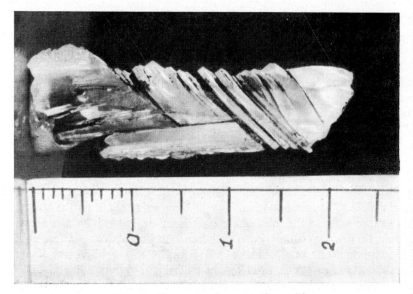

FIG. 39. Pseudomorph of quartz after calcite.

axis by only 15°. Compromise growth surfaces were preserved at both ends of the crystal, so that there can be no doubt as to the simultaneous growth of this quartz and of the next generation of calcite, synchronous with the quartz.

It is not easy to account for this odd phenomenon, however, by a simple contact between the crystals of the two minerals. We are dealing here, it appears, with a replacement of the older "paper spar" resulting in the formation of this unique pseudomorph.

Inasmuch as the quartz has practically none of its own crystal faces, it appeared highly desirable to ascertain the origin of this specimen in the deposit. The specimen proved to be very abundant in primary inclusions giving the following series of the homogenization temperatures: 244–220–212–171–168–158 and 150°C.

This range of temperatures in the deposit corresponds to the growth of thick prismatic quartz and the accompanying precipitation of the bulk of the sulfides.

In this case, if we are dealing indeed with a replacement process and with a "cleavage pseudomorph" after the primary mineral, we may conclude that the process was a slow one, by all appearances, and occurred over a wide range of gradually decreasing temperatures of the solutions (from 250 to 150°C).

On Unity of the Hydrothermal Metamorphism of Rocks and of the Formation of Minerals in "Alpine" Fissure Veins

Alteration of host rocks in contact with ore veins and pegmatites is a well-known phenomenon. Evidence of an appreciable leaching of host rocks of the veins and of a re-deposition of this substance in fissures and pores of the host rocks is found wherever we deal with mineral veins of the Alpine type, specifically, with quartz veins. The extensive alteration of quartzites containing "Alpine" and hydrothermal veins in Aldan were previously described [34, pp. 68–69]. However, for the sake of a better understanding of the alteration and for the sake of relating it to the

FIG. 40. Crystal quartz overgrowing quartzite (Aldan).

formation of quartz crystal veins, it appeared worthwhile to us to make an examination of secondary inclusions in the host rocks and of primary inclusions in quartz crystals in the vein-filling itself.

The specimen shown in Fig. 40 was taken by us from the Zasontitski Plot. The photograph shows clearly the boundary between the gray quartzite and the transparent crystals of quartz. The latter grew on a wall of a vein fissure, in many directions, depending on the orientation provided for them by quartz granules in their substratum. There is a conspicuous resemblance between the composition of the host rock and the vein-filling substance both of which contain 95.9 to 96.6 per cent silica, according to our analyses.

The rock-forming quartz grains belong genetically to quartz of granites and gneisses: their edges are dentate or, more rarely, rounded. They are strongly metamorphosed and are transformed into a very firm and practically monomineralic massive rock. The end-stage of their metamorphism has an expression in the filling of the multitude of "hair-like" fissures, running in all directions, by exceedingly fine veinlets of quartz in which numerous secondary inclusions were preserved (secondary, in reference to the rock-forming mineral) containing aqueous solutions.* The inclusions in the quartz crystals of the veins have a diversity of shapes, but the most common one of all is a regularly-faceted cavity, of the type we have previously described [35, p. 69, Fig. 7].

Figure 40 shows three relatively large crystals of quartz inclined to each other at different angles. It shows, on the right, also several small crystals belonging to a different generation [24]. These small crystals, in our particular case, grew in different positions on the large individuals of the druse, often as fillings of the empty space between the individuals.

Thermometric examination of the large *quartz crystals* gave the following temperature series for the primary inclusions: 221–192–172–167–160–150°C. The homogenization temperatures of the secondary inclusions were: 102–92–90–88–84–79°C. These temperatures were particularly characteristic of primary inclusions in the very fine crystals of quartz.

The following two series of temperatures were established by homogenization of the secondary inclusions in quartzite: (1) 234–180–178–160–154 and 150°C; (2) 94–90–87–83°C.

The self-evident similarity of the temperatures shown by the primary inclusions in the crystals of the vein quartz of two generations and of the secondary inclusions in quartzite allows us to maintain that the hydrothermal metamorphism of the host rock of the vein and the formation

---

* Curiously, among the secondary inclusions in quartzite, fairly often one may observe also some complex inclusions of two immiscible liquids (aqueous solution, carbon dioxide) with a large gas bubble consisting of carbon dioxide and water vapor. The volume ratios of the phases are not consistent. In cases where there is only a little water vapor in an inclusion (up to 15 or 20 per cent of the volume), the homogenization takes place in two stages: the liquid carbon dioxide disappears at about 30°C, whereupon the aqueous solution is volatilized gradually, so that, at 220°C, the inclusion becomes homogeneous in the gaseous phase (carbon dioxide and water vapor).

of the minerals in the fissures constituted *one single and synchronous process* [35, 37].

On Homogenization Temperatures of Inclusions in Twin Crystals and Temperatures of Formation of Datolite and Apophyllite

We examined a twin crystal of transparent calcite from one of the large vugs in a lead–zinc deposit in DVK. This crystal is shown in Fig. 41. Closely-spaced inclusions of ilvaite are visible near the surface of the

FIG. 41. Twin of calcite.

crystal. The preponderant forms of scalenohedron, rhombohedron, and bipyramid, V [21$\bar{3}$1] [20$\bar{1}$], l [01$\bar{1}$2] [110], γ [8.8.$\overline{16}$.3] [91$\bar{7}$], were established in this crystal. The basal rhombohedron r [10$\bar{1}$1] [100], the rhombohedron h [03$\bar{3}$2] [55$\bar{4}$], and the scalenohedron [6.5.$\overline{11}$.1] [60$\bar{5}$] are not so well developed. There is a weak development of the bipyramid [22$\bar{4}$3] [31$\bar{1}$] and of the series of vicinal scalenohedra in the l/r band. The twin plane is C(0001); the twin axis is Z.*

---

* The crystallographic orientation of the calcite is by G. L. Piotrovskii.

Examination of inclusions in the central part of the twinned calcite crystal gave homogenization temperatures of 81–82°C, and, in one case, of 102°C.

Analyses of the central part of the individual on the left gave the following temperature series: 82–76–74–73–72–71–70°C and temperatures of 56–54°C closer to the outer faces of the crystal.

The homogenization temperatures of two-phase inclusions of aqueous solutions in the individual on the right were found to be quite similar: 81–76–72–70–68–61°C.

Also, there were single-phase inclusions with probable homogenization temperatures below 50°C.

These results are not surprising and they indicate that the transparent twinned calcite of scalenohedral habit, on the whole, is a low-temperature

FIG. 42. Low-temperature datolite.

mineral that crystallized at a temperature lower than 100°C. As we see, this crystal has two terminations, both of which were growing concurrently—and this is by no means a common case in nature. Specifically the common doubly-terminated crystals of quartz, the so-called crystals of free growth, develop their second termination at a later time, by a regeneration of the crystal cut off from its substratum (see p. 163).

This second regenerated termination, as a rule, differs from the first one both morphologically and by its many defects, so characteristic of the place at which the crystal was attached.

The mechanism of growth of our specimen remains obscure, in this particular case, because of its highly symmetrical form, since it was impossible to determine the place at which it was attached to its substratum. The crystallization temperature of ilvaite was also low, since the ilvaite grew contemporaneously with the deposition of the latest zone of the calcite.

Perfectly transparent crystals of datolite and apophyllite, with clearly defined faces, are found in the same vugs of the deposit. A well formed datolite crystal is shown in Fig. 42.

A skin of very fine crystals of apophyllite is often seen on the datolite. The length of some individual datolite crystals may be up to 6 mm, along the long axis (Fig. 43).

Fig. 43. A druse of platy datolite and apophyllite.

Datolite is a very peculiar mineral and is generally regarded as a typical one for mineralization at shallow depths, judging by its distribution and occurrence. At the same time, datolite is believed to be a high-temperature mineral.

Crystalline granular olive-green datolite is often found in an early association with quartz and platy calcite, in the deposit from which we had obtained some very interesting test minerals for our study. Datolite, in association with quartz and platy calcite, in the "crystal channel" of the deposit, gives inclusion homogenization temperatures higher than 300°C. On the other hand, the transparent platy datolite shown in the photographs contains chiefly solid inclusions, single-phase inclusions of aqueous solutions, and, much more rarely' two-phase inclusions. We succeeded in homogenizing the latter at a maximum temperature of 110°C, but were compelled to assume the general temperature of formation of the datolite as being considerably below 100°C. The apophyllite overgrowing the datolite contained only single-phase inclusions of solution and, generally speaking, no two-phase inclusions at all could be found by us in this mineral. This circumstance provides a reason for the belief that the typical temperature at which the host mineral was formed was lower than 50°C.

The facts here ascertained, together with others already described incline us to the conclusion that minerals crystallizing over a wide range of temperature ("transcendent") are far more abundant in nature than is generally believed. This further reduces the group of minerals called "geological thermometers" whose presence in a deposit is still being construed as an indicator of the temperatures of the highly involved process of formation of minerals, the process which depends on a whole series of variables among which the temperature is fully as variable as any other factor.

Utilization of Inclusions in Certain Tectonic Conclusions

There is nothing surprising in the fact that different homogenization temperatures of secondary inclusions in healed fissures within minerals may serve occasionally as indicators of heterochronous moments of tectonic crushing of mineral veins and may help in our correlation of these moments with stages in the mineral genesis. One may easily appreciate the importance of the inclusion studies in microtectonics and in the tectonics of fissures. We aim here to offer an illustration of such usefulness in the instance of geotectonics, the subject that is in need of additional facilities in our exact understanding of natural phenomena.

Figure 44 shows a well-defined crystal of transparent quartz with an overgrowth of large crystals of calcite appearing dark from the surface. This specimen was collected by us from Vein No. 6 of a deposit in Pamir. The overwhelming majority of primary inclusions in this quartz was of the multiphase type: aqueous solution–gas bubble–two transparent isotropic crystals of cubic habit or only one such crystal, in the instance of three-phase inclusions.

In every one of our experiments with the homogenization of these inclusions, the smaller one of the "captive" crystals will be dissolved at 60–61°C, while the other one would disappear only at the temperature of the disappearance of the gas bubble (or after a short delay), at 130–135–138°C, and higher. The first crystal, as we see, with a high coefficient of

FIG. 44. Calcite overgrowing crystal of quartz (Pamir).

thermal solubility, was sylvite; the second one, with the low solubility coefficient, was halite.*

In three-phase inclusions, which are probably *expressions of the next moment in the change of the mother liquor's composition and concentration, there is only one crystal, sylvite, which is dissolved at 60°C*. The inclusions homogenize at 114–102°C.

Finally, two-phase inclusions of aqueous solutions were also found in this quartz crystal with average homogenization temperatures of 85°C.

Crystals of calcite overgrowing the quartz contain only two-phase and single-phase inclusions of aqueous solution. The homogenization temperature series for the two-phase inclusions is as follows: 82–71–68–65–62–60 and 52°C. It appears that not in a single instance could we prove a homogenization temperature of an inclusion that would exceed even the lowest temperature for the quartz.

* A specific example of application of the physico-chemical method to studies of the composition of "captive" minerals.

Locally, at the very surface of the quartz crystals, with their so very well-developed faces, we find traces of compromise growth surfaces produced by contact with the crystals of calcite. This fact, alongside the homogenization temperature series, leads to the conclusion that there was no break in the temperature between the time of formation of the two minerals and that, somewhere between 90 and 80°C, the termination of the crystal growth of quartz coincided, in time, with the beginning of the growth of calcite.*

Elsewhere in the vein, calcite grows on crystals of siderite and on some other still older minerals. This case is exemplified by Fig. 45.

We had to become convinced that both kinds of the calcite belong to one and the same temperature interval of deposition from bicarbonate

FIG. 45. Growth of calcite on siderite (Pamir).

solutions. For that reason, we measured the homogenization temperatures of inclusions in the surficial zones, the bases, and the middle portions of these crystals. The first series was found to be 48–53–54–58–59 and 60°C; the second one, involving clearly outlined inclusions, had homogenization temperatures of 68°C and somewhat higher. These results prove that we

* The deposit contains also a different kind of calcite of a somewhat earlier generation, syngenetic with quartz, with inclusions whose homogenization temperature is 100–120°C.

were dealing in both instances with a low-temperature calcite belonging to one and the same generation.

The rounded appearance of faces, edges, and terminations of these calcite crystals is conspicuous at first glance. There is clear-cut evidence of solution visible on the surface with the aid even of an ordinary lens. As to the low temperatures of the solutions responsible for the phenomenon, we may judge them from the numerous *single-phase* secondary *inclusions* [37].

As one may see from the previously reported figures, a discrete gas bubble originates in the included solutions of this type at a temperature higher than 48–52°C. We must conclude therefore that the solutions corroding the surfaces of the calcite crystals and penetrating these crystals along cleavage fissures had temperature below this threshold.

We find it difficult to give an exact estimation of the true temperatures for these end-products of thermal solution activity in the deposit, because we do not know the magnitude of the pressure. Despite very good surface exposures, a reconstruction of the geological profile gives us no opportunity for a clear-cut opinion on thickness of the overburden at the time of the mineral genesis.

However, judging by the very low temperatures of homogenization and by the size of the geothermal gradient, it is difficult to believe that the deposit could have been formed at a depth exceeding 2 km. The depth was probably shallower and the observed temperatures may be very close to the true temperatures.

The deposit is situated in a zone that was subjected to drastic disturbances at the time of the Alpine folding. By reasoning from our data on the inclusions preserved until now, we maintain that the host rocks of the deposit were never sunk to depths exceeding the limit here indicated. It could not have happened either before the formation of the single-phase secondary inclusions in the crystals of calcite nor after the period of action of the solutions by which these inclusions were formed. On the contrary, there are reasons to believe that only uplift accompanied by erosion have been experienced by the area since the formation of the deposit.

Even two-phase inclusions of solutions homogenizing at 50°C, for example, could not have remained in the calcite, had the deposit been sunk to a depth of 2.5 km, because they would be *superheated* and would *explode*. At such depths, one would expect temperatures of the order of magnitude of 90°C.

In our experiments at atmospheric pressure, at 10–15°C overheating of the inclusions above their homogenization temperatures would result invariably in a *decrepitation of the inclusions* in calcite accompanied by a loss of the liquid into fissures along the cleavage planes. An overheating by 40°C, even at an increased external pressure, would give inevitably the same result. This was not the case, however, with the secondary single-phase inclusions of aqueous solutions which, unlike the two-phase ones, had no "buffer" in the form of the gas bubble. Heating of such inclusions leads therefore to a still earlier explosion, provided the external pressure is not too high.

We have pointed out, in the past, the value of inclusion studies on minerals of sedimentary rocks [37, p. 14] for stratigraphic purposes (correlation of barren horizons and sedimentary bodies) as well as in paleogeography (recognition of the zones of erosion). We have taken here the opportunity to demonstrate the value of liquid inclusion studies in the solution of certain types of problems in tectonics.

THERMOMETRIC STUDIES OF SOME MINERAL DEPOSITS

We gained our first experience in applications of thermometric research to mineral deposits and mineralogic provinces in 1941–1943, in examinations of the sources of optical minerals in Central Asia [30, 31, 32, 33]. Later on, our experience was expanded to include pegmatitic, hydrothermal, and "Alpine" sources of crystal quartz and also certain sources of ores in other territories of the U.S.S.R.

Since we had already reported on geology and origin of most of these deposits in a series of articles some of which were published [30, 33, 33a, 34, 34a], we shall now treat these aspects of the problem only in brief, as our main purpose is to characterize intervals and variations in the temperature regimes of solutions in the course of the formation of mineral deposits. Some very brief descriptions of the geology of the deposits are given only insofar as they are required in the definitions of time, depth, and general environment of mineral genesis.

In the present study, oriented toward methods, we do not endeavor to offer complete characterization of the thermal environments wherein mineral deposits of different types have been formed. Our principal aim is merely to suggest the direction of further developments of the research and to illustrate applications of thermometric analysis, as a method, in certain concrete problems.

On Temperatures of Formation of Calcites in Central Asia and Crimea

Every occurrence of Iceland spar found in Central Asia has formed in limestones. In contrast with the hydrothermal deposits in basic effusives (trap rocks), these deposits have only a very small commercial value.

Deposits of Iceland spar in limestones are characterized by a variety of structural environments of formation. There are examples of every one

of the four types of mineralization we had previously identified [33]:
(1) Deposits and vugs in fracture cavities; (2) in ancient karst caves;
(3) in caverns formed by hydrothermal solution of limestones; (4) in zones
of fissuring and coarse brecciation of the rocks. The first three types are
widely represented in the districts of Magian, Marguzor, and Ugam, where
there are tens of localities containing crystals of calcite and Iceland spar.
The fourth type is represented by the Debryud.

(1) Calcite veins and vugs of the first type are fairly monotonous, on
the whole, and, for that reason, we shall give here only a brief description
of some of their typical representatives. Vein No. 4, Magian, was formed
in thickly layered Ludlow limestones, in a tectonic fissure. In the place
where both the vein and the fissure are wide, there is a cave with the following structure to the walls: the host limestone is in a clearly defined
direct contact with limestone–calcite breccia, up to 2 m thick, grading into
a white partially transparent calcite toward the center of the cave. This
calcite is overgrown by large crystals of Iceland spar, with edges up to
46 cm long, chiefly of scalenohedral habit. The crystals show combinations
of scalenohedron with basal rhombohedron, as well as pure scalenohedron
and its combination with a rhombohedron or a prism. The surfaces of
most of the crystals are coated with a dark "shirt", but their cores are
transparent and yellowish, as a rule.

Vein No. 4, Marguzor, resembles structurally the vein just described
and is associated also with a tectonic fissure. The bulges in the calcite vein
contain vugs of very large crystals of a highly transparent calcite. The
breccia in the vein's contacts grades into a milky-white calcite overgrown
by crystals of Iceland spar in the central section.

(2) The most striking example of a deposit of the second type is found
also in the Magian District. It was there, in 1936, that we discovered the
large cave of Dzhumbayir, up to 50 m long, consisting of six chambers
[33]. The cave is in the Ludlow limestones, at 20–30 m depth below the
ancient erosional surface which is overlain unconformably by Upper Paleozoic sandstones and shales with the combined thickness of 500 m.

The ceiling and the walls of three chambers, the farthest one from the
entrance to the cave, are overgrown abundantly by druses of fissured
Iceland spar of rhombohedral habit. Some crystals are up to 30×30×
40 cm in size and up to 60 cm long, along the rhombohedral edge. In addition to the basal rhombohedron, the crystals in the cave show also combinations of rhombohedron and scalenohedron, scalenohedron, short prism
and rhombohedron, and prism, scalenohedron, and rhombohedron. Twins
are common among the druse crystals. There is practically no deposition
of the milky-white vein calcite in the cave and the crystals are growing
directly on their limestone substratum. The position of the farthest part of
the cave does not allow us to relate its formation to the modern topo-

graphy, while the presence of finely disseminated sulfides is an indirect evidence of their origin in thermal solutions that entered the cave, most likely in pre-Mesozoic times, and had converted the cave into a gigantic reservoir–crystallizer.

There is a large number of smaller caves occupying up to 10–15 per cent of the volume of the rock wherein they are contained to the east of the Marguzor Lake, in the Kamir-Surak Mountains, in Ludlow limestones, close to the ancient erosion surface. Transparent and semi-transparent crystals of calcite are found in nearly every one of these ancient karst cavities.

(3) There are caves in the Chorrag Ridge, Marguzor District, that show no relation whatsoever either with the ancient or the modern erosion surfaces. Cave No. 3 is the most typical one in this respect. The cave was formed at the intersection of two fissures: a meridional vertical one and a tectonic fissure dipping at 20°. The space of the cave, 5 m long, 4 m broad, 2.5 m high, was half-filled with a blocky breccia in whose cavities there was a development of transparent crystals of calcite. Some sections of the cave's walls are composed of a silicified breccia whose limestone fragments were leached, so that the quartz veinlets by which the limestone was formerly cemented have now the appearance of a skeleton. The largest crystals of Iceland spar, up to 20 cm along the rhombohedron edge, are generally hanging from the ceiling or are growing on lower surfaces of the blocks filling the cave. Most of the crystals are combinations of a hexagonal prism and a rhombohedron.

This cave is very interesting, in connection with the sequence of the formation of hypogene minerals in poly-mineral deposits of Iceland spar. Milky-white quartz is the earliest mineral, in the cave here described. The numerous veinlets in limestone are composed of this mineral. Afterwards, toward the end of the silicification phase, there was crystallization of an ore mineral. Aggregates of violet and greenish fluorspar, in the form of veinlets and of inclusions in cavities, were deposited somewhat later. Fluorite cubes (edge up to 0.5 mm) and fine crystals of an ore mineral were deposited also in cavities, in places, on top of the druse of fine crystals of transparent quartz. Milky-white calcite and Iceland spar were the last minerals formed by the hydrothermal process. Hydrothermal leaching of the rocks was taking place early in the process; it was succeeded by the deposition of the minerals here discussed.

(4) The Debryud deposit, at the headwaters of the Pasrud River, was formed in a tremendous zone of fissuring and breciation, up to 12 m across, of Upper Silurian limestones near their contact with shales. Milky-white calcite forms a dense network of veins and veinlets in the breccia. Vugs of semi-transparent calcite developed at intersections of these veinlets and veins and in blow-outs of the veins, between blocks of limestone [33,

Fig. 3]. In many of these vugs, calcite grows on a druse of siderite crystals among which small grains of chalcopyrite may be found occasionally. Crystals of transparent calcite attain the size of $60 \times 25 \times 20$ cm and most of them are of scalenohedral habit. As a rule, they are covered by a non-transparent "shirt" of calcite.

Calcite deposits in the Pskem-Ugan District (Kumungur, Boguchelpak, Akburkhan, Kubrek, Khozartek, Susingen, and others) are very similar to the types just described and do not require any additional characterization.

The problems of origin of Iceland spar in limestones, with examples of the deposits in Central Asia, were examined by us in detail in a special publication [33]. We wish now merely to point out that deposits of this optical mineral owe their origin to a circulation of low-temperature hydro-thermal solutions which became naturally mixed with ground waters and metamorphic waters, as they moved over long distances from the intrusions, and that calcium and carbonate are acquired by these solutions from the carbonate host rocks.

The results of our measurements of homogenization temperatures of inclusions in Iceland spar are summarized in the following table:

TABLE 22

No. in sequence	Source	Crystal No. in author's collection	Average homogenization temperature (°C)	Per cent gas bubble*
1	Magian	33	74	—
2	Marguzor	104	98	—
3	Marguzor	13	78	—
4	Marguzor	39, 40	70–71	3.6
5	Kumungur	108	89–110	4.3
6	Buguchelpak	109, 110	84–88	—
7	Akburkhan	120, 121	67–84–100	—
8	Kubrek	126, 127	82–78–60	3.3
9	Khozartek	128, 129	71–69–63	—
10	Susingen	107, 111	76–84	—
11	Tyuya-Muyun	122, 123	74–88 to 190	—

* By volume [V.P.S].

The table shows that the average temperature of crystallization of Iceland spar from Central Asiatic deposits is below 100°C, as a rule (uncorrected for pressure). However, transparent calcite may be formed also at much higher temperatures, in entirely different geologic environments such as Tyuya Muyun. Iceland spar from the skarn of Chatkala and Pskem, in specimens No. 130 (Kara-Arda) and No. 136 (Ak-Bulak), gave the homogenization temperatures of 180–195°C and 230–275°C respectively.

The following succession of crystallographic forms, in the course of mineral genesis, from the earliest basal rhombohedron through scaleno-hedron and down to crystals of prismatic habit, was indicated by our

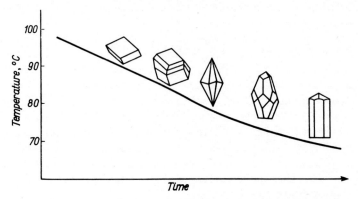

FIG. 46. Schematic evolution of crystallographic forms of calcite in vugs from Magian and Marguzor.

studies of calcite crystals from the Magian and the Marguzor deposits (Fig. 46).

In this case, we came upon the fact that this kind of *sequence of forms may take place occasionally within a very narrow range of the temperature* (Fig. 46) and that the phenomenon can be scarcely explained only by the temperature variation. This relationship will be shown also later, with the example of calcites from the DVK. However, in view of wide variety of natural phenomena, this subject must be approached with great caution and, among other things, one must consider the highly probable effects of different substances present in mineral-forming solutions on the crystal-line forms produced.

By way of comparisons of these results with the widely known calcites of Crimea, we undertook several measurements of homogenization tem-peratures of inclusions in calcite crystals from Sudak (Specimen Nos. 1–4), Baydar Gate* (Nos. 6 and 6a), Al-Todor (No. 7), and Kastel' (Kara-Dag) (No. 5).† The results were reported in Table 23.

These results show that the Crimean calcites (Baydar Gate, Sudak) were formed chiefly at temperatures lower than 100°C. Moreover, the very last moments of the crystallization of some of them occurred in lukewarm and possibly even in cool solutions, as indicated by the presence of both

---

* Baydarskiye Vorota, the point on the Crimean Plateau (the Yayla) from which the descent to the Crimean Riviera begins [V.P.S.].

† The author is greatly indebted to G. P. Barsanov, Doctor of Geologic–Miner-alogical Sciences, who kindly placed at our disposal these and several other speci-mens from the Mineralogical Museum of the Academy of Sciences of the U.S.S.R.

primary and secondary single-phase inclusions. We obtained only a single cleavage fragment of the crystal from Kara-Dag that gave homogenization temperatures much higher than the rest of the crystals.

TABLE 23

Specimen No.	Source	Homogenization temperature (°C)	Remarks
1	Sudak	Up to 60	Single-phase inclusions also abundant
2	Sudak	75–80	The most typical temperature 80°C
3	Sudak	60–80–100–110	Columnar calcite
4	Sudak	40	Many single-phase inclusions
5	Kastel'	177–185 (primary) 105–135 (secondary)	From effusive rocks
6	Baydar Gate	Up to 55–60	Many single-phase inclusions
7	Al-Todor	25–35	Carbon dioxide present

Several fragments of transparent calcite from Yakutia were transmitted to us for an examination. Crystals of "pyramidal" calcite from tubular veins and from zones of fragmentation in diabase pegmatites gave the following series of homogenization temperatures for their inclusions: 240–232–215–185 and 165°C.

Crystals from calcite–zeolite vugs and veinlets amidst trap rocks were found to be relatively low-temperature ones: 136–120–115–110 and 100°C. It is highly probable that these deposits of the mineral were formed in two successive stages of mineral genesis.

Our brief discussion of the processes by which calcite is formed shows that this mineral is formed, on the whole, *within a wide range of temperature of the solutions. Variation in the crystallographic forms of calcites, on the contrary, may take place within a narrow range of the temperatures and the use of these forms as mineralogical thermometers is accordingly difficult to justify.* Variations in composition and concentration of bicarbonate solutions appear to have just as much influence in the evolution of the crystallographic forms of calcite as the temperature.

On Temperatures of Formation of Some Fluorite Deposits in Central Asia and in Transbaykalia

Characteristics of the temperature environments of the formation of fluorite deposits of Tadzhikistan and south-western Kazakhstan are here presented in brief. These deposits contain optical varieties of fluorite and of other transparent minerals, in addition to fluorspar, which served as the best-suited test materials for the purposes of the thermometric analysis, in the first stage of our research.

Deposits of Central Tadzhikistan. The thick Upper Silurian sequence whose limestone horizons contain the Zeravshan deposits plays the most important role in the geologic structure of the territory. Devonian and Lower Carboniferous limestones are also prominent in the geologic section of the district. Strongly dislocated Middle Paleozoic sediments are overlain unconformably by Upper Paleozoic formations represented by flysch in the west and by effusive porphyries and clastic volcanic rocks in the east, in the basin of the Kaznok River.

Mesozoic and Tertiary sediments of composition typical for Tadzhikistan lay on top of the Paleozoic rocks with a strikingly angular unconformity.

These same sediments overlay also the hydrothermal veins of barite and calcite in the vicinity of the Munor Pass (Pereval), thereby defining a pre-Mesozoic age for the fluorite deposits of the Zeravshan–Gissar mountain system.

The overburden thickness above these veins varied from 0.5 to 2 km during the formation of the deposits, as shown by a restoration of the geologic section.

The geologic position of the deposits here discussed indicates therefore that they were formed in the upper zone of circulation of hydrothermal solutions. The contents of these mineralized solutions were derived chiefly from a deep magmatic source, with the exception of calcium bicarbonate with which they were probably enriched during passage through the Middle Paleozoic limestones. Antimonite, cinnabar, realgar, and other such minerals, found occasionally and in very small quantities in some deposits of optical minerals, are evidence that the solutions have travelled far from the parent intrusions. The most important prerequisite for the formation of these deposits was the combination of the fluorine- and barium-bearing solutions with the limestones.

Development of brecciated zones, in conjunction with the screening effects of shales, in different limestone series, was an especially favorable factor. In places where the flow of mineralizing solutions was particularly intensive, in zones of contacts and of brecciation of the limestones, there was a deposition of massive ores of fluorspar and barite and optical varieties of these minerals were crystallized only in small cavities inside the ores.

In the best deposits of optical fluorite, the mineral solutions entered the zones where the vugs and caverns of crystals were being formed as fairly weak currents, feeding the reservoir-crystallizers slowly and uniformly. The cavernous character of the rock in which the vugs of optical fluorite and barite were formed originated by tectonic processes and by subsequent solvent action on the limestones by earlier apparently undersaturated solutions. The caverns, the natural reservoir-crystallizers, served not merely to provide space for crystal growth but also to assure a fairly stable and favorable physico-chemical regime for crystallization of the minerals.

There was an inter-formational slipping leading to intensive fragmentation of the rocks and the formation of breccias which were cemented eventually by barite and quartz, as the result of activity of hydrothermal solutions, in the "*Northern*" *deposit* of fluorite, along the contact between limestones and the overlying shales. Depending on their constituents, we recognize barite–shale–limestone and quartz–limestone breccias both of a highly varying thickness. Locally in the breccias there is an almost complete replacement of limestone fragments by barite and quartz and, more rarely, by violet fluorspar.

Microstructures of the deposit are characterized by brecciation zones inside the limestones oriented obliquely to the contact plane, as well as by fracture fissures and, to a somewhat lesser extent, by drag fissures.

The brecciated zones and the mutually intersecting fissures proved to be the most favorable places for the formation of the largest vugs and caverns of optical fluorite during the subsequent mineralization. The dolomitized limestones were found to be fragmented also by a network of minute fissures, whose development may have been associated with dolomitization, in addition to the fissuring and the brecciation already described. These fine fissures also played an important role in the slow and very weak circulation of hydrothermal solutions participating in the mineralization of the cavities.

Four stages of mineralization are fairly definitely recognizable in the deposit. Minerals of the first stage are developed chiefly in the breccias situated directly in the limestone–shale contact and are associated with the primary silicification and dolomitization of the limestones. These minerals are represented by milky-white quartz, hornsfels-like [fine grained?—Ed.] quartz, massive pinkish white non-transparent barite, violet fine-grained feldspar, dolomite, ore minerals, and by finely and sparsely disseminated galena, sphalerite, chalcopyrite, and pyrite in the breccias.

All mineral formations of the first stage are cut by veins and veinlets of non-ore minerals belonging to the second and the *principal stage of the deposit's* formation, characterized by sugary quartz and chalcedony, greenish blue fluorspar and optical fluorite, optical barite, white calcite, and transparent Iceland spar. Occasional crystals of tetrahedrite, realgar, and auripigment belong also to this relatively low-temperature stage at the end of the hydrothermal process.

Formation of minerals of the third stage is associated with the very last influx hydrothermal solutions to the site. It is represented by dickite, filling the core of the vugs and crystal quartz, in the form of fine free crystals, found together with optical fluorite and palygorskite in some caverns.

Malachite, azurite, and limonite were formed in the fourth supergene stage.

Of all the minerals here enumerated, only quartz, barite, fluorite, and dickite are abundant in the deposit. Optical fluorite is found almost invariably with optical barite, overgrowing the barite crystals.

Fluorite crystals are, for the most part, colorless and are notable for their high transparency. Only occasionally does one observe a bluish tinge in these crystals or, still more rarely, a lilac tinge. Most of the fluorite crystals are cubes. Tetragonal trisoctahedron and hexoctahedron faces beveling the cube adges are extremely rare. Crystals of optical barite have a platy appearance and may be up to 20 cm along their largest edge. They are found often as a fan-shaped growth of several joined crystals. Crystals of Iceland spar are rare in the deposit; they grow generally on optical fluorite. As a rule, all the optical minerals are found in cavities of various sizes commonly knows as vugs ("gnyozda"). The larger cavities, larger than one-quarter of one cubic meter, are called caverns ("pogreba"). Vugs and caverns, as a rule, are distributed irregularly in the deposits hornfelsitized and dolomitized limestones, at distances up to 12 m from the contacts with the shales. The leaching of the limestones preceding the main stage of mineral formation played a conspicuous part in their formation.

Only the second, main stage of mineralization, with its well faceted crystals of barite, fluorite, and calcite, was examined in detail for temperature of crystallization. Our measurements of the homogenization temperatures of primary and pseudo-secondary inclusions, uncorrected for pressure, are reported in Table 24.

As shown in the table, all of the hydrothermal optical minerals in the deposit here examined fall within the range of 139–192°C. The temperature range [corrected for pressure–Ed.] of barite, fluorite, and calcite is 159–192,* 141–176, and 139†–148°C respectively. The most typical mean temperature for the deposit is 178°C for barite and 141°C‡ for fluorite and calcite.§

All of the measured temperatures proved to be in exact agreement with the established sequence of crystallization of the minerals of the deposit, from barite through fluorite to calcite. Not a single instance was found of contradiction between the sequence of crystallization and the

---

* Probably a misprint; should be 202°C [Ed.].

† Probably a misprint; should be 129°C [V.P.S.].

‡ Total thickness of the deposit's overburden was 2 km assuming its depth at 1.5 km below the pre-Upper Paleozoic erosion surface and taking 0.5 km as the thickness of the overlying Upper Paleozoic materials. The corresponding probable correction for pressure would be 40°C, as here employed.

§ Apparently a misprint; 162°C is the mean for the fluorite, according to Table 28 [V. P. S.].

TABLE 24

No. in sequence	No. of vugs, names of parts of deposit	No. of prepared sections here examined	Mean temperatures (°C)		
			Barite	Fluorite	Calcite
1	1	51, 52	135	116	—
	6	100	—	123	—
	9	55	—	124	—
	10	53, 54	131	120	—
	14	56	—	133	—
	19a	57	—	126	—
	21	58, 67	141	128	—
	22	59	—	122	—
	24	60	—	114	—
	25	61, 88	146	130	—
	30	62	—	124	—
	31	63	—	126	—
	34	64	—	121	—
	36	65, 89	137	118	—
	38	66, 67	134	115	—
	39	68	—	126	—
	41	70, 50	143	126	—
	42	71	—	125	—
	43	72	—	121	—
	44	73, 91	133	116	—
	45	74	—	128	—
	46	75	—	133	—
	47	76, 92, 37	152	135	107
	48	77	—	106	—
	49	78	—	109	—
	50	79	—	117	—
	51	80	—	129	—
	52	81	—	127	—
	53	82	—	124	—
	54	83	—	136	—
	55	84, 93	149	132	—
	56	85	—	104	—
	57	86	—	134	—
2	Central part	14	—	119	—
		18	—	123	—
		26	—	123	—
		32, 35	135	126	—
		45, 94	136	125	—
		101	—	125	—
		4	129	—	—
		25	140	—	—
		36	—	—	108
3	Western part	27	—	101	—
		8	119	—	—
		12	—	—	101
4	Eastern part	30	—	108	—
		20	—	—	89

[continued on p. 198]

TABLE 24 (continued)

No. in sequence	No. of vugs, names of parts of deposit	No. of prepared sections here examined	Mean temperatures (°C)		
			Barite	Fluorite	Calcite
5	Temperature range of the mineral		119 to 162	101 to 136	89 to 108
6	Mean temperature of the formation of the mineral, uncorrected for pressure		138	122	101
7	Same, after probable correction for pressure*		178	162	141

* 40°C [Ed.].

homogenization temperatures, as indicated in the table, for different crystals from a given vug. Thus, the mean (corrected) homogenization temperature of inclusions in barite, vug No. 47, was found to be 192°C, and the means for fluorite and calcite were found to be 175°C and 147°C respectively (see Fig. 35, p. 173).

The crystallization of minerals from barium–fluoride–bicarbonate solutions in the deposit took place at slowly and progressively decreasing solution temperature and at different degrees of saturation. In the first hydrothermal stage of formation of optical minerals, in some natural reservoir-crystallizers, supersaturation with barium sulfate was attained by cooling down to 192°C. When the solutions reached temperatures of 176–175°C, all of the barite was crystallized out and the formation of fluorite began. Nucleation and growth of fluorite to small and large crystals, in one and the same vug took place at temperatures down to 147°C. The smallest crystals, however, yield the lowest homogenization temperatures for primary inclusions. Later on calcite began to separate; it continued down to 129–130°C. At still lower temperatures, very fine crystals of quartz formed and dickite was deposited.

Crystallization of the minerals of this deposit was first represented by us on a true ("absolute") temperature scale Fig. 35, using the geochemical diagrams suggested by Fersman. The temperature range for different minerals in the deposit as a whole, of course, was found to be wider than the range in individual caverns and vugs.

We made an attempt to ascertain the mean temperatures, typical for fluorite in different vugs at different depths, taking advantage of the exposure of the deposit by mining works to depths exceeding 50 m. We succeeded in drawing isotherms for the main stage of fluorite deposition on the basis of our findings for a specifically chosen series of vugs. The highest mean temperatures of crystallization of fluorite were found to be in vugs in the central part of the deposit, the part which was disturbed rather severely by tectonic fissures. There also we found the steepest temperature gradients and the most intensive fluoritization. In the central open cut, as well as in open cut No. 12, the mean temperatures of vugs 18 to 20 m apart vertically were found to differ by as much as 14°C (for example, vugs No. 47 and No. 10). The mean temperatures for the bulk of the crystals in vugs in the deep central part of the deposit were somewhat higher.

The overall amplitude of the crystallization temperatures of optical barite, fluorite, and calcite was 33, 25, and 19°C respectively, as shown by the results of thermometric studies of 60 mineral specimens from different vugs and veins.

It was also observed that the more intensive is the vein mineralization in vicinity of a given vug, the higher is the homogenization temperature of inclusions in crystals of optical barite and fluorite in the vug. It is evident that a larger number of channels leading to the vug will yield a larger combined *conducting capacity,* and will result in a higher temperature isotherm reaching the site of the given vug. In this connection, a group of occurrences of fluorspar and optical fluorite to the south of the deposit here discussed and close to intrusions of alkali syenites, are highly interesting.

The *"southern"* deposit is associated with limestones which seem to belong to the same Upper Silurian beds which compose the "fluorite" rock. These limestones are 50 m thick. They are part of the southern edge of the previously mentioned Chimtarga Syncline. The Middle Paleozoic rocks, well developed in the vicinity of the deposit, with their sharp angular unconformities laterally and down dip, are overlain by Upper Paleozoic tuff–agglomerates, tuff–breccias, tuffs, and, in their lower half, by porphyries, with a combined total thickness of 1200 m. The deposit is situated at about 300 m below the ancient erosion surface, so that the net depth at which the deposit was formed may be defined as 1.5 km. Intrusive alkali rocks are also fairly prominent in the vicinity of the deposit where they form five sizeable bodies lying in an ellipse showing a northeast–southwest orientation.

Indications of fluorite mineralization in the district are associated with the inner part of this intrusive zone.

Together with I. V. Belov, we established the following succession of rocks in the intrusive complex of the district: granitoids of the adamellite type with alkali granites; alkali syenites; nepheline syenites and alkali pegmatoids; vein alkali syenites and nepheline syenite porphyries; camptonites and lamprophyres. We must note here that *fragments of alkali syenites are present in the basal horizons of the Upper Paleozoic volcanogenic formation,* while camptonites and lamprophyres pierce all of the horizons of the latter.

The host limestones of the "southern" deposit are overlain by silicified stanzaites and lyditites. Along the contact plane which dips steeply to the north there has been tectonic movements, as now indicated by the slickensides and by the rock flour. Transverse fragmentation zones in the limestones functioned as the principal paths for the hydrothermal solutions entering the site of the deposit. A system of relatively short steeply dipping fissures (at 60–85°) within the mineralized zone is conjugate with the principal disturbance structures antedating the mineralization. These short fissures complicate the "pre-ore" disturbance features and they also cut through the earliest aggregations of minerals, while serving as the sites of deposition of minerals belonging to the next stage of mineralization.

Fluorspar is preponderant over the other minerals in the main mineralized field. This fluorspar was produced in the first stage of mineral genesis and is represented by massive–granular aggregates of crystals of milky-white, bottle-green, emerald green, and blue colors. In the transverse fragmentation zones in the limestones, it formed deposits of banded fluorspar ores alternating, in places, with siderite and brown ironstone.

The fluorspar ores were cut by veins of other minerals in the second stage of mineral genesis. The minerals belonging to this second and main stage of mineralization may be enumerated as follows: vein calcite, siderite, flesh-colored barite, semi-transparent fluorite, chalcopyrite, and pyrite were laid down in the fissures; *at the same time,* in vugs and caverns, there was a successive crystallization of transparent and semi-transparent calcite, and optical fluorite. A fair abundance of embedded chalcopyrite and pyrite is observed locally in crystals of the optical minerals. Cavities, functioning as natural crystallizer-reservoirs, are as large as caverns in some of the zones of contact between the host limestones and the fluorspar ores, while cavities situated inside the fluorspar ores are very small in size. The large cavities were produced apparently by a hydrothermal solution of the limestone at the places of intersection of the "pre-ore" fragmentation zones with the fissures developed within the mineralized horizons.

Isolated cubical crystals and druses of optical fluorite, commonly together with platy crystals of barite, overgrow crystals of transparent calcite or, more often, grow directly on top of non-transparent calcite and fluorspar of the veins. Our analyses of optical fluorite and fluorspar from cavern No. 17 gave the following results (in percentages) (Table 25).

The loss on ignition in these analyses was particularly interesting to us. It was proved definitely that *the greater the amount of liquid inclusions present in fluorite, the greater is the loss on ignition.* Such inclusions are easily ruptured on ignition (by overheating above the homogenization temperature) with the resulting escape of the volatile substance, chiefly water.

TABLE 25

No. in sequence	Minerals and their inclusions	CaF_2	SiO_2	Fe_2O_3 and FeO	Al_2O_3	R_2O_3	Loss on ignition
1	Colorless optical fluorite (few inclusions)	98.28	0.96	0.16	0.12	0.28	0.06
2	Bluish optical fluorite (practically no inclusions)	98.57	0.80	0.16	0.06	0.22	0.00
3	Greenish fluorspar (abundant inclusions)	94.48	2.00	0.32	0.18	0.50	1.35

Kaolin (dickite?) and aragonite, minerals of the third stage of the mineral genesis, are found in the inner part of the productive vugs.

The fourth supergene stage of mineral genesis in the deposit is represented by tenorite, malachite, azurite, and limonite. Ten typical crystals of optical fluorite and fluorspar from the deposit were studied in detail and the result of their thermometric analysis are summarized in Table 26.

The possible correction for pressure may not exceed $+30°C$ as the depth of the deposit is 1.5 km. In such case, the temperature range of the formation of optical fluorite must be set as 129–166°C.

TABLE 26

No. in sequence	Nos. of vugs from which the crystals were taken	Crystal No. (author's collection)	Average temperature for fluorite, °C, uncorrected for pressure	Temperature for iron carbonate	Presence of zonal inclusions of chalcopyrite in fluorite crystals
1	1	96	136	—	+
2	3	98	108	—	—
3	9	97	122	—	—
4	11	99	106	—	+
5	19	95	128	—	+
6	22	21	112	—	—
7	23	22, 28, 29	{ fluorspar 109 / optical fluorite 99 }	108	+
8	—	7	106		+
9	—	23	104	—	—
10	—	24	107	—	—

In order to clarify genetic relations of the deposit here described to the intrusions of alkali syenites, we undertook a determination of traces of fluoritization in these intrusives. A small vug with fluorite crystals was found in one of the eastern intrusions of the alkali syenites. Inclusions in crystal No. 31 from this vug gave a mean homogenization temperature of 131°C, within the temperature range of formation of the deposit.

Our measurements of the temperatures support the proposition that it is not possible to connect directly the formation of fluorite, in the deposits here discussed, with any derivatives of the exposed alkali syenite intrusives in direct proximity of the deposits, even though the intrusions may contain, in places, veins of fluorspar and vugs with optical fluorite. Were there a direct genetic relationship between the intrusions and the deposits of fluorite, one should expect without doubt much higher temperatures of formation of fluorite than the temperatures we found. It should be noted also that the biggest fluorite veins in the deposit, right next to a small outcrop of nepheline syenite, *failed to yield homogenization temperatures for liquid inclusions in fluorite in excess of the fluorite range (134–147°C).** This fact also strengthens our conviction that the intrusions of nepheline syenites now outcropping on the surface are not the source rocks of fluorite in the deposits we examined. These deposits were formed by some deep volcanic hearth, the one that gave origin to the veins of camptonites and lamprophyres.

A deposit in south-western Kazakhstan. Our very first acquaintance with this deposit showed that it contains a whole series of generations of fluorite and quartz as well as of barite and calcite. The fluorite is found extensively in the from of varicolored crystals, often fairly large. The initial application of thermometric analysis to different generations of fluorite had posed at once a whole set of difficult problems whose ultimate solution we failed to attain, because of our departure from Central Asia.

A series of fundamental important questions was resolved successfully by Grushkin [28, 29] afterwards, who continued our investigation in Central Asia and who made use of the thermometric method in determining the origins of hypogene deposits. Grushkin's genetically important conclusions, based on his studies of these deposits, are cited below.

The fluorite deposit in question is highly interesting mineralogically, because of the great variety of its minerals and generations. Five generations of fluorite and four of quartz are particularly well developed, in addition to various sulfides (pyrite, chalcopyrite, sphalerite, galena, tetra-

---

* 134 to 147°C seems to be the homogenization range for liquid inclusions in fluorite from that particular vein. Yermakov does not say whether these temperatures were corrected for the pressure. If they were not, they are much higher than the uncorrected temperatures reported in Table 26 [V.P.S.].

hedrite) associated almost entirely with a quartz–barite–fluorite breccia. Barite was deposited in a close association with the sulfides; calcite and nacrite were laid down at the very end of the hydrothermal process. Secondary minerals, chiefly hydroxides of iron and copper and carbonates of lead and zinc, were produced in the supergene phase of the mineral genesis.

Grushkin's sequence [28, 29] of the deposit's hypogene minerals is as follows, with certain refinements: *Fluorite* I—dark-violet; II—light-violet zonal; III—colorless or bluish, transparent; IV—greenish, semi-transparent; V—pinkish; transparent and semi-transparent *barite;* pyrite, chalcopyrite, sphalerite, galena, tetrahedrite; *quartz* I—columnar; II—"crested"; III— finely crystalline, needle-like; IV—hornfels-like; *calcite,* with transitions from rhombohedron to scalenohedron, and down to prism; finally, *nacrite.*

Colorless optical fluorite of the third generation, with colorless or honey-yellow semi-transparent calcite of rhombohedral habit, is found in cavities inside the hornfelsitized rocks. Water-clear crystals of optical barite were discovered in a fragmented clayey flint rock. Optical fluorite and calcite are found on top of a greenish fluorspar lining the walls of the vugs, in most cases. Crystals of optical fluorite are often blunted by faces of a pyramidal cube (tetrahexahedron). The cube's edges are blunted occasionally by faces of a trapezohedron and a hexaoctahedron occurring together. Faces of fluorite crystals are often corroded by etch figures and their edges are often truncated by pseudo-faces produced by solution. The crystals examined by us have fairly ordinary type zonation. Their most important internal defect, however, is a multitude of globular, wedge-like, and ellipsoidal pores filled with liquid and with bubbles of gas [36]. These bubbles are often associated with the octahedral faces and their size varies from 0.005 to 0.04 mm.

Smol'yanikov [97] cites the following results of chemical analyses of the violet fluorspar and of the optical fluorite from this deposit (as percentages):

TABLE 27

No. in sequence	Mineral	Ca	F	SiO_2	O_3	BaO	Fe_2O_3	Al_2O_3	CO_2	H_2O lost at 105°
1	Violet fluorspar	51.38	49.10	0.04	none	none	0.01	0.05	none	0.03
2	Optical fluorite	51.43	48.95	none	trace	trace	0.02	0.04	none	none

The loss on ignition for No. 1 is 0.09 per cent; none in No. 2.

The fluorite generations, identified in the deposit, are here described according to B. Krasil'nikov and G. G. Grushkin. The first generation is represented by dar-violet fluorite.

It forms clusters of fine ladder-like crystals of cubic habit with edges averaging 4 mm long. Replacement of this fluorite by quartz is observed often along octahedral cleavage planes.

Our measurements of the homogenization temperatures (in parentheses) and Grushkin's (without parentheses) established the following series: 149–147–(146) and 131°C.

The second generation is represented by a light-violet fluorite. Its well defined crystals, in cavities, are colored uniformly on the inside, but their color on the periphery is conspicuously zonal in its distribution. The faceted crystals are cubical; their average edge length is 3 cm. The homogenization temperature series for their primary inclusions is as follows: 180–172–168–164–147–(138)–133°C. In the vugs such crystals are overgrown by transparent optical fluorite of the next generation.

The third generation is represented by a colorless or bluish transparent or semi-transparent fluorite growing exclusively in the form of clearly defined crystals, generally in vugs and in druses. Crystals growing on the walls of vugs have a random orientation with respect to each other. However, where they overgrow crystals of the preceding generations, the orientation of the optical fluorite coincides with that of the previously formed crystal. Despite their considerable size, the optical fluorite crystals of the deposit have no industrial value because of the abundance of inclusions and fissures. Their inclusions gave the following series of the homogenization temperatures: 160–(149)–(143)–135°C.

The fourth generation is a semi-transparent greenish fluorite growing in cavities, on broken surfaces and on faces of crystals of the preceding generation, in the form of ladder-like clusters with a parallel orientation. The size of the crystals in the clusters varies from 0.3 to 1.2 cm. The earmark of the fluorite of this generation is its selective capacity for being replaced by nacrite. The replacement is parallel to the cube faces and consists of a gradual parting of the layers of the fluorite, from the crystal surface inwards. The inclusions showed the following homogenization temperature series: 190–156–151–147–(137)–131–(130)–113 and 105°C.

The fifth generation is a pink transparent or semi-transparent fluorite separated, it appears, by a considerable interval of time from the preceding generations. The relative abundance of different crystal forms, becoming progressively more involved toward the end of the crystallization, is highly typical of this last generation of fluorite. The homogenization temperatures of its primary and pseudo-secondary inclusions are: (121)–119–115–101 and 90°C.

In the instance of fluorite of some of the generations here described, Grushkin [29] had traced changes in the homogenization temperatures of inclusions in different growth zones of individual crystals in which there was evidence of a radical lowering of the temperatures toward the end of the crystallization. He represents these changes as curves *3, 4,* and *5* in Fig. 47.

Temperatures of the sulfide-barite stage of the deposit's mineralization remain obscure, but the next stage, the stage of activity of silica-bearing

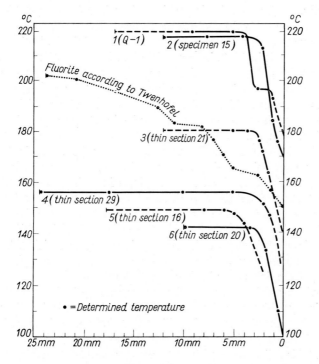

FIG. 47. Curves of homogenization temperatures in crystal growth of quartz and fluorite.

solutions responsible for the deposition of quartz has now an entirely satisfactory explanation, thanks to the Grushkin's mineralothermal research.

The earliest variety, semi-transparent columnar or coarsely crystalline milky-white quartz, found in fissures or in large cavities inside the ore body, was crystallized between 219°C (the inner part of the crystals) and 193°C (the outer zone of the crystals).

The second and the third varieties, the pseudo-pyramidal and the short-columnar crested quartz respectively, were formed apparently between 168 and 144°C.

The fourth variety is the transparent needle-like quartz forming a brushwork on walls of fissures and cavities; its tentatively estimated mean temperature is 138°C, by secondary inclusions in quartz I.

The fifth variety is the finely crystalline quartz, replacing limestone and fluorite, deposited in the end period of the activity of the silica-bearing solutions at temperatures below 129°C.

Finally, the homogenization of inclusions in calcite, crystallized at the very end of the hydrothermal process, suggest temperatures of 96–70°C.

We gave the following brief characterization of the hydrothermal activity in this deposit in 1942, in our article [30, pp. 185–186]:

"The principal non-ore minerals were formed chiefly in consequence of a metasomatism of limestones brought about by powerful flows of solutions containing silica and fluorine. These solutions, arising from the intrusion through the numerous fissures in limestones antedating the mineralization, with the limestones being contemporaneous with the formation of the core of the anticline, were arrested by the Tournais shales functioning as a screening horizon. The solutions spread out under the shales, with the resulting intensive transformation of the limestones in the brecciated contact zone and the deposition of fluorspar, quartz, and other minerals. In the course of the replacement reactions with the limestones and of the formation of calcium fluoride, there was a liberation of large quantities of carbon dioxide with which the solutions became enriched. This served to increase reactivity of the solutions and the accompanying intensive leaching of the limestones in the zone of the deposit.

"Cavities produced in the limestones eventually became the natura reservoir-crystallizers as they were filled by the succeeding flow of silica and bicarbonate solutions. It is evident that these accessions to the cavities were *periodic* depending on the extent of the opening-up of fissures inside the ore. This filling resulted in a temporary conservation of the vugs and cessation of the in-flow of the solutions. The process was repeated severa times, it appears, with the resulting production of the six generations o fluorite. The temperature of the solutions was relatively low and it varied in different stages of the mineral genesis, depending on the degree of open ing of the fissures and intensity and concentration of the hydrotherma flows ascending from the intrusion."

Grushkin's subsequent geologic and mineralothermal investigation [29a] served substantially to refine these concepts of the deposit's origir He designed recently a very clear-cut and original pattern (Fig. 48) of th succession of crystallizations and temperatures in the formation of th hypogene minerals of the deposit. According to this pattern, *showin*

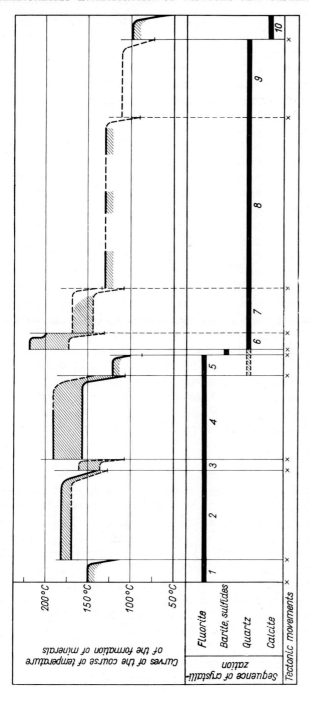

FIG. 48. Sequences of crystallization and temperatures of formation of hypogene minerals.

1. Dark-violet zoned fluorite
2. Violet zoned fluorite
3. Bluish transparent fluorite
4. Greenish fluorite
5. Pink fluorite
6. Columnar quartz
7. Crested quartz
8. Finely crystalline needle-like quartz
9. Hornfels-like quartz
10. Calcite (rhombohedron → scalenohedron → prism)

discontinuities in the deposit-forming process against the background of changing temperatures, the heavy line representing every mineral or every generation of the mineral is a relative quantitative expression of the proportion of the mineral constituent. The width of the shaded fields represents typical ranges of crystallization temperature of the minerals, including the relatively abrupt lowering at the end of the crystallization. Incidence of the tectonic disturbances causing renewed circulation of the hydrothermal solutions is indicated by crosses at the bottom of the diagram. Grushkin came recently to the following interesting conclusions, on consideration of the mineralothermometric data on the deposit:

"The beginnings of the ore-forming process were against the background of a general rise in the temperatures succeeded by their general and gradual lowering. The results suggest that the span of the temperatures, as indicated by the measurements, for every stage of the process, is broadened toward the breaking point between the rise and the fall of the temperatures shown in the pattern. This is indeed how it should be, on the assumption that the temperature spans of different stages of the ore-forming process depend on the difference between the temperature of the in-flowing solution and of the host rocks, at the given depth and the given stage of the process. The same factor may be responsible for the temperature differences of fluorite in different vugs at Kulikolon [32]. The ore-forming process was not a continuous one. Throughout its duration, the process involved a series of successive interruptions. The interruptions we identified corresponded either to a succession of one generation of a mineral by the next one or to a succession of one mineral by another one. For most of the generations (interruptions), the succession coincides with the appearance of [tectonic—V.P.S.] movements within the mineralized zone rejuvenating the process.

"Finally, the general shape of the temperature curve of any one of the generations, with its conspicuous falling-off toward the end of the crystallization, indicates a disturbance in the physico-chemical system, a depletion or a decrease in the concentrations of mineral-forming substances in the solution, and a disruption of the unity of the process" [29a].

Variations in the temperature regime of mineral-forming solutions, as we had already shown, cannot be classified. The different types of such variations are determined by the very multiplicity of environments of the formation of hypogene deposits. Nevertheless, the abrupt fall of temperature toward the end of the crystallization of a given mineral is one of the typical happenings arising on sudden changes in the mineral-forming environment as well as resulting from interruptions in the accession of hydrothermal solutions to sites of their activity.

Let us consider one more example, for the sake of comparison of the fluorite deposits of Central Asia with some others elsewhere.

Temperatures of formation of fluorite in Transbaykalia. We gave Yakzhin more than forty specimens of fluorite from different sources in the Transbaykalia. As it is well known, the origin of these deposits is explained by many foreign investigators (Norwood, Schaler, Emmons, Hornung, and others) by a downward movement of waters by which the vein materials were extracted [and segregated—V.P.S] from the surrounding rocks. Some others (Ulrich, Tanger) attribute the formation of these deposits to ascending waters originating in a magmatic hearth. In this latter view, however the mineral solutes, including fluorine, were acquired by the ascending waters from the surrounding rocks.

In any case, it is believed at this time that the fluorspar may be produced in highly variable environments, from pneumatolytic to epithermal, and even in cold-water sediments of marine basins.

The hydrothermal origin of the fluorite deposits of Transbaykalia is a long-established view based on the research of our scientists (P. P. Pilipenko, N. A. Smol'yanikov, A. V. Gulyayeva, A. A. Yakzhin, and others).

This view is fully and definitely sustained by the character of the homogenization of inclusions in fluorites from Transbaykalia involving a complete filling of the vacuoles with the liquid. However, we had proved the presence also of some essentially-liquid single-phase inclusions in the youngest generations of pink fluorites indicative of a cold-water or a tepid-water origin of the host crystals [37].

As to the conclusions by some of our investigators in regards to a pneumatolytic origin of the Kalanguy fluorites, they found no confirmation in our results on inclusions in minerals of this deposit.

The monotony of the vein minerals and the absence of well-faceted crystals in the samples we procured made our identifications of different genetic groups of inclusions extremely difficult. The hydrothermal origin of the crystals, nevertheless, was demonstrated sufficiently reliably and found to be in four stages: 255–200, 190–155, 140–135, and lower than 100°C. Thermometric investigations showed accordingly that the deposits in Transbaykalia belong to the medium-temperature and the low-temperature stages of hydrothermal mineral genesis. The Solonechnoye deposit and that of Konduy were found to belong to the high-medium stage, with average homogenization temperatures of 215–200°C and 255–250° and down to 155°C respectively.

Both medium-and low-temperature fluorites are found in the Otsoluy deposit. Thus its violet, colorless-pale, and light-green crystals show homogenization temperatures of 245–240, more than 215, and 160–155°C respectively. The homogenization temperatures of secondary inclusions in fluorites from all these deposits were 135–155°C. These inclusions were indicative of temperatures of the end-stages of the circulation of the hydrothermal solutions which had already ceased to play any important role in the deposition of the minerals.

The Abagaytuy deposit belongs to the low-temperature type, according to our data on inclusions in fluorites and barites from that source. Specifically, the temperatures of the green fluorites fluctuated in the vicinity of 190°C; the yellow barites showed about 180°C; the light-colored occasionally greenish crystals—160–155°C; the colorless and transparent crystals—140°C, and lower.

In the instance of the fluorites from Kalanguy, we not only failed to find any inclusions with the type II homogenization (see Chapter 7), but had proved that, on the whole, the Kalanguy temperatures were the lowest ones among the temperatures of the other deposits here considered. The highest homogenization temperatures of the Kalanguy fluorites were 165–160°C. Moreover, the pink and the yellow varieties of fluorspar deposited in the uppermost zone of the "cockades" contain single-phase essentially-liquid inclusions shown by us to be typical for minerals of the cold-water origin [37, p. 53].

If hydrothermal deposits are to be classified by their temperatures under a series of stages and phases, so that the medium-temperature stage is defined by the homogenization temperature from 350 to 200°C (phase 1 at 350–275°C; phase 2 at 275–200°C) and the low-temperature stage as from 200 to 50°C (phase 1 at 200–125°C; phase 2 at 125–50°C) we may suggest the following sequence in the formation of fluorites from Transbaykalia, on the temperature scale based upon the data we have obtained (Table 28):

TABLE 28

No. in sequence	Deposit	Medium-temperature		Low-temperature		Cold water
		phase 1	phase 2	phase 1	phase 2	
1	Konduy		—|————|—			
2	Otsoluy		—|————|—			
3	Solonechnoye		—|—|—|			
4	Abagaytuy			—|—|—|		
5	Kalanguy			—|————|——	——	

We had no opportunity to visit these deposits or to examine the reports on their exploration. It is possible also that mineral collections were incomplete. Just the same, it is unlikely that there will be any future changes in our fundamental conclusions to the effect that the fluorite deposits of Transbaykalia were formed beginning with phase 2 of the medium-temperature stage of the hydrothermal process and down to the stage of tepid-water or cold-water hydrotherms (Kalanguy).

On Temperatures and Other Problems of the
Formation of Quartz in Aldan

We examined the problems of origin and of classification of the sources of crystal quartz in Aldan and defined the genetic types of quartz-bearing vugs and caves in our earlier publications [33a, 34]. Prospecting and exploration for this odd type of deposit were discussed also at an earlier time [34a]. The experience justifying these publications was acquired in our previous studies, chiefly in the large territories of Pamir and Aldan.

We began our studies of the formation temperatures of these deposits in 1942, but the need of building the required body of data permitted publication so far of only fragmentary results pertinent to the problem. We shall omit here, for all practical purposes, the information on origin and geologic structure of the deposits in Aldan and in Pamir, because it may be found in the reports by Laz'ko [60 and others] and Morozenko [66], not to speak of our earlier publications. On our recommendation, Zakharchenko too [44] became involved in the research on the quartz of Pamir, in 1949; these studies revealed many interesting aspects of the temperatures of formation of these deposits. For these reasons, we are reporting here on temperatures of the formation of crystals quartz only in Aldan.

We are offering here only a most general character of the environments in which crystal quartz is formed in Pamir and in the Plita* of Aldan, as an introduction to the discussion of the temperatures of the mineral's crystallization based entirely on our publications already cited.

The quartz veins of Aldan are found in the Archaean quartzite series. In Pamir, they lie in granitoids, Paleozoic sandstones, and, more rarely, in Permian–Triassic porphyrites. The veins are associated invariably either with tectonic fissures or with zones of cleavage and fragmentation in the rocks.

The origin of the accumulations of crystal quartz are still obscure in the literature, up to the present time. Even less attention has been devoted to type definitions of crystal quartz veins and caves.

The principal types of quartz veins were represented by us, in 1945 [33a], schematically as follows:

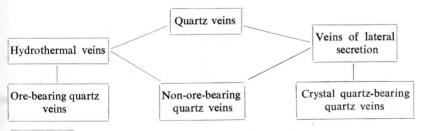

* Plita is a part a platform overlain by horizontally bedded sedimentary overburden [V.P.S.].

Two main groups of quartz veins are recognizable genetically by their mineral composition: hydrothermal veins produced by deposition of magmatic distillates, and lateral-secretion veins resulting from hydrochemical solution and redeposition of substances derived from host rocks by hot waters of different origins circulating in host rocks.

The typical features of ore-bearing, ore free, and crystal quartz-bearing quartz veins are summarized by us in Table 29.

TABLE 29

Indicators	Ore-bearing quartz veins	Ore-free quartz veins	Quartz veins with crystal quartz
1. Ore minerals	Ore minerals are present in economic concentrations	Ore minerals either absent or very sparsely disseminated	Ore minerals rare or absent in crystal quartz periphery
2. Cavities with crystal quartz	Generally absent; rarely small cavities with fine crystal quartz	Cavities with crystal quartz are found commonly inside the vein quartz	As a rule, cavities of appreciable size containing crystal quartz and other minerals
3. Vein-filling	Grayish white or tinted massive coalescent or porous quartz, occasionally of a highly varied texture	Milky-white occasionally glassy quartz, commonly uniformly granular, rarely crested or rod-like in texture. Vein carbonates, sericite, or chlorite present occasionally	Quartz does not form a continuous vein body; it forms only linings on walls of cavities and caves filled with crystal quartz and often also with clay
4. Contacts with host rocks	Sharply defined clear-cut contacts, as a rule; in the case of replacement, the banding of the veins becomes vague and tortuous and the host rocks bear evidence of alteration	Character of the contacts is determined by the host rocks and is variable accordingly	Contacts are uneven and tortuous. The quartz linings generally grade into the altered host rock

The ore-bearing crystal quartz veins are of no importance from the industrial point of view. The ore-free quartz veins are common and are important locally as sources of piezo-quartz, in different districts. The lateral secretion veins constitute valuable sources of piezo-quartz, as a rule.

A special type, *the Alpine-type of vein formation,* was recognized already for a long time in the Alps, by its characteristic geological environment, its mineral paragenesis, and the proved sequence in the order of crystallization, recurring uniformly in a large number of veins. The crystal quartz-bearing veins of lateral secretion origin in the Aldan resemble the Alpine veins, to some extent, while also showing certain distinctions, worthy of notice, as shown in Table 30.

Some of the special features of the Aldan crystal quartz veins are the results of the characteristic fissure-tectonics, and of an exceptionally high silica content of their highly uniform host rocks. This latter circumstance was conducive to the absolute predominance of crystal quartz over the other minerals of the veins.

The crystal quartz veins of Aldan were produced almost entirely by leaching of their host rocks with hot waters of diverse origin and by crystallization of the quartz from true solutions. "Metamorphogenic" waters, secreted during the metamorphism of the host rocks, appear to have played a major part in the formation of the veins.

TABLE 30

Indicators	Veins of Alpine type	Veins of Aldan
1. Host rocks	Diverse types containing 45 to 70 per cent silica	Very uniform quartzites containing more than 95 per cent silica
2. Mineralogic composition	Highly variable; up to 60 mineral species known	Highly uniform; not more than ten known mineral species
3. Relation to structures	The veins are associated with gently sloping drag fissures across the structures	The veins are associated with fissures and cleavage zones in the overburden of the structures; fissures and cleavage are nearly vertical, as a rule
4. Morphology and size of veins	Lens-like and, locally, rosary-like small veins not over 20 to 30 m long	Typical veins and vein zones are either very long, hundreds of meters, or constitute short vein bodies of indefinite shapes

The ore-free quartz veins are intermediate genetically between the ore-bearing hydrothermal veins and the crystal quartz veins of the Alpine type. They were formed, it appears, at an early stage, as the result of a deposition of silica gel in the fissures followed by a deposition of anhydrous silica in the cavities of a growing vein. The latter crystallized from true solutions and formed well-faceted crystals of perfect structure.

Diagenesis of the vein substance laid down in the first stage was very important in the development of cavities inside the veins and in the subsequent formation of the vugs of crystal quartz in these cavities, which took place in part from residual solutions, of low concentration.

Depending on origin and type of the crystal quartz veins, we proposed the following grouping of genetic and morphologic types of cavities serving as sites of the formation of crystal quartz (Table 31):

TABLE 31

Genetic type of cavity / Type of quartz vein	Diagenetic cavities inside veins	Tectonic fissure cavities	Caverns of leaching in cleavage zones of rocks
Ore-free quartz veins	1. Diagenetic; lens-like cavities	3. Lens-like cavities in dislocation fissures	
	2. Irregularly shaped cavities in incompletely filled fissures	4. Irregularly shaped cavities at intersections of fissures	
			5. Irregularly tubular caverns of leaching
Crystal quartz veins			6. Multi-chamber caves with caved-in roof

Despite the many measurements of the homogenization temperatures of inclusions in crystal quartz from Aldan collected at very different sources often at long distances from each other, the range of temperatures was found to be remarkably constant for the entire province.

Only in cases where the crystal quartz vein is situated in direct proximity to outcrops of pegmatites associated with Proterozoic granites was there a marked increase in homogenization temperatures of the inclusions in quartz and even *change in the type of homogenization*. The first fact is evidence of the unity of the hydrothermal metamorphism and the epithermal metamorphism in the south-western part of the Plita of Aldan, while the second one indicates a direct relationship between the intrusions of Proterozoic granite–pegmatites and the formation of some of the crystal quartz veins. While discussing examples of determinations of the lower and upper temperature limits of formation of crystals and druses of quartz earlier in the book (pp. 154–157) and the formation of crystals by discontinuous processes (p. 158–159), in ascertaining the unity of hydrothermal metamorphism of rocks and mineral genesis in fissure-veins, we have already made some use of the data we collected in the Aldan. Without going deeply into such details, we shall report here only the general results on homogenization temperatures of inclusions in quartz crystals from different mineralized sites, identified by their tentative names and scattered over an immense territory. These general results are summarized in Table 32.

The temperatures reported in Table 32 are cited without any corrections whatsoever and they represent therefore the minimum temperatures, in our summation of the principal thermometric results on crystals and crystal deposits of the Aldan.

Corrections for pressure are contingent on availability of clear-cut proof of (1) association of the deposit with derivates of a given intrusive body (by age and composition) and (2) the consequent estimation of thickness of the overburden at the time of the emergence of the intrusions and of the formation of the deposits.

As we know, there are many difficulties in the objective solution of such problems in the majority of deposits and districts. In the case of the Aldan, these problems are complicated further by the presence of the various expressions of the *Upper Archaean* intrusions described by D. S. Korzhinskii (normal alaskites, biotite granites, alkali-albite alaskites, leucocratic and biotite–hornblende granites, etc.), the presence of the *Proterozoic* granites and plagio–granites with widely distributed small intrusions of granite–pegmatites (Ye. M. Laz'ko, G. B. Mitich, and others), of monzonite–diabase–spessartite veins up to 100 km long, of *Post Cambrian* quartz–porphyries, *Post-Jurassic* syenite–porphyries, augite syenites, aegerine granites, and various nepheline syenites described by Yu. A. Bilibin.

As we see, the investigator has a wide choice here in deciding, if only by the age, with which particular intrusions he should connect the ore-free and the crystal quartz veins, situated almost entirely in quartzites of the middle part of the Upper Archaean. Naturally, this problem is important not only theoretically but also in prospecting in the field. It seems to us that an objective solution of this problem would be helped considerably by *the investigation of inclusions in minerals from veins in direct proximity as well as at a distance from the intrusions suspected of being genetically related to the veins in question. Variations in the homogenization temperatures and in the homogenization types of inclusions in minerals* from veins at different distances from the intrusives or, conversely, the absence of such variations, are the criteria in checking the accuracy of the hypothesis.

In our case, against the general backround of a fairly uniform low-temperature range of formations of crystal quartz, developed extensively in a large territory, in veins next to the bodies of porphyroid granite–pegmatites, we discovered abrupt variations in the homogenization types (from type I to type II), and in the homogenization temperatures of the

TABLE 32

Crystal No.	Source	Temperature series (°C)		Remarks
4	Western section (quarry 10)	310 to 270	Secondary inclusions and regeneration at 160–150 and 140°C (the first type)	Homogenization of primary inclusions accompanied by inversion [37]. Source close to a granite–pegmatite body.
43	Same	260		
24	Western section (quarry 8)	260		
48	Same	225–180–175		Homogenization as in type I. Some inclusions contain CO_2. Platelets of hematite and chlorite present occasionally in the outer zone. Crystal growth ceases at 130°C. Secondary inclusions at 124–109–80°C. Inclusions in the compromise growth faces at 138–130°C.
53	Same	210–190		
11	Same	200–190–182–170–160		
42	Same	217–204–192–180–170–162–151––148–142–140–130		
20/52	Central section (quarry 1)	180–155–140		
19	Eastern sections (quarries 3, 7, 9)	165–148–140–130		
41	Same	156–135		Temperature of 120°C in fine finger-like crystals
16	Same	195–180–175–155–150		Cream-colored crystals
41a	Same	190–185–180–150		
12	Khrustal'noye (quarry 15)	210–185–165–160		Interior of phantom crystal
	Same	130–120		Exterior of phantom crystal
30/31	Khrustal'noye (quarry 15)	180–170		Crystals with truncated termination. Regeneration of the formation at 140°C.
46	Same	230–210–150		
23	Same (vein 4)	220–190–155–150		
47	Sosnovskoye	210–155–140–130		*Crystals in graphite envelope*
35/2	Same	190–185–140		No envelope

TABLE 32 (continued)

Crystal No.	Source	Temperature series (°C)	Remarks
10	Sosedka	160–80	80°C in the outermost zone
18	Rovnoye	100–90–80	
13	Morion	260 (with inversion)–215–140 (homogenization of type I of secondary inclusions)	Creamy-colored ("pale") crystal from vein near granite pegmatite
33	Same	160–150–145–140	Thick prismatic colorless crystal from vein away from the pegmatite
46c	Slannikovoye	180–170	Short prismatic yellowish crystal
28	Novopustynnoye	Crystal I: 225–230–235 (type II homogenization at 400°C), 450° (type I homogenization) Crystal II: 220–225–230 (type II homogenization	Joined growth of two individual crystals separated by biotite, from a pegmatitic body. Homogenization of multiphase inclusions as in type I (Fig. 50)*
45	Same	180–160–150	From quartz vein
15	Pustynnoye	198–190–180–160–150–135	Some inclusions with CO_2
37	Zasontitskoye	220–190–172–160–150	Secondary inclusions at 100–90–80°C
38	Same (vein 5)	160–140–120–110	
36/44	Severnoye	235–210	Sylvite and hematite in some primary inclusions. Secondary inclusions at 120°C
26	Oyon	150–140	Secondary inclusions at 100°C
46/9	East Oyon	190–175–160–150–140	
No number	Yarogu, Vein 5	180–130–125	
No number	Yarogu, Vein 4	220–210	Scales of chlorite in inclusions Secondary inclusions at 110°C
29	Kurumkan	145–140–125	A curious transverse dissolution of edges and faces of crystals. Secondary inclusions at 90–80°C
39	Berezovoye	150–140–130–120	Three-phase inclusions with sylvite also present
47a	Avilova	210–205–200–190	
40	Kilerchi	212–200–186–182 160–148–140–132	First generation of crystals. Second generation of crystals, 1st epoch

* Probably a misprint for Fig. 49 [Ed.].

TABLE 32 (continued)

Crystal No.	Source	Temperature series (°C)	Remarks
No number	Olekma	128–120–115–102–92 190–170	Second generation of crystals, 2nd epoch

inclusions. This is particularly conspicuous on the western flank of one of the deposits and in the eastern part of the Morion vein (see Table 32, specimens 4 and 13).

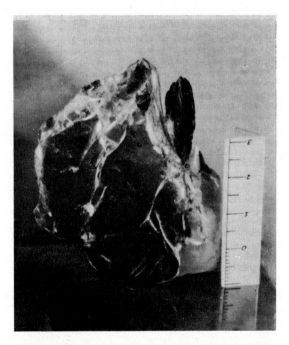

FIG. 49. Crystal of biotite grown between two crystals of quartz.

Specimen No. 28 (Fig. 49) extracted from a vug in the Novopustyn-noye pegmatitic body is especially interesting. We see a joined growth of two individuals of crystals quartz between which, at one stage in their growth, a crystal of biotite began growing. Both of the crystal quartz individuals show type II gaseous homogenization of their inclusions, the earliest one in the general process of the alteration of magmatic derivatives, with the temperature range of 220–235°C.* Later on, when the mineral-forming environment was transformed from a gaseous solution into a liquid aqueous solution, there developed hydrothermal inclusions in healed fissures in the crystal, secondary with respect to the crystal core, with homogenization temperatures exceeding 450°C.

We recognize that *this is the very first experiment in the application of the homogenization types and temperatures of inclusions in minerals in the determination of their genetic kinship with intrusives.* These humble facts, however, still act as a proof of the relationship between the crystal quartz accumulations in Aldan and the Proterozoic (Pre-Cambrian) intrusions of granites and of their pegmatitic bodies.

Thus we may assume that a certain part of the Proterozoic rocks, with an average thickness of 750 m, was the top horizon of the overburden of the deposits. On the other hand, not knowing of the Pre-Proterozoic erosion of the Upper Archaean rocks in every particular case, we have no way of finding an expression, in definite numbers, for the depths at which the deposits were formed and to arrive, in such manner, at the possible pressure correction, so as to obtain the true temperatures on the basis of observed homogenization temperatures of the liquid inclusions. If we consider the complete absence of certain upper series of the Upper Archaean in the region (for example, the Charokitovaya series), the Pre-Proterozoic erosion becomes appreciable indeed. Further evidence to the same effect is found also in the positions of the present outcrops of the Proterozoic rocks on the lower course of the Chug River and on the left bank of the Yarog River resting on most highly diverse horizons of the Upper Archaean, including the middle-Upper Archaean horizons. These geologic findings limit the estimate of the thickness of cover at not more than 2 or 3 km.

Thus even the most exacting corrections for pressure, when they become feasible and necessary, could scarcely have any serious effect on the still fairly low temperatures of the formation we have determined for the crystal quartz in the Aldan.

It is worthy of note that there is no substantial difference in the temperatures of veins containing very little of the milky-white quartz (the veins produced by impoverished hydrothermal fluids and veins of the "Alpine" type) and the "ore-free" veins composed chiefly of milky-white quartz (the Nimger mineralized group). All of the region's most important deposits were formed between 235 and 120°C.

Two generations of crystal quartz are indicated at the Kholodnoye; higher than 250°C and lower than 225°C. The latter generation had several epochs of crystal quartz. The last one of these epochs, in the form of

---

* The lower the homogenization temperature of this type (II), the more "high-temperature" is the pneumatolytic mineral, in the sense of being the earlier one in the general process of the mineral genesis (see the next section of the book).

fine crystals, took place at 130–80°C, at the time when the larger and older crystals were forming their secondary inclusions and when the terminations of the druses were completing their growth. Curiously, at the Sosnovoye, *graphite was being laid down from aqueous solutions, as an envelope around the crystals.*

The majority of the crystals at the Khrustal'noye were formed during the first phase, at 210 to 160°C. The completion of their growth and their regeneration were accomplished later, during the second phase, at 140–120°C.

We have already discussed (pp. 159–160) the definitely established generations of quartz at the Kilerchi, with the two epochs of crystals in the second phase of the mineral genesis, and the corresponding temperatures were reported in Table 32.

Different deposits had different ranges of temperatures of their generations and epochs of quartz (narrow or wide as they might be) and *the rate of the crystallization,* determined apparently by the rate of temperature decrease, was one of the expressions of their individuality.

On the Temperatures of Formation of Certain Lead–Zinc Deposits

Nagol'nyi Kryazh. Notwithstanding the fact that after Samoylov's [80] brilliant mineralogic investigations, most of the researchers expressed themselves in favor of a juvenile origin of these ores, rather than of their infiltrational origin, the problem is still "unsupported by any adequate documentation" [102].

The common arguments in favor of such origin of the deposit include the localization of the ore in certain definite fissures, the sulfide (not sulfate) composition of the ore, the presence of milky-white quartz which depends allegedly on gas in the solution that can be injected only by juvenile processes, etc. Obviously, this sort of proof of a hypogene origin of ore deposits does not look particularly convincing to everyone.

On the assumption of a hydrothermal origin of the mineralization in the Nagol'nyi Kryazh, some investigators attempted also to determine the possible temperatures of the mineral genesis. Taking the prismatic form of the quartz crystals of the deposit as their guide (Maucher's type III), some of the investigators estimated these temperatures at 365–250°C. Others, in the wake of Niggli, because of the presence of iron-poor and cadmium-poor sphalerite, ascribed 200–400°C as the temperature of formation of the deposit. Still others (K. N. Vifanskii), without any proof whatsoever, determined the temperatures of ore deposition as 150-200°C.

One may admit just as well, on the whole, that such debates and contradictory views of origins of mineral deposits were and still are rather common. They are ended generally by some arbitrary victory, on either side, so that the most eminent geologists join the winner without having contributed the least bit (or nearly nothing) of new evidence in support of the victorious side. As we know, however, appraisals of the origin of mineral deposits have not merely an academic but also a very practical interest. It seems to us that personal opinions in such problems may be eliminated only by studies of inclusions in the minerals, so as to determine objectively the state of aggregation and the temperatures of the mineral-forming solutions.

With this purpose in mind, we endeavored to obtain at least some data on the Nagol'nyi Kryazh, limited as it might be. As one may see, the existing veins in regard to a hypogene origin of the ores and the tempera-ture range of the solutions, at least in the instance of the high-temperature focus of the mineral genesis, the Ostryy Bugor, were an encouragement for the assumption that not only hydrothermal but also pneumatolytic solutions were participating in the formation of the ore deposits in the area. Our investigations of homogenization of inclusions in minerals from the Nagol'nyi Kryazh, highly preliminary as they are, suggest only a hydrothermal origin of the deposits.

All of the inclusions, two-phase and heterogenous at room tempera-tures, would homogenize by filling their vacuoles by the liquid phase. As will be shown later, one would have some evidence in support of the vadose origin of the ores, were there any primary inclusions in the miner-als that appear homogeneous at room temperatures.

Figure 50 shows a vein quartz overgrown by crystal quartz. No defi-nite inclusions could be detected in the milky-white quartz from the banded vein. A chainwork of clearly defined primary inclusions, along the growth course of the crystal termination, was found in the cut section through the crystal on the left, parallel to the crystal's long axis. Four inclusions near the present termination of the crystal gave a temperature of 110°C; the more deeply seated inclusions gave 115°C; inclusions in the core of the crystal (at the level of the edges between the rhombohedron and the prism) gave 120°C.

We had no opportunity to estimate the upper limit of the tempera-tures at which the druse crystals of quartz began their growth, but their lower limit, 110°C, could be determined rather exactly. Crystal quartz of the small druse in the center of the specimen crystallized at 70–88°C (as appraised by secondary inclusions in the quartz "mat" under the crystals). Other specimens of crystal quartz from Yesaulovka gave homogenization temperatures of 120–130°C for their primary inclusions.

The determined homogenization temperatures of primary inclusions in quartz crystal overgrown by ankerite, from Nagol'naya Tarasovka, were 198–201°C. The same source contains also transparent quartz of an earlier generation, with homogenization temperatures of primary inclusions at 115–117–130–140°C.

Multiphase inclusions and complex (with CO_2) inclusions may be found in quartz crystals from Ostryi Bugor. There is a multitude of

FIG. 50. Quartz druse from veins of Nagol'nyi Kryazh.

two-phase and multiphase microinclusions* in milky-white quartz from the Ventilyatsionnaya and the Varvara Tunnels, the largest ones of which homogenize at 195–200–210–220°C. Later generations of faceted quartz crystals are also found here, with inclusion homogenization temperatures of 180–170–160°C and 140–130–120–110°C. Our data on the temperatures of formation of the sulfides are very limited, so far.

Crystal quartz from the Zhuravka Gulley, formed simultaneously with galena, gave temperatures of 130–140°C. The minimum temperature of 115°C was established for quartz overgrown by a transparent sphalerite (Nizhnii Nagol'chik), while the temperature for the *sphalerite* itself was 105°C. *Pyrite* grows locally on top of the sections of the quartz crystals whose temperature was indicated as 115–150°C.

The ankerite from Yesaulovka, with small needles of boulangerite, has measured temperatures of 110–150°C. This leads us to believe that the boulangerite was crystallized at a temperature somewhat higher than 150°C.

---

* Unfortunately we have been unable so far to procure quartz from the high temperature fraction.

We have indeed very few objective data for an appraisal of the depth of the deposition of the ore within the confines of the Nagol'nyi Kryazh. However, if we accept Tanatar's calculations [102] of a depth of about 2000 or 2500 m, the possible correction for pressure could not exceed the determined temperatures by more than 30 or 40°C. The previously cited initial research data on the state of aggregation and the temperatures justify even now the conclusion to the effect that the polymetallic mineralization in the Nagol'nyi Kryazh was caused, in the main, by low-temperature *hydrothermal* solutions.

A deposit in the Soviet Far East. The deposit presently to be discussed had been investigated in sufficient detail by a whole series of scientists (V. I. Smirnov, Ye. A. Radkevich, F. V. Kozlov, and others). Its host rocks are chiefly Upper Triassic limestones overlain by clastic materials and by effusive rocks. The depth at which the deposit formed did not exceed 1 km, according to the majority of the investigators. The deposit's mineralogic composition is highly diversified, apparently as the result of a multistage development.

Two of the stages are recognized definitely by all of the investigators, the early and the late one, involving deposition of silicates and of ores respectively. An odd kind of a deposition of minerals in cavities, locally called "vents", had also accompanied the late stage. Rather abundant and diverse materials representing chiefly the late stage of the mineralization were placed at our disposal by Kozlov, for a thermometric examination.

Specifically, we received samples of weakly mineralized quartz–datolite–calcite ores developed directly after the deposition of the bulk of the silicates in skarn and tactite [86] bodies; samples of quartz–calcite veins containing the bulk of the lead–zinc ores; finally, some well-faceted minerals from the "vents" showing no evidence of any direct association with the deposition of the ores.

Several investigators became engaged in correlation of these diverse materials. The problem was found to be extremely difficult, because some members of the mineral groups were found to be disassociated spatially and because the very conspicuous and striking multiplicity of crystallographic forms of one and the same mineral in the deposit. Quartz and calcite, the two most common vein minerals, showed a typical multiplicity of forms. It was by these minerals, as well as by axinite, datolite, and apophyllite that our principal attention was directed to the application of thermometric methods in the problem. We made more than 400 determinations of homogenization temperatures of the inclusions, in different specimens, by which we established some fairly definite temperature series for some of the minerals. The main results of these studies are summarized in Table 33 (p. 224).

TABLE 33

Speci-men No.	Minerals and para-genesis in brief	Homogenization temperatures (°C)		Remarks
		primary and pseudo-secondary inclusions	secondary inclusions	
2	(1) Granular quartz lining on hedenber-gite	300–290–280	135–130–125	With galena and chalcopyrite
	(2) Prismatic quartz	285–260–240–220–200	122–115–112	Sulfides embedded in outer zone of prismatic quartz
	(3) Arsenopyrite, chalcopyrite	—	—	—
	(4) "Rash" of finest quartz crystals	135–125–115	—	Di-pyramidal shape of crystals is indicated
	(5) Calcite with em-bedded galena and sphalerite	145–130–125	120–115	Blunt rhombohe-dral forms pre-sent
	(6) Ore-free calcite	120–115–112	90–80	
3	Transparent apohyl-lite from Verkhnii Rudnik	Single-phase inclusions	—	Turns white, like porcelain, on heat-ing to 200°C
4	Quartz–datolite rock from Khrustal'nyi Otvod	540 and higher	245–240–220–210	Measured in quartz
5	(1) Calcite as basal rhombohedron	265–260–220	140–120	Volume of gas bubble in prim-ary inclusions 35–37 per cent
	(2) Film of colloidal substance	—	—	Over dissolved surface of calcite
	(3) Short prismatic quartz	190–180	—	
6	Late scalenohedron of calcite from Ver-khnii Rudnik	105–102–100–82–76–70–68–61–54	Single-phase	
8	(1) Granular quartz	285–280	—	
	(2) Calcite, basal rhombohedron	210–170	140–130	
	(3) Short prismatic quartz	198–187–150	100–90	Terminations of crystals look like warts covered by a rash of di-pyramidal quartz

TABLE 33 (continued)

Speci-men No.	Minerals and para-genesis in brief	Homogenization temperatures (°C)		Remarks
		primary and pseudo-secondary inclusions	secondary inclusions	
	(4) Calcite; a blunt-ed rhombohedron (completely twinned)	170–140–135–130–128	90; single-phase inclusions also present	
	(5) A "rash" of di-pyramidal quartz	100–90	—	
36	Axinite from a skarn rock	—	280 and higher	
40	Thick prismatic quartz (fine crystals from a small cavity)	230–220	—	
41	Platy calcite	285–280–278–275	250	
42	Phantom quartz crystal			
	(1) Axial, long pris-matic	280–250	—	
	(2) Axial, short pris-matic	200–150	127–108–86	
	(3) Di-pyramidal quartz	130–100	—	
43	Calcite (blunted rhombohedron, prism)	140–135–130–125–110	Single-phase	
45	Scalenohedron with prism	110	—	
47	"Branched" calcite	50–38	Single-phase	38°C for a single inclusion with an extremely small bubble
49	Scalenohedron, transparent, from an ilvaite–datolite association	110–85	Single-phase	
251	Quartz pseudo-morphs after "pa-per spar" (calcite) in skarn bodies	244–220–215–171–158–150	100	
261	Quartz–datolite rock	320–300	220–210	Measurements on quartz with very small inclu-sions

TABLE 33 (continued)

Speci-men No.	Minerals and para-genesis in brief	Homogenization temperatures (°C)		Remarks
		primary and pseudo-secondary inclusions	secondary inclusions	
554	Crystal of quartz with zones and with multinucle-ated growth	—	—	From cavities in hedenbergite from Verkhnii Rudnik. Over-growth on white quartz
	(1) Central section growing on white quartz	300–275–260–240	130–120–110–105–90	
	(2) Central section; solution effects	190–180–152	—	
	(3) Outer section of the multinucle-ated crystal	120–110–100	—	
604	Short columnar crystals of quartz in skarns	—	—	From Verkhnii Rudnik
	(1) Base of crystals	290	—	
	(2) Crystal quartz with solution cap ("hood")	235–225–220	—	
	(3) A "rounding-out" termination	140	—	
785	Short columnar quartz	210–150	—	

The previously discussed examples of calcite crystal growth, with interruptions and re-solution (Fig. 28), of the phantom crystal of "di-pyramidal" quartz (Fig. 33), of "checkered" or "feathery" quartz (Fig. 34), of the prismatic crystal quartz in paragenesis with sulfides and calcite (Fig. 36), of the quartz pseudomorph after "paper spar" (Fig. 39), of the calcite twins (Fig. 41), of the datolite and apophyllite crystals (Figs. 42 and 43)—they all belong to the deposit here discussed and help to simplify our problem accordingly. With the aid of these data and of the data previously tabulated it becomes possible even now to offer a general characterization of the crystallization sequence and of the temperatures at which the minerals of the deposit were formed.

The earliest sub-stage of the silicate mineralization was represented in the order of crystallization by hedenbergite and ilvaite, garnet and epidote, late hedenbergite and early datolite, axinite and andradite; our data are very scarce on these materials. Inclusions in these earliest minerals are extremely small, so that our measurements were not too satisfactory at the ordinary microscopic magnifications we employed. The homogenization of inclusions in green garnets consisted of a filling of the vacuole with the gaseous phase (homogenization type II), while inclusions in axinite, possibly secondary, would homogenize in the liquid phase, as in type I [37] at temperatures exceeding 280°C.

We succeeded in making exact measurements only in quartz whose inclusions homogenized by the gas filling the entire vacuole at 540°C and still higher temperatures. In the main, this stage of mineralization was apparently pneumatolytic. On the other hand, quartz from the quartz–datolite association gave temperatures of 300–320°C, and higher, with the homogenization consisting obviously of a complete filling of the vacuoles by the liquid. Secondary inclusions in the crystal showed temperatures of 245–210°C. Insofar as this quartz, formed after the deposition of the bulk of the silicates and some associated early quartz, is generally contemporaneous in time of crystallization with granular crystalline datolite, the quartz temperatures may be indicative also of the lower temperature limit of crystallization of the datolite. Fairly large crystals of *platy* calcite, in the same association gave type I homogenization temperatures of 275–280–285°C.

Thus the temperature range in which the hydrothermal quartz–datolite association has developed may be defined as 275–320°C, and somewhat higher.

The vein minerals accompanying the deposition of the ores may be arranged in the following sequence, by the homogenization temperatures of their inclusions:

Crystalline–granular lining on quartz I	280–300°C and higher
Platy calcite I	285–275°C
Long prismatic quartz II overgrowing quartz I	285–240°C
Calcite II, as basal rhombohedron	265–210°C
Gel-like substances	240–230°C
Short columnar or thick prismatic quartz III (the rounding out of the long prismatic quartz, Fig. 52)	230–150°C
Calcite III, as blunted rhombohedron	170–125°C
Gel-like substances	150–130°C

These data may lead to the conclusion that the three morphologic varieties of calcite and quartz, I–II–III, followed each other in the sequence of their deposition but that they are practically contemporaneous. In parallel with the deposition of quartz and calcite, within a wide range of temperature from 300 to 125°C, there was also a synchronous deposition of the bulk of the sulfides, together with granular crystalline quartz and calcite.

The mineral-forming process took place with interruptions in its gradual character resulting in the successions of crystallographic forms and in

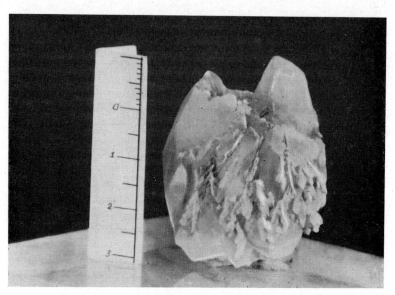

FIG. 51. Low-temperature scalenohedral and "branched" calcite.

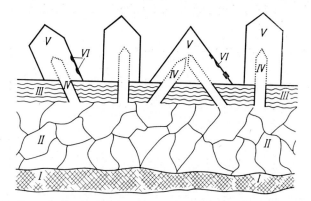

FIG. 52. Pattern of interrelations of long prismatic and short prismatic quartz.

I Ray-like hedenbergite   IV Long prismatic quartz
II Granular quartz   V Short prismatic quartz
III Gel-like substance   VI Ilvaite (late) *

* IV, V, and VI corrected from original misprints [Ed.].

the deposition of the gel-like substances during the interruptions. For example, the interrelations of quartz II and III are especially illustrative, as shown in Fig. 52, and have no need of supplementary explanations.

The prismatic quartz III was subjected later to solution and regeneration by the deposition of the multinucleated quartz IV ("checkered" or "feathery" quartz, Fig. 34) at 130–90°C. The gel-like substances were

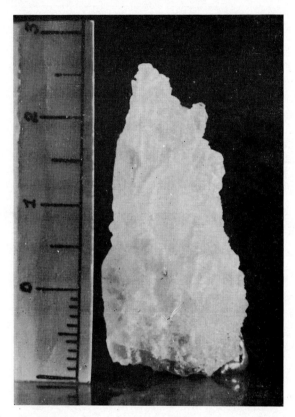

FIG. 53. Complex form of a crystal of low-temperature calcite.

deposited prior to that and even concurrently. Elsewhere, simultaneously with the "checkered" quartz, the di-pyramidal quartz was being deposited, but from the already pure and true solutions, in the form of a "coat" over the prismatic quartz crystals (Fig. 33) or of a fine "rash" of quartz (Fig. 36).

Calcite IV, in the form of a blunted rhombohedron or of a prism–scalenohedron combination, was deposited together with this quartz.

Beginning with the temperatures of 110–105°C, there was crystallization of late ilvaite II and of the scalenohedral calcite V, in combinations with a prism, rhombohedra, and a di-pyramid (Fig. 41), as well as of calcites of highly involved forms (Figs. 51 and 53). The lowermost of the established temperature limits of crystallization of these calcites is 38°C.*

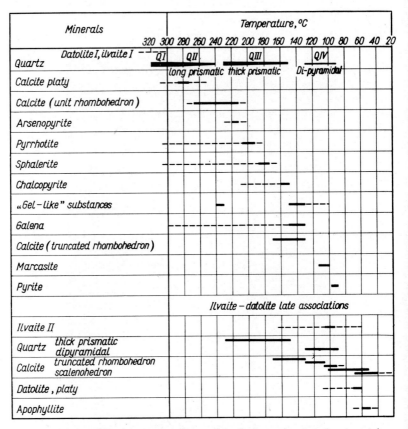

Fig. 54. Crystallization temperatures of hydrothermal minerals at certain lead-zinc deposits in the Soviet Far East ("DVK").

It seems that the crystallization of large transparent individuals of platy datolite II, with its solid inclusions and the multitude of single-phase liquid inclusions (Fig. 42), began simultaneously with that of calcite V, or a trifle earlier. The two-phase inclusions gave temperatures of 110°C, and lower. After the datolite and concurrently with the late forms of calcite V, there was crystallization of an entirely transparent apophyllite containing single-phase liquid inclusions only (Fig. 43).

---

* Only in one single case did we find an extremely rare inclusion with a very small "pinpoint" gas bubble which disappeared at that temperature.

Such is the history of the formation of minerals in the deposits of the Tetyukhe Group, in its main features, brought to light with the aid of our method of thermometric investigation. Figure 54 represents our data in the form of a paragenetic table of the minerals of the deposits in the framework of the temperatures that are nearly true.

The next figure (Fig. 55) shows the sequence of crystallographic forms of quartz and calcite in relation to the decreasing temperatures of the mother liquor. As one may see, the determined homogenization temperatures do not agree with the temperatures assigned to the different forms of these minerals by Kalb [190] and Maucher [191], the fathers of the morphogenetic method in mineralogical thermometry.

It appears that standard schemes of universal validity fail to grasp the multiform variety of natural phenomena.

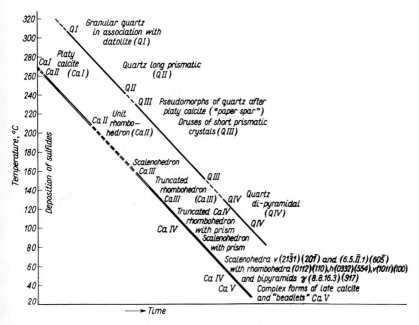

FIG. 55. Pattern of evolution of crystallographic forms of hydrothermal vein minerals in relation to decreasing temperatures of solutions.
Symbols: – – – quartz; ==== calcite.

We had no opportunity to visit the sources of our test materials and to become acquainted with the detailed reports on mineralogy of these deposits. Kozlov, who placed these materials at our disposal, provided us only with very fragmentary information on their mineralogenetic sequences. Such circumstances will enable geologists who are personally acquainted with this group of mineral deposits to make objective evaluations of reliability of the method we employed.

Particularly important is the combination of the thermometric studies with the methods of determination of the state of aggregation of the solutions, as discussed in the next chapter. We had to run somewhat ahead of the discussion already, in several specific cases, for the sake of illustrations of the usefulness of this combination.

CHAPTER 7

Methods and Results of Research on State of Aggregation of Mineral-forming Solutions

ESSENCE AND SIGNIFICANCE OF THE METHODS

In the course of the development of the previously described "visual" method of determining the temperatures (the method of empirical curves), we proceeded from measurements of stable phase-ratios in inclusions at room temperatures to measurements of every variation in these ratios brought about by heating the inclusions. Because the apparatus we had built was adapted for this type of work within a wide range of the temperatures, it did not take a long time to discover substantial differences in the course of the homogenization of inclusions in minerals of different origins. These distinctions were represented, for the first time, in diagrams of the types of homogenization of mineral-forming solutions included in topazes [37, p. 45].

Further work in ascertaining the course of homogenization of inclusions in other minerals from geologically different sources confirmed definitively that these new homogenization types and variants have a general validity.

It developed that in topaz, beryl and tourmaline of pegmatitic veins and deposits in contacts with or in proximity to intrusions, the homogenization of primary inclusions by heat is made effective by the filling of the vacuoles by the gas and not by the liquid as in the case of minerals from ordinary hydrothermal deposits. It was shown, moreover, that the filling of the inclusion's vacuole with gas, as the result of heating, does not always occur in the same manner.

All these observations led to the necessity of measuring the phase ratios in the inclusions simultaneously with observing the progress of the homogenization. The required determinations are made under the microscope, with the aid of the thermochamber and of the eyepiece micrometer.

Elongated tubular inclusions (see p. 122), suited for linear measurements, are selected for the purpose. The initial phase ratios (at room temperature) are determined accurately prior to the experiment, whereupon, while the heating is on, variations in the phase ratios are determined after every 30 or 50°C increase in the temperature. The observations are generally concerned with contractions or expansions of the gas bubble, as

[233]

indicated by the number of micrometer divisions at the given temperature as against the initial one. It is possible occasionally to make simultaneous measurements of one or two solid phases, if present in the inclusion. After completion of the homogenization, the results are calculated as percentages and the experiment is repeated, as a control.

These investigations require a very slow heating, pauses in heating, and repeated measurements of every registered temperature, for the sake of accuracy of the results. The determined points are plotted on a temperature–volume (gas or liquid) diagram.* The points are joined to yield different curves, the objective expressions of the original state of the dynamic mineral-forming environment. The general appearance of the curves is not affected by the rate of the heating.

It develops that four types and shapes of homogenization curves are typical of the four definite ranges of variation in the phase ratios of primary and pseudo-secondary inclusions at room temperatures. These four ranges of variation represent the clearly defined successive stages of the mineral-forming process.

Thus the substance of the method here proposed consists of ascertaining the course of homogenization of inclusions, expressed as curves typical of minerals of different origins in geologically different depositional environments. *A mineral reveals objectively its identification with a given stage (and sub-stage) of variations in the mineral-forming solution of a state of aggregation, by the course of homogenization of its primary and pseudo-secondary inclusions.*

We endeavored to demonstrate in the preceding section of this book the need of a purposeful orientation in the use of the homogenization method, in systematic successive examinations of inclusions *in different growth zones of a mineral,* in order to trace variations in the temperature regime of the solution. This approach to the utilization of inclusions in the capacity of self-registering thermometers, the first one of its kind, is the goal of the method of thermometric analysis we proposed.

As one may see, however, this method by itself does not yet guarantee discoveries of multiform orderly relationships in natural mineral genesis. It is not enough to determine only the final temperature of homogenization. One must follow the progress of the homogenization, that is, the direction of the sequence of variations in the phase ratio under the influence of the applied heat. It is necessary also, on the temperature scale, to watch the *rate of the heterogenization* of solutions homogenized by heat. A very rapid, nearly instantaneous appearance of the gaseous phase in a liquid inclusion or of the liquid phase in a gas–liquid inclusion may be accompanied occasionally by a boiling of the solution 2 or 3°C below

---

* Preparation of such diagrams is explained below.

the point of the homogenization. Such boiling is an indication that the mother liquor was sealed in the mineral at a temperature in the vicinity of the condensation of the gas (vapor) into liquid, so that even a small lowering of the pressure may cause the liquor to boil.*

The investigator must not be indifferent to the problem as to what particular phase and in what particular manner the inclusion homogenizes, or to the features of the inclusion's heterogenization. It was for that very reason that we proposed still another method of examination of inclusions aimed at ascertaining the state of aggregation of mineral-forming solutions sealed hermetically in the crystal's pores.

The main results obtained by the latter method are considered later in this book, with the use of concrete examples of the inclusion studies in topaz and quartz from different sources.

THE COURSE OF HOMOGENIZATION OF INCLUSIONS IN TOPAZ

There is an appreciable degree of variation in the phase ratios and in gas-filling coefficients among primary, pseudo-secondary, and secondary inclusions in topaz from Volynia and from other sources. The gas bubble in primary inclusions generally occupies more than one half of the inclusion's total volume. Multiphase inclusions of essentially-liquid solutions are found chiefly in pseudo-secondary and secondary inclusions (Plate VII, 1–4).

In the identification of the genetic types of inclusions, the highest reliability may be attained, of course, only in the instance of the intergrown well-faceted topaz crystals (Fig. 56) in which secondary inclusions intersect the compromise growth surfaces. Inside these multiphase inclusions one may see under the microscope, as a rule, six or more different crystals (potassium and sodium chlorides and fluorides and apparently also various compounds of aluminum, silica, etc.) (Fig. 57).

Identification and study of such "captive" minerals involves very serious difficulties, as was already discussed (pp. 58–59). In order to avoid errors, we shall identify them tentatively only by numbers, arranged in decreasing order of their volume ratios at 20–30°C.

Plate VI, 1 shows a large black bubble and, above the bubble, an isotropic crystal "I" of a nearly cubical habit; mineral "II", to the left of the crystal is commonly rounded and isotropic.† The upper corner of

---

* Large quantities of dissolved carbon dioxide in a liquid or a "gas–liquid" solution also may cause the solution to boil.

† The indices of refraction were determined with the aid of immersion fluids injected into the inclusions. The results were as follows: Crystal I, $N = 1.549 \pm 0.001$; Crystal II, $N = 1.490 \pm 0.001$. This leads us to believe that Crystal I is halite and Crystal II is sylvite.

the inclusion contains an anisotropic mineral "III", $\gamma = 1.600$, $\alpha = 1.590$ ± 0.001. Two small six-sided crystals of the inner mineral IV are visible by the lower left corner of crystal I on top of which there is a growth of a

FIG. 56. Intergrowth of topaz crystals.

black mineral V, possibly an ore mineral, as in the case illustrated by Plate VII, 4.

A prismatic transparent slightly bluish anisotropic mineral VI grows on the bottom of crystal II. All of these inner "captive" minerals and the gas bubble are in equilibrium with the saturated liquid mother liquor filling the inclusion. This solution, of course, is in equilibrium also with the walls of its vacuole on which some amount of substance cognate to the host crystal had been deposited on cooling.

We assembled prepared sections that would permit us to observe, in one and the same zone of the topaz crystal, both large inclusions (up to 0.25 mm long) and relatively small but tubular inclusions in which all of the phases were situated in a row, so to speak. A simultaneous homogenization of both large and small inclusions was a proof of their identity. The measurements were made during the homogenization at regular temperature intervals, indicative of the progressive changes in the phase ratios. Such multiphase inclusions, homogenizing at 300–310°C, had the following phase ratios in their initial stage (at ordinary temperature): 50 per cent aqueous solution; 19.6 per cent gas bubble; 25.4 per cent solid phases. The included crystals had the following volumes, as percentages of the total volume of

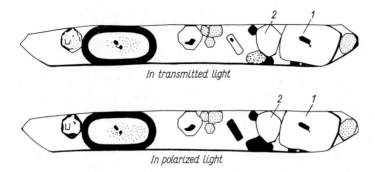

In transmitted light

In polarized light

The course of homogenization in multiphase inclusions

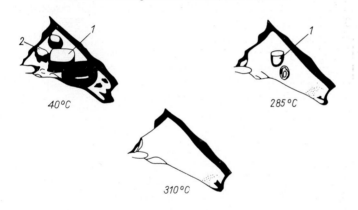

40°C

285°C

310°C

Different phase ratios in inclusions

1. Halite
2. Sylvite

FIG. 57. Multiphase inclusions in topaz crystals from Volynia. Well-faceted multiphase inclusion with a captive mineral in Volynian topaz. Dimensions; length 2.6 mm, width 0.7 mm

the solid phase: 60 per cent I; 21 per cent II; 12 per cent III; 4–4.2 per cent IV; 1.5 per cent V; 1.3 per cent VI.

In the experiment documented by Plates V and VI, in inclusions V, 1 and VI, 1 the common phase ratios at 40°C were found to be as follows: 56.5 per cent saturated aqueous solutions; 19.6 per cent gas bubble; 14.9 per cent I; 5 per cent II; 3 per cent III; 1 per cent IV; 0.55 per cent V; 0.45 per cent VI. The temperature rose only from 20 to 40°C, after the thermochamber was closed. Even this slight warming was sufficient, however, to produce some rounding of the edges of crystal I whose original appearance was as shown in Plate VII, 2.

We succeeded in measuring only the gaseous phase and solid phase I during the homogenization. Photomicrographs of the prepared section were taken concurrently, as control-records of the measurements.

In the photomicrographs, the gas bubble of the tubular inclusion is situated between the following lines of the scale: in Plate V, 1—between 3.5 and 4, with the solid phase (white) at 5 (the vertical thread); in Plates V, 2, 3 and 4—at 5 to 5.5 and 6.5 to 7 respectively. These phases show clearly in Plate VI, 1–4, so that one may see that the homogenization was made effective by a progressive decrease in the volume of the gas bubble with the accompanying dissolution of the solid phases. The course of the homogenization by heat is indicated by the results summarized in Table 34.

The times of the observations (Table 34, column 1) correspond to the following photomicrograph numbers: 1—Plates V and VI, 1; 3—Plates V, 2 and VI, 2; 4—Plates V, 3 and VI, 3; 6—Plates V, 4 and VI, 4. In the range from 70 to 100°C, crystals II, III, and VI were melted first; crystals IV and V successively decreased in their size and became dissolved completely at 290–310°C. The halite crystal was the last one to go into solution or to melt,* at 310°C, and the inclusion was left with its liquid phase only.

During the restoration of the heterogeneous state of the inclusion, on cooling to 290°C, the crystal I began to grow, together with the reappear-

TABLE 34

Obser-vation No.	Tempera-ture (°C)	Gas (%)	Solid phase (%)	Obser-vation No.	Tempera-ture (°C)	Gas (%)	Solid phase (%)
1	40	19.9	14.9	6	275	2.5	3.4
2	100	15.6	12.75	7	280	2.2	3.0
3	150	12.25	10.2	8	290	1.0	2.5
4	180	10.0	8.6	9	300	0.0	1.5
5	250	5.0	5.0	10	310	0.0	0.0

* There is no fundamental difference between solution and melting in the presence of the liquid phase.

ance of the gas bubble, and acquired at once its sharp edges and flat faces, whereupon the other solid phases also began to crystallize, in the reverse sequence of their dissolution. The more rapid was the cooling, the more disorderly was the separation of the captive crystals, and the less perfect their crystalline form. We failed to restore the inclusion exactly to its original state, with the characteristic crystal perfection of its captive minerals, as the rate of cooling in nature must be immeasurably slower. However, the phase ratios in these still confined systems are preserved and the experiment may be repeated many times, with the same results, as long as there is no superheating.

The prepared section with the inclusions here described was heated very slowly (the experiment lasted 270 min), so that the included solution could come to equilibrium with the host mineral. However, no important changes in the inclusion's shape could be observed. Only a small difference in the outlines of the inclusion's lower boundary is indicated, on comparisons of Plates VI, 1 and 2 with Plates VI, 3 and 4, as a certain fraction of the cognate substance at this boundary had passed into solution.

The curves in our diagram (Fig. 58) represented all of the types and species of homogenization of inclusions in topaz crystals, as revealed, for the first time, by our studies of concrete examples. As it will be shown later in this book, the general relationships brought out in the diagram are typical also of some other minerals (beryl, quartz) containing the same types of inclusions.

The lower abscissa of the diagram shows percentages of the gaseous phase of inclusions; the zero-point on the left represents 100 per cent gas and 0 per cent liquid, and the one on the right 0 per cent gas and 100 per cent liquid. The numbers on the lower abscissa indicate the intermediate gas contents of inclusions, in percentages; the corresponding percentages of the liquid phase are shown on the upper abscissa. The vertical dotted line represents 50 per cent gas and 50 per cent liquid and marks approximately the field of change in the homogenization types. Segments of vertical lines on the left are the diagram's field boundaries; they delineate sections representing different varieties of homogenization belonging to the same type, with the characteristic gas and liquid precentages in heterogeneous gaseous inclusions at room temperature. The same kind of lines on the right represent more or less arbitrarily defined sections of the field based on the volume ratios of the phases in the essentially-liquid inclusions. The curves on the diagram, of course, do not begin at the abscissa, since we did not measure the phase ratio in inclusions at 0°C, feasible as that would be with the aid of our recently constructed microfreezer.

The results of the above experiment with inclusions in the wine-yellow topaz crystals from Volynia were plotted on curve *I* of the diagram

(Fig. 58). The solid line represents the course of the homogenization, as tracked by the gas bubble; the dotted line represents the same course as

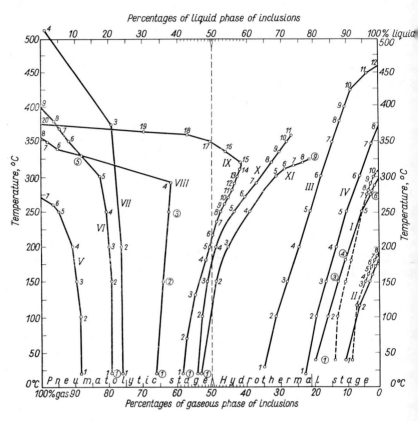

FIG. 58. Diagram of the homogenization of inclusions of a mineral-forming medium in the topaz crystals from the Volynia and Sherlova Gora.

indicated by crystal I, in the same inclusion. The figures on the curves stand for the observation numbers (as in Table 34). The figures in circle refer to the observation numbers of Plates V–VI by which the observed phase ratios in the inclusions, in the course of the experiment, are docu mented. We see that the rate of decrease in the volume of the gas bubble a point 5, at 250°C, becomes greater than the rate of melting of mineral I The two curves intersect at point 5, because the gas bubble disappears a 300°C and the relics of the solid phase disappear only at 310°C. A com plete homogenization of the inclusion takes place at that temperature and even a small degree of additional heat ruptures the confined system and results in an abrupt decrepitation of the prepared section.

Two-phase inclusions homogenize at temperatures up to 200°C, as was shown previously, with the examples of quartz, fluorite, barite, calcite, and other minerals, with the inclusions containing up to 21 per cent gas and 79 per cent, and more, of the liquid. We could not find any two-phase inclusions of this type in topaz crystals. Presence of solid phases in inclusions in topaz and, consequently, of *the very high concentrations of the associated solutes in the mineral-forming solutions, in similar inclusions, serve markedly to raise the homogenization temperatures,* up to 300 or 310°C.

Curve *II* of the diagram (Fig. 58) is analogous to curve *I* but is based on secondary inclusions typical of latest periods of activity of hydrothermal solutions in the pegmatites of Volynia. These solutions healed fissures in large topaz crystals extending to the surface of the present crystal face. At 40°C, this type of inclusions contains 79 per cent aqueous solution, 10.4 per cent gaseous phase, and 10.6 per cent solid phases. The latter consist of 8.6 per cent mineral I, 1.3 per cent II, 0.6 per cent III, and 0.1 per cent IV. Solid phases V and VI are most likely to be absent. In any case, we could not see them even at appreciable microscopic magnifications. The course of the homogenization is illustrated by the following figures in Table 35:

TABLE 35

Obser-vation No.	Tempera-ture (°C)	Gas (%)	Solid phase I (%)	Obser-vation No.	Tempera-ture (°C)	Gas (%)	Solid phase I (%)
1	40	10.4	8.6	5	170	1.0	2.2
2	115	6.4	8.8	6	180	0.0	1.0
3	150	2.8	4.0	7	185	0.0	0.4
4	160	1.8	3.2	8	190	0.0	0.0

Construction of curve *II* requires no explanations. We may merely point out the homogenization of two-phase inclusions with the gas–liquid ratio of 10.4 : 89.6 occurred below 150°C in the other minerals. Thus here too, the high concentration of substances in the mineral-forming solution causes an appreciable increase in the homogenization temperatures.

Homogenization of inclusions in topaz from Sherlova Gora, with their relatively low volume percentages of solid phases, is made effective by a complete filling of the pore by the liquid. At 40°C, the inclusion contained 34.5 per cent gas bubble, 64 per cent liquid, and 1.5 per cent solid phases. The progressive increase in the volume of the liquid (and the corresponding decrease in the volume of the gas bubble) is characterized by the following figures.

(2) 68%   at 100°C;   (6) 82.5% at 300°C;   (10)   93.1% at 425°C;
(3) 72.4% at 150°C;   (7) 85.9% at 350°C;   (11)   94.8% at 440°C;
(4) 75.9% at 200°C*; (8) 88.0% at 380°C;   (12)   96.6% at 450°C;
(5) 79.3% at 250°C*; (9) 89.5% at 400°C;   (13) 100%   at 462°C

(and 0 per cent gas in 13). (Here and later, the first measurement represents the initial phase ratio.)

As shown by the figures, the course of the homogenization is slow and smooth up to 400°C, whereupon, at 400–440°C, its tempo is accelerated and becomes even more rapid at the higher temperatures. This course is represented by curve *III* in the diagram.

Secondary inclusions in topaz from Volynia contain more of the solid phase than was found in the foregoing experiment, but less than in the experiment represented by curve *I*, while their gas content is 22.6 per cent at ordinary temperatures. The course of their homogenization was exceptionally uniform and the disappearance of their gaseous phase, as a slow progressive decrease in the volume of the gas bubble, is shown in the diagram not as a curve but as a practically straight line, *IV*. The progress of the homogenization, in this case, may be appraised by the following measurements:

(1) 22.6% gas at   25°C;   (5) 9.7% gas at 250°C;
(2) 19.4% gas at 100°C;   (6) 5.8% gas at 300°C;
(3) 16.1% gas at 150°C;   (7) 2%   gas at 350°C;
(4) 13.0% gas at 200°C;

the gas bubble disappeared completely at 375°C, but a small quantity of the solid phase was still visible.

We did not suceed in performing a complete homogenization of the inclusion because one of the "captive" minerals had begun its growth at the temperature at which the inclusion was still incompletely isolated from the solution wherein the growth of the host topaz crystal was taking place. In the experiments here described, as we have seen, the gas bubble occupied less than 50 per cent of the inclusion's volume. Homogenization of such inclusions by heat terminates invariably in a complete disappearance of the gas bubble, in a dissolution of the "captive" minerals, and in a complete filling of the entire pore with the liquid aqueous solution. Moreover, the greater the per cent of gas in the inclusions, the higher is the homogenization temperature. *Such a course of homogenization*, previously known but poorly investigated, up to the present time, was called by us *type I homogenization*.

An entirely different view results from our studies of the essentially gaseous inclusions in which the gas bubble occupies 76 per cent, and more,

---

* Temperature misprints corrected to agree with Fig. 58 [Ed.].

of the inclusion's volume, as well as of the gas–liquid inclusions, with the gas bubble's volume at 50 to 76 per cent of the total.

Application of heat to essentially gaseous inclusions causes a gradual filling of the inclusion by a gas and not by a liquid. Also, there is an observed inverse relationship between the homogenization temperature and the phase ratio. The higher is the proportion of the gas phase in such inclusions (76 to 95 per cent gas, and more), the lower is the temperature at which the homogenization becomes effective by a complete filling of the inclusion's pore with the gas. Thus primary inclusions in topaz crystals from Volynia, with a gas content of 88.2 per cent of the total volume, homogenized at 270°C; at 79.3 per cent gas, the homogenization temperature was 400°C (Plate II, 3); at 76 per cent gas the homogenization temperature was 510°C, with the accompanying total filling of the inclusion's pore with gas.

In our opinion, the recorded homogenization temperatures of the essentially gaseous inclusions, in the majority of the cases, may be referred to temperatures characteristic of the natural process. They indicate some kind of minimum temperature *whose deviation from true temperature increases with decrease in the inclusion's content of the liquid phase*, as observed at room temperature. Specifically, it may be that in the last example, the homogenization of the inclusion containing 24 per cent liquid phase may be taken as a satisfactory approximation of the true temperature. Much work is still required here, analogous to the work that was essential in developing the basis for the utilization of the two-phase essentially liquid inclusions in the capacity of self-registering thermometers.

Our diagram (Fig. 58) represents the homogenization curves of primary essentially gaseous inclusions in topaz at these particular phase ratios. Curve *V* represents the first example, at 11.8 per cent liquid and, correspondingly, 88.2 per cent gas, involving a gradual decrease in the volume of the liquid caused by the application of heat. The course of the homogenization was as follows:

(1) 11.8% liquid at   20°C;   (5) 4.4% liquid at 250°C;
(2) 11.8% liquid at 100°C;   (6) 2.9% liquid at 260°C;
(3) 10.3% liquid at 150°C;   (7) liquid vanished at 270°C,
(4)   8.8% liquid at 200°C;

and gas filled the entire inclusion. The conversion of liquid into gas in the confined system, in inclusions of this kind, is accelerated toward the end of the homogenization.

The initial state of the inclusion, in the second example, is recorded in Plate II, 3. Its homogenization followed the course as expressed by curve *VI*:

(1) 20.8% liquid at   20°C;   (6) 7.3% liquid at 350°C;
(2) 20.8% liquid at 150°C;   (7) 4.4% liquid at 370°C;
(3) 19.8% liquid at 200°C;   (8) 3.0% liquid at 380°C;
(4) 18.8% liquid at 250°C;   (9) at 400°C, the liquid, as
(5) 16.7% liquid at 300°C;

visible plainly in the left part of Plate II, 3 (light) and occupying 2.5 divisions of the scale on the right, vanished completely and the entire inclusion turned black.

The third example of the homogenization of inclusions containing 24 per cent liquid and 76 per cent gas is illustrated by curve *VII* showing that the percentage phase ratios remained practically unchanged up to 375°C. The liquid phase began to disappear fairly rapidly only above 375°C. The inclusion was filled with gas at 510°C and the homogenization became complete. The subsequent cooling led to a gradual heterogenization of the inclusion whose course followed the same curve, but in the opposite direction. The gas bubble was growing smaller gradually, while the liquid's volume was increasing back to its initial volume at room temperature. *The course of homogenization of inclusions by the filling of their entire volume with the gaseous phase is* called by us *homogenization type II* and the variant involving a gradual filling with the gas is called *species 1 of this type of the homogenization.* An increase in the quantity of liquid in the essentially gaseous inclusions may be obtained only by artificial cooling, but our studies of inclusions at temperatures below zero had not yet acquired a systematic character.

Most of the gas–liquid inclusions in topaz crystals from Volynia contain gas bubbles occupying 55 to 75 per cent (inclusively) of the inclusion's total volume. We shall consider now three typical homogenization curves for this range of the volume phase ratios.

The inclusion shown in Plate II, 2 contains 66 per cent gas (vapor) and 34 per cent liquid at ordinary temperatures. The principal points in the homogenization of this inclusion, and of others of the same type, are recorded in Plate IX, 1, 2, 3 and by curve *VIII* of the diagram (Fig. 58).

Changes in the phase ratio of the inclusion were as follows:

(2) 64%   gas at 150°C   (6) 96%   gas at 340°C;
          (Plate IX, 1);   (7) 99%   gas at 350°C;
(3) 62.5% gas at 250°C;   (8) 100% gas at 355°C
(4) 62.0% gas at 290°C;   (Plate IX, 4).
(5) 88.8% gas at 333°C
          (Plate IX, 3);

After cooling by 10–15°C, the situation, as in *6*, was restored, with the subsequent rapid regression to *5* (Plate IX, 3), etc.

As shown by the preceding examples, the uniform and the very slow decrease in the size of the gas bubble, resulting from the application of heat, was succeeded at 300°C by its very rapid growth, at the rate of about 1 per cent per 1°C of the progressively increasing temperature. Beginning at 330°C, this growth was retarded and one could see that the interphase boundary was advancing as if by kicks, moving forward at one time, recoiling, and moving forward again, while the temperature was increasing steadily. The homogenization occurred only at 355°C. For these reasons, another change in the slope of the curve took place at point 6.

Curve *IX* illustrates a different phase ratio (58.2 per cent gas and 41.8 per cent liquid) and a less drastic change in the slope occurring at a different point. The course of the homogenization of this very fortunately shaped inclusion was as follows:

(2) 57.1% gas at 75°C;	(12) 43.3% gas at 290°C;
(3) 54.6% gas at 130°C;	(13) 42.6% gas at 300°C;
(4) 51.6% gas at 180°C;	(14) 41.8% gas at 310°C;
(5) 50.5% gas at 200°C;	(15) 41.7% gas at 320°C;
(6) 49.5% gas at 215°C;	(16) 46.2% gas at 340°C;
(7) 48.4% gas at 235°C;	(17) 50.5% gas at 350°C;
(8) 47.3% gas at 250°C;	(18) 59.3% gas at 360°C;
(9) 46.2% gas at 260°C;	(19) 70.3% gas at 365°C;
(10) 45.1% gas at 270°C;	(20) 100% gas at 375°C.
(11) 44.3% gas at 280°C;	

As shown by the results, the gas bubble was contracting slowly up to the temperature of 315°C and was expanding, from then on, to 350°C, revealing the change in slope or inversion at 315–320°C. Beginning at 350°C, where the bubble occupied 50.5 per cent of the volume, and on to 375°C, the homogenization became very rapid, as the interphase boundary was advancing into the liquid. The gas bubble was growing at the rate of 2 per cent per 1°C.

A very similar type of homogenization, with a change in slope, was followed in inclusions shown in Plate X, 3 (with the end result in Plate X, 4) and in Plate I, 3.

In this latter case, in the initial state, the gas occupied 55 per cent of the inclusion's volume (and the liquid 45 per cent). Thus the inclusion was an extreme example, within the particular range of variation of the phase ratio in the scope of our diagram. There was practically no visible decrease in the gaseous phase on heating up to 150°C. Between 150 and 330°C, the bubble's volume was reduced to 42 per cent, whereupon the bubble began to grow slowly, up to 360°C, where it recovered its initial volume. This was followed by a very rapid growth of the bubble, up to the moment of the homogenization at 380–390°C.

For the range of the diagram, for the phase ratios of 55–76 per cent gas (vapor) and, accordingly, of 45–24 per cent liquid, it was established by the whole series of the experiments that the typical homogenization curves have a definite inversion point. Homogenization of this kind is called by us *type II, species 2*, or *homogenization with an inversion point*. The greater is the percentage of gas in such inclusions (within the range as here indicated), the lower are the homogenization and inversion temperatures.

The course of homogenization is different still in inclusions whose gas (vapor)–liquid ratios are very close (1:1) (2 to 4 per cent more gas). Such inclusions, with 54 per cent gas are recorded in Plate I, 1. Their homogenization proceeds as follows:

(1) 54% gas at 20°C; (7) 37.0% gas at 300°C;
(2) 52.7% gas at 100°C; (8) 32.4% gas at 320°C;
(3) 51% gas at 150°C; (9) 32.2% gas at 335°C;
(4) 48.6% gas at 200°C; (10) 30% gas at 350°C;
(5) 43.2% gas at 250°C; (11) at 360°C, there
(6) 40% gas at 270°C;

was an *instantaneous thrust* of the phase boundary *into the liquid* and a sudden homogenization occurred at 362°C. At the same time, it was difficult to decide, which one of the phases, the liquid or the gas, had filled the inclusion. We had to cut off curve X of the diagram. Replicate tests produced the same situation.

In order to clarify this picture, we succeeded in selecting a particularly large tubular inclusion, about 0.5 mm long and 0.05 mm wide. This inclusion is shown in Plate X, 1 and 2. Its homogenization, represented by curve XI in the diagram, had the following course:

(1) 53% gas at 20°C; (6) 28.5% gas at 310°C;
(2) 48.5% gas at 150°C; (7) 25.7% gas at 315°C;
(3) 45% gas at 200°C; (8) 23.0% gas at 320°C;
(4) 28.5% gas at 250°C*; (9) 21.0% gas at 325°C,
(5) 31.0% gas at 300°C;

and an instantaneous "sliding" of the phase boundary *into the liquid,* so rapid that there was no chance of any measurement, even at the slowest rate of the heating. *The gas bubble, after its decrease in volume, gradually grew neither larger nor smaller, but vanished instantaneously, while it was still fairly large* (21 per cent of the inclusion's volume), *and would reappear or disappear just as instantaneously* at a slightest cooling or heating of the section below 325°C or above 324°C. Such homogenization is called by us *type II, species 3, or homogenization with a "critical point".*

* Probably misprint for 38.5% [Ed.].

In our work with inclusions whose ratios were very close to these ratios in the two preceding examples, *the phenomenon of boiling preceding the complete homogenization, in the gaseous as well as in the liquid phase, was definitely established.*

The inclusion shown in Plate XXII, 1 was homogenized in the gaseous phase at 352°C; the one in Plate XXII, 2 was homogenized in the liquid phase at 367°C. We shall refer to them, from here on, as *the first* and *the second* inclusions respectively. It appears that both of these inclusions belong to fragments of one single large crystal of topaz from Volynia. Their classification under a given *genetic type* (pseudo-secondary or secondary) could not be determined, because the fragments had no outer crystal faces to show. Both of the inclusions are pseudo-secondary, in all probability.

Moreover, the gas bubble in the first inclusion was somewhat larger than 50 per cent (between 50 and 60 per cent), while the second inclusion's gas bubble was smaller than 50 per cent (between 40 and 50 per cent) and the presence of the cognate substance in both inclusions, as a lining, was a matter of interest to us, in view of the possibly erroneous interpretation of this lining as representing a cognate substance laid down in an already formed (hermetically sealed) inclusion.

The very thin boundary between this "lining" and the host crystal shows plainly in Plate XXII, 1, both in the upper and in the lower parts of the inclusion. It is as if this boundary were separating the "teeth" of the topaz, protruding into the inclusion and disrupting the inclusion's originally regular form, from the substance of the host crystal by which the original form of the inclusion was formerly defined.

The same kind of "teeth" are visible also in the second inclusion, in the lower part. One of them protrudes into the gas buble and, at the base of this tooth, a thin boundary separating it from the rest of the crystal is clearly visible.

There develops a possibility of an optical identification of this boundary, by the small difference in the indices of refraction of either substance, by comparing the topaz substance of a relatively later age with the age of the inclusion's vacuole. Experiments, in this connection, have a twofold purpose:

(a) a still more detailed tracking of the course of homogenization and heterogenization of the inclusions in question and

(b) a determination whether the "dentate" inner topaz crystals were deposited on the vacuole's walls *before the hermetic sealing of the inclusion* or *after the isolation of the included droplet from the free solutions from which the minerals were crystallized.*

The first inclusion. Seven solid phases, in the form of very small crystals, barely visible in the photomicrograph (identified by numbers, in

TABLE 36

Obser-vation No.	Time*	Temperature attained (°C)	Changes observed inside inclusion
1	11.55	30	
2	12.10	100	
3	12.20	134	
4	12.30	150	
5	12.45	200	Definitely visible decrease in the volume of the vapor. Barely noticeable solution of solid phase I
6	13.00	230	Solid phases I dissolved; solid phase VI became invisible
7	13.10	250	Solid phases III and VII begin to dissolve
8	13.20	268	Solid phases III and VII dissolved. A new gas bubble, isolated from the main one, appears and begins to increase
9	13.30	280	The vapor bubble and the new gas bubble coalesced
10	13.45	300	
11	13.55	310	Small gas bubbles began to emerge at the site of the solid phases, to migrate, one after another, to the opposite part of the inclusion, where the main bubble is, and to coalesce with the main bubble
12	13.55	310–300	A non-transparent root-like branched solid phase VIII (an ore mineral) grew very rapidly on the vacuole's wall near the inclusion's center; small twigs appeared on top of solid phase V
13	14.10	320	Boiling. Numerous gas bubbles in the right part of the inclusion coalesce rapidly into one single large bubble which moves slowly to the left where the gaseous phase still persists and which has become appreciably smaller in size. While the large bubble is still in motion, it is being overtaken and augmented in its volume by numerous small gas bubbles. All the while the main ("the primary") gas bubble is rapidly growing smaller
14	14.30	340	The second gas bubble contacts the original one, but the bubbles do not merge. Their combined volume is about the same as at the end of the observation 12
	14.30'20″	340–342	The two gas bubbles coalesce into a single large one

TABLE 36 (continued)

Obser-vation No.	Time*	Temperature attained (°C)	Changes observed inside inclusion
15	14.40	340–342	A repetition of observations 13 and 14. A continuous procession of gas bubbles. This is accelerated by a small rise of the temperature. Gas bubbles are set loose from every wall of the vacuole in contact with the liquid
16	14.50	350	A nearly continuous stream of gas bubbles is flowing into the left part of the inclusion and merging directly with the "main" gas bubble. The size of that gas bubble is beginning to increase appreciably and the liquid–gas boundary is becoming less definite.
17	15.00	320	The situation as in observation 13 is restored. The "growing-up" of solid phase III
18	15.40	350	Recurrence of the phenomena, as in observations 13, 14, 15, 16
19	15.40′15″	351–352	A very rapid movement of the poorly visible interphase boundary in the direction of the liquid and a very rapid filling of the inclusion's pore with the gaseous phase. (The homogenization is near its critical point.) "Branched" solid phase VIII and relics of solid phases IV and V are visible. No visible changes in the outlines of the inclusion
20	15.45	340	A continuing circulation of gas bubbles
21	15.50	345–350	A nearly massive stream of gas bubbles driven from the right to the left part of the inclusion. The volume of the main gas bubble stays constant when the temperature stays constant
22	20.20	350	The solution in the inclusion "boils" continuously for 2 hr 30 min without any visible changes in the outlines of the vacuole. Only dark pinpoint dots develop on the vacuole's walls

TABLE 36 (continued)

Obser-vation No.	Time*	Temperature attained (°C)	Changes observed inside inclusion
23	20.25	360	Explosions of the inclusion and of the others, of the same type, shortly after their homogenization. Examination of the vacuole's wall at high microscopic magnifications shows presence of odd-looking pinpoint dots resulting from the solution [of the walls?—V.P.S.], that were entirely undetectable at temperatures below the homogenization

* The experiment lasted from 11.55 to 20.25 o'clock, i.e. from 11.55 a.m. to 8.25 p.m. The first two digits stand for hours; the next two for minutes; the seconds were noted only in Nos. 14 and 19 [V.P.S.].

the order of their decreasing relative volumes) were recognized in the right part of the first inclusion. We shall now describe in some detail our experiments with this inclusion (including the temperature record in Table 36).

This experiment, running continuously for 8 hr 30 min, showed a continuous and very energetic boiling of the confined fluid,† in inclusions whose gas bubble occupies nearly the entire inclusion and whose homogenization involves a critical point at a constant temperature (1 or 2°C below the temperature of the homogenization).

Some faint boiling occurs also at a temperature of 40°C below the homogenization temperature. The boiling increases in intensity as the solution approaches the homogenization point, but ceases entirely at the homogenization temperature, i.e. at the point where the pressure becomes sufficiently high (in the given case, the confining pressure of the vacuole walls counteracts the vapor pressure at the homogenization temperature).

Possibilities of transfer and redeposition of the ore substance by the fluid, as in the case of the root-like, branched solid phase VIII, were manifested definitely in the course of the experiment. The growth of the "branches" of that crystal was particularly energetic (at a relatively small lowering of the temperature) *in the wake* of the chain-like migration of gas bubbles which served apparently to stimulate and perhaps even to cause the transfer of the substance within the confined system.

† Here and elsewhere, by the fluid we mean the state of the solution as it appears at the time of the homogenization of gas–liquid inclusions, namely, as a compressed saturated vapor, intermediate between gas (in the common sense of the term) and a liquid aqueous solution, with respect to density and index of refraction.

There were *no changes in the outlines* of the inner "dentate" small crystals lining the vacuole during the 8.5 hr of heating, although *extremely small etching figures indicative of a small degree of solution of the topaz under the influence of the applied heat* did develop on these crystals (and, in general, on the inclusion walls). The insolubility of the topaz lining the inclusion shows that the lining was formed prior to the hermetic sealing of the inclusion, when the included droplet was still in contact with the crystal-forming solution.

However, even after complete sealing off of the droplet, i.e. after the final formalization of the gas–liquid inclusion, certain small amounts of the cognate substance were deposited on the inclusion walls, alongside the "captive" minerals. It was this portion that redissolved during homogenization, resulting in the formation of *the solution figures* on the inclusion walls, as here observed (Plate XXI, 1).

The solid phases IV, V, and VIII are not typical "captive" minerals, since it appears that their growth had begun even before the complete sealing of the inclusion. To some extent therefore they are syngenetic with the "dentate" topaz in the inclusion lining.

We cannot understand the cause of the formation of the *insoluble* solid phase VIII. We may think of it merely as a newly-formed very sparingly soluble substance of an unknown composition (most likely an ore mineral) originating from substances brought into solution in the relatively rapidly fluctuating temperature of the artificial environment.

The second inclusion. The second *two-phase* inclusion (Plate XXII, 2), with a gas bubble volume estimated at 50–40 per cent of the total, homogenized *in the liquid phase* at the ordinary rate. The course of its homogenization, however, resembled that of the one already described.

An abridged record of the observations of the experiment, which was of ordinary duration, is presented in Table 37.

There was no visible change in the outlines of the inclusion throughout the experiment. In a replicate test, the inclusion "boiled" continuously for five hours straight, at a temperature considerably lower (4–7°C) than the homogenization temperature, but with the same result. There was no appreciable solution of the "dentate" crystals of "inner" topaz.

The boiling of *the liquid* solution somewhat below the homogenization temperature, as recorded, was taking place within a narrow range of the temperature (within 7°C), as against its wider range in the first inclusion, where boiling at different intensities continued for 41 or 42°C.

The two experiments here described indicate the fluid density to be somewhat below the critical one and the aqueous solution density to be just barely above the critical one, so that *even the slightest change in temperature and pressure of the system results in a turbulent boiling.*

TABLE 37

No. in sequence	Time	Temperature (°C)	Changes observed inside inclusion
1	11.30	20	
2	12.15	100	No appreciable change in the volume of the gas bubble
3	13.10	200	An appreciable decrease in the size of the gas bubble
4	15.20	360	Gas bubble is much smaller than at the start. The boiling, already under way, results in the formation of fine gas bubbles merging with the main one, but without any increase in its total volume. The main bubble is moving continuously
5	15.50	365	A stream of finest gas bubbles merges with the main one whose volume has decreased abruptly
6	15.52	367	The gas bubble has vanished and the boiling has stopped suddenly. Homogenization in the liquid phase is complete

Within the field of conversion of the solutions from state to state (in our diagram, this field corresponds to 45 or 46 per cent to 55 or 56 per cent volume of gas) it appears that *turbulent boiling phenomena are common in natural environments, precisely controlled by very small alterations in temperatures and pressures.*

The results of the work we did proved definitely the existence of *two groups of inclusions* in topaz crystals from Volynia, *strikingly different in their degree of filling at room temperatures and in their type of homogenization.* The *first* type is represented by multiphase inclusions with the gas bubble occupying less than 50 per cent of the inclusion; the *second* type contains a gas bubble occupying 76 per cent, and more, of the total volume.

Inclusions of the first group are associated *entirely with healed fissures extending to the surface of topaz crystals.* As we saw, they were formed after the crystal was already complete.

Inclusions of the second group are associated chiefly with inner zones of crystals and they are distributed in relation to the crystal form of their host mineral. More rarely, such inclusions are found also in fissures that do not extend beyond the core of the crystal.

Finally, we established the existence also of a third group of inclusion containing 50–75 per cent (inclusive) of gas phase. Their homogenization as in the second group, consists of filling of the entire inclusion by gas, but the course of their homogenization is not the same (as it involves the inversion, the critical point, and, on occasions, the boiling phenomena). In order to render even an approximate account of the distribution and abundance of the different inclusion groups, we undertook a detailed and tedious statistical study, using fragments of wine-yellow and blue topaz crystals and a small crystal of colorless topaz. The ratio of the volume of the gas bubble and the total volume of the inclusion's pore was determined in 513 inclusions (chiefly of regular tubular shape). It developed that, quantitatively, about 5 per cent of the inclusions belong to *the first group* and *the second group* includes about 20 per cent of the total. The bulk of the inclusions (75 per cent), however, contained gas bubbles occupying 50–75 per cent of the total volume (the third group).

The results of our statistical studies are presented in Fig. 59 (p. 254) and in Table 38.

TABLE 38

No. in se- quence	Color of topaz crystals (blue and wine-yellow are common in the same crystal)	Number of detected inclusions		
		inclusions contain- ing more than 76 per cent gas	inclusions with 50 to 75 per cent gas	inclusions with less than 50 per cent gas
1	Wine-yellow	69	161	11
2	Blue	27	177	7
3	Colorless	2	50	9
	Total	98	388	27
	Per cent	20	75	5

Thus it was found that the majority of the inclusions belong to the third or intermediate group, in regards to their gas content (50–75 per cent).* These inclusions bear the earmarks of primary origin, judging by their distribution, although they cluster toward the outer growth zones rather than toward the cores of the crystals. They are found also in the central zones of the crystals where they are associated invariably with healed fissures that do not extend to the outer zones (pseudo-secondary inclusions).

---

* There is a possibility of a greater relative abundance of the first group of the inclusions (up to 10 or 15 per cent). The tubular form is rarer in multiphase liquid inclusions than the others.

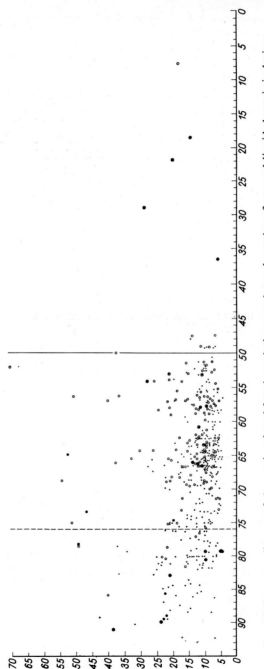

Fɪɢ. 59. Summary diagram of changes in mineral-forming solutions, as shown by ratios of gas and liquid phases in inclusions in topaz crystals from Volynia (prepared by N. P. Yermakov, 1948)

⊛Recordered by photomicrographs; ●Fully reliable measurements of phase ratios; ○ Reliable measurements of phase ratios; · Moderately reliable measurements of phase ratios. On the abscissa: degree of filling of inclusion by gas phase; on the ordinate: ratios between length and width of tabular inclusions. Vertical dotted line is the boundary between the pneumatolytic and the gas-aqueous stages; solid vertical line is the boundary between the pneumatolytic and the hydrothermal stages.

The gas–liquid ratio in these inclusions was found to be variable, at a given room temperature, and it was found also that the nearer the inclusions are to the crystal periphery, the lower is their gas content and the higher is their content of liquid and solid phases. On the whole, however, volume per cent of solid phases is much lower in this group than in the first group of inclusions. Such variability of the phase ratios in primary and pseudo-secondary inclusions, from the crystal's core to its periphery, did not seem to be accidental to us. This variability appears to be an expression of an orderly change in the mineral-forming media, from almost "dry" gases* to gases more or less saturated with water vapor.

We had no opportunity to analyze these gases, but it is probable that they are strong acids and carriers of various solutes in the gaseous phase.

The name "gas–liquid" is applied by us rather arbitrarily to inclusions containing 50–75 per cent of the gas phase. We do not consider the liquids observed in such inclusions at room temperatures to be pure water, in the majority of the cases. They are rather mixtures of various acids, including such weak acids as carbonic in the instance of complex inclusions (see below). Judging by inclusions in which the proportion of solid phases increases progressively toward the crystal's periphery, one may be led to believe that the acid fluid, to the measure of its enrichment with water vapor, is able to transfer and redeposit increasingly greater quantities of dissolved substances and to participate that much more energetically in the genesis and pneumatolytic metamorphism of minerals and rocks.

At the end of the pneumatolytic process, however, there is apparently a radical decrease in the concentrations of solutes in supercritical solutions, since we found no solid phases whatsoever in primary inclusions in the peripheral zones of the crystals, particularly in inclusions showing the critical point during their homogenization. In the experiment recorded by curve X in our diagram (Fig. 58), the proximity of the critical point (362°C) to the critical temperature of pure water may be a sign that we were dealing with a "spent" water vapor containing practically no dissolved substances, except small quantities of some volatile ones (possibly CO_2) by which the temperature of the critical homogenization was lowered. On the other hand, the position of the critical point at 325°C on curve XI may be an indication that the supercritical solution already contains an increased quantity of acids of some kind responsible for the lowering of the solution's critical point.

It is difficult, of course, to draw any conclusions in such problems, in

---

* An arbitrary term. Apparently, these are gaseous substances existing at super-critical pressures and temperatures. They produce up to 10 per cent of the liquid phase after their hermetic sealing in the mineral's cavities and after cooling to 18 or 20°C.

the initial stage of the research, when we still have no definite idea about the chemical composition of gaseous and gas–liquid inclusions.

As the result of our statistical studies of inclusions in pneumatolytic minerals, we gained the impression that there can be no two inclusions with absolutely identical phase ratios in different zones of a crystal's growth and that this fact in itself is an expression of continuity of the changes going on in mineral-forming solutions. The summary diagram (Fig. 59) includes the statistical and the experimental data only for inclusions in topaz crystals from Volynia. It stands to reason that the points from left to right along the abscissa of that diagram, depending on the gas phase content of the inclusions at room temperature, are indeed expressions of the continuity of the change and that the abundance of these points gives us an approximate idea as to what particular range the given stage of the topaz-formation belongs.

Let us consider now, in brief, the results of similar studies of some other common vein minerals, as a proof that the types and the species of homogenization of inclusions in mineral of hypogene origin, as here determined, also have a general significance.

THE COURSE OF HOMOGENIZATION OF INCLUSIONS IN QUARTZ

The ordinary and already known course of homogenization of aqueous inclusion in hydrothermal minerals was first shown by us using examples of inclusions in low-temperature quartz crystals from Middle Ural [37]. Plate III, 2 shows these liquid inclusions, common in hydrothermal quartz, with a bubble of gas that is small, relative to the inclusion's total volume. Plate III, 3 shows the same inclusion, but homogenized at 130°C. Plate III, 4 is a record of the moment of their heterogenization, when, on cooling down to 115°C there was a "boiling", in the inclusion on the right, and the fine bubblets of gas merged for a moment into two bubbles of vapor. The two combined into a single gas bubble, in the next moment of the cooling and the original appearance of the inclusions was restored at 30°C (Plate III, 2).

The irregularly shaped inclusions shown in the photomicrographs were unsuited for measurements of their phase ratios at different temperatures concurrently with observations of the course of the homogenization. Only tubular inclusions, very rarely found in quartz, are convenient for that purpose. They are represented in the photomicrographs of quartz from Transbaykalia. The inclusion in Plate III, 1 has the shape of a negative crystal and a tubular form. The upper and the lower inclusions were found to have exploded by overheating above their homogenization temperatures. The fine fissures into which the liquid contents of these inclusions were forced instantaneously are clearly visible in the photomicrograph. These fissures do not extend to the crystal surface. The cavities of the exploded inclusions were found to be filled entirely by gas and they appeared black under the microscope for that reason.

Plate IV, 1–4 shows the same zone of the crystal at a higher magnification. There, under the faceted inclusion, some tubular inclusions are visible that are suited for sufficiently reliable observations of changes in their phase ratios resulting from heating. In the initial state, at 30°C (Plate IV, 1) one may see a black gas bubble under the vertical thread of the eyepiece, occupying 21 per cent the inclusion's volume. The progress of the homogenization was marked, in this case, by a consistent decrease of the bubble volume, as illustrated by the following record:

(2) 13.0% gas at 140°C (Plate IV, 2);
(3) 11% gas at 160°C;
(4) 9% gas at 170°C;
(5) 8% gas at 180°C (Plate IV, 3);
(6) 0% gas at 200°C (Plate IV, 4).

Further heating resulted in explosions of the liquid inclusions.

It was considerably more difficult to follow the course of homogenization of multiphase liquid inclusions of high-temperature hydrothermal solutions. Effects of high concentrations and of high external pressures are serious complicating factors in thermometric investigations and requires tediously painstaking work, which we have already begun.

A relatively simple case is presented by three-phase inclusions, with only one "captive" mineral in addition to the liquid phase and the gas bubble, as in quartz crystals from Aldan and Pamir, where the mineral generally has a cubical habit (NaCl or KCl). However, in the instance of relatively high-temperature minerals, a whole collection of inner isotropic and anisotropic "captive" minerals is generally found, all different in their crystallographic forms and optical properties, in addition to the liquid and the gas. We have already described the course of the homogenization of such inclusions in topaz crystals from Volynia and recorded it in Plate V–VII. Primary inclusions in quartz crystals from Pamir are shown in Plate VIII and are represented in Fig. 60.

We again had no opportunity to track and record the homogenization course for these and for other similar inclusions, by means of exact measurements of their phases at different temperatures. For that reason, we are presenting here only the general results of the temperature measurements at the moments when a given phase would vanish in the inclusion, as plainly seen in Plates VI, 3 and VIII, 2–4. There is no need here to repeat the explanatory text of the photomicrographs.

As already shown (pp. 63–65), among the "captive" minerals, in quartz crystals from Pamir, we generally find *halite, sylvite, carbonate*

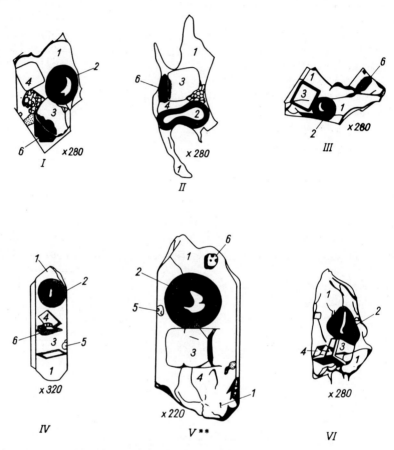

FIG. 60. Multiphase inclusions in crystals of quartz from Pamir. (Reproduced from photomicrographs)

Fillings of inclusions: *1.* Mother liquor; *2.* Gas bubble; *3.* Sylvite; *4.* Halite; *5.* Carbonate; *6.* Specularite*.

* Captive minerals are identified tentatively.

** *V* is reproduced from G. G. Lemmlein's photomicrograph.

(dolomitic calcite), and—of ore minerals—hematite [specularite?]. The first two of these inner minerals occupy the largest volume in inclusions. For example, in an elongated inclusion in quartz from Odudi, our rather exact measurements showed that while the saturated aqueous solution occupies 46.66 per cent of the inclusion's volume and the gas bubble occupies 13.34 per cent, *the solid phases* make up 40 per cent of the volume. If we consider that the solution is at equilibrium with the other phases and has a solute content of at least 26 per cent at room temperature, the total chloride concentration in an inclusion of this sort is estimated at about 52–53 per cent. The inclusion in Plate VIII, 2 belongs to this very type. In the others, Plate VIII, 1 and 3, the volume of the solid phases varies from 15 to 20 per cent, on the average, but is not over 10–12 per cent in the last one of the series (Plate VIII, 4). In the remaining cases (crystals from miscellaneous sources) the solid phases are represented sometimes only by a single "captive" mineral (halite) and their volumes are smaller still (less than 10 per cent).

As we see, composition and concentration of the solutions are variable, particularly so in time, since both the volume and the quantity of solid phases in inclusions within the inner zone of some of the Odudi crystals differ from those in inclusions in the peripheral zones. Variations in composition and concentration of the solutions are related to variations in their temperatures.

The lowest of the homogenization temperatures of two-phase inclusions vary from 82°C (vein No. 6) to 158–160°C. Homogenization temperatures of inclusions in quartz from veins in porphyrites were determined by us at 216–220°C [32, p. 41]. At the same time, inclusions with 15 per cent solid phases, by volume (approximately), on the average, are homogenized at 245–265°C, but the calcite and the halite they contain dissolves only at higher temperatures.

On the whole, inclusions containing large volumes of solid phases (30–40 per cent, or some such order of magnitude) could not be homogenized completely and any attempts to do so would result in their explosions. Sylvite is generally the first one to dissolve, at temperatures up to 100–110°C, after which halite is either melted or dissolved at temperatures up to 300–310°C; carbonate is the last one to vanish, generally at 330–340°C. In not a single case did we succeed in dissolving completely the red scales of hematite. They would turn conspicuously dark at temperatures over 200°C, would grow appreciably smaller in size, but would never disappear completely even at 420°C. In such inclusions, 370–380°C was the most characteristic temperature of disappearance of the gas bubble.

We failed occasionally also in attaining a complete dissolution of the halite crystal. In such cases, we were led to the conclusion that the halite

Curve No.	Point No. on homogenization curves									
	1		2		3		4		5	
	gas (%)	°C	gas (%)	°C	gas (%)	°C	gas (%)	°C	gas (%)	°C
XXX	74.0	40	72.0	150	70.6	200	69.0	250	69.0	260
XXXI	85.1	30	85.1	100	86.2	200	90.4	250	95.7	270
XXXII	94.0	30	94.2	100	94.9	150	95.6	165	96.4	175

began to grow in the crystal's cavity before the pore was sealed, i.e. before effective isolation of the inclusion.

In all the examples of homogenization of inclusions in quartz described here, the application of heat led to decrease and ultimately to a disappearance of the gas bubble, as well as to a complete dissolution of the solid phases formed within the inclusion from droplets of the isolated mother liquor. We observed this type I of homogenization in every specimen of hydrothermal quartz and crystal quartz from veins of the Alpine type we examined.

An entirely different picture is presented by homogenization of inclusions in quartz from the vicinity of intrusives or from pegmatitic veins near the deposit. Gas bubbles occupy appreciable volumes in such inclusions (more than 50 per cent). Application of heat to such inclusions, as with the inclusions in topaz, leads in the conversion of the entire inclusion into the gas phase. The course of the homogenization, however, is not always the same, as in topaz. This may be seen in Fig. 61 representing homogenization curves* of the three types characteristis of the quartz here discussed. The course of the homogenization of the inclusions represented by the curves is shown also in Table 39, a summary only of the exact measurements of the phase ratios at different temperatures.

As shown by the data, the volume of the gas bubble in a tubular inclusion in quartz from the Ukrainian pegmatites (curve *XXX*) decreases very slowly on heating up to 260°. The gas bubble begins to grow on further heating and becomes larger than it was initially (at 40°C) by 280°C. Between 280 and 308°C the entire inclusion is rapidly filled with gas. The inclusion's initial condition is restored on cooling and a repeated heating yields the same results as before, with the inversion point on the curve at 260°C. Accordingly, the curve is the characteristic one for the homogenization of gas–liquid inclusions (type II, species 2).

Curve *XXXI* is typical of the essentially gaseous inclusions observed in the inner zones of large quartz crystals from the Ukraine. On heating

---

* The rarity of tubular inclusions in quartz does not allow us, so far, to derive a larger number of such curves.

Point No. on homogenization curves

6		7		8		9		10		11	
gas (%)	°C	gas (%)	°C	gas (%)	°C	gas(%)	°C	gas(%)	°C	gas (%)	°C
72.0	270	75.0	280	80	290	84	295	90	300	100	308
100.0	290	—	—	—	—	—	—	—	—	—	—
97.1	180	98.5	190	100	202	—	—	—	—	—	—

such essentially gaseous inclusions, they display a continuous increase in
the gas phase and a gradual decrease of the liquid phase, down to its

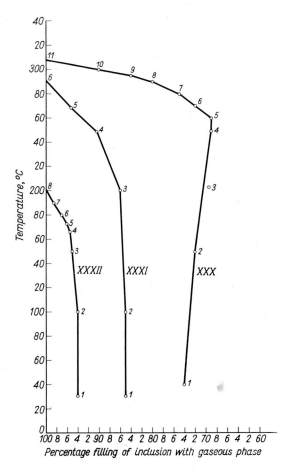

FIG. 61. Homogenization curves of inclusions in pneumatolytic quartz crystals.
XXX, XXXI — Volynia, *XXXII* — Vyshovo (Transcarpathia).

disappearance. Their phase ratios are not the same in different growth zones of the crystal. The higher the per cent of the liquid (up to 24 or 25 per cent), the higher is the temperature of complete homogenization of type II, species 1. The same crystals of quartz may contain also systems of fissures formed at various times whose late healing produced the obviously secondary inclusions. These latter inclusions homogenize as in type I at various temperatures, down as low as 90–100°C.

We found essentially gaseous primary inclusions with a very high content of gas phase at room temperature* in quartz crystals from fissures in the propylitized granodiorite porphyries of Transcarpathia. The long tubular form of these inclusions enabled us to make reliable observations on the course of their homogenization, given by curve *XXXII* of the diagram. As shown, inclusions containing 6 per cent liquid in their initial state were completely filled with the gaseous phase by 202°C. One must suppose that inclusions of "dry" gases [37, p. 28] containing up to 10 per cent liquid at room temperature are characterized by type II, species 1, of the homogenization at temperatures below 250°C.

Quartz–carbonate veins showing some evidence of a poly-metallic mineralization are found within the boundaries of the same intrusion. They are situated near the already mentioned ore-free quartz veins. The examination of primary inclusions in quartz crystals from the ore-bearing veins proved that they belong to *the essentially liquid* category and are homogenized (i.e. as in type I) by a complete filling with liquid at 185–190–200–206–210 and up to 240°C. The same temperature series and the same homogenization type was found in *the secondary inclusions* in quartz from ore-free veins and veinlets.

This suggests a conclusion that the evidence of ores in the intrusives is associated with an appreciably later process of a *hydrothermal* mineralization in which the aqueous silica-bearing solutions healed fissures in crystals of quartz in the earlier ore-free veins produced by gaseous solutions.

An exact elucidation of the course of homogenization of inclusions, accompanied by construction of the curves, is especially difficult in the instance of quartz, as we have already explained. As a rule, inclusions in quartz are faceted, rounded, or irregularly shaped. We have always succeeded, however, in ascertaining the manner of the homogenization whether the filling was with the liquid or with the gas) in inclusions of practically any shape, i.e. we were able to identify the type of the homogenization and to determine the final temperature at which the homogenization was made effective. In the majority of gas–liquid inclusions we were able to determine also the rather nebulous inversion point as well as the exact

---

* Fissures with such quartz crystals are ore-free, since their quartz was formed apparently in an early stage of the autopneumatomorphism of the intrusions.

homogenization temperature. All this constitutes the minimum of essential data which were never taken into account previously, before the development of our method, as here proposed, for ascertaining the state of aggregation of mineral-forming solutions, the kind of data that, by all appearances, will become very important in objective identification of the environments of formation of hypogene mineral deposits.

We must turn now, once again, to the discussion of the course of homogenization of inclusions in *different growth zones of quartz crystals* from pegmatites, so as to make clear the normal variations in the types and the species of homogenization produced by the progressive action of magmatic derivatives responsible for a given type of the mineral-forming environment.

THE COURSE OF HOMOGENIZATION OF INCLUSIONS IN BERYL AND TOURMALINE

Every type and every species of homogenization, as previously described by us for inclusions in topaz and quartz crystals, were discovered also in beryls, as the result of applications of the thermometric method to a large number of beryl crystals from different sources. We did not succeed in finding species 3 involving a critical point, however.

Examination of inclusions in beryl is very difficult because of frequent fissuring of the mineral on heating. For that reason, not more than 20 per cent of the experiments we undertook could be carried through to completion.

Our most important results are summarized in Table 40 and are represented diagrammatically in Fig. 62, as ten different curves which show also the variations in the phase ratios in the inclusions during the heating.

We determined that all inclusions containing up to 50 per cent gas phase homogenize by filling their entire volume with the liquid. However, the fact that some of the curves for the essentially liquid inclusions with a relatively low percentage of gas phase (curves *XIV* and *XVIII*) intersect with some others (curves *XV, XIX, XX*) representing inclusions with larger volumes of the gaseous phase, at room temperatures, certainly merits our attention. The cause of that lies apparently in different concentrations of substances in the inclusions in minerals from different sources or else in a heterochronous character of the solutions in crystals from a given source.

All other things being equal, inclusions of the more concentrated solutions homogenize at higher temperatures. Variations in the composition of inclusions also play an important part in this connection. For example, even a relatively small concentration of carbon dioxide in an inclusion serves to lower substantially the inclusion's homogenization temperature, as shown below. As the result, the corresponding curves flatten out in the last stage of the homogenization, because of the expansion of the liquid in which the carbon dioxide is dissolved. All of these factors produce variations in the rate of homogenization and the unlike homogenization temperatures of heterochronous inclusions in high-temperature minerals from one and the same deposit.

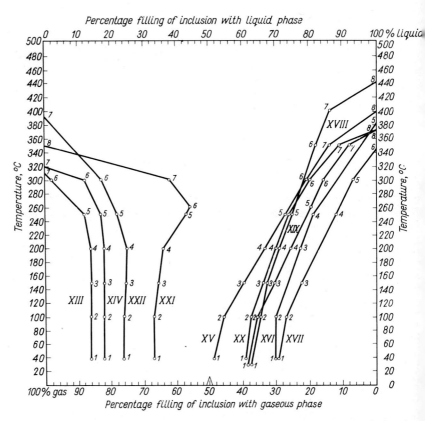

Fig. 62. Homogenization types of inclusions of mineral-forming media in beryl.
Homogenization type I — *XV, XX, XIX, XVIII, XVI, XVII;*
Homogenization type II — *XIII, XIV, XXII, XXI.*

These effects may be illustrated by the example of a small but thoroughly investigated crystal of hydrothermal beryl (specimen 43) from a high-temperature deposit. The course of homogenization of different inclusions, from the crystal core to its periphery, is reported (Table 41) showing variations in the gas volumes in the inclusions under the influence of heat.

One of the primary two-phase inclusions with 30 per cent gas, in the same crystal, gave a homogenization temperature of 286°C, while some of the multiphase inclusions with about the same gas content homogenized at 318–334°C and up to 402°C.

As shown by the data in the preceding table, *our "visual" method for an approximate determination of the temperature is completely unsuited for high-temperature hydrothermal minerals, on account of the strong influence of concentrations of the solutions responsible for a significant lowering of the temperature in the growth of even one and the same crystal.*

A crystal of beryl (No. 94, author's collection) contains primary two-phase inclusions of a long, drawn-out, tubular form (length about 0.5 mm; width 0.004 mm), so very convenient for the application of our method (Plate XIV, 3), with the gas bubble occupying 39 per cent of the volume. Examination of such inclusions made it possible for us to draw curve XX. They homogenize as in type I at 370°C. Secondary inclusions in the same crystal have an irregular and a generally flattened shape (Plate XV, 1) and homogenize at 212–218–223°C, and at lower temperatures (down to 150°C).

In another crystal from the same source (No. 45) we found also tubular but three-phase inclusions with the same size of gas bubble (39 per cent of the volume). Their solid phase, represented by a very small "captive" mineral, could not be identified. However, the presence of this solid phase was sufficient to raise the homogenization temperature to 384°C. The course of the homogenization of these inclusions was as follows: 39 per cent gas at 20°; 38.8 per cent at 50°; 36.1 per cent at 100°; 32.2 per cent at 150°; 26.6 per cent at 200°; 20.0 per cent at 250°; 15.5* per cent at 300°; 8.3 per cent at 350°; 0 per cent at 384°C. The solid phase persisted even at 400°C, since its growth had started apparently when the inclusion was still incompletely sealed. Secondary inclusions in beryl crystals from the same mountain also gave the type I homogenization at different temperatures, in the range of 212–223, 168–172, and 152–160°C.

An abundance of two-phase and multiphase inclusions, strung out along the mineral's length, is found in small crystals of aquamarine from a certain source. The multiphase inclusions contain five different "captive" minerals, in addition to the gas bubble and the liquid (Plate XV, 2). These inclusions should be considered as primary, by virtue of their positions in the crystals. Solid phase I, an isotropic crystal in the left part of the inclusion, dissolves completely at 75°C and is probably sylvite. Above the gas bubble there sits a six-sided anisotropic "captive" mineral (solid phase II), and, on the left of the gas bubble, a fairly large and also anisotropic crystal III; next to which, on the left, there is a non-transparent black crystal IV, probably an ore mineral, surrounded by fine greenish worm-like crystals (solid phase V).

---

* "155.5%" in the original [Ed.].

TABLE 40

	Point No. on								
Curve No.	1		2		3		4		5	
	gas phase (%)	°C	gas phase (%)	°C	gas phase (%)	°C	gas phase (%)	°C	gas phase (%)	°C
XIII	86.0	50	86.0	100	86.0	150	86.0	200	88.0	250
XIV	82.0	50	82.0	100	82.0	150	82.0	200	83.0	250
XV	48.6	50	45.7	100	39.8	150	33.0	200	27.0	250
XVI	30.0	50	30.0	100	22.6	200	19.0	250	0	378
XVII	29.5	50	27.0	100	22.7	150	11.8	250	7.0	300
XVIII	37.6	30	34.8	100	32.8	150	29.0	200	25.2	250
XIX	38.4	30	35.3	100	30.0	150	25.7	200	19.8	250
XX	39.0	40	37.2	100	33.6	150	29.8	200	26.2	250
XXI	67.0	40	67.0	100	65.6	150	63.9	200	57.3	250
XXII	76.0	40	76.0	100	75.3	150	75.3	200	78.4	250

Most of these worm-like crystal dissolve at 170–190°C. The black mineral IV and crystals II and III begin to dissolve noticeably at 280–300°C. The pale-greenish worm-like mineral dissolves completely at 350°C and the gas bubble vanishes at 382°C. The experiment was continued for four hours without any further increase in the temperature and a certain decrease in the size of the solid phases II–III–IV was observed. However, their complete dissolution could not be attained without a further increase

TABLE 41

Prepared section No.	Temperature (°C)								Homogenization temperature type I (°C)
	40–50	100	150	200	250	300	350	400	
	Volume of gaseous phase (%)								
I (with solid inclusions)	30.7	26.1	23.0	18.4	15.3	10.8	7.0	0.5	402
II (with two-phase inclusions)	33.6	—	30.6	24.5	18.2	4.0	—	—	310
III (with two-phase inclusions)	34.0	31.0	25.0	15.0	11.0	3.0	—	—	312
IV (with two-phase inclusions)	36.0	31.6	28.3	23.3	16.7	10.0	5.0	—	362
V (with CO₂)	42.8	38.0	35.7	33.5	28.0	21.4	10.0	—	350–358

homogenization curves

6		7		8		9		10		11	
gas phase (%)	°C	gas phase (%)	°C	gas phase (%)	°C	gas phase (%)	°C	gas phase (%)	°C	gas phase (%)	°C
98.0	300	100	310	—	—	—	—	—	—	—	—
88.0	300	100	320	—	—	—	—	—	—	—	—
20.6	300	14.3	350	0	398	—	—	—	—	—	—
—	—	—	—	—	—	—	—	—	—	—	—
0	342	—	—	—	—	—	—	—	—	—	—
18.3	350	14.4	400	0	438	—	—	—	—	—	—
16.1	300	8.0	350	0	368	—	—	—	—	—	—
20.0	300	11.3	350	0	375	—	—	—	—	—	—
56.0	258	62.3	300	10	349	—	—	—	—	—	—
83.0	300	100	392	—	—	—	—	—	—	—	—

in the temperature. The inclusion was restored to its initial state after cooling.

The data here presented on the homogenization of primary inclusions in beryl are indicative of type I homogenization. They are also evidence of the high-temperature hydrothermal origin of some beryls.

The type II homogenization is observed in the majority of beryl crystals, however. Their two-phase inclusions, with more than 76 per cent gas, become gradually filled with the gas phase, on heating. As shown by curves *XIII, XIV,* and *XXII,* the greater the liquid content of such inclusions, at room temperature, the higher is the temperature of their homogenization (Fig. 62).

We recognized from one to three solid phases in the multiphase secondary inclusions in such beryls (Plate XVI, 1, 2 and 4). We are reasonably sure only of the sylvite, seen as a cubical crystal and showing a very high temperature coefficient of solubility. This cubical crystal becomes rounded noticeably even at 60°C; its volume decreases to about one half of its original size by 70°C; at 78–82° this "captive" mineral dissolves entirely. In case the other three [two?—V.P.S] phases are also present, their noticeable dissolution begins only at temperatures exceeding 250–260°C.

Some of the inclusions in beryls in the author's collection contain a completely black gas bubble, as seen in the microscope. The color is caused merely by the characteristic reflection of light resulting from the large difference between the indices of refraction of the gas and of the crystal.

A continuous pulsation of the gas bubble develops, from 260°C on, during the homogenization of one of such complexly shaped inclusions (Plate XIV, 4). It is as if minute gas bubbles were emanating from the main gas bubble, through the fine tube beneath the inclusion. These minute gas bubbles pass through the tube into the inclusion's left part, after which they stream back to their source and merge with the main gas bubble. This circulation of gas is accelerated at rising temperatures and attains its peak at about 370°C, when the main gas bubble is already very small. Here again, as in topaz, we come across the typical boiling phenomenon. In keeping pace with the rising temperature, the light-colored part of the inclusion, occupied by the liquid, becomes progressively darker. Finally, at 376°C, the gas bubble looks as if it were "dissolved" and the whole inclusion becomes uniformly dark gray. This phenomenon indicates *a substantial decrease in density of the liquid and in its index of refraction*, in the process of the homogenization. The inclusion's initial appearance is restored on cooling. Repetition of the experiment produced no differences whatsoever in the course of the homogenization.

Primary inclusions containing 71 per cent gas and 29 per cent liquid were found in one of the beryl crystals (No. 42, author's collection). Their homogenization temperature was found to be very high and apparently involved an inversion point at a low temperature. The course of the homogenization proved to be as follows:

71% gas at 50°C;	85% gas at 400°C;
67–68% gas at 150°C;	91% gas at 460°C;
71% gas at 250°C;	94% gas at 500°C;
74% gas at 300°C;	97% gas at 530°C;
80% gas at 350°C;	100% gas at 550–560°C.

Secondary inclusions, homogenizing as type I, at different temperatures, are often found in such beryls: two-phase ones homogenize at 125–142°C; three-phase and multiphase ones at 295–317°C and 366–412°C respectively. Two small anisotropic "captive" minerals were observed in the latter group. One of them dissolved at temperatures up to 136°C; while becoming progressively smaller in size. The size of the second one remained unchanged up to high temperatures, but its boundaries with the liquid phase grew more and more fuzzy, so to speak, so that when the mineral vanished at last somewhere near 400°C, the exact moment of its disappearance was very difficult to identify. It was as if this "captive" mineral had seeped out into the liquid phase (melting).

Primary inclusions in beryls from one of the provinces homogenize with an inversion, as a rule, of the type represented in curve *XXI*. We did not succeed, however, in determining the point of inversion exactly, because of an insufficient quantity of test material. The average gas content of the inclusions is 66 per cent at room temperature. The size of the gas bubble is reduced approximately one and one half times at temperatures up to 300–315°C, whereupon it increases rapidly and a homogenization of type II, species 2, takes place at 350–352°C. Secondary two-phase essentially liquid inclusions in aquamarines homogenize as in type I at 168–242°C.

Inclusions in beryls from a source in the West homogenize as in type II and most of them have an inversion point, in their homogenization (curve *XXI*). The inversion point, on the whole, is not so clearly expressed. For that reason, it should be more appropriate, perhaps, *to draw a semicircle* between points 6 and 7 of the curve. The homogenization temperature is raised and the inversion temperature is lowered with increasing relative amounts of liquid in the inclusion. This trend is illustrated by a juxtaposition of the two extremes (among the cases encountered) in Table 42.

TABLE 42

Percentage gas at room temperature	Point of inversion (°C)	Homogenization temperature (°C)	Percentage liquid at room temperature
67	258	349	33
56	225	428	44

As we see, inclusions of gaseous and aqueous solutions in crystals of beryl from most diverse sources homogenize in the same manner as the inclusions in quartz and topaz.

Multicolored tourmalines from various places (Ural, Borshchevochnyi Kryazh) give the same picture of variations in the course of homogenization of their inclusions. Their essentially liquid inclusions in type I, however, had to be classified by us as secondary, in the few specimens we examined. The homogenization curves for tourmalines could not be drawn, so far, because of the absence of regularly tubular inclusions in the specimens. The homogenization type was determined sufficiently reliably, nevertheless, even in the instance of irregularly shaped inclusions.

For example, primary inclusions in tourmaline from Murzinka show a small decrease in the size of their gas bubble on heating up to 270°C. However, the gas bubble begins to recover its initial volume from 280°C on, and, after 310–325°C, there is a rapid growth of the inclusion's gas phase (type II, species 2, of homogenization). The inclusion becomes completely filled with gas at 340–355°C. The essentially liquid secondary inclusions in healed fissures gave homogenization temperatures from 264 to 295°C, type I. We found a single three-phase inclusion with a small gas bubble and a homogenization temperature of only 103°C. We may draw here certain conclusions, without any further overloading of the text by descriptions of our additional experimental findings.

The new, *the second type* (type II) of homogenization (and the variants of the progressive homogenization involving the point of inversion and the critical point) proved to be typical for primary inclusions in topaz, quartz, beryl, and tourmaline from high-temperature deposits regarded as pneuma-tolytic. *Not in a single case was this second type of homogenization encountered in quartz or any other mineral from the large number of hydrothermal and "Alpine" deposits we examined.* At the same time (rarely as that may be) we found primary multiphase inclusions in fine crystals of topaz and beryl from certain sources with homogenization as in type I This leads us to the supposition that small crystals of topaz and beryl may be produced, on occasions, in aqueous solutions, i.e. by hydrothermal process.

THE COURSE OF HOMOGENIZATION OF MIXED INCLUSIONS OF AQUEOUS SOLUTION AND CARBON DIOXIDE

Our consideration of the course of homogenization of inclusions in minerals would be incomplete, were we to omit a brief discussion of the rather widespread occurrence of complex inclusions in minerals. Such inclusions contain two fluids, immiscible at room temperatures, one of which is an aqueous solution and the other one is liquid carbon dioxide A gas bubble consisting of water vapor and carbon dioxide is present inevitably in such inclusions. Also, one or several solid phases are found occasionally in the liquid part of the inclusion.

There are several specific features about the course of homogenization of complex inclusions, the main one of which is *the completion of the homogenization in two stages.* Also, the presence of carbon dioxide causes a marked lowering of the homogenization temperature, as compared to the temperature that one would expect from the size of the gas bubble Even the presence of solid phases, in complex inclusions, is unable to counteract this lowering of the homogenization temperature. *The first stage of the homogenization* occurs due to the fact that *liquid carbonic acid turns into gas invariably at temperatures below 31°C.* Thus by the beginning of the second stage of homogenization the gas bubble occupies, on occasions, 70–80 per cent of the inclusion's total volume (Plate XVIII, and 4). When complex inclusions attain a certain definite temperature, on heating, they become filled either with the liquid or with the gaseous phase

The course of homogenization involving a very rapid filling of the inclusion's space with the liquid phase was demonstrated, for the first time by us with the aid of curve *XII* of the diagram [37, pp 44–45], although at that time, in 1948, the reason for the radical bend in the curve was still obscure to us.*

---

* The volume of the gas bubble was measured on the microscope stage warmed by the microscope light, so that the second aqueous phase (carbon dioxide) was overlooked.

Figure 63 shows the homogenization curves for mixed inclusions (aqueous solution–carbon dioxide) in topaz crystals from different sources. For the sake of comparison, we added three more curves obtained for inclusions of aqueous (*XXVII*) and of gaseous (*XXVIII* and *XXIX*) solutions in topaz crystals (Fig. 63).

In one of the prepared sections of a colorless topaz from Volynia we found inclusions containing 30 per cent gas, 29 per cent aqueous solution,

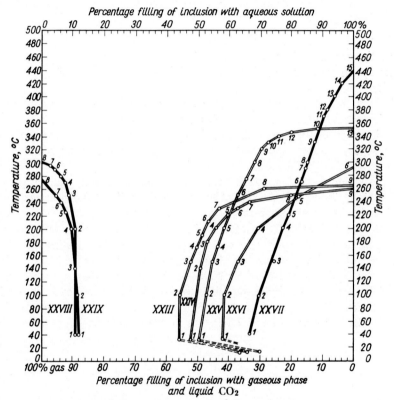

FIG. 63. Homogenization curves for mixed inclusions in topaz compared with curves for ordinary essentially gaseous inclusions.

Homogenization curves
= Curves for mixed inclusions with CO_2); *XXIII, XXIV, XXV, XXVI*.
— Curve for aqueous solutions; *XXVII*.
— Curves for gaseous solutions; *XXVIII, XXIX*.
XXIII, XXIV, XXVIII and *XXIX*—topaz from Ural; *XXVI* and *XXVII*—topaz from Transbaykalia; *XXV*—topaz from Volynia.

Phase rations in mixed inclusions at 20°C

Curve No.	Gas bubble	Liquid CO_2	Solid phases	Aqueous solution	Temperature at the time of observation
XXIII	34.2%	21.5%	about 2.5%	41.8%	19.6°C
XXIV	36%	17%	about 8%	39%	19.7°C

20 per cent liquid CO_2, and 1 per cent solid phase. Changes in the phase ratios, by the application of heat, indicated the following course of homogenization:

(2) 47% gas at 100°C;   (8) 31.0% gas at 300°C;
(3) 44.8% gas at 150°C;   (9) 29.5% gas at 320°C;
(4) 43.5% gas at 170°C;   (10) 27.6% gas at 330°C;
(5) 41.4% gas at 200°C;   (11) 24.1% gas at 340°C;
(6) 37.1% gas at 250°C;   (12) 20.0% gas at 345°C; and
(7) 34.5% gas at 275°C;   (13) a very rapid dissolution

of the still large gas bubble, by a rapid advance of the interphase boundary into the gas, with the volume increasing at the rate of 4 per cent per 1°C increase in temperature. Homogenization took place at 350–352°C, while relics of the solid phase were still demonstrably present in some of the inclusions. A lowering of the temperature by only 3 or 4°C caused a very rapid restoration of the gas bubbles, appearing first at the end of the inclusion opposite the site of the homogenization and coalescing into a single large gas bubble. This course of the homogenization may be seen in curve *XXV* (Fig. 63).

Complex inclusions were found in a topaz crystal from Lipovka Village (Central Ural). In one of these inclusions, it was possible to determine the following phase ratios very accurately at 19.6°C: 41.8 per cent aqueous solution; 21.5 per cent liquid carbon dioxide; 34.2 per cent gas bubble; about 2.5 per cent two "captive" minerals. Heating to 31°C resulted in a disappearance of the phase boundary between the gas bubble and the liquid carbon dioxide. We have shown the typical course of this initial stage of homogenization with an example of a complex inclusion in quartz from Pamir; (see Plate XI, 2, 3 and 4). The volume of the gas bubble at 35°C was found to be 55.7 per cent of the total inclusion volume. The

TABLE 43

Curve No. in diagram	Point No. on							
	1		2		3		4	
	gas (%)	°C	gas (%)	°C	gas (%)	°C	gas (%)	°C
XXIII	55.7	35	55.7	100	52.1	150	50.0	170
XXIV	53.0	35	49.0	140	46.5	180	44.0	200
XXVI	42.0	35	41.2	100	36.3	150	30.3	200

course of homogenization is shown in Table 43 and by curve *XXIII* (Fig. 63).

The following volume ratios of the phases were determined at 19.7°C in a tubular inclusion in a crystal of yellowish topaz from the Shaytanka

Mountain (Ural): 39 per cent aqueous solution; 17 per cent liquid carbon dioxide; 36 per cent gas bubble; about 8 per cent solid phases (curve *XXIV*, Fig. 63). The exact volume of liquid carbon dioxide could not be determined in a complex inclusion in topaz from Transbaykalia (the Urul'ga River) (curve *XXVI*, Fig. 63). The further course of the homogenization of these inclusions is clearly shown by the table below.

The break in the homogenization curves of complex inclusions seems to represent the moment when carbon dioxide mixes with the aqueous solution and serves to increase very appreciably the coefficient of thermal expansion of the solution. Homogenization curve *XXVII* is typical of the essentially liquid multiphase inclusions in topaz crystals containing no carbon dioxide. This curve, like curves *XXVIII* and *XXIX* representing the essentially gaseous inclusions, is included in the diagram entirely for comparison purposes.

We did not trace exactly the course of homogenization of complex inclusions with a large gas bubble and an appreciable quantity of carbon dioxide. Such inclusions are found not only in topaz but also in beryl (Plate XV, 4) and are especially common in quartz.

The presence of liquid carbon dioxide in inclusions speaks for itself of a very high pressure in the inclusion system. This pressure grows so high on heating that we met with an intensive decrepitation of inclusions in all our experiments before the homogenization temperature could be reached. There were many tubular inclusions in the crystal of quartz from Pamir. In the course of our experiment with the prepared section of this crystal, we had to observe three analogous inclusions simultaneously. The first stage of homogenization of these complex inclusions was completed at 28.5–31.1°C *by the transition of the liquid carbon dioxide into the gaseous super-critical state.**

homogenization curves

5		6		7		8		9	
gas (%)	°C	gas (%)	°C	gas (%)	°C	gas (%)	°C	gas (%)	°C
48.6	190	46.4	210	42.9	230	28.6	260	0.0	265
40.0	220	37.0	230	33.0	240	20.0	250	0.0	260
18.1	250	0.0	293	—	—	—	—	—	—

* If we designate the volume of the gas bubble at 20°C as 100 per cent it becomes 90 per cent already at 23.5°C, 80 per cent at 27°C, 73 per cent at 27.5°C, and at 28.5°C the gas bubble vanishes completely, on account of an intensive expansion of the liquid carbon dioxide.

Further heating of the inclusions resulted in an appreciable increase in the size of the gas bubble. One of the inclusions ruptured at 160°C. A strong explosion of another one at 170°C broke one half of the section into several small pieces. The third inclusion, in the remaining part of the section, exploded at 220°C, when it still contained an appreciable quantity of the liquid phase.

Inclusions of pure carbon dioxide in low-temperature hydrothermal minerals and complex inclusions in high-temperature minerals are extensive in their wide distribution and *contribute evidence of the high degree of participation of carbon dioxide in mineral-forming processes.*

In every case of the application of the method here described for the determination of the state of aggregation of mineral-forming solutions, it is important to ascertain presence or absence of carbon dioxide in the inclusions, because carbon dioxide, as we have seen, has a substantial bearing on the cause of their homogenization. Presence of carbon dioxide in gaseous inclusions was proved by us in a number of cases, but, so far, it had not appeared possible for us to elucidate its influence on the course of the homogenization. We may merely assume that, within the range of variations in mineral-forming solutions, from "dry" gases to aqueous solutions, some kind of enrichment in it takes place, not only with water vapor but also with carbon dioxide gas. This supposition may be proved only as the result of micro-analysis of the inclusions for their gaseous constituents, analyses that we are not yet able to undertake. Having understood so far, only very approximately, the influence of carbon dioxide on the course of homogenization of inclusions, we are omitting entirely a discussion of inclusions of alien petroleum-like liquids homogenizing in the gaseous phase, even when the size of the extant gas bubble is relatively small.

VARIATIONS IN THE COURSE OF HOMOGENIZATION OF INCLUSIONS IN DIFFERENT GROWTH ZONES OF CRYSTALS

Delineation of the products of hydrothermal activity and of pneumatolysis, in a multistage development of hypogene deposits, involve well-known difficulties. Removal of these difficulties is one of the main problems in the modern theory of the formation of ores. Our present study also is largely subordinate to this problem.

The experience gained in applications of the methods we developed for studying inclusions of mineral-forming solutions must be supplemented by studies of individual crystals from pegmatitic deposits. This in indispensable for ascertaining variations in types and varieties of homogenization of inclusions in different growth zones of crystals.

Description of the sources of our test materials is omitted here, on the whole, for several reasons. It may be said only that pegmatitic veins and bodies of irregular shapes are associated with contact zones of a great plutonic granitic massif in the Ukraine. These pegmatites contain large and small cavities in which certain well-faceted minerals had crystallized; chiefly quartz, more rarely topaz, and others still more rarely. Paragenetic relationships of these minerals are not entirely clear and our first attempt therefore is to draw certain conclusions pertinent to the subject.

Figure 64 shows two crystals of topaz (*1* and *2*) and one crystal of morion (*3*) from one and the same vug in the pegmatites. They were

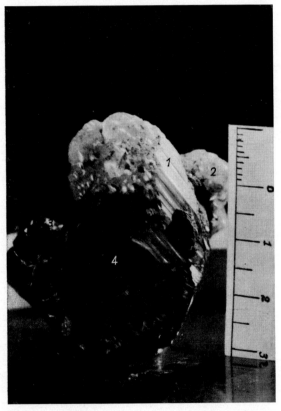

Fig. 64. Crystals of topaz and morion cemented by limonite.

probably in a druse at one time, but the now disengaged crystals were found to be cemented by limonite (*4*). It was desirable to determine, by their inclusions, whether the quartz and the topaz crystallized synchronously or in a sequence, one after the other.

The results on a large number of primary inclusions in these crystals are shown (as averages) in Table 44.

One may see in the table that the average temperatures are close to each other. The only observed discrepancy is due to the presence of liquid carbon dioxide in the inclusions in topaz and to its absence in the inclusions in quartz. The type and the species of homogenization were also the same. All of this suggests synchronous or nearly synchronous growth of the crystals.

TABLE 44

Type and species of homogenization	Homogenization temperature (°C)			Remarks
	Topaz 1	Topaz 2	Morion 3	
II (without inversion)	220	220	315	Liquid CO_2 in topaz
II (with inversion)	350–355	340	345	No CO_2

A crystal fragment of pneumatolytic quartz from the Ukrainian pegmatites is shown in Fig. 65, where its zonal structure is clearly visible.

The inner zone of this gray quartz abounds in primary gaseous inclusions, but its outer transparent zone is practically inclusion-free.

All inclusions in the inner zone, parted by a narrow band of transparent quartz, homogenized, with an inversion point, consistently at 310-

FIG. 65. Fragment of quartz from pegmatite. The outer zone is transparent; the inner zone is gray and is superabundant in gaseous inclusions.

330°C. The very scarce inclusions in the outer zone homogenized, also with an inversion, at 330–335°C.

This crystal is of considerable size (about 20 cm between the faces of the prism) and appears to have been formed during one single stage of the process and within a relatively small decrease of temperature (25°C) of the supercritical solutions.

Figure 66 represents a crystal of quartz whose inner zone is overflowing with gaseous inclusions, while the outer zone is transparent and has no inclusions at all. The boundary between the two zones is very sharp.

FIG. 66. A fragment of quartz crystal. The inner zone is full of primary gaseous inclusions.

Such structures of quartz crystals are typical of the pegmatites of the region.

We examined also a gigantic crystal from a pegmatitic body. Its zonal structure was clearly defined and its weight exceeded one ton.

The width of the prismatic faces of this crystal is 80 cm and the length of the edge between the rhombohedral faces is 1 m.

The outer transparent zone of the crystal, 16 cm thick, was smoky, but its inner zone consisted of gray quartz, of the same kind as in Figs. 65 and 66, with an immense number of primary inclusions by which *the specific gravity of the mineral was significantly lowered.*

In a sample taken from the crystal's center, 41 cm from a face of the prism, the homogenization of primary inclusions occurred at 305°C.

type II (without inversion). Among secondary inclusions in healed fissures of the crystal, we recognized two groups homogenizing as in type I at 240–280°C and at 145–195°C.

In another sample of the central zone of the crystal, taken 28 cm away from the outer face of the prism, primary inclusions homogenized at 320°C, type II (without inversion).

The very rare secondary liquid inclusions in the fissures of the crystal homogenized at the same temperatures as in the first sample already described.

In a sample from the gray zone, taken 24 cm away from the crystal's surface, the very abundant primary gas–liquid inclusions, homogenized as in type II, *with the point of inversion,* at 310–330°C. Their approximate inversion temperatures ranged from 200–230°C. The secondary inclusions homogenized as in type I and at the same temperatures as in the samples previously described.

In a sample of gray quartz, taken 1 cm from the contact with the smoky outer zone and 17 cm from the surface of the prism face, the inclusions homogenized as in type II, at 340–350°C and with the point of *inversion at 270°C.* The course of the homogenization was the same, but its temperature was 330°C, for inclusions in the smoky contact zone (15 cm from the crystal's surface).

Homogenization of inclusions in the smoky outer zone, with its point of inversion and with the critical point, took place apparently within the range 325–275–240°C. Moreover, essentially liquid secondary inclusions were also found in this zone, corresponding to two healing periods at 215–275°C and 55–90°C, together with some probably pseudo-secondary inclusions homogenizing at 310–327°C.

It should be pointed out that multiphase liquid inclusions homogenizing at 302–310–320°C, type I, were also found in isolated positions *outside the fissures,* in a specimen broken off [and rehealed?—Ed.] from the prism's surface (to a depth of 1 cm). A very rapid disappearance of the gas bubble accompanied by boiling at the end of the heating, of the kind previously described for topaz, was a special feature of the homogenization of these inclusions.

Definitely secondary inclusions homogenizing at 55–90°C, 140–190°C and 215–275°C, were found in fissures next to the crystal surface. The first two systems were healed probably concurrently with the very late formation of opal and chalcedony in the deposit.

The locally broken off inner part of the crystal was found to be regenerated by transparent smoky quartz in which we found inclusions typical of the subsurface part of the crystal (homogenization type II at 240–257–260°C and type I at 300–307°C).

Examination of this giant crystal was very useful in our investigation. We had the opportunity of following through the sequence of types and species of homogenization of the inclusions evidently caused by variations in the solutions during the growth of one single crystal. These variations were clearly expressed, from the crystal core to the smoky outer zone.

The inclusions were essentially gaseous (88–84.7 per cent gas) in the inner part of the crystal (deeper than 25 cm below the surface of the faces of the prism) and their homogenization was as in type II (species 1). The inclusions were gas–liquid, in the interval from 25 to 16 cm below the crystal's surface, with the proportions of liquid (as observed at room temperatures) increasing progressively toward the crystal's periphery. In our experiments, this increase was *accompanied by increasing temperatures of homogenization* (type II, species 2, with inversion), from 310–312°C to 350°C.

The smoky zone proper, yielding materials that generally meet the technical specifications, was formed mainly during the end-stage of the pneumatolytic process characterized by a lowering of homogenization temperatures of *gas–liquid* inclusions that are *found together with primary* (apparently the original ones) *essentially liquid inclusions* homogenizing in the liquid phase and with boiling. In one case, *in a healed fissure of the identical zone in a different crystal* we had the luck to observe definitely *the most highly varied ratios of the phase volumes in the inclusions.* This is characteristic, in our opinion, *of the environments of crystallization and healing of minerals in a boiling aqueous solution that had just arisen from a supercritical solution.*

A similar pattern of change, from the core to the periphery, is observed in inclusions in a quartz crystal from the same district.   The distance between the prismatic faces of this crystal was 25 cm.* The crystal's outer zone is also composed of transparent smoky quartz; its inner zone is gray. Primary inclusions in the inner zone homogenized at 270–280–285–290–305–310°C, with inversion. The homogenization temperatures rose to 335–340°C at the contact of the inner with the outer zones. Gas–liquid inclusions in the smoky outer zone showed again a radical lowering of the homogenization temperatures, from 305 to 205°C. Moreover, in addition to the gaseous inclusions this zone contained also some essentially liquid inclusions whose positions in the crystal did not always justify their classification as secondary with respect to the zone. The homogenization temperature series (type I) for these latter inclusions proved to be: 303–252–247–240–230–228–203°C, i.e. the same as in the first example of homogenization in the liquid phase.

---

* Placed at our disposal by Yu. Yu. Yurk, Senior Scientific Associate, Academy of Sciences of the U.S.S.R.

One would think that the simultaneous presence of gas–liquid and of essentially liquid inclusions homogenizing within the same range of the temperature may be explained only by boiling of the crystal-forming solution at the time of formation of the crystal's outer zone.

Comparisons between results obtained for the latter two crystals lead us to the conclusion that the second one is *of a younger age* than the first one. Its crystallization began when the inner part of the first one, the giant, was already produced from gaseous solution and had already attained its substantial dimensions. The larger crystal's zone at 28–17 cm below the existing faces of the prism is contemporaneous with the second crystal's inner zone. Both crystals finished their growth at the same time, in the same end-phase of the mineralization, characterized, it appears, by boiling of the mineral-forming solutions.

It should seem doubtful that such large crystals could be formed mainly from gaseous solutions, i.e. as the result of pneumatolysis. However, the tremendous numbers of undoubted primary gaseous and gas–liquid inclusions are objective indications of that origin of the crystals. Even if we consider the fact that essentially gaseous solutions are not highly concentrated (the same cannot be said about gas–liquid solutions in the inclusions), it is still probable that a very long stage of crystallization, of a nature unknown to us, may discourage any speculations on this subject.

THEORETICAL CONSIDERATION OF TYPES AND SPECIES OF HOMOGENIZATION OF INCLUSIONS IN MINERALS

We recognize two types and three species of homogenization of gaseous and liquid solutions included in minerals, in the summation of our discussion of the course of homogenization represented as curves in the diagrams (Figs. 58, 61, 62 and 63).

The different spans of variations in the phase ratios indicated in the diagrams have their own types and species of homogenization, it appears. *The first type of homogenization* is characteristic of the essentially liquid inclusions. Application of heat to such inclusions is accompanied by a smooth decrease in the size of the gas bubble, down to a pin-point, and by its ultimate disappearance, as well as by disappearance of the solid phases in the inclusion. In the case of liquid *two-phase* inclusions in low-temperature hydrothermal minerals, *the size of the gas bubble and the temperature of homogenization* are interrelated (the larger the gas bubble, the higher the temperature). This interdependence is sustained at temperatures up to 200°C and at gas bubble sizes from 1 to 21 per cent of the inclusion's total volume. *Presence of solid phases* in inclusions *serves to raise the homogenization temperature appreciably* and upsets the previously indicated relationship.

The first species of the second type of homogenization is characterized by a progressive increase in the size of the gas phase, by which the inclusion is finally filled. In contrast with the first type, type II, species 1, is characterized by an *inverse relationship between the size of the gas bubble,* occupying more than 76 per cent of the inclusion's volume at ordinary temperatures, *and the homogenization temperature* (the larger the gas bubble, the lower the homogenization temperature). Solid phases are rarely found in such inclusions; they appear as minute crystals forming "ripples" on the inclusion's walls.

The second species of the second type of homogenization (with an inversion point) is characteristic of the central sections of our diagrams, where the ratio of the gas bubble to the inclusion's total volume ranges from 55 to 76 per cent. Within this range, *the size of the gas bubble is inversely proportional to the homogenization temperature* and the inversion temperature tends to be lower, as a rule, if the gas bubble, at room temperature, occupies a relatively large volume of the inclusion, within the limits here indicated.

The third species (of type II) *of homogenization, with a critical point, is characterized by a sudden disappearance of the interphase boundary or by its instantaneous movement into the liquid,* as illustrated by curves *IX* and *XI* (Fig. 58). This variant is typical for a narrow field in our diagrams where the relative volume of the gas bubble is 51 to 55 per cent of the inclusion volume.

It has been demonstrated that, at a short distance from this narrow field, both on its right and on its left, as well as, to a certain extent, within the field itself, there is a boiling of the fluid and of the aqueous solution which is particularly energetic just before the instant of complete homogenization in the gas or in the liquid phase. It appears that, in the end stage of pneumatolysis and in the beginning stage of hydrothermal activity, even minute fluctuations of the temperature or of the pressure produce a violent boiling of the mineral-forming solutions.

The different types of homogenization are expressions of differences in the physical state of mother liquors sealed in minerals. As shown, the course of homogenization is undoubtedly influenced also by composition and concentration of the included solutions.

The nature of the homogenization of the first type, characteristic of hydrothermal minerals, was already discussed in detail (pp. 42–45). The gas bubble of these essentially liquid inclusions is vapor filling the vacuum. The gas bubble is produced as the result of the contraction of the hot solution on cooling and of a decrease in the volume of the cooled vacuole. Since the contraction coefficient of a liquid (solution) is much greater than of a solid substance, the different between the two volumes is compensated by gas (vapor) and the size of the resulting gas bubble will be proportional to the temperature of the included solution, at the time of its isolation, all other things being the same.

Depending on the extent of cooling [i.e. from the temperature of trapping—Ed.], there is a drastic *decrease also in the internal vapor pressure of the inclusion system*. In the case of pure water, this pressure is only 15 atm at 200°C; it becomes 1 atm at 100°C and 1/100 atm at 10°C. The vapor pressure of saturated KCl solution is merely 8.58 atm at 190°C and is 7.27 atm at 183°C for saturated NaCl, etc. The internal pressure becomes dependent only on composition of the liquid and the temperature as soon as the gas bubble appears in the inclusion. The vapor pressure should be very low at room temperatures in the case of included aqueous solutions.

In essentially liquid inclusions, the mean density of the two phases is always greater than the critical density of the included solution and the specific volume is always lower than the specific volume at the critical temperature (Fig. 18). If the solution is a concentrated one, its cooling may result not only in the formation of a vacant space wherein the gas bubble may develop, but also in a precipitation of solid phases which is undoubtedly related to a positive thermal coefficient of solubility of the solutes.

If the mother liquor included in the mineral's pores at a high temperature and a high pressure was a liquid aqueous solution with a specific volume smaller than the critical volume, the course of the homogenization of such inclusions will be as in type I, terminating in a complete filling of the inclusion's vacuole with the liquid phase, as we saw in every instance of inclusions in hydrothermal and Alpine type minerals.

In cases when the mother liquor was *a gaseous solution* at the time of its sealing off in the mineral's pores, we encounter the *second type of homogenization* of inclusions. The mean density of such solution, whatever its composition may be, must be invariably lower than its critical density, but its specific volume must exceed its volume at the critical temperature.

If we assume that the most common case (type II) involves presence in the inclusion of water vapor and its various solutes, we shall be dealing again with heterogeneous systems. At the originally high vapor pressure (but still not as high as the critical pressure), a liquid (aqueous solution) will be produced, in addition to a relatively large (more than 75 per cent of the inclusion's total) volume of free space which will be occupied by a gas phase at equilibrium with the liquid. Naturally, applications of heat to confined systems of this kind will result in a complete filling of the inclusion with gas.

The homogenization temperature of such essentially gaseous inclusions is the temperature at which $V = m/d$, where V is the volume of the inclusion, m is the mass of the given substance in the inclusion, and d is the density of vapor occupying the space at the given temperature.

Species 2, type II, of homogenization, with the point of inversion, as in species 1, had never been encountered by us in inclusions in minerals at any appreciable distance from the parent intrusion of hydrothermal mineral deposits or of Alpine mineral veins.

Changes of gaseous solutions with time take place apparently in the direction of a progressively increasing saturation with water vapor and of an increase in the density of gaseous solutions, even though this density still remains lower than the critical density of the solutions, up to the certain moment of transition of the medium from one state into another one. Such increase in density is easily traced in inclusions that become heterogeneous at lower temperatures and whose content of liquid is relatively high (25–45 volume per cent). By way of distinction from the essentially liquid or the gaseous inclusions, we call such inclusions gas–liquid or gaseous–aqueous, and the solutions they had captured—gas–liquid solutions.

The liquid of these inclusions, of course, is not pure water. The liquid is an aqueous solution containing apparently both strong and weak acids which tend, on the whole, *to lower their critical temperature,* notwithstanding the opposite effect of their non-volatile solutes. A cooling of the hermetically isolated supercritical solutions in the inclusions, down to room temperature, leads to their conversion into heterogeneous, occasionally three-phase or multiphase systems analogous to the system represented by the lower-right sketch in Fig. 57. As a rule, the volume of their solid phases is insignificant, compared to the inclusion's total volume. Since the pressure increases very rapidly, within the inclusions, on heating, their liquid phase, over an appreciable range of the temperature, up to the point of inversion, not merely fails to vanish, but, on the contrary, expands considerably, while decreasing in its density which tends to approach the density of the inclusion's gas phase. In the end, *at a certain definite temperature, the gas is enabled not only to dissolve the liquid phase but also to dissolve the previously precipitated solid substances.* This stage of rapid dissolution is expressed by a more or less abrupt turn of the homogenization curves to the left (Figs. 58, 61, 62). In practice, it appears, one may be dealing with solutions of this kind in high-pressure boilers, where there is an intensive transfer of substances by the gas phase and the resulting plugging of the turbine blades.

As shown in the diagram (Fig. 58), there is a rise in the inversion temperature with increasing quantities of liquid in gas–liquid inclusions, as observed at room temperature. If the liquid content of such inclusions amounts to 46–50 per cent, *the inversion temperature, on our curves, coincides with the critical point of the captured fluids.* In this extreme case of type II homogenization, we find species 3 (with the critical point). The decrease in the liquid density, accompanied by appreciable expansion of

TABLE 45

Point No.	Gaseous phase at room temperature (%)	Homogenization temperature (°C)	Type and species of homogenization	Source of specimen	Solid phase (%)	No. of phases in inclusion at room temperature
			Beryl			
18	81.0	320	II, 1	—	—	2
19	86.0	310	II, 2	—	—	2
20	82.0	320	II, 1	—	—	2
21	48.6	398	I	—	—	2
22	30.0	378	I	—	—	2
23	29.5	342	I	—	—	2
24	37.6	438	I	—	—	2
25	38.4	368	I	—	—	2
26	39.0	370	I	—	—	2
27	67.0	349	II, 2	—	—	2
			Topaz			
1	10.4	180	I	Volynia (curve II)	10.6	6
2	19.6	300	I	Volynia (curve I)	25.4	8
3	22.6	375	I	Volynia (curve IV)	present	2
4	33.2	445–450	I	Adun-Cholong	small	2
5	34.5	462	I	Sherlova Gora (curve III)	1.5	2
6	50.0	350 to 352	—	Volynia (curve XII)	$1.0+CO_2$	2
7	54.0	360 to 362	II, 3	Volynia (curve X)	—	2
9	58.2	371	II, 2	Volynia (curve IX)	—	2
10	59.7	370	II, 2	Volynia (curve IX)	small	2
11	64.3	355	II, 2	Volynia (curve IX)	—	2
11	66.0	350	II, 2	Volynia (curve VIII)	—	2
13	75.0	310	II, 2	Volynia (curve VIII)	—	2
15	79.2	400	II, 1	Volynia (curve VI)	—	2
16	88.0	275	II, 1	Murzinka, Ural	—	2
17	88.2	270	II, 1	Volynia (curve V)	—	2
			Pneumatolytic quartz*			
40	85.1	290	II, 1	—	—	2
41	94.0	202	II, 1	Transcarpathia	—	2

* The other data on the homogenization temperatures employed in drawing of the curves were previously cited (Fig. 16).

the liquid (up to 1/3 increase in the original volume), on heating, goes far enough for the liquid to bring its density conspicuously near the density of the gas. After that, there is an instantaneous homogenization of the inclusion system characterized, it appears, by a solution of a rather simple composition. *At this point, the density of the solution captured by the mineral equals the solution's critical density, while its specific volume equals its volume at the critical temperature.*

We prepared a special diagram (Fig. 67), as an illustration of types and species of homogenization of inclusions with the aid of our experi-

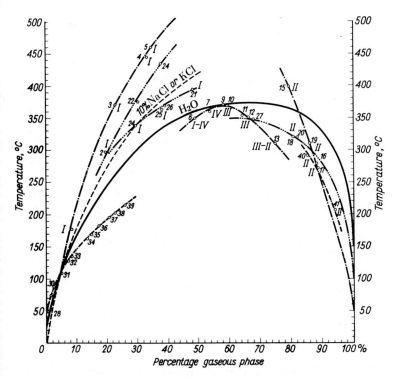

FIG. 67. Homogenization temperature curves for pure water and mother liquors for inclusions in topaz, beryl and quartz crystals.

Curves of ratios between degree of filling and homogenization temperature
  — Empirical curve for water
  — — — Empirical curve for 10 per cent solution of NaCl or KCl
  —·—· Determined curves for topaz (reference points *1* through *17*) frcm Volynia, Ural, Sherlova Gora, and Adun-Cholong
  —·····—···· Determined curves for beryl (reference points *18* through *27*)
  —·—·—· Determined points for quartz (reference points *18* through *41*) from Aldan, Ural, Volynia, Transcarpathia).
I, II, III, IV, types and species of homogenization. Multiphase inclusions at points *1* and *2*. A mixed inclusion (with CO_2) at point *6*.

mental data. The curves in this diagram show the relationship between the degree of filling of inclusions in topaz, beryl, and quartz crystals with homogenization temperatures of the inclusions. For the sake of comparisons, the diagram also contains analogous curves for pure water and for 10 per cent solutions of chlorides. The numerical data employed in the construction of the diagram are reported in Table 45 (p. 284).

As evident from the diagram, the inclusion curves for different minerals do not coincide. Moreover, curves for one and the same mineral also fail to coincide, as, for example, for beryl. If the first kind of the non-coincidence is explanable by differences in the temperature coefficients, the second one is due entirely to difference in the composition and the concentration of the included solutions.

All of the curves become farther apart in the field of high temperatures, but in the field of low temperatures and weak concentrations (the left part of the diagram) all of them practically coincide.

The extreme right of the diagram represents solutions in the supercritical state [sic]. Here too there is a non-coincidence and even intersection of different curves for inclusions in different minerals. These curves lead us theoretically to expect homogenization temperatures at 100°C and even at 50°C, for inclusions of "dry" gases with a very low content of liquid (at room temperature). In reality, however, the lowest determined homogenization temperature for inclusions of this kind was 200°C.

Let us now look at the low-temperature position of the homogenization curves involving the inversion and the critical points. As shown, the temperatures of these curves are lower than the curve for pure water derived for the same degree of filling. The plausible explanation here lies in the probable presence of strong and weak acids in the inclusions, conducive to lowering of the [homogenization?—Ed.] temperature of the inclusion-forming solutions. We should remember that the critical temperature of HCl is only 51.4°C (84.5 atm), and of CO_2 only 31.1°C (75.5 atm).

In our view, the diagram may be useful in determining the position of the inclusion-bearing mineral against the general background of successive variations in mineral-forming solutions, from the early stage of "dry" gases, to the late stage of liquid cold-water hydrothermal solutions, by means of the homogenization type and of the degree of filling of the inclusions. Our published schematic diagram of the stages and sub-stages of evolution of mineral-forming magmatic derivations [37, p. 56] discussed below (Fig. 68) was intended for this purpose. The types and the species of homogenization of inclusions, as illustrated by the giant crystal of quartz, allow us to recognize variations with time in the mother liquor. They provide us with the opportunity to determine objectively the range of participation of a solution, in a given state of aggregation, in the crystallization of inclusion-bearing minerals and in the formation of hypogene mineral deposits.

Homogenization type II is never found in inclusions in minerals from hypogene sources far removed from the parent intrusions and of an undoubtedly hydrothermal origin. This type *must be recognized as the characteristic one for minerals of pneumatolytic origin deposited by supercritical solutions.*

Homogenization species 2 (with a point of inversion) and 3 (with a critical point) are typical of inclusions in minerals produced in the terminal stage of the pneumatolytic process, *while species 1 (type II) is found in inclusions belonging to the early stage of the action of supercritical solutions.*

If it becomes necessary in the future, even as before, to recognize the group of "pneumatohydatogenic" minerals and mineral deposits, gas–liquid inclusions will probably become the indicators of such origin of their host minerals. The phenomena of violent boiling *at a slightest downward fluctuation of the temperature and the pressure* is typical of the end-phase of this stage.

We must add now a few words in reference to the extent of suitability of the homogenization temperatures of essentially gaseous and gas–liquid inclusions for an estimation of the true temperatures and pressures of pneumatolytic mineral genesis. If one and the same zone of a mineral contains primary inclusions homogenizing as in types I and II and at the same temperature, i.e. when we are dealing with a mineral that was formed in the environment of a boiling fluid, we may be able to determine the temperature and the pressure exactly from the composition.

In other cases, the temperature required for the conversion of the very last drop of liquid into vapor will be only the minimum temperature and the pressure will be also the minimum pressure. Moreover, the larger the volume of the gas bubble in the inclusion, the farther away is the observed homogenization temperature from the actual temperature of the formation of the mineral. Consequently, in the instance of essentially gaseous inclusions, so far, *we do not consider it possible to determine even the minimum temperatures on the basis of the temperature at the point of the homogenization.* The still unknown corrections for pressure and concentration would be too high. Only within the range of 80–70 per cent gas and 20–30 per cent liquid, as observed in inclusions at room temperature, might they be reasonable. A large body of experimental work is still required, with the accompanying careful physico-chemical interpretations of the results, for a productive solution of the many problems involved in the studies of gaseous inclusions as a group.

IN REFERENCE TO THE POSSIBILITY
OF DIFFERENTIATING BETWEEN PRODUCTS
OF PNEUMATOLYSIS AND PRODUCTS OF HYDROTHERMAL
AND COLD SOLUTIONS IN MINERAL DEPOSITS

In Chapter 3 of our study, we undertook correlations of composition and state of inclusions in minerals with progressive and orderly development of the mineral-forming hypogene process, as well as correlations of the experimentally obtained data on inclusions of mother liquors, as discussed in Chapters 5 and 6 of this book; these demonstrated the possibilities of objective identifications, in mineral deposits, of pneumatolytic products and of products laid down by hot or cold liquid aqueous solutions. Understanding of the true nature of various inclusions, in addition to the experimental work, must provide the key to unlock new doors, in ascertaining physico-chemical environments of the formation of hypogene deposits of various kinds.

We shall summarize very briefly, in the present chapter, the indicated possibilities in the problem and consider in some detail, the meaning of single-phase essentially liquid inclusions that are homogeneous at room temperature.

The presence of essentially liquid heterogeneous inclusions, homogenizing as in type I, is evidence of a hydrothermal or an "Alpine" origin of their host minerals.

We encountered single-phase liquid inclusions in our studies of hydrothermal deposits of fluorite in Transbaykalia. The significance of such inclusions, in regards to the origin of their host minerals, has been completely obscure up to the present time.

Such inclusions are by no means rare in hydrothermal minerals *of the very latest generations* and they are common in minerals known to be of cold-water origin,* as it was proved by our studies of a large number of minerals crystallized in different environments, including supergene ones. We observed large numbers of such inclusions in gypsum crystals from sedimentary beds, in analcite from the Archangel'sk area (Cape Chaytsyn), in celestite from Pinega and from the vicinity of Kislovodsk, and in inyoite from Inder Lake. Natrolite from the northern territories contains essentially liquid inclusions of an odd type, without any gas bubble, but with small crystals (liquid+solid phase). We were able to produce two-phase inclusions in crystals of alum (liquid+sylvite crystals) grown artificially at temperatures below 70°C. This was proof that inclusions of this type may be produced in warm solutions, *provided the solutions are highly saturated with substances that are alien to the host mineral.*

---

* With the exception of easily-soluble minerals, such as halite and sylvite developing also anomalous gas bubbles in their inclusions, in the absence of hermetic sealing of the inclusions [37, p. 51].

It is curious that heating of two-phase (liquid–solid) inclusions in natrolite leads to their homogenization at a low temperature, up to 40° or 50°C. The solid "captive" minerals are dissolved in the process. Further heating (overheating) leads to formation of heterogeneous inclusions. In one of our experiments, gas bubbles appeared in 5 per cent of the large number of the inclusions observed, even at 50°C. In some others, the gas bubbles appeared at 90°C and at 105°C. This kind of heterogenization is related to solution of the vacuole walls and decrepitation of the mineral permitting a gradual leakage of the included liquid into the fissures. All of the inclusions were found to be "empty" (without liquid) at 130°C, so that their subsequent cooling failed to restore their original state.

Any disturbance in the hermetic sealing of the vacuole is followed by a practically instantaneous leakage of the liquid into the fissures, in the case of two-phase and of multiphase inclusions.

Our other experiments, with crystals grown artificially in aqueous solutions, showed that a discrete gas bubble can be found at room temperature in crystals formed at temperatures as low as 65–70°C. This threshold is subject to fluctuations, depending on the temperature coefficient of solubility of the host mineral and on the shape and the size of the inclusion. After cooling, the volume of such bubbles, in crystals formed at 65–90°C, varies from 1.5 to 3 per cent of the volume of the cavity.

Discrete gas bubbles in secondary and primary inclusions of natural solutions at lower temperatures were found by us only in quartz crystals from the Northern Ural, where they occupied 0.7 per cent of the inclusion's volume and homogenized at 55°C, and also in the last generation of calcite from the Soviet Far East where the gas bubble amounted to 0.5 per cent of the inclusion's volume and would disappear at 38–40°C.

As shown by experiments and by examination of many natural minerals, discrete gas bubbles are not produced in included solutions trapped at temperatures below 40–50°C.

Single-phase liquid inclusions in transparent crystals of quartz from the agate of Akhaltsikh, the "diamanths"* from Marmarosh, apophyllite and calcite from the Soviet Far East, late pink fluorite from Kalanguy, and other minerals of the hydrothermal paragenesis are interpreted by us as evidence to the effect that such minerals were formed from solutions whose temperatures had fallen below 50°C.

The problem as to whether the mineral-forming solutions are vadose or juvenile in their origin is highly complicated by the fact that both vadose and juvenile solutions become mixed, undoubtedly, in the upper zone of circulation.

---

* Probably a trade name for ornamental quartz [V.P.S.].

Moreover, solutions of "metamorphic origin" also play an important role in the mineral-forming process, as was shown by A. N. Zavaritskiy for pyritic deposits and by A. G. Betekhtin for deposits of manganese. Controversies about the origin of deposits of piezo- and optical minerals [33, 34, 60, 66, etc.] bring out the fact that it is by no means possible, in all instances, to differentiate between hot solutions of metamorphic origin producing deposits of the Alpine type and solutions whose mineral content is closely related to a magmatic source, i.e. hydrothermal solutions in the strict sense of the term. It is difficult, however, to visualize the latter as being purely magmatic and unenriched by any mineral constituents of the host rocks, whose alterations along the extensive paths of movement of the solution are widely known. Activity of the hydrothermal fluids is undoubtedly enhanced in the presence of carbon dioxide which plays a major part in the formation of minerals and is often found in inclusions.

In such manner, we run into great difficulties in the very definition of the concept "hydrothermal solution". The long-standing debate on this subject can hardly be assumed to be terminated conclusively. There is no doubt that, in the upper zone of the earth's crust, there is a mixing of genuine hydrothermal solutions with heated metamorphic ones and even with vadose waters, so that pseudohydrothermal fluids ("pseudohydrotherms") [34] are the result. Proceeding from geologic premises and taking into account the whole of the history of the evolution of the mineral-forming process, in every given case, we are generally able, of course, to determine with a high degree of probability whether the mineral-forming solutions had a magmatic or surficial origin. This is particularly successful for mineral deposits where we may draw on our considerable experience with the alteration of minerals under the influence of definitely surficial solutions [95].

Vadose waters, circulating even at 1 km depths, in zones unaffected by surficial temperature fluctuations (the band of perennial temperatures) could hardly be heated above 34°C [75] and, for that reason, the products of their deposition (except in the previously noted anomalous cases) cannot contain any two-phase liquid inclusions. On the other hand, we find single-phase inclusions, typical of cold-water and tepid-water minerals, also in the products of the final stages of an undoubtedly hydrothermal process (fluorites from Transbaykalia, certain minerals from Tetyukhe and other sources). Consequently, while speaking of the lower temperature limit of the hydrothermal process, we must always bear in mind that *cold-water minerals*, that need be subdivided genetically into *magmatogenic* and *exogenic* ones, are found also among the hydrothermal products.

We examined tens of thousands of inclusions in many kinds of minerals, in the course of our research in the temperatures and the state of aggregation of mineral-forming solutions. The inclusions showed definitely that minerals, such as quartz, may be crystallized in very different environments. If, for example, the majority of beryl and topaz crystals contain the essentially gaseous or the gas–liquid inclusions homogenizing as in type II, it does not mean necessarily that a pneumatolytic origin must be ascribed to all beryl and topaz, as was done before. For example, the early topaz crystals from the Il'men' Mountains indeed do contain primary inclusions homogenizing as in type II, at temperatures up to 580°C, while inclusions in the later topaz crystals from the Akulova Pit homogenize at 250–260°C only, and the colorless very small crystals of topaz from the Kosaya Mountain suggest still lower temperatures, from 195 to 240°C. On the other hand, zircon and almandite contain among their primary inclusions only "dry" gases or *single-phase essentially gaseous* inclusions, as evidence it appears of the very earliest stage in the evolution of pneumatolysis.

As was demonstrated in the preceding chapter, such inclusions, following our experimentation, make it possible for us not only to refer their host mineral to the pneumatolytic or to the hydrothermal stage of the mineral genesis but also to ascertain in what particular sub-stage or phase (within the stage) did it crystallize. *In mineral deposits of a multistage origin, pneumatolytic and hydrothermal products may be identified as such on the basis of the studies of their inclusions.*

For example, in certain deposits in Transbaykalia, to be described in detail by other geologists (I. F. Grigor'ev), primary inclusions in quartz from greizens homogenized as in type II (without inversion) at an average temperature of 360°C. Inclusions in a later quartz (quartz I, pre-cassiterite) are homogenized at 320–330°C, with an inversion. Inclusions in cassiterite from the same source homogenize as in type I at 280–240°C, on the average. Not in a single case could we find inclusions in the post-cassiterite quartz of various generations that would homogenize as in type II. They showed homogenization temperatures of 248°C, and lower. We were able to find some primary inclusions in some fine and apparently late crystals of topaz homogenizing as in type I and indicating a hydrothermal origin of their host mineral.

All of these minerals, by themselves, could offer no clues to geologists concerning their origins; opportunities of that kind were provided by the inclusions, as we have seen.

Extensive applications of the thermometric analysis of minerals, as here described, together with determinations of the state of aggregation of mineral-forming solutions, will enable us in the future to develop orderly general patterns of the evolution of magmatic derivations and the sequence of hypogene formation of minerals in their endogenic deposits.

As the first approximation to this purpose, by way of an elaboration and refinement of the patterns proposed by Fersman, we take the liberty here to suggest a still very crude skeleton of a pattern of the principal stages and sub-stages* of the evolution of mineral-forming magmatic derivations (Fig. 68), based on our results with the inclusion studies and on the experience of many Soviet geologists with various types of hypogene mineral deposits, as described in the publications listed under Bibliography.

---

* In the original, "etapy i stadii" ("etapes and stages") respectively, here and throughout the text [V.P.S.].

CHAPTER 8

Schematic Pattern of Principal Stages and Sub-stages in Hypogene Formation of Minerals

THE majority of geologists and mineralogists assume that pegmatites are mineral formations arising *from residual magmatic solutions* saturated with volatile constituents (graphic granites) and that pneumatolytic deposits are produced by deposition of minerals *from gas-like solutions,* at temperatures above or below the critical temperatures of the gas, and that hydrothermal deposits are produced *by hot aqueous solutions* in their liquid state, by way of the fundamental distinction between the processes of the development of hypogene mineral deposits. However, these concepts lose practically all of their clarity on their practical application to exo-magmatic deposits* because of the absence of objective criteria in recognition of the origins of the minerals.

American geologists, whose concepts of the process of endogenic formation of minerals tend toward simplification and emasculation of the idea of evolution, are trying to bring under the category of hydrotherms not only hot and chiefly aqueous liquids but also any water-enriched hot fluid in the gaseous state. A series of other geologists, such as Rosenbusch, believe that even "graphic granites" were formed from fluids.

It is not possible for us, in the present work, to consider all of the mutually contradictory opinions regarding the processes of hypogene formation of minerals. We do not aim, in this part of the book, to give an account of the many kinds of accomplishments of Soviet geologists in ascertaining physico-chemical processes and geologic environments of formation of minerals. Such reviews are already on record [9, 53, 92]. We should wish merely to outline, in a fragmentary way, only the accomplishments of Soviet scientists that helped substantially in the making of our pattern and in the development of our concepts in the theory of the

---

* Under the term "exo-magmatic", in contrast with "endo-magmatic", we include all mineral formations, related genetically and in time, to the long life of a magmatic source, but developing outside its boundaries. Exo-magmatic deposits are products of synmagmatic and not of post-magmatic gaseous and liquid solutions.

formation of ores. It is essential also to consider some of the defects that compel us even now to propose this pattern in its first variant.

The presence of a clearly defined line of demarcation between the magmatic stage, in the strict sense, and the next stage in the succession, as recognized by many Soviet geologists, is essential for an understanding of the evolution of the exo-magmatic mineral-forming process. However, the problem as to where exactly this line is to be drawn, in every specific case, is still not entirely solved. An orderly development of magmatic sources, like any other development in time, is unthinkable unless it is accompanied by qualitative changes in composition of the magma and of its mineral products. This is brought out in a series of contributions by Soviet petrographers. Studies in the development of endo-magmatic deposits by Russian scientists such as V. A. Krat, A. N. Zavaritskii, A. G. Betekhtin, P. M. Tatarinov, G. A. Sokolov, and others was a major contribution to the theory of ore formation. The endo-magmatic group of ore deposits is probably the only one whose origin and classification were determined in such detail as to have left no doubts whatsoever. In foreign countries, on the other hand, this group has not been clarified even now, including specifically such a typical member as Sudbury.

Our Soviet scientists were just as definitely ahead of the American school of ore geologists in the problem of pneumatolytic ore deposits as they were in regards to endo-magmatic deposits. This was made manifest, first of all, in the classification of endogenic deposits from which Lindgren et al. excluded pneumatolytic deposits a long time ago [151a, 155].

This latter group represents an important stage in the evolution of magmatic derivatives and holds the place of honor in Obruchev's classification [72, 73], most widely accepted by our geologists. More recently, however, some of our outstanding geologists were inclined to combine it with the hydrothermal one [105], "in view of the practical absence, so far, of any objective criteria, at our disposal, for separate identification of materials deposited by gaseous vs. liquid solutions" [88, p. 157].

Indeed, we are not aware, so far, of any even partially reliable criteria of pneumatolysis, although the inconsistency of the denials of transfer and redeposition of substances in gaseous solutions was already demonstrated by the experiments of eminent Soviet scientists, such as Khitarov, Ivanov [110, 111, 112, 113], and Syromyatnikov [101]. Supporting evidence is provided by Belyankin [4], in his observations on gaseous transfers in technological processes.

Nikolayev [67, 68], on the basis of his equilibrium diagrams for binary systems, concluded that fluid solutions are very important [as carriers of mineral substance—V.P.S.] within a very wide range of temperatures and pressures, over and above their critical points, and that there is a definite break between magmatic solutions and their gaseous residues. His diagrams are highly valuable scientifically.

These works, as well as the works of Zavaritskii [42 and others] lead to the invalidation of several of the concepts and diagrams of Vogt and Niggli and refute the enunciations of such American geologists as Graton and Lindgren.

One must admit, nevertheless, that observations and experiments of this type and theoretical conclusions devoid of objective natural criteria, could still not be accepted as proof of the critical phenomena effective in natural mineral genesis. It has been pointed out correctly that geologic observations also fail to yield sufficient data that would make it possible to distinguish the pneumatolytic stage of mineral genesis from the hydrothermal one. Moreover, for example, some minerals believed to be pneumatolytic are very common in pegmatitic and even in hydrothermal veins. It follows therefore that they could have been formed equally well from gas-saturated magmatic solutions as from aqueous solutions. Under such circumstances, the existence and the effective range of the "pneumatohydatogenic" formation of minerals [14] becomes still more obscure.

It is extremely important for our correct understanding of the hypogene formation of minerals whether this phenomenon takes place in confined or in open systems. This problem was solved by Soviet geologists on the basis of geologic facts, laboratory findings, and their physico-chemical interpretations, chiefly in connection with research in pegmatites. Although different investigators had different views as to the degree of confinement or of openness of the systems, in the different stages of the evolution of magmatic derivations (A. Ye. Fersman, A. N. Zavaritskii, V. A. Nikolayev), they arrived at the correct conclusion in regards to the *relative* meaning of these concepts, namely, that the distinctions in question are not mutually exclusive but mutually complementary, that a confined system is simultaneously an open one, to a certain degree, and that, in the dimension of time, a *preponderantly* confined system is succeeded by a *preponderantly* open one, etc. Hydrothermal solutions participate in mineral genesis in relatively more open environments, in a discontinuously pulsating system, as against, for example, a preponderantly confined physico-chemical environment of mineral genesis operative in the crystallizer cavities in Alpine veins.

The geochemical studies of V. I. Vernadskii and A. Ye. Fersman, outstanding in their significance, gave us the principles of the historical understanding of mineral genesis, in many respects.

Specifically, Fersman's pattern of geophases served as the starting point of our schematic diagram (Fig. 68) founded on studies of relics of mineral-forming solutions preserved in inclusions.

Physico-chemical interpretations of laboratory data and of results of geologic–mineralogic research depend significantly on the work of D. S.

Korzhinskii who proved the equally valid applicability of the phase rule to confined physico-chemical systems and to open systems at dynamic equilibrium.

His "temperature levels", based on reactions involving up-take of water (Collected Papers, *Micas of the U.S.S.R.*), are highly important in comparative mineralogic thermometry.

S. S. Smirnov has developed the concept of a pulsating character of mineral-forming solutions given off by a magmatic source and of their orderly variations, in space and time. Smirnov and, next to him, Yu. A. Bilibin, developed the premises of the metallogenic concept of the multistage character of the formation of parent intrusions and of the ore-bearing intrusive complexes orderly succeeding each other, in time. They demonstrated the need of taking into account the entire complex of variations in geologic environments of deposition of minerals, as a prerequisite to understanding of the stabilization of various hypogene exo-magmatic deposits of minerals.

A. G. Betekhtin gave us a powerful weapon for bringing to light the successions and phases of mineralization in ore deposits, in his method of investigation of textures and structures of ores. His method is the means of determining the age relationships in aggregates of ore minerals. One of the most difficult problems in the origin of ores, involving the ore minerals, was resolved by Betekhtin's method. More recently, Betekhtin developed the theoretical basis of paragenetic relationships of minerals in ores, in relation to various sulfur and oxygen regimes, temperatures, and other factors present in different quantities in mineral-forming solutions, by which the deposition of the minerals is effected.

Problems involved in interactions between mineral-forming solutions and the surrounding rocks were examined theoretically by D. S. Korzhinskii using polymetallic mineralized skarns as examples. The theory of "bimetasomatic" origin of the skarns, in conjunction with the principles of the "filtrational effect" had opened new pages in science, in our understanding of relationships between mineral-forming media and geologic environments. These interactions are clearly illustrated also by the exceptionally thorough studies of scheelite-bearing skarns (by Kh. M. Abdullayev) and of wolframite-bearing greisen veins (by O. D. Levitskii).

A. N. Zavaritskii's principle, namely, that pegmatites formed after the graphic phase are products of metasomatic processes, has a cardinal significance in the problems of interactions between gaseous media and geologic environments. Quantitative expressions of these interactions, bound inseparably with qualitative variations in the media and in the environments, were demonstrated to science, for the first time, by K. A. Vlasov. The ore-tectonics researches of A. V. Korolev, F. I. Vol'fson, A. V. Pek, and others, constitute an essential link in our understanding of the dependence of natural physico-chemical systems, in regards to their becoming open or confined, on tectonic movements. The latter may produce either renovations in the migration paths of gaseous and liquid solutions or may block their migration paths, with the resulting formation of confined, or more accurately, practically confined environments of formation of minerals, for a period of time. The works of F. V. Chukhrov and, to some extent, of O. D. Levitskii, in ascertaining the role of colloids in hydrothermal mineral genesis amplify significantly the views of Soviet geologists on hypogene formation of ore deposits.

It is not possible, of course, to bring forth here all of the attainments of the Soviet school of ore geologists that created the basis of the new theory of the formation of ores, in an adequate degree of completeness and with their characteristically comprehensive approach to the solution of this most highly involved problem. We presented here only very brief information, by way of an illustration of the most favorable background and creative daring of the young Soviet geologists, as well as of the unbreakable bond and the dependence of our work on the advancements of the entire school of Soviet ore geologists based on the most progressive and the solely correct scientific world outlook.*

However, notwithstanding all of these undoubtedly great accomplishments, our liberation from concepts alien to the Soviet school is still too slow. It may be sufficient here merely to remember that we are still at peace with many obscurities and especially with the lack of sufficient objectivity in the research on the relatively low-temperature hydrothermal processes of mineral formation. As an example, we may cite identification of hypo-, meso-, epithermal, etc., deposits by the means of the so-called typomorphic minerals which, as everybody knows, are themselves in need of identification in regards to their true origin (with the exception, perhaps, of some genuinely low-temperature minerals, such as antimonite, cinnabar, and realgar).

It may be sufficient here to remind that, at one time, the "imported" concepts of tin deposits as typically pneumatolytic ones became firmly rooted with us, with the consequent adverse effect of both on prospecting and on genetic conclusions. The presence of cassiterite in an ore was deemed to be a sufficient proof of a pneumatolytic origin of the ore deposit. However, Smirnov's discovery of sulfide-cassiterite deposits had led to the abandonment of cassiterite as an indicator of a hydrothermal† origin of the ore deposits [89].

Some of the very common sulfides are found also in the early stages of pegmatitic mineral genesis, as well as in skarns and in hydrothermal deposits. There is no assurance therefore that they could not have been

---

* Dialectic materialism, in its philosophic–scientific applications [V.P.S.].

† It appears that, in this place, the original does not differentiate between hydrothermal and pneumatolytic ore deposits [V.P.S.].

formed from gaseous solutions or even from magmatic solutions. Finally, one may see many examples (Transcaucasia, etc.) in which it is not possible to decide whether the deposit is hydrothermal or supergene, in view of the presence of gypsum, calcite, and other such minerals. The lower temperature limit of hydrothermal mineral genesis and the source of the solutions remain obscure in these cases

American geologists, like Hulin [126*], for example, in his latest publications, in 1947, believe that hydrothermal solutions are characterized by temperatures below the critical temperature of water (374°C) but above its boilling point at the earth's surface (100°C). Smith [133]† believes that the upper temperature limit of the hydrothermal process is approximately 290°C.

We cannot accept such liberties in setting up the temperature limits of the hydrothermal action. As already proved, there is nothing to prevent the existence of concentrated aqueous solutions, in the liquid form, at much higher temperatures. Their boiling points also need not coincide with 100°C, in the upper zone of the earth's crust, on account of the presence of their solutes in different concentrations.

In principle, there is also nothing to prevent the assumption of the existence of tepid liquid hydrothermal solutions participating in the formation of mineral deposits at temperatures considerably below 100°C. According to our findings in the research on inclusions, the limits of hydrothermal activity, in regard both to temperature and to the depth, are broadened considerably, in either direction. Moreover, *the temperature boundaries cannot be stable, as a rule.* Hydrothermal mineral genesis is often superimposed on the products of pneumatolytic processes, so that the new low-temperature hydrothermal minerals are often confused with the earlier products of high-temperature hydrotherms. Formation of a very large number of exo-magmatic deposits was a multistage process.

The fragmentational subdivision of hydrothermal deposits into hypo-, meso-, lepto-, epi-, and telethermal, introduced by Lindgren [125]‡ and elaborated by other American geologists (Graton) was subjected to a just criticism by our geologists, chiefly because these designations involve not only the temperature but also the depth factor. Thermometric investigations of minerals indicate that the majority of hydrothermal deposits and even isolated crystals were formed in a span of appreciably decreasing temperatures, as, for example, within the mesothermal to epithermal range. Formation of the deposits, in time, was accompanied by pulsations of the solutions which were responsible for variations in the products of the hydrothermal process.

---

* Erroneous citation—Hulin does not appear in the Bibliography.

† [133] in the Bibliography is Zirkel. 1893 [V.P.S.]. Refs 176 and 194 are by Smith [Ed.].

‡ [125] in the Bibliography is Brewster, with the dates of 1827 and 1835 [V.P.S.].

The above does not mean that we should ignore or belittle the temperature factor in determining origins of mineral deposits. The temperature factor plays undoubtedly a leading role in hydrothermal mineral genesis. However, as we have shown the temperatures in question must be determined for individual minerals formed within a more narrow range of temperature than the range of the given deposit, as a whole. The problem of the over-all range of temperature for the deposit is to be solved on the basis of temperatures of its minerals in which certain definite fixed moments of the hydrothermal mineral genesis are determined by thermometric analysis (see Chapter 6).

Notwithstanding the fact that the entire genetic classification of hydrothermal deposits is essentially a many-storied edifice built on the temperature, our knowledge of the temperatures of the natural processes is still very small. Referring of hydrothermal deposits to a given category have generally been based on occurrences of a key mineral or a group of minerals to which a given range of temperature and mode of formation are assigned. In reality, however, many minerals (the example of cassiterite is cited above), previously believed to be diagnostic of certain types of deposit, were found to have formed within a wide range of temperature and to have crystallized from solutions in different states, when the more exact methods of study were applied to the problem of their origin.

A series of the so-called "transient" minerals is widely known, minerals that cannot be considered characteristic of any particular genetic type of mineral deposit. At the same time, the previously limited circle of "geologic thermometer" minerals, considered by mineralogists to have formed within narrow temperature boundaries, becomes progressively more limited, as new data on the subject continue to be accumulated. These and related minerals were performing a responsible job, whatever it was, on probation, of determining the origin and particularly the temperatures of formation of mineral deposits. The total inadequacy of such methods of recognizing the unknown by the means of something not-too-well-known is obvious.

In mineralogy and in prospecting for mineral deposits, the problem of ascertaining the origin of minerals becomes altogether too complicated if they fall into the investigator's hands not directly from their original source, with a definitely known paragenesis, but *from panned samples or as constituents of sedimentary rocks*. A correct objective determination of the origins of minerals in the light fraction, in the latter case, is not only of cardinal importance in practice, as for example in correlations of barren sedimentary series, but also theoretically, as for example in reconstructions of paleogeologic and paleogeographic environments as well as in certain fields of petrography of sedimentary rocks.

Thus, despite the very substantial accomplishments of the advanced school of Soviet geologists, in practice and in theory, and the very large body of accumulated observed facts, painstaking mineralogic descriptions and analyses, responsible for a whole series of profound theoretical constructions, prognoses, and conclusions, it becomes perfectly clear that a great deal of work is still required for the creation of a new Soviet theory of the formation of ores.

We hope that applications of the new methods of study of the mineral-forming environments to individual mineral deposits may be a contribution to the problem. Their extensive applications in deciphering the complicated processes of the formation of ores, however, requires even now some kind of schematic representation that will be elaborated and refined undoubtedly in the future. We can no longer remain satisfied with the scholastic schemes, not subject to any objective proof, of the sort that was developed chiefly by the American school of ore geologists.

A schematic representation of the sequence of stages and sub-stages in the evolution of mineral-forming magmatic derivatives [37, p. 57] was offered by us, for discussion and use, based as it was on the research of our outstanding scientists, but only as the first approximation, by integration with the results of study of relics of mineral-forming solutions preserved in the inclusions.

In harmony with the purposes of the present work, we are offering here some brief explanations that refer mainly to the evolution only of pneumatolytic and of hydrothermal processes.

The period of magmatic activity giving birth to groups of minerals in hypogene deposits of different kinds is subdivided into *stages* and *sub-stages,* in our scheme, both of which are defined by the objective criteria brought to light for the first time. The hypogene mineral-forming process, as a whole, may be characterized accordingly by its sections. The term "stage of mineralization" is employed by us in place of the ordinary term, "phase of mineralization", and the term "sub-stage" is used as a designation of the successively evolved separations of paragenetic mineral groups within the stage. The "increment of mineralization", in our understanding of the terms, embraces a still more narrow segment of the process, i.e. is a section of the sub-stage.

In our tentative layout (Fig. 68) every stage of mineralization is defined by the limits of activity of the mineral-forming medium, the over-all *state of aggregation* of which remains the same, within the given stage, notwithstanding the medium's variations in space and in time. The stages are separated from each other by the relatively rapid transformations of the medium resulting in abrupt qualitative and quantitative changes in the groups of minerals, in their structures and textures.

The sub-stage embraces a certain span of the evolutionary process within the limits of a given stage. This span is characterized by certain changes in a series of physico-chemical variables, as expressed not in a transformation of the general state of the medium, but in certain qualitative and quantitative specifications within the given span of evolution of the process. For example, the first sub-stage of the pneumatolytic process is characterized, as observed, by a progressively increasing quantity of wate vapor (up to 25 per cent), while, toward the end of the second sub-stage, before the transformation of super-critical gaseous solutions into liquid ones, the water vapor begins abruptly to dominate the system, judging by the quantities of liquid in the inclusions (45–50 per cent).

We may succeed eventually in a further subdivision of different sub-stages into smaller entities (increments). Specifically, the "dry" gas increment of mineralization is indicated, by the inclusions, in the early first sub-stage, at the beginning of the evolution of pneumatolysis. The level of relatively rapid conversion of the critical solutions into liquid is indicated at the end of the late, second sub-stage of pneumatolysis. At the same time, the already-formed fraction of liquid appears to be in a state of boiling. Both gaseous and liquid inclusions are produced simultaneously in minerals crystallizing at this level of transition to hydrothermal solutions. Homogenization of both kinds of inclusions is accompanied by a series of features that are characteristic of rapid transformations of solutions from one state of aggregation into another one.

Mineral genesis within a given sub-stage or even in a given increment is by no means a regular and quiet process. It is accompanied by a continuous change in chemistry of the medium and by minor or major changes of the temperature and of the pressure.

This continuous process is *discontinuous* at the same time, in the sense that, on occasions, because of the development of various generations and modifications of the minerals, some of the previously-formed minerals may undergo dissolution. Even individual crystals, as in those showing growth zones, betray a whole series of minute and ultraminute interruptions in the continuity of the process that are especially clearly expressed in the development of growth zones, in changes of the crystal habit, in solution, and in regeneration, etc. We may speak therefore only of a *relatively* quiet evolutionary development within a given stage, as against the *relatively* rapid transformations at the stage's boundaries accompanied by marked disruptions of the mobile equilibria and in the corresponding ratios of the basic physico-chemical parameters (T–P–X).

Our schematic representation (Fig. 68, section 10) indicates the preponderant role of the principal minerals within the limits of every stage. This appears to be the result of a *natural selection* among the minerals, the selection taking place in the course of the variations in the mineral-forming environment. However, the evolutionary process is recognizable even in individual minerals (changes in composition and in crystallographic forms, color, optical properties, density, etc.).

The arrangement of the stages and the sub-stages in our scheme (Fig. 68), *left to right,* shows the direction of the evolution of the mineral-forming environment in a definite chronologic sequence, In such manner, the scheme gives an idea also in regards to the relative *age status* of the deposits of the groups of minerals *produced over the range of activity of one and the same magmatic source.*

The arrows in section 3 of the scheme indicate the range of existence of magmatic solution enriched with supercritical "dry" gases, of strongly acid supercritical gaseous solution (evolving into an acid and possibly even into a neutral gas–liquid solution), and of alkaline aqueous solution whose solutes subsequently undergo a partial conversion from the molecular to the colloidal state.

Sections 4, 5, 6, and 7 of the scheme (Fig. 68) represent the heretofore non-existent objective physico-chemical data obtained by direct observations on natural minerals and partially confirmed by experiments with artificial crystals. They are the backbone of the entire scheme and they make it possible objectively to distinguish the different stages and sub-stages in the development of mineral deposits, as we have shown in the present work.

Any hypogene mineral deposit and its generations of minerals may be set in the appropriate place within the mineral-forming process, as a whole, on the basis of the study of its inclusions.

The upper and the lower temperature limits of the pneumatolytic and the hydrothermal stages, shown in section 8, were determined with the aid of many thousands of experimental measurements of the homogenization temperatures of inclusions. These limits may be subject to minor changes, depending on supplementary research, chiefly in regards to the lower limit for pneumatolytic minerals and the upper limit for hydrothermal ones.

There is no doubt as to the importance of concentrations of the solutions and of the external pressure, both of which vary within a wide range, for different deposits, when it comes to the phase-transformations of the mineral-forming medium. Specifically, it is highly probable that the presence of strong acids in gaseous solutions tends to lower their critical temperature. If the external pressure is low, the critical temperature may be found to be less than 200°C, but it may be even higher than our datum of 500°C at high pressures and high concentrations of substances in solution [*sic*].

As already shown, a determination of one single parameter—the temperature—for a natural physico-chemical P–T–X system, at a mobile equilibrium with other variables, sheds a definite light on the direction of variations in the process, as a whole.

Section 9 of the scheme (Fig. 68) illustrates the general character of the vein-filling for different stages of the process. Section 10 should be helpful in the field, in assigning the place of a given deposit in the general pattern of the ore-forming process. However, while this section is reliable only in its general features, it still requires additions and corrections, depending on further studies of mother liquor inclusions in minerals. The series of minerals set in the table and based on the immense experience of many geologists, if taken by themselves, provide only a poor and schematic expression of the evolution of the mineral kingdom and of the limits in which the different minerals originate, against the general background of the evolution of magmatic derivatives. Depending upon temperature and on other variations in the parent medium, the magmatic derivatives alter their composition, form, specific gravity, optical properties, and color, which are closely interdependent, since they are functions of the same variables upon which the evolution itself depends.

An interdependence of the physical properties of minerals is indicated in nature, as, for example, between color and crystallographic form, whose discovery, unfortunately, so far has escaped the attention of investigators. It appears that the general direction of the process of variation in the solutions and of the crystallization of minerals, in every period of magmatic activity, is toward progressively more complicated structures and stereochemistry of progressively more homogeneous crystal systems [Fersman, 108]. On the other hand, we observe a certain recurrence of properties in every stage of the process, but on a different base, as shown most clearly, for example, in the succession of colors of the minerals (see beryl, tourmaline, fluorite, quartz). These orderly relationships require a thorough study of minerals, in order to bring them to light, research that must be integrated with studies of inclusions of mineral-forming solutions.

Section 11 represents the sequence of replacement processes in multistage mineral genesis, involving products of the preceding stage or sub-stage and minerals of the host rocks. As previously shown, determinations of the course of metasomatic alteration, so widely occurring in nature, are facilitated substantially by studies of secondary inclusions of solutions participating in the process. As a matter of course, the new products of the given stage are deposited on the already altered products of the preceding stage.

It is essential now to summarize some of the data on the stages, as we consider our scheme in its vertical orientation. Since problems of endo-magmatic mineral genesis were not touched upon in our study, the scheme contains practically no data pertinent to that subject. Our discussion begins with the last sub-stage of the magmatic stage, called "epimagmatic" by A. Ye. Fersman, which is also the earliest one of the exo-magmatic derivatives. In the dimension of time, the predecessors of this stage could be only the very first moments of a very complicated process of development of contact deposits, omitted here from consideration, the moments belonging to the initial period of penetration by the intrusion, when the intrusion had not yet begun its normal development but had already produced a pyrometamorphism of its host rocks and had given off the first fractions of its volatile constituents.

The normal evolution of this source begins only after its establishment as a confined system, or, more exactly, as a *periodically and relatively confined* system, aided by the formation of a solid peripheral magmatogenic shell around the active source. From that time on, magmatic mineral genesis may be regarded as a progressively evolving process resulting, among other things, in an enrichment of the intrusion's upper section with volatile substances and the accompanying production of a magmatic solution most heavily enriched with gases. When under the influence of an increasing internal pressure as well as of external, e.g. tectonic, factors, the confinement of the system becomes upset, a situation recurring many times, magmatic derivatives begin their prolonged evolution, as they move upwards on their migration paths, with the accompanying processes of exo-magmatic deposition of minerals.

During the first, initial stage, there is a "squeezing-out" of the magmatic solutions into fissures. This magmatic solution is "residual" only for the given moment of release of confinement of the system and, as we know, generally there may be several such moments [58] after the recurring confinements of the system and the accompanying regression of the active part of the magmatic source into the depths. A rapid cooling and escape of volatile substances from the magmatic solution of this sort results in the formation of aplites characterized by the crystallization of quartz with its own crystal faces, as distinct from the "graphic" granites. The aplites are characterized also by the development of plagioclases and, in places, by zonal deposition of garnet and magnetite. This may occasionally be the end of mineral genesis, in these fissures, particularly in narrow ones.

In other and more common instances, aplites form only the outer lining of the fissures, while the inner part becomes completely or partially filled with oligoclase crystals and mica plates, followed by crystals of orthoclase or microcline with embedded quartz on which the characteristic graphic structure of pegmatitic bodies depends.

In case of a radical preponderance of silica in the magmatic solution the excess of silica may be deposited in the middle part of the pegmatitic vein, as a mass of quartz, forming the so-called silexites that are observed in pegmatites with blocky structures. If this particular moment coincides with a firm "sealing-off" of the fissure, the process of mineral genesis may be cut short, in the veins, and the later portions of the magmatic deriva tives will have to follow some other migration paths in their upward movement.

Unfortunately, it is not possible for us here to consider the very important problem of origins, existence, and terminations of the migration paths of the magmatic derivatives. These paths, developing for various reasons, tend to be blocked rapidly, on account of the vertical and lateral pressures, opposed as they are by the pressure from the magmatic source, transmitted through the magmatic and other solutions. In the complex process of formation of veins, the thickness, mineralogic composition, and structure are determined partially by the outcome of the contest between the two mutually opposite tendencies, as here indicated.

In our view, the first, the aplite–pegmatitic stage of mineral genesis is the shortest one, in time, although this "residual" solution, highly enriched with gases, may be squeezed out several times, outside the boundaries of the intrusive body, in connection with recurring disruptions in the confinement of the magmatic source. The relative confinement of the latter is not particularly characteristic of the first period of its history. It is during this very period that the main bulk of exo-magmatic deposits is produced, starting with the moment when the accumulated high pressures inside the magmatic source serve to rupture its crust and to squeeze out the magmatic derivatives, as an odd kind of a "residual" solution containing large quantities of gas phase.

Following a lowering of the pressure, the magmatic derivatives are distilled upwards, entirely in the form of gaseous substances, where they become the pneumatolytic media of mineral genesis, on their migration paths, most commonly through the central parts of veins in the graphic granites. This change in the medium is not a gradual one; the pegmatitic solution does not last very long outside the magmatic source, under various conditions of pressure and temperature, but becomes crystallized relatively rapidly, in the lower sections of its migration paths, yielding its place to pneumatolysis, a very important mineral-forming process.

The action of supercritical solutions is effective within a wide range of temperatures and pressures. Duration of their effectiveness is contingent upon the prolonged pulsating character of the distillation of metalliferous gases and aqueous vapors. Quantitative proportions of the latter are subject to change, *with time,* because the saturation limit of the solution and the pressure of the gas are not the same for different volatile constituents. The composition of the gaseous medium of mineral genesis varies both in time and in space (along the migration paths).

Variations in the mineral-forming solutions, in time, depend not only on variations in temperature and pressures, but also on variations in the external *geologic environments* which must not be identified with *the* *media.** These variations determine the deposition of a given product in the *horizons of mineral genesis differing with respect to the intrusion's contact,* succeeding each other to the measure of the regression of the active part of the magmatic source into depth.

The high content of various acids and of saturated water vapor in the third stage of development of magmatic derivatives produces substantial changes in the further course of the exo-magmatic mineral genesis and, at a certain definite moment, leads to the formation of liquid aqueous solutions.

Many investigators assume, with attention to vapor pressures of different constituents, that gaseous solutions display an acid reaction which becomes weaker progressively, while liquid aqueous solutions are already in possession of alkaline characteristics. This idea is based on observations on volcanic emanations and on the fact that carbonates are not characteristic of the pneumatolytic stage but are so very common in the hydrothermal stage of evolution of magmatic derivatives. *By way of a proof of the correctness of such representations, they adduce now some direct measurements of acidity and alkalinity and even of the* pH *of inclusions.*

The coming progress in research, like the one on inclusions in minerals, will be incomparably more useful to science than the productions like the well-known article by L. Graton ("The Nature of Ore-forming Fluid") which caused an extensive but not a very productive discussion in the pages of American journals.

Concentrations of substance in gaseous solutions are appreciably lower, on the whole, than in hydrothermal solutions. It is possible to reason, however, on the basis of inclusions, that this concentration increases gradually, from the "dry" gas on, although we still have no numerical expressions for the increase.

We made some calculations, on the basis of three-phase and multiphase inclusions, which show occasionally, in the fourth stage† very high concentrations of salts,‡ chiefly chlorides,§ up to 60 per cent. Thus the high-temperature hydrotherms existing at high pressures, at one of the early increments of the hydrothermal stage, appear to be *salt solutions with solute concentrations still not encountered in the surficial environments of the earth* ("*hydrothermal brines*").

---

* We may merely distinguish *the medium of stabilization of intrusions,* the rock containing the magmatic source, and *the medium of mineral genesis,* in the form of magmatic solutions, supercritical gaseous and liquid aqueous solutions from which crystallization of minerals takes place.

† By the "fourth stage", Yermakov means probably the first sub-stage ($T = 200–500°C$) of his third stage (Fig. 68) [V.P.S.].

‡ V. A. Nikolayev's "C" constituent.

§ Many metals, including iron, are also present, it appears, as chlorides (and fluorides), in addition to petrogenic elements.

Such inability of the brines to part with their sodium and potassium salts within a wide range of temperatures and pressures, while still in the liquidus field, presumably, makes them *ideal carriers of various substances participating in the formation of hydrothermal deposits.*

The widespread opinion abroad with regard to a severe dilution of ore-forming solutions, at least in the early phase of the fourth stage of their evolution, lacks any justification whatsoever in our observations on inclusions in minerals. Insofar as it is possible to judge by the homogenization curves and by all of the experiments with inclusions here described, the relative concentration of substance in the solutions decreases briefly only at the threshold of the transition from the pneumatolytic to the hydrothermal stage, in the field where boiling phenomena are most common, and, later on, decreases radically in the medium-temperature and the low-temperature sub-stages of the process.

Composition of the solutions changes continuously, depending on variations in the other factors of mineral genesis. The solutions are especially active, in the pneumatolytic stage, with respect to their host rocks and the previously-formed minerals. The substance of minerals deposited in any given sub-stage (except the first one) has not merely a magmatic origin but is very often a re-deposited substance—"metamorphogenic" [19, 20].

After the formation of mineral deposits at a given depth, the "spent" solutions continue to be active in mineral genesis in the upper horizons, not as much at the expense of their "original" magmatic constituents, as by virtue of their acquisition of new substances by their interactions with the host rocks along their migration paths. At these levels, the hydrotherms begin to blend with the solutions from which Alpine veins are produced and, beginning at depths of 3–4 km below the surface, it becomes progressively more difficult to tell them apart from heated vadose solutions.

The role and the relatively high importance of the colloidal transfer of substances from which veins and ore minerals are formed is beginning to be understood more and more exactly in the fields of hydrothermal mineral genesis. Colloidal solutions seem to develop from true solutions, as the result of a lowering of temperature and pressure, as well as of reactions with the other solutions encountered of unlike composition and origin (juvenile, metamorphic, and vadose). The previously noted reactions of the solutions with wall rocks along the migration paths may play an important role, on occasions, in transformations of the hydrotherm and in the development of colloids. Partial conversions of molecular solutions, particularly of solutions of silica, into colloidal solutions appear to be especially probable in the field of transition from the high-temperature to the low-temperature stages of the hydrothermal process.

Unfortunately, we find only submicroscopic liquid inclusions, in tremendous quantities, in the products of colloidal origin. These inclusions are identifiable only after a pulverization of the mineral and by examination of the powder in immersion liquids at extremely high microscopic magnifications. For that reason, our experiments with determinations of the temperatures and the types of these inclusions have failed, so far, to yield the desired results.

Only two principal sub-stages and the third one, the sub-stage of cold-water hypogene mineral genesis, are differentiated by us within the hydrothermal stage represented in the scheme. This stage could be subdivided, of course, into three or five sub-stages and even into a still larger number of segments, because we have the means of determining the lowest true temperatures of formation of minerals, on the basis of their liquid inclusions of mother liquor. However, there is no practical need for such fragmentation.

Everybody knows that even high-temperature minerals are often found together with low-temperature minerals at the same depth and in the same ore body. In this connotation, mineral deposits are multistage products, most commonly, and any elaborate break-down of mineral genesis into stages, phases and of the deposits into small classes is, to a considerable degree, senseless. On the other hand, a differentiation of hydrothermal deposits into two or three large categories is more useful, in view of the now indicated "antipode" incompatible minerals, such as, for example, wolframite and cinnabar, beryl and antimonite, etc. Moreover, *three-phase and multiphase liquid inclusions* are most characteristic of the high-temperature class of mineral deposits.

We should preserve, perhaps, the tripartite subdivision of hydrothermal deposits into high-temperature (500–350°C), medium-temperature (350–200°C), and low-temperature (200–50°C), if only to avoid upsetting the traditions too rudely. Every one of these stages [sub-stages?—V.P.S.] may be broken down into two levels or phases, in case of a need that arises in comparisons between deposits, as we did in the instance of the fluorite deposits of Transbaykalia (p. 209).

The future genetic classification of mineral deposits must fully take into account, in addition to the principal criterion, *the state of aggregation of mineral-forming solutions, the very important temperature factor, and the factor of depth, and the degree of the distance of the deposit from the active magmatic source.* Under such conditions, it will be possible to distinguish in nature "*deep*" (chiefly pneumatolytic), "*moderately deep*" and "*shallow*" deposits, as well as "*proximate,*" "*distant,*" and "*far removed*" ones (in reference to the magmatic source). Combinations of these terms with the principal index of the classification will give us a fairly exact position of the given deposit not only in the pattern of the progressive development of the mineral genesis, but also to a certain extent in the geologic environment [37].

Of course, we do not aim and we cannot embrace here the entire multitude of factors by which the appearance of various deposits is determined. The attainments of Soviet geologists in different fields of the theory of economic ore deposits had already dispensed with such needs. As already shown, our geologists had accomplished a lot in the creation of the Soviet theory of hypogenetic formation of ores (see also the Bibliography).

Collective efforts in the next years must be directed toward a coordination of the vast body of data on mineral deposits with the results on the inclusions of mineral-forming media which fell outside the range of scientists' vision for many decades. The time has come for a quantitative reading of the mineral-forming processes—and then the mineral kingdom will arise before us in all of [its] continuous motion and evolution. If not, there can be no further new and radical advances in our understanding of the exceptionally difficult process of the formation of ores.

Smirnov said in 1947, in his critical appraisal of the present state of the theory of ore-formation: "In the present state of our knowledge, a geologist engaged in the study of ore deposits must keep his mind open, when it comes to the accepted theories of ore-formation: these theories are still too imperfect. The keys to the problem have not yet been found" [96].

We endeavored to show in our study that the missing "keys", the very ones that are most important, were preserved for us by nature, in the form of relics of the parent medium inside minerals and that the method of their investigation must be introduced as a part of the standard equipment of geologists engaged in studies of the conditions of formation of mineral deposits associated with magmatic activity.

As shown, the inclusions provide us with the required criteria for evaluations of the temperatures and the states of aggregation of mineral-forming solutions. Both the scientific and the practical importance of this fact require no explanations, since a correct solution of the problem of origin of mineral deposits has a direct influence on their appraisal and on the orientation of prospecting in the field.

CHAPTER 9

Scientific Practical Importance and Perspectives
of Investigations of Inclusions in Minerals

WE ATTEMPTED to show in the present work that the history of formation of minerals and hypogene mineral deposits is recorded sufficiently
completely in the inclusions of the parent medium (magmatic solution,
supercritical gases and liquid aqueous solutions) from which the inclusion-
bearing minerals were produced and that special investigations of such inclusions serve to open new vistas for a deeper study of the mineral-forming
processes.

In order to learn how to read *the biography of minerals,* a special technique had to be developed, together with a series of methods and procedures which served substantially to facilitate the solution of the problem.

As one may see from the contents, our work had a *methodical orientation* and we allow ourselves to hope that it will help Soviet geologists, in
the shortest time, to take possession of these supplementary methods and
procedures in the research in physico-chemical conditions of formation of
hypogene minerals and mineral deposits.

The thermochamber attachment we built, for the microscope, in combination with other apparatus, makes it possible to investigate inclusions of
mother liquors in minerals within a wide temperature range. *The method of
experimentation* on the included solutions, developed on the basis of this
new technique, as shown, is suited for practical applications *in the research
on temperatures and on the state of aggregation of the included solutions.*

The natural classification of various inclusions in minerals suggested in
this work, on the basis of composition and state of the inclusions, constitutes an essential prerequisite of a further development of these investigations of inclusions, as witnesses of the medium in which the crystallization
of minerals took place. *The different groups, types, and species of inclusions in minerals are fixed records of certain definite stages, sub-stages, and
increments of the orderly evolution of the processes of hypogene mineral genesis.*

Up to recent times, in the genetic classification of inclusions themselves, only primary inclusions were distinguished, the inclusions associated
with previous forms of the crystal's growth, and secondary inclusions
originating in the course of healing of fissures in minerals. Inclusions of the

[310]

first type were believed to be suited for genetic investigations of minerals, while data obtained on inclusions of the second type were referred to the subsequent mineral-restoring processes and not to the processes of growth of minerals themselves.

We discovered a new and a very common genetic type of "primary–secondary" or, better, of *pseudo-secondary* inclusions showing the earmarks of both of the other types. *The majority of inclusions formerly believed to be secondary* and situated in healed fissures of the earlier growth periods of crystals *proved to be suited* for use accordingly *as the sources of data on physico-chemical environments of formation of minerals.*

A new, "visual", method of investigation, requiring no special apparatus, is suited for an approximate estimation of the temperatures of formation of minerals, on the basis of two-phase inclusions of weak aqueous solutions, within the range of up to 200°C. This method is based on the derivation of empirical curves for different minerals from the phase ratios in the inclusion and from the homogenization temperatures. A mathematical analysis of these curves, derived for the most important vein minerals, quartz and calcite, made it possible for us to arrive at some simple empirical equations with the aid of which we could estimate the probable temperatures of formation of low-temperature hydrothermal minerals.

On the basis of the method of homogenization of inclusions by heat, we proposed *a new methodology of thermometric investigations* (analysis) *of minerals the* hallmark of which is a separate study of inclusions in different growth zones and different sections of crystals. Practical applications of this analysis showed that *variations in the temperature of the solutions during the crystal growth do not always occur in the same manner.* The variation may be a progressive and gradual decrease in the temperature becoming more rapid toward the end, or it may be an abrupt drop in the temperature after a certain pause in a gradual growth of the crystal, or a temporary increase in the temperature of formation of the crystal's outer zone which may be accompanied, on occasions, by some dissolution of the faces of the crystal's inner zone, or, finally, in the instance of some zonal growth crystals, a rapid oscillatory variation, for different zones, caused by a pulsating accession of the solutions at the site of the crystal growth.

Determination of the sequence of crystallization of minerals is not an easy problem, and had not yet been entirely solved methodologically. An important supplementary step now exists in the methods of mineralo-thermal analysis, as here suggested. *The classification of crystals by their generations and nucleations and the synchronization of minerals* of the same composition but of a different external appearance *may often be made with the aid of the new methods of study of the inclusions of mother liquors.*

The growth of individual crystals of a definite polythermal generation of minerals takes place occasionally within ranges of decreasing temperatures so wide that any temperature boundaries (for example, the epithermal–mesothermal one, at 200°C) *accepted in the classification of hydrothermal deposits lose their meaning and there is no point in their mechanical applications.* If we adhere to the subdivision of the deposits into the tele-, epi-, meso-, and hypothermal categories established by American scientists, we shall be obliged to apply this classification also to individual crystals, in the sense of meso-, epi-, tele-, thermal formations—a senseless endeavor. Some minerals begin to crystallize above 200°C and conclude their growth below 100°C. The crystallization temperatures must be determined in different growth zones of individual minerals of different generations, whereupon *it becomes possible to reconstruct the different types of variations in the temperature regime of the parent solutions by which a given hypogene deposit was formed, as a whole.*

Experiments in conversions of heterogeneous systems of inclusions (at room temperature) into homogeneous ones, conducted on the basis of special methods of observations and measurements of the phase ratios in these inclusions, on heating, brought to light the various types and species of homogenization. *From the course of the homogenization of inclusions, one may judge objectively the type of the original state of aggregation of the solutions from which the host minerals of the inclusions were produced. One of the newly discovered types of homogenization (type II) proves the phenomena of pneumatolysis and confirms the existence of critical phenomena* in the mineral-forming processes. In deposits of a multistage origin, *such investigations of the inclusions in heterochronous minerals allow us to differentiate between pneumatolytic and hydrothermal products.*

Hydrothermal solutions (occasionally, an extremely super-saturated "hydrothermal brine") *participate in mineral-forming processes at temperatures considerably above the critical temperature of pure water.* On the other hand, *hypogene solutions may deposit minerals in tepid-water and cold-water environments*, at temperatures below the boiling point of water at the pressure of one atmosphere. Such *minerals are characterized*, at room temperatures, *by the presence of single-phase essentially-liquid inclusions of aqueous solutions.*

As previously shown, every investigator interested in solidified, gaseous, or essentially-liquid inclusions is bound to come across relics of mineral-forming media that are important in the construction of a new and of a better genetic classification of mineral deposits associated with magmatic activity.

Qualitative changes in the medium, in time (and in space), by which the formation of minerals is accompanied and determined, after they lead up to certain quantitative ratios, are no longer able to continue their further development gradually, whereupon transition of the medium from one state into another one becomes the result. *These continuous and recurring changes and transformations in the physico-chemical process of the formation of hypogene mineral deposits has now become accessible, for the first time, to objective evaluations based on studies of relics of mineral-forming media sealed hermetically in minerals. Because of that, it is possible now to distinguish a series of major, intermediate, and minor "steps" within the mineral-forming process.* These various steps are called stages, sub-stages, and increments of the evolution of magmatic derivatives, in the diagrammatic representation of the process we designed (Fig. 68).

Transformations at the pneumatolytic–hydrothermal stage boundary are identified exactly by the type distinctions in the homogenization of inclusions and by the course of their homogenization involving the critical point.

Evolutionary changes within the limits of a given stage are recognized by the homogenization types and by the temperatures of homogenization of inclusions of gaseous and aqueous solutions and, to some extent, by composition and concentration of the solutions. The sub-stages and the increments in our scheme are defined on that basis.

It becomes possible, in such manner, on the basis of direct investigations of exhalations of a magmatic source, preserved as inclusions in minerals, to recognize the process by which a given hypogene deposit was formed, part-by-part, and to determine the sequence of formation of minerals in the general course of the evolution of the process.

As we know, the majority of American geologists have already excluded the pneumatolytic stage from the classification of mineral deposits a long time ago and went right on, in their largely subjective ideas, along the line of the emasculation of the idea of an evolution of the process, in their publications, along the line of denying the wealth of possibilities of the natural mineral genesis.

Soviet geologists, having made use of different kinds of methods and procedures in their many-sided approach to the subject, succeeded in coming closer to an understanding of mineral-forming processes, in their details, but had merely outlined the paths leading to a deeper knowledge of the principal factors governing these processes.

The great accomplishments in physico-chemical interpretations of natural mineral-forming processes, based chiefly on experiments with artificial systems, are in an urgent need of a "bridge" from the laboratory data to natural processes and phenomena. The utilization of inclusions of mother liquors, in science and in practice, is put forth in the present study as a support for such a "bridge." Our studies show that the heterogeneous *natural systems* sealed hermetically in minerals are susceptible to reconstitution into their original state and are suited for exact qualitative and quantitative analysis and measurement.

The former underestimation of the importance of inclusions, the most common phenomenon in minerals, resulted in their neglect in interpretations of quantitative chemical and spectrographic analyses of minerals showing unexpectedly, as it were, presence of elements alien to the test materials. The losses on ignition, in a series of minerals, can be explained only by explosions of liquid inclusions and by losses of their volatile constituents. Variations in the specific gravity of one and the same mineral from different sources may be often explained by variations in their inclusion content. Sub-microscopic liquid inclusions have some importance, it appears, also in the thermal analysis of some hydrated minerals, etc.

Research in metallogeny, in its present development in our country, may acquire additional means of prospecting and appraisals of hypogene mineral deposits with the aid of the multi-purpose utilization of inclusions of mineral-forming solutions.

Even the first attempt in the applications of thermometric studies reported in this book has already opened new possibilities for ascertaining of a whole series of intimate features in the formation *not only of individual crystals but of entire mineral deposits.*

Specifically, minerals in hydrothermal deposits may be arranged in paragenetic schemes within the boundaries of true (or nearly true) temperatures. The stepwise discontinuous character of variations in *the temperature* of mineral-forming solutions and, consequently, also of the factors of mineral genesis that depend on the temperature, may be glimpsed in the case of deposits formed under complex tectonic conditions. The unlike homogenization temperatures of secondary inclusions in minerals are helpful in ascertaining heterochronous dislocations within the mineralized zone causing fragmentation and fissuring of minerals. Variations in temperatures, types, and species of homogenization of inclusions in minerals from veins situated in areas of intrusions differing in their composition and time may be of aid in ascertaining genetic connections of the mineralization and a given type of intrusions, which is essential in the correct orientation of prospecting in the field. It may become possible in the future even to outline foci of mineralization and to refine the present concepts of zonations in the distribution of minerals by means of thermometric analysis (aided, of course, also by other methods) of minerals of one generation common in the area of the deposit or in an area comprising a group of mineral deposits.

These highly promising perspectives in metallogenic studies do not exhaust all of the various possibilities of scientific and practical utilization of inclusions.

All-inclusive comprehensive studies of confined natural systems of inclusions will enable us to design procedures which do not now exist, for crystallization of a series of minerals of which there is a shortage. Chemical and microchemical analyses of included solutions, in conjunction with the homogenization experiments, will teach us how to transfer the immense experience of the laboratory of nature into the laboratories of Soviet scientists adapted for production of synthetic crystals.

The homogenization temperature of the given inclusions is an index of the minimum temperatures that must be attained experimentally, while the homogenization type is the index of the optimum state of aggregation of the solution from which the given mineral is to be crystallized.

Chemical composition of inclusions and concentrations of constituents alien to the crystal will indicate both kind and quantity of the required admixtures to the synthetic media of crystal growth.

Substances cognate to the substance of the mineral must be used in an excess, of course, in the crystallization chamber or the bomb, to assure a supersaturation of the solution even at high temperatures. The optimum degree of filling of the bomb may be determined easily from the coefficient of filling of the inclusions in corresponding minerals. Application of heat to the hermetically sealed crystallization chamber will bring [the system— V.P.S.] to the homogenization temperature, at the minimum pressure, as operative in natural mineral-forming environments.

The path of research, from observations and experiments with natural systems of inclusions to artificial reproductions of these systems and the crystallization of the desired minerals, will lead to further opportunities in the future and to an additional objective verification of our knowledge of the theory of the formation of ores.

Studies of inclusions in the light fraction of panned samples and in minerals from sedimentary rocks, in ascertaining the primary origin of the minerals (by the criteria here proposed) will undoubtedly yield new data, so essential for correlations of barren horizons and in determining the sources of erosion. The observed preservation of essentially-liquid inclusions in minerals of rocks composing areas which were subjected to intensive tectonic disturbances, particularly to oscillating movements, may provide a geologist–tectonist with important data on the depth of burial of such rocks. On the contrary, exploded liquid inclusions that are observed occasionally in minerals from hypogene rocks and mineral deposits serve as evidence of a subsequent overheating, to a high degree, of the minerals, either because of their sinking to great depths or by an emergence of some new intrusion in their vicinity.

The series of propositions we have given here, in connection with the possible practical use of data obtained by the inclusion studies in problems of metallogeny, in artificial crystallization of minerals, and in tectonic and mineralogic problems of sedimentary rocks, based as they are on the contents of our book, are still in need of a large amount of supplementary team-work, on the part of geologists, some of which has already begun at several cities (Moscow, Tashkent, Leningrad, L'vov, Kiev, and others).

If we remember that the "precious substance" of inclusions is the very same "juice of the earth" from which minerals are produced, we ought not be surprised (or to interpret it as a whim of the author) at its so very extensive importance in so many different fields of geologic–mineralogic sciences.

The many-sided research in inclusions of mother liquors in minerals should be of interest not only to geologists engaged in studies of hypogene deposits, mineralogists, geochemists, petrographers, and crystallographers, but also to scientists in other geologic and non-geologic fields (such as the physical and chemical fields). The problem of many-sided utilization of inclusions in the socialist science and practice may be resolved, in all its body, only by a collective effort.

We should emphasize once more, however, that investigations of inclusions require a high degree of fineness and delicacy and that interpretations of the results require much caution. In the present-day practice of genetic investigations, groups, types and species of inclusions, as well as types and species of homogenization of included solutions, may be accepted as entirely suitable criteria for recognizing environments wherein minerals were formed. As to the developed techniques of thermometric analysis of minerals, one needs to remark that they are suited for obtaining the minimum temperatures (but close enough to the true ones) only in the instance of two-phase inclusions of dilute solutions typical for minerals from low-temperature hydrothermal deposits at shallow depths. In determinations of relative temperatures and of the temperature range of growth of individual crystals, the present techniques are suited for all well-crystallized transparent and semi-transparent hydrothermal and "Alpine" minerals, by way of a first approximation.

An immense experimental and analytical work in determining composition and concentration of substances in included solutions is still ahead of us. Physico-chemical interpretations of its results must play a decisive part in introductions of corrections for the concentration, so as to bring the determined homogenization temperatures of the formation of mineral closer to the true ones. Work of this type will broaden considerably the scope of the measurement of temperatures in products of the hydrothermal process and will supply the premises for solutions of many genetic problems in the origins of ores, some of which were already suggested.

Solutions of technical and theoretical problems in future research promising so much for our deeper understanding of natural mineral-forming processes, require a conversion from the present "home-made" experiments of individual scientists to special laboratories, equipped with modern technical facilities. The work already begun in several cities re quires a co-ordination by one single center. This can be made real only in the environment of our planned socialist system by which the amazing progress in the solution of the most intricate scientific problems of modern times has been assured.

The author would be very thankful to any scientific workers and to practicing geologists who might wish to make critical remarks on his book. He will accept them with gratitude and will take them into account in his future studies.

The author wishes to render any aid, within his means, in the organization of studies of inclusions of mineral-forming solutions to all comrades who are interested in the problems discussed in this book.

April 16, 1950.

The Laboratory of Thermometric Analysis

The State University of L'vov

L'vov, Lomonosov Street, 8

BIBLIOGRAPHY TO PART I

1. ABDULLAYEV, KH. M., *Geologiya sheelitonosnykh skarnov Sredney Azii.* (Geology of Scheelite-bearing Skarns of Central Asia.) *Izd. AN SSSR*, Tashkent, 1949.
2. BELENETSKII, A. M., O "mineralogii" Al'Biruni. (About the "Mineralogy" of Al-Biruni.) *Vest. AN SSSR*, No. 4, p. 59, 1949.
3. BELYANKIN, D. S., O vode v magme i magmaticheskikh gornykh porodakh. (On Water in Magma in Reference to Magmatic Rocks.) *Geolog. vest.* No. 1-3, 1926.
4. BELYANKIN, D. S., Naskol'ko zhe v deystvitel'nosti rastvoryayetsya kremnekislota v vodnom pare nizhe kriticheskoi temperatury? (What, after all, is the Actual Solubility of Silicic Acid in Water Vapor below the Critical Temperature?) *Sb. Sovet. geolog.* No. 3, 1944.
5. BELYANKIN, D. S., K voprosu o sovremennom sostoyanii i perspektivakh ucheniya o magmakh i magmaticheskikh gornykh porodakh. (In Reference to the Present State and the Perspectives of the Theory of Magma and of Magmatic Rocks.) *Izv. Akad. Nauk SSSR, ser. geolog.* No. 5, 1947.
6. BARSANOV, G. P. and YU. F. POGONYA, Samorodnyi vismut kak geologicheskii termometr. (Native Bismuth as a Geological Thermometer.) *Trudy mineralog. muzeya Akad. Nauk SSSR*, I, 1949.
7. BETEKHTIN, A. G., O klassifikatsii rudnykh mestorozhdenii. (In Reference to the Classification of Ore Deposits.) *Izv. Akad. Nauk SSSR, ser. geolog.* No. 2, 1939.
7a. BETEKHTIN, A. G., O teksturakh i strukturakh rud. (In Reference to Textures and Structures of Ores.) *Sovet. geolog.* No. 9, 1934.
8. BETEKHTIN, A. G., Kal'kopirit. (Chalcopyrite.) *Mineraly SSSR*, Vol. I, p. 371.
8a. BETEKHTIN, A. G., O geneticheskikh tipakh margantsevykh mestorozhdenii. (In Reference to Genetic Types of Deposits of Manganese.) *Izv. Akad. Nauk SSSR, ser. geolog.* No. 4, 1940.
9. BETEKHTIN, A. G., YU. A. BILIBIN, F. I. VOL'FSON, D. S. KORZHINSKII, O. D. LEVITSKII, G. A. SOKOLOV *et al.*, Razvitiye nauki o rudnykh mestorozhdeniyakh za gody stalinskikh pyatiletok. (Development of the Sciences of Ore Deposits in the Years of Stalin's Five-year Plans.) *Izv. Akad. Nauk SSSR, ser. geolog.* No. 1, 1950.
10. BILIBIN, YU. A., Lokalizatsiya zolotonosnosti v svyazi s tektonikoi Severovostoka. (Localization of Auriferousness in Relation to Tectonics of the Northeast.) *Prob. sovet. geolog.* No. 5-6, 1937.
11. BILIBIN, YU. A., Obshchiye printsipy metallogenicheskikh issledovanii. (General Principles of Metallogenic Investigations.) *Izv. Akad. Nauk SSSR, ser. geolog.* No. 5, 1947.
12. BONSHTEDT, E. M. *et al.*, Sputnik geokhimika i mineraloga. (Geochemist's and Mineralogist's Companion.) *Zap. VMO*, Pt. 76, I, 1937.
13. BOGDANOVICH, K. I., *Rudnyye mestorozhdeniya.* (Ore Deposits.) Pt. I and II, 1912.
14. BOLDYREV, A. K., A. G. BETEKHTIN *et al.*, *Kurs mineralogii.* (Course of Mineralogy.) ONTI, 1936.
15. BOLDYREV, A. K., *Ocherki vysshei mineralogii.* (Essays in Advanced Mineralogy.) *Izd. zh. "Kolyma"*, 1944.
16. BRESHENKOV, B. K. and N. P. YERMAKOV, Marguzorskiye sur'myanyye mestorozhdeniya. (The Antimony Deposits of Marguzor.) *Sb. TPE*, 1935.

17. VERNADSKII, V. I., *Istoriya mineralov zemnoi kory.* (History of Minerals of the Earth's Crust.), Vol I, Pt. 1, 1923.

17a. VERNADSKII, V. I., *Ocherki geokhimii.* (Essays. in Geochemistry.) 2nd ed., 1936.

18. VIROVLYANSKII, G. M. Kvarts kak geologicheskii termometr. (Quartz as a Geological Thermometer.) *Zap. VMO*, Pt. 67, No. 3, 1938.

19. VLASOV, K. A., Kataliticheskaya rol' fluora v protsesse desilikatsii pegmatitov i genezisa berilla. (The Catalytic Function of Fluorine in Desilicification of Pegmatites and in the Genesis of Beryl.) *Trudy Lomonosov. inst. seriya geokhim.* No. 9, 1938.

20. VLASOV, K. A., O teorii desilikatsii granitnykh pegmatitov. (In Reference to the Theory of Desilicification of Granitic Pegmatites.) *Izv. Akad. Nauk SSSR, ser. geolog.* No. 2, 1938.

21. VOL'FSON, Otnosheniye orudeneniya endogennykh mestorozhdenii k krupnym tektonicheskim narusheniyam. (Relation of Mineralization in Endogenetic Deposits to Major Tectonic Disturbances.) *Izv. Akad. Nauk SSSR ser. geolog.* No. 6, 1948. No initials given in original; probably F.I.[V.P.S.]

22. VADILO, P. S., Etyudy po mineralogicheskoi kristallografii. (Essays in Mineralogic Crystallography.) *Mineralog. Sb. L'vov. geolog. obshch.* No. 4, 1950.

23. GAVRUSEVICH, B. A., K mineralogii i geokhimii pegmatitov Volyni. (In Reference to Mineralogy and Geochemistry of Pegmatites of Volynia.) *Trudy mineralog. muzeya Akad. Nauk SSSR.* No. 4, 1930.

24. GRIGOR'EV, D. P., Generatsiya i zarozhdeniye mineralov. (Generation and Origin of Minerals.) *Mineralog. Sb. L'vov. geolog. obshch.* No. 3, 1949.

25. GRIGOR'EV, D. P., K voprosu o razlichenii pervichnykh i vtorichnykh zhidkikh vklyuchenii v mineralakh. (On the Subject of Recognition of Primary and Secondary Liquid Inclusions in Minerals.) *Mineralog. Sb. L'vov. geolog. obshch.* No. 2, 1948.

26. GRIGOR'EV, D. P., O genezise mineralov. (On Origins of Minerals.) *Zap. VMO*, Pt. 76, No. 1, 1947.

27. GRUSHKIN, G. G., K metodike opredeleniya temperatur gidrotermal'nykh kvartsev po zhidkim i gazovym vklyucheniyam. (On the Subject of Methods of Determining the Temperatures of Hydrothermal Quartz by its Liquid and Gaseous Inclusions.) *Dokl. Akad. Nauk Uzb. SSR* No. 2, 1948.

28. GRUSHKIN, G. G., Temperatury obrazovaniya kvartsev mestorozhdeniya Aurakhmat. (The Temperatures of the Formation of Quartz in the Aurakhmat Deposit.) *Izv. Akad. Nauk Uzbek. SSR* No. 2, 1948.

29. GRUSHKIN, G. G., Nekotoryye itogi izucheniya temperatur obrazovaniya kvartsevi fluoritov. (A Summation of Studies in the Temperatures of the Formation of Quartzes and Fluorites.) *Akad. Nauk Uzb. SSR, trudy inst. geolog.* No. 4, 1949.

29a. GRUSHKIN, G. G., Nekotoryye voprosy genezisa mineralov. (Certain Problems in the Genesis of Minerals.) *Mineralog. Sb. L'vov. geolog. obshch.* No. 4, 1950.

30. YERMAKOV, N. P., *Geologiya mestorozhdenii opticheskikh mineralov Sredney Azii i temperatury ikh obrazovaniya.* (Geology of Deposits of Optical Minerals in Central Asia and the Temperatures of their Formation.) (Theses.) Samarkanda, 1943.

31. YERMAKOV, N. P., Opredeleniye temperatur obrazovaniya gidrotermal'nykh mineralov issledovaniyem zhidkikh vklyuchenii. (Determination of the Temperatures of Formation of Hydrothermal Minerals by Studies of their Liquid Inclusions.) *Dokl. Akad. Nauk SSSR*, Vol. 45, No. 5, 1944.

32. YERMAKOV, N. P., Temperatury obrazovaniya mestorozhdenii opticheskikh mineralov Sredney Azji. (The Temperatures of Formation of the Deposits of Optical Minerals in Central Asia.) *Sb. Sovetskaya geologiya* No. 1, 1944.

33. YERMAKOV, N. P., Geologicheskiye usloviya formirovaniya mestorozhdenii islandskogo shpata Sredney Azji. (Geological Environments of the Formation of the Deposits of Iceland Spar in Central Asia.) *Zap. VMO*, Pt. 7, 1, 1945.

320 RESEARCH ON THE NATURE OF MINERAL-FORMING -SOLUTIONS

33a. YERMAKOV, N. P., Geneticheskiye tipy khrustalenosnykh zhil i pogrebov Aldana. (Genetic Types of Quartz-Bearing Veins and of 'Quartz Vugs of Aldan.) *Dokl. Akad. Nauk SSSR*, Vol. 48, No. 1, 1945.

34. YERMAKOV, N. P., O proiskhozhdenii kwartsevykh zhil i mestorozhdenii gornogo khrustalya. (On the Subject of Origin of Quartz Veins and of Deposits of Quartz Crystals.) *Sb. Sovetskaya geologiya*, No. 12, 1946.

34a. YERMAKOV, N. P., O poiskakh i razvedkakh mestorozhdenii p'yezo i opticheskikh mineralov. (On the Subject of Prospecting and Exploration for Deposits of Piezo and Optical Minerals.) *Sb. Sovetskaya geologiya*, No. 17, 1946.

35. YERMAKOV, N. P., Proiskhozhdeniye i klassifikatsiya zhidkikh vklyuchenii v mineralakh. (Origin and Classification of Liquid Inclusions in Minerals.) *Mineralog. sb. L'vov. geolog. Obshch*. No. 2, 1948.

36. YERMAKOV, N. P., Ispol'zovaniye defektov v kristallakh fluorita dlya izucheniya yestestvennoi istorii minerala. (Utilization of Defects in Crystals of Fluorite in Investigation of the Natural History of the Mineral.) *Mineralog. Sb. L'vov. geolog. obshch*. No. 2, 1948.

37. YERMAKOV, N. P., Kriterii poznaniya genezisa mineralov i sreda rudoobrazovaniya. (Criteria for Ascertaining Origins of Minerals in Reference to the Ore-forming Environments.) *Mineralog. sb. L'vov. geolog. obshch*. No. 3, suppl. 1, 1949.

38. YERMAKOV, N. P., O pervichno-vtorichnykh vklyucheniyakh v mineralakh. (About the Primary-Secondary Inclusions in Minerals.) *Mineralog. sb. L'vov. geolog. obshch*. No. 3, 1949.

39. YERMAKOV, N. P. and R. F. SUKHORSKII, Krivaya dlya vizual'nogo opredeleniya temperatur obrazovaniya gidrotermal'nogo kvartsa. (A Curve for the Visual Determination of Temperatures of the Formation of Hydrothermal Quartz.) *Mineralog. sb. L'vov. geolog. obshch*. No. 3, 1949.

40. YERMAKOV, N. P. and E. M. LAZ'KO, Zhidkiye vklyucheniya v geologicheskoi termometrii. (Liquid Inclusions in Geological Thermometry.) *Mineralog. sb. L'vov. geolog. obshch*. No. 3, 1949.

41. YERMAKOV, N. P., Metodika termometricheskogo analiza mineralov iz gidrotermal'nykh mestorozhdenii. (Methods of Thermometric Analysis of Minerals from Hydrothermal Deposits.) *Mineralog. sb. L'vov. geolog. obshch*. No. 4, 1950.

41a. YERMAKOV, N. P., Metod rastreskivaniya v mineralogicheskoi termometrii. (The Decrepitation Method in Mineralogical Thermometry.) *Mineralog. sb. L'vov. geolog. obshch*. No. 4, 1950.

42. ZAVARITSKII, A. N., Osnovnoi vopros fizicheskoi khimii protsessa obrazovaniya pegmatitov. (The Fundamental Problem in Physical Chemistry of the Formation of Pegmatites.) *Izv. Akad. Nauk SSSR, ser. geolog*. No. 5, 1944.

43. ZAKHAROV, E. E. and S. A. YUSHKO, Ocherki po geokhimii Urala. (Essays in Geochemistry of the Ural.) *Trudy IMS*, 75, 1935.

44. ZAKHARCHENKO, A. I., Rezul'taty izucheniya zhidkikh vklyuchenii v gornom khrustale Pamira. (Results of Studies of Liquid Inclusions in Crystal Quartz from Pamir.) *Mineralog. sb. L'vov. geolog. obshch*. No. 4, 1950.

45. IVANTISHIN, N. M., Galenitovyye rudoproyavleniya na podol'skoi paleozoiskoi polose. (Indications of Galena Ores in the Paleozoic Belt of Podolia.) *Geolog. zh. Akad. Nauk Ukrain. SSR*, Vol. VIII, No. 3, 1947.

46. KANIBOLOTSKII, P. M., Ob osnovnykh prichinakh rudootlozheniya v gidrotermakh. (In Reference to the Fundamental Causes of the Deposition of Ores in Hydrotherms.) *Nauch. zap. Dnepropetrov. Gosuniversiteta*, Vol. XVIII, No. 1, 1940.

47. KARPINSKII, A. P., O nakhozhdenii v mineral'nykh veshchestvakh zhidkogo ugol'nogo angidrida. (On the Presence of Liquid Carbon Dioxide in Mineral Substances.) *Gornyi zh.*, Vol. 2, No. 4–5, 1880.

48. KOZERENKO, V. N., Analiz glubinnosti intruzii pri poiskakh rudnykh mestorozh-denii v sredney chasti Zapadnogo Tyan'-Shanya. (Analysis of the Intrusions' Depths in Prospecting for Ore Deposits in the Central Part of Western Tien-Shan.) *Sovet. geolog.* No. 17, 1946.

49. KORZHINSKII, D. S., Zhidkiye vklyucheniya kak prichina mnimoi pelitizatsii polevykh shpatov. (Liquid Inclusions as the Cause of the Pseudo-pellitization of Feldspars.) *Dokl. Akad. Nauk SSSR*, Vol. 29, No. 2, pp. 115–117, 1940.

50. KORZHINSKII, D. S., Obrazovaniye kontaktovykh mestorozhdenii. (Formation of Contact Deposits.) *Izv. Akad. Nauk SSSR, ser. geolog.* No. 3, 1945.

51. KORZHINSKII, D. S., Faktory mineral'nykh ravnovesii i mineralogicheskiye fatsii glubinnosti. (Factors in Mineral Equilibria and Mineralogic Facies of the Depths.) *Trudy IGN, Akad. Nauk SSSR*, No. 12, 1940.

52. KORZHINSKII, D. S., Fil'tratsionnyi effect i ego znacheniye v geologii. (The Fil-trational Effect and its Significance in Geology.) *Izv. Akad. Nauk SSSR, ser. geolog.* No. 2, 1947.

53. KORZHINSKII, D. S., Metodicheskiye napravleniya v fiziko-khimicheskoi petrologii (Trends in the Methods of Physico-chemical Petrology.) *Yubileynyi sb. Akad. Nauk SSSR*, Vol. II, 1947.

54. KORZHINSKII, D. S., Petrologiya tur'yinskikh skarnovykh mestorozhdenii medi. (Petrology of the Skarn Deposits of Copper at Tur'yinsk.) *Trudy inst. geolog. nauk, seriya rudnykh mestorozhdeniy*, 68, No. 10, 1948.

55. KOROLEV, A. V., *Structura rudnykh polei i mestorozhdenii.* (Structures of Ore Fields and of Ore Deposits) *Izd.* SAII Tashkent, 1935.

56. KOROLEV, A. V., Sostoyaniye predstavlenii o genezise i usloviyakh lokalizatsii postmagmaticheskikh mestorozhdenii Srednei Azii. (The Present State of Ideas Regarding Origin and Requirements for the Localization of Post-magmatic Depo-sits of Central Asia.) *Trudy inst. geolog. Akad. Nauk Uzbek. SSR*, 2, 1948.

57. KOROLEVA, Z. A., *Parageneticheskiye sootnosheniya gipogennykh mineralov v me-storozdeniyakh Karamazara.* (Paragenetic Relationships of Hypogene Minerals in the Karamazar Deposits.) *Izd.* Uzbek. filiala Akad. Nauk. Tashkent, 1941.

58. KUZNETSOV, V. I., O protsesse stanovleniya granitnykh pegmatitov, (In Reference to the Process of Stabilization of Granitic Pegmatites.) *Mineralog. sb. L'vov. geolog. obshch.* No. 2, 1948.

59. KUZNETSOV, V. I., K metodike nabluydenii zhidkikh vklyuchenii v prozrachnykh mineralakh s pomoshch'yu immersionnykh zhidkostei. (On the Subject of the Methods of Observation of Liquid Inclusions in Translucent Minerals with the Aid of Immersion Liquids.) *Mineralog. sb. L'vov. geolog. obshch.* No. 3, 1949.

60. LAZ'KO, E. M., Geologicheskiye usloviya formirowaniya aldanskikh mesto-rozhdenii gornogo khrustalya i ikh geneticheskiye osobennosti. (Geological En-vironments of the Formation of Quartz Crystal Deposits in Aldan and Their Genetic Characteristics.) *Trudy Moskov. inst. tsvetnykh metallov i zolota*, No. 16, 1947.

61. LAZ'KO, E. M., Zhidkiye vklyucheniya kak geologicheskii barometr. (Liquid Inclusions as a Geological Barometer.) *Zap. VMO*, Pt. 78, No. 4, 1949.

62. LEVITSKII, O. D., *Mestorozhdeniya redkikh i malykh elementov SSSR.* (Deposits of Rare and Minor Elements in the USSR.) *Izd. Akad. Nauk SSSR*, Vol. II, 1939.

63. LEBEDEV, A. P., O kvartsevo-kal'tsitovykh vklyucheniyakh v laboradoritakh iz Golovina (severo-zapadnaya Ukraina). (On the Subject of Inclusion of Quartz–Cal-cite in Labradorites from Golovino, Northwestern Ukraine.) *Sbornik "Akademiku D. S. Belyankinu"* Izd. Akad. Nauk SSSR, 1946.

64. LEMMLEIN, G. G., Mineralogicheskiye svedeniya al Biruni. (al Biruni's Minera-logic Knowledge.) *Vestnik Akad. Nauk SSSR*, No. 4, pp. 60 and 61, 1949.

64a. LEMMLEIN, G. G., Sootvetstvuyet li nablyudayemyi sovremennyi ob'yom vklyuche-niya pervonachal'nomu? (Does the Observed Present Volume of an Inclusion Correspond to its Original Volume?) *Dokl. Akad. Nauk SSSR*, Vol. 72, No. 4, 1950.

65. LUKSHO, P., Vklyucheniya zhidkostei v kvartsakh granitov Finlyandii. (Inclusions of Liquids in Quartz from Granites of Finland). *Zap. mineralog. obshch.* Ser. 2, Vol. IX, p. 106, 1874.

66. MOROZENKO, N. K., Genezis khrustalenosnykh zhil Pamira. (Origin of the Quartz Crystal Veins of Pamir.) *Sovet. geolog.* No. 9, 1947.

67. NIKOLAYEV, V. A., O protsesse otdeleniya letuchikh soyedinenii iz magmy. (In Reference to the Process of Parting of Volatile Substances from Magma.) *Izv. Akad. Nauk SSSR, ser. geolog.* No. 5, 1944.

68. NIKOLAYEV, V. A., Diagramma ravnovesiya binarnykh sistem tipa silikat–voda i otdeleniye letuchikh soyedinenii iz magmaticheskikh rasplavov. (The Equili-brium Diagram for Binary Systems of the Silicate–Water Type and the Separation of Volatile Compounds from Magmatic Solutions.) *Zap. VMO*, Pt. 75, No. 1, 1945.

69. NIKOLAYEV, V. A., O troynykh sistemakh s letuchimi komponentami i etapakh glubinnogo magmaticheskogo protsessa. (On the Subject of Ternary Systems with Volatile Components and Stages of the Deep Magmatic Process.) *Zap. VMO*, Pt. 76, No. 1, 1947.

70. NIKOLAYEV, V. A., O nekotorykh osobennostyakh reaktsii metamorfizma s ucha-stiyem vody i uglekisloty. (On the Subject of Certain Features of the Metamorphism with the Participation of Water and Carbon Dioxide.) *Izv. Akad. Nauk SSSR, ser. geolog.* No. 4, 1947.

71. NEKHOROSHEV, V. P., Tektonika i metallogeniya yugo-zapadnogo Altaya. (Tec-tonics and Metallogeny of the Southwestern Altay.) *Izv. VGRO*, Vol. 51, 15, 1932.

72. OBRUCHEV, V. A., Printsipy klassifikatsii rudnykh mestorozhdenii. (Principles of Classification of Ore Deposits.) *Vest. moskov. gornoi akademii*, I, 1922.

73. OBRUCHEV, V. A., *Rudnyye mestorozhdeniya.* (Ore Deposits.) ONTI (2nd ed.) 1934.

74. OBRUCHEV, V. A., *Obrazovaniye gor i rudnykh mestorozhdenii.* (Formation of Mountains and Ore Deposits.) (2nd ed.) 1944.

75. OVCHINNIKOV, A. M., O gidrotermal'nom rezhime zemnoi kory. (About the Hydrothermal Regime of the Earth's Crust.) *Dokl. Akad. Nauk SSSR*, Vol. 53, No. 7, 1946.

76. PEK, A. V., *Treshchinnaya tektonika i strukturnyi analiz.* (Fissure Tectonics and Structural Analysis.) Moscow–Leningrad, 1939.

77. PEK, A. V., Issledovaniya v oblasti paragenezisa khimicheskikh elementov v sul'fid-nykh, mednykh, tsinkovykh i svintsovykh rudakh. (Studies in the Field of Para-genesis of Chemical Elements in Sulfide, Copper, Zinc, and Lead Ores.) *Trudy MGRI*, Vol. 8, 1937.

78. PILIPENKO, P. P., Skarny i orudeneniye. (Skarns and Mineralization.) *Trudy MGRI*, Vol. 13, 1939.

79. SAAK'YAN, P. S., K voprosu o metallogenii. (On the Subject of Metallogeny.) *Izv. Akad. Nauk SSSR, ser. geolog.* No. 3, 1949.

80. SAMOYLOV, YA., Mineralogiya zhil'nykh mestorozhdenii Nagol'nogo Kryazha (Mineralogy of Vein Deposits in the Nagol'nyy Kryazh.) *Materialy dlya geologi Rossii*, Vol. XXIII, Izd. Mineral. og. obshch. 1908.

81. SATPAYEV, K. I., Osnovnyye cherty geologii i metallogenii dzhezkazganskogo mednorudnogo rayona. (The Fundamental Features of Geology and Metallo-geny of the Dzhezkazgan Copper Ore District.) *Trudy Kazakhstan. bazy Akad. Nauk SSSR*, 7, 1935.

82. SAUKOV, A. A., Geokhimiya rtuti. (Geochemistry of Mercury.) *Trudy geolog. inst. Akad. Nauk SSSR, mineralog. geokhim. ser.* 78, 1946.

83. SEMENENKO, N. P., Pegmatitovyi protsess grafitovykh mestorozhdenii. (The Pegmatitic Process in Deposits of Graphite.) *Izv. Akad. Nauk SSSR, ser. geolog.* No. 6, 1937.

84. SMIRNOV, V. I., *Rtutno–sur'myanyye mestorozhdeniya yuzhnoi Fergany.* (Mercury–Antimony Deposits of Southern Ferghana.) Gosgeoltekhizdat, 1947.

85. SMIRNOV, V. I., Glavnaya zona razlomov Tyan'-Shanya i eye s'vyaz' s orudeneniyem. (The Main Zone of Fractures in Tien-Shan and its Connection with Mineralization.) *Sovet. geolog.* No. 11, 1940.

86. SMIRNOV, V. I., *Problemy sovetskoi geologii.* (Problems of Soviet Geology.) No. 1, 1935.

87. SMIRNOV, S. S., Zametki po nekotorym voprosam ucheniya o rudnykh mestorozhdeniyakh. (Remarks on Certain Aspects of the Theory of Ore Deposits.) *Izv. Akad. Nauk SSSR, ser. geolog.* No. 3, 1946.

88. SMIRNOV, S. S., Retsenziya na knigu P. Niggli "Sistematika magmatogennykh rudnykh mestorozhdenii" (Review of P. Niggli's Book "The Systematics of Magmatogenic Deposits of Ores"). *Izv. Akad. Nauk SSSR, ser. geolog.* No. 1, 1947.

89. SMIRNOV, S. S., Nekotoryye zamechaniya o sul'fidno–kassiteritnykh mestorozhdeniyakh. (Certain Remarks on Sulfide–Cassiterite Deposits.) *Izv. Akad. Nauk SSSR, ser. geolog.* No. 5, 1937.

90. SMIRNOV, S. S., V. I. MIKHEYEV and I. I. SHAFRANOVSKII, O kristallakh dipiramidal'nogo kvartsa iz tetyukhinskogo svintsovo–tsinkovogo mestorozhdeniya. (About Crystals of Di-pyramidal Quartz from the Lead–Zinc Deposit of Tetyukhi.) *Zap. VMO,* Pt. 76, No. 4, 1947.

91. SMIRNOV, S. S., K voprosu zonal'nosti rudnykh mestorozhdenii. (On the Subject of Zoning in Ore Deposits.) *Izv. Akad. Nauk SSSR, ser. geolog.* No. 6, 1937.

92. SMIRNOV, S. S. and A. G. BETEKHTIN, Uspekhi v oblasti teorii obrazovaniya magmatogennykh rudnykh mestorozhdenii. (Advancements in the Field of the Theory of Origin of Magmatogenic Deposits of Ores.) *Yubileynyi sbornik Akad. Nauk SSSR,* Vol. II, 1947.

93. SMIRNOV, S. S., *Ocherk metallogenii vostochnogo Zabaikal'ya.* (Outline of Metallogeny of Eastern Transbaykalia.) Gosgeolizdat, 1944.

94. SMIRNOV, S. S., Polimetallicheskiye mestorozhdeniya vostochnogo Zabaikal'ya. (Polymetallic Ore Deposits of Eastern Transbaikala.) *Trudy VGRO,* 327, ONTI, 1934.

95. SMIRNOV, S. S., *Zona okisleniya sul'fidnykh mestorozhdenii.* (The Oxidized Zone of Sulfide Deposits.) ONTI, 1936.

96. SMIRNOV, S. S., O sovremennom sostoyanii teorii obrazovaniya magmatogennykh rudnykh mestorozhdenii. (On the Present State of Theory of Origin of Magmatogenic Deposits of Ores.) *Zap. VMO,* Pt. 74, No. 1, 1947.

97. SMOL'YANIKOV, N. A., Flyuoritovyye mestorozhdeniya Srednei Azii. (Fluorite Deposits of Central Asia). *Trudy TPE,* 27, 1935.

98. SOBOLEV, V. S., *Vvedeniye v mineralogiyu silikatov.* (Introduction to Mineralogy of Silicates.) Izd. L'vov. Gosuniversiteta, 1949.

99. SOKOLOV, D., *Rudovodstvo k mineralogii.* (Manual of Mineralogy.) Pt. I, pp. 536–537, Leningrad, 1932.

100. STRELKIN, M. F., K voprosu ob olovonosnykh pegmatitakh. (In Reference to Stanniferous Pegmatites.) *Izv. Akad. Nauk SSSR, ser. geolog.* No. 6, 1938.

101. SYROMYATNIKOV, F. V., K voprosu o gazovom perenose kremnekisloty. (On the Subject of Gaseous Transfers of Silicic Acid.) *Trudy soveshchaniya po eksperimental'noy mineralogii i petrografii,* 1934–1935.

102. TANATAR, I. I., Geokhimicheskaya kharakteristika polimetallicheskikh mesto-

rozhdenii Nagol'nogo Kryazha. (Geochemical Characteristics of the Polymetallic Deposits in Nagol'nyi Kryazh.) *Probl. sovet. geolog.* No. 4, 1934.

103. TATARINOV, P. M., Uspekhi v izuchenii nemetallicheskikh poleznykh iskopaye-mykh. (Successes in Studies of Non-metallic Mineral Raw Materials.) *Sb. Sovetskaya geologiya za 30 let,* 1947.

104. USANOVICH, M. I., O kislotakh i osnovaniyakh. (About Acids and Bases.) *Zh. obshch. khim.* Vol. IX (XXI), 2, 1939.

105. USOV, M. A., *Kratkii kurs rudnykh mestorozhdenii.* (A Brief Course in Ore Deposits.) (2nd ed.) Kubuch. Tomsk, 1933.

106. URAZOV, G. G. and N. N. NOGINOV, Eksperimental'noye issledovaniye poryadka vydeleniya sul'fidov zheleza, medi, i svintsa iz ikh odnorodnykh zhidkikh rastvorov. (Experimental Studies of the Sequence of Separation of Sulfides of Iron, Copper, and Lead from Their Homogeneous Liquid Solutions.) *Trudy TsNIGRI,* 19, 1935.

107. FERSMAN, A. E., *Geokhimiya.* (Geochemistry.) Vols. I, II, III, IV, 1933–1939.

108. FERSMAN, A. E., *Pegmatity.* (Pegmatites.) Vol. I (3rd ed.), Izd. Akad. Nauk SSSR, 1940.

109. FERSMAN, A. E., *Geokhimicheskiye i mineralogicheskiye metody poiskov poleznykh iskopayemykh.* (Geochemical and Mineralogical Methods of Prospecting for Mineral Deposits.) Izd. Akad. Nauk SSSR, 1939.

110. KHITAROV, N. I., L. A. IVANOV and L. E. ROTMAN, K poznaniyu kriticheskikh yavlenii v prirodnykh protsessakh. (In Reference to the Understanding of Critical Phenomena in Natural Processes.) *Sovet. geolog.* No. 2, 1939.

111. KHITAROV, N. I., O sostoyanii ostatochnogo magmaticheskogo rastvora (po eksperimental'nym dannym). (On the State of the Residual Magmatic Solution (on the basis of experimental data). *Sovet. geolog.* No. 7, 1939.

112. KHITAROV, N. I. and L. A. IVANOV, Eksperimental'nyye dannyye po kharakteristike vodnykh rastvorov v oblasti kriticheskikh temperatur (v prilozhenii k voprosam geologii). (Experimental Data in Regards to Characteristics of Aqueous Solutions in the Field of Critical Temperatures (in Reference to Geologic Problems).) *Trudy 17-i sessii mezhdunarodnogo geologicheskogo kongressa,* Vol. V, Moscow, 1940.

113. KHITAROV, N. I. and L. A. IVANOV, Parovaya i gazovaya faza sistemy kremnezyom-voda. (The Vapor and the Gaseous Phase in the Silica-Water System.) *Sovet. geolog.* No. 2, 1944.

114. CHIRVINSKII, P. N., Nakhodka kvartsa bez prismy v donetskom basseyne. (A Find of a Quartz without the Prism in the Don Basin.) *Zap. VMO,* Pt. 77, No. 3, 1948.

115. SHADLUN, N. A., *Vvedeniye v kurs rudnykh mestorozhdenii.* (Introduction to Course in Ore Deposits.) Sverdlovsk-Moscow, 1936.

116. SHAFRANOVSKII, I. I. and D. P. GRIGOR'EV, O poverkhnostyakh soprikosnoveniya kristallicheskikh individov. (On the Subject of Surface-contacts between Crystalline Individuals.) *Zap. VMO,* Pt. 77, No. 3, 1948.

117. SHUBNIKOV, A. V., *Kristallografiya.* (Crystallography.) Ekaterinburg, pp. 48–49, 1923.

118. SHUBNIKOV, A. V., *Kak rastut kristally?* (How do Crystals Grow?) Izd. Akad. Nauk SSSR, 1935.

119. SHKBARA, M. N., Kal'tsit kak geologicheskii termometr. (Calcite as a Geological Thermometer.) *Zap. nauch. issledov. inst. khar'kov. Gosuniv.* 1940.

120. SHCHERBINA, V. V., *Geokhimiya.* (Geochemistry.) Moscow, 1939.

121. SHTERNBERG, A. A., Vliyaniye neodnorodnostei kristalla na skorost' narastaniya granei. (Influence of Heterogeneity in a Crystal on the Rate of the Accretional Growth of the Faces.) *Uchenyye zap. LGU, ser. geolo-pochven.,* 13, 1945.

122. SHCHERBAKOV, D. I., Geneticheskiye usloviya olovorudnykh proyavlenii Sredney Azii. (Genetic Environments of the Expressions of Ores of Tin in Central Asia.) *Sb. Nauchnyye Itogi Rabot TPE*, Izd. Akad. Nauk SSSR, 1937.

123. YAKZHIN, A. A., K metallogenii Nagol'nogo Kryazha. (In Reference to Metallogeny in the Nagol' nyi Kryazh.) *Sovet. geolog.* No. 8, 1945.

124. DAVY, H., *Phil. Trans.*, pp 367–376, 1822.

125. BREWSTER, D., (1) *Edinb. Phil. J.*, Vol. IX, pp. 94–95, 1823. (2) *Edinb. Roy. Soc. Trans.*, Vol. X, pp. 1–43, 1826. (3) *Edinb. J. Sci.*, Vol. VI., pp. 155–156, 1827. (4) *Geol. Soc. Trans.*, Vol. III, pp. 455–460, 1835.

126. NICOL, W., (1) *Edinb. New Phil. J.*, Vol. V, pp. 94–96, 1828. (2) *Edinb. New Phil. J.*, Vol. VII, pp. 111–113, 1829.

127. FRANKENHEIM, M. L., *Poggend. Ann.* Vol. XXXVII, pp. 516–527, 1836.

128. SORBY, H. C., (1) *Geol. Soc. J.* Vol. XIV, pp. 443–500, 1858. (2) *Phil. Mag.*, Vol. XVIII, pp. 81–91, 1859.

129. SORBY, H. C. and P. BUTLER, *Proc. Roy. Soc.*, Vol. XVII, pp. 291–302, 1869.

130. SÖCHTING, E., *Zeitschr. gesammt. Naturw.*, Vol. XIII, pp. 417–442, 1859.

131. DANA, J. D., *Mineralogy* (5th ed.), p. 761, 1868.

132. ZIRKEL, F., (1) *Sitz. Ber. Akad. Wien*, Vol. XLVII, 1, pp. 226–270, 1863, (2) *N. Jahrb. Mineral.*, p. 802, 1870.

133. ZIRKEL, F., *Lehrbuch der Petrographie*. Vol. I, 1893.

134. VOGELSANG, H., *Poggend. Ann.* Vol. 137, pp. 257–271, 1869.

135. PFAFF, F., *Poggend. Ann.* Vol., 143, pp. 610–620, 1871,

136. HUNTER, J. and E. Sang, *Edinb. Roy. Soc. Proc.*, Vol. VIII, pp. 126–130, 1873.

137. PHILLIPS, J. A., *Geol. Soc. Quart. J.* Vol. 31, No. 123, pp. 319–345, 1875.

138. JUDD, J. W., *Geol. Soc. Quart. J.* Vol. 32, p. 33, 1876.

139. ALLPORT, S., *Geol. Soc. Quart. J.*, Vol. 32, pp. 407–427, 1876.

140. WARD, J. C., *Geol. Soc. Quart. J.*, Vol. 31, No. 124, pp. 568–589, 1875.

141. LEA, I., *Acad. Nat. Sci. Proc.*, pp. 98–107, Philad., 1876.

142. HARTLEY, W. N., *Chem. Soc. J.* Vol. 1, pp. 137–143, 1876; *ibid.*, Vol. 2, pp. 237–250.

143. GÜMBEL, C. W., *Akad. Sitz. Ber. München*, Vol. 10, pp. 241–254, 1880; *ibid.*, Vol. 11, pp. 321–368, 1881.

144. HAWES, G. W., *Amer. J. Sci.* Vol. 21, pp. 203–209, 1881.

145. PRINZ, W., (1) *Annal. Soc. Belg. Micr.*, 1882; (2) *Bull. Soc. Belg. Geol.*, Vol. 32, pp. 63–82, 1908.

146. HIDDEN, W., *N. Y. Acad. Sci. Trans.*, Vol. 1, pp. 131–136, 1881–82.

147. KHRUSHCHEV, K. V., *Min. Petr. Mitt.*, Wien, 1882.

148. LASAULX, A., *Niederrhein. Gesell. Sitz. Ber.*, pp. 4–6, Bonn, 1883.

149. JULIEN, A. A., *Am. Min. Micr.*, Vol. 5, No. 10, p. 189, 1884.

150. RENARD, A. F., *L'analyse microscopique des roches et les enclaves des minéraux*, pp. 28–33, Louvain, 1887.

151. SJÖGREN, H., *Upsala Geol. Inst. Bull.*, Vol. 1, No. 2, 1893.

151a. LINDGREN, W. and STEIGL, *Geol. Survey. 17th Ann. Rept.*, Vol. 2, 130, 1895–96.

152. KÖNIGSBERGER, J., *N. Jahrb. Mineral.*, Vol. 14, p. 43, 1901.

153. KÖNIGSBERGER, J. and W. MÜLLER, *Centralbl. Mineral.*, pp. 72–77, 341, 1906.

154. TRONQUOY, R., *Bull. Soc. Fr. Min.*, Vol. 35, 1912.

155. LINDGREN, W. and W. WHITEHEAD, *Econ. Geol.* Vol. 9, No. 5, pp. 455–460, 1914.

156. SPENCER, A., *Geol. Survey Prof. Pap.*, Vol. 96, pp. 63–100, 1917.

157. YONSEN, A., *Sitz. Ber. Bayr. Akad. Wiss.*, pp. 321–328, 1920.

158. ROSENBUSCH, H. and E. WÜLFING, *Mikroskopische Physiographie der petrographisch-wichtigen Mineralien*, I, Stuttgart, 1904.

159. NACKEN, P., *Centralbl. Mineral.*, pp. 12–20, 35–43, 1921.

160. DALE and NELSON, *U.S. Geol. Survey Bull.*, Vol. 738, pp. 17–26, 1923.
161. HOLDEN, E. F., The Cause of Color in Smoky Quartz and Amethyst, *Am. Min.*, vol. 10, No. 10, pp. 203–252, 1925.
162. HULIN, and D. CARLETON, Factors in the Deposition of Hydrothermal Ores (abs.), *Econ. Geol.*, vol. 42, pp. 413–414, 1947.*
163. LEMMLEIN, G. G., *Zeitschr. Kristal.*, Bd. 75, H. 3, 1929.
163a. LEMMLEIN, G. G., *Zeitschr. Krist.*, Bd. 75, H. 1–2, 1930.
164. SEIFERT, H., *Fortschr. Min. Krist. Petr.*, Vol. 14, T. 2, 1930.
165. BUERGER, M., (1) *Am. Min.*, Vol. 17, No. 6, 1932; (2) *ibid.*, Vol. 19, No. 12, 1934.
166. NEWHOUSE, W., *Econ. Geol.*, Vol. 27, No. 5, pp. 419–436, 1932.
167. NEWHOUSE, W., *Econ. Geol.*, Vol. 28, No. 8, pp. 744–750, 1933.
168. EDGE, A., *Canad. Min. J.*, Vol. 55, p. 406, 1934.
169. BADER, H., *Schweiz. Min. Petr. Mitteil.*, Vol. 14, pp. 319–441, 1934.
170. CONNELY, D. and J. LORD. *J. Am. Cer. Soc.*, Vol. XX, 1, pp. 10–16, 1937.
171. INGERSON, E., *Am. Min.*, Vol. 32, No. 3–4, 1947.
172. INGERSON, E., *Am. Min.*, Vol. 32, No. 7–8, 1947.
173. TWENHOFEL, W., *Econ. Geol.* Vol. XLII, No. 1, 1947.
174. TABER, S., *Am. Min.*, Vol. 32, No. 3–4, 1947.
175. SCOTT, H., *Econ. Geol.* Vol. XLIII, No. 8, 1948.
176. SMITH, F., *Econ. Geol.*, Vol. XLIII, No. 8, 1948.
177. PEACH, P., *Am. Min.*, Vol. 34, No. 5–6, 1949.
178. DREYER, R., R. GARRELS and A. HOWLAND, *Am. Min.*, Vol. 34,, No. 1–2, 1949.
179. BAILEY, S., *J. Geol.*, Vol. 57, No. 3, 1949.
180. ADAMS, E., *J. Geol.* Vol. 20, pp. 97–118, 1912.
181. BRIDGMAN, P., *Am. J. Sci.*, Vol. 45, pp. 243–268, 1918.
182. FARMIN, R., *Econ. Geol.*, Vol. XXXVI, No. 2, 1941.
183. SOSMAN, R., *Am. J. Sci.*, Ser. 5, Vol. 35, pp. 353–359, 1938.
184. BOWEN, N., Geologic thermometry, *Laboratory investigations of ores*, 671, New York, 1928.
185. RAMDOHR, P., (1) *N. Jahrb. Min.*, Vol. 54, pp. 320–379, 1926; (2) *Zeitschr. prakt. Geol.*, Vol. 331, 1931.
186. MÜGGE, O., (1) *N. Jahrb. Min.*, Festband, pp. 181–196, 1907; (2) *Centralbl. Min.*, pp. 609–615, 641–648, 1921; (3) *Zeitschr. Krist.*, Vol. 83, p. 460, 1932; *ibid.*, Vol. 86, p. 439, 1933.
187. WRIGHT, F. and E. LARSEN, *Am. J. Sci.* (4), Vol. 27, pp. 421–447, 1909.
188. HEIDE, F., *Zeitschr. Krist.*, Vol. 67, pp. 33–90, 1928.
189. SCHWARIZ, H., *Econ. Geol.*, Vol. 22, 1927; *ibid.*, Vol. 23, 1928; *ibid.*, Vol. 26, 1931.
190. KALB, G., (1) *Centralbl. Min.* (A), Vol. 10, pp. 337–339, 1928; (2) *Zeitschr. Krist.* (A), Vol. 86, pp. 439–465, 1933; (3) *ibid.*, Vol. 90, 1935, etc.
191. MAUCHER, W., *Die Bildungsreihe der Mineralien als Unterlage für die Einteilung der Erzlagerstätten*, Freiberg i.S., 1914.
192. STIRNEMANN, E., *N. Jahrb. Min.*, Vol. 53 (A), pp. 59–94, 1925.
193. DAUBREE, Ac., *Annales des mines*, 5 sér., Vol. XII, p. 289, 1857.
194. SMITH, F. G., *Econ. Geol.*, Vol. XLII, No. 6, 1947.

* The original reference 162, as given: "HOLDEN, E. and EDWARD F., *Am. min.*, Vol. 10, 1925, pp. 215–220." [Ed.]

PLATE I.

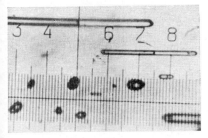

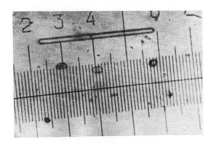

1. Tubular–rounded gas–liquid inclusions in topaz from Volynia at room temperature. Gas bubbles (dark) occupy 54.45 per cent of the volume of the inclusions. Characterized by homogenization with the critical point at 362°C. 100 ×.

2. Tubular–flattened gas–liquid inclusions in topaz from Volynia. The gas bubble is recognizable by its meniscus at the boundary of the liquid phase. At room temperature the gas bubble occupies 54 per cent of the volume of the inclusion. 100 ×.

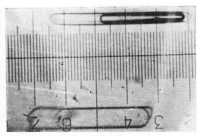

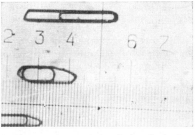

3. Gas–liquid inclusions in topaz from Volynia; a tubular one on top, flat one below. 55 per cent gas at 20°C. The homogenization takes place in the gas phase, as in variant 2, at 390°C. 100 ×.

4. Flattened–rounded tubular inclusions in topaz from Volynia. 60.74 per cent gas at 20°C. Homogenization as in variant 2. 100 ×.

PLATE II.

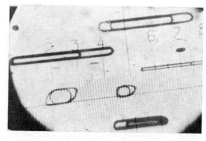

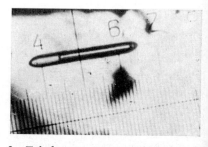

1. Tubular, flattened–tubular, and flattened gas–liquid inclusions in topaz from Volynia. 66.27 per cent gas, homogenization as in variant 2.

2. Tubular gas–aqueous inclusion in topaz from Volynia. 66 per cent gas at 20°C. Homogenization as in variant 2. 180 ×. [See also Plate 9–Ed.]

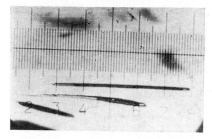

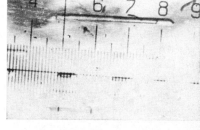

3. Tubular–rounded and irregularly tubular gaseous inclusions in topaz from Volynia. Relative volume of the gas is 79.31 per cent at 20°C; volume of the liquid observed at the tips of the inclusions is 20.69 per cent. Homogenization in the gas phase, as in variant 1, at 400°C. 100 ×.

4. Rounded–tubular gaseous inclusions in topaz from Volynia. 82.76 per cent gas 17.24 per cent liquid, at 20°C. Homogenization as in variant 1. 100 ×.

PLATE III.

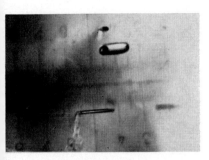

1. A. faceted two-phase inclusion in quartz from Transbaykalia. Bottom: an exploded tubular inclusion filled with gas. The fissure into which the liquid was squeezed begins from the left tip of the inclusion. On top: a small oval inclusion, also exploded on heating. 100×.

2. Two-phase inclusions in low-temperature quartz from Middle Ural at room temperature. 100 ×.

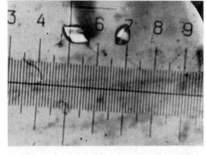

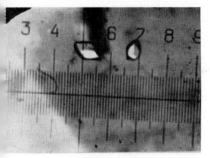

3. Same inclusions homogenized by heating to 130°C. 100 ×.

4. Same inclusions after cooling to 115°C. This was accompanied by an "effervescence" in the right inclusion; numerous fine bubbles coalescing into two gas bubbles which, in turn, in the next moment are going to coalesce into one common bubble, whereupon the inclusion will assume the same appearance as is shown in No. 2. The reconstitution of the gas bubble in the left inclusions was delayed by 2–3°C. 100 ×.

PLATE IV.

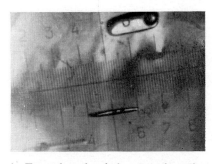

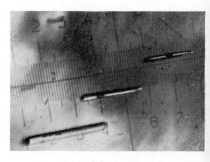

1. Faceted and tubular two-phase inclusions in quartz from Transbaykalia (same as Plate III, 1, but magnified 180 times). The gas bubble occupies 21 per cent of each inclusion at room temperature.

2. Same as Plate IV, 1, but at 140°C. The gas bubble occupies 13 per cent of the volume of each inclusion. The larger inclusion was removed from the field of vision, since the measurements were type. I. The gas bubbles have disappeared. 180 ×.

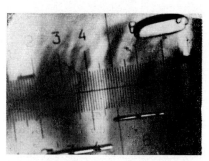

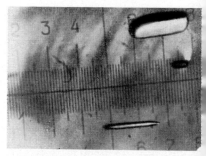

3. Same as Plate IV, 1, but at 180°C. The abrupt shrinkage of the gas bubble is clearly noticeable, as its volume now is 8 per cent of the total. 180 ×.

4. Same as Plate IV, 1, but with the inclusions homogenized at 200°C, as in type. I. The gas bubbles have disappeared. 180 ×.

PLATE V.

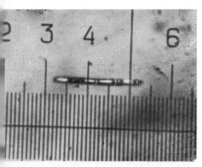

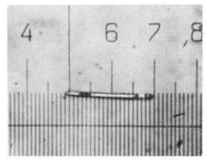

1. A rounded–tubular inclusion in topaz from Volynia at 40°C. A saturated aqueous solution occupies 56.5 per cent of the volume; the gas bubble (black) occupies 19.6 per cent of the volume. Solid phase No. 1 (halite, white) is situated under the vertical line and occupies 14.9 per cent of the volume. Solid phases No. 2 (sylvite) and No. 3 (white) are situated between the gaseous bubble and the No. 1 solid phase; they occupy 5 per cent and 3 per cent of the volume respectively. Homogenization as in type I. 180 ×.

2. Same as No. 1, but at 150°C. Of the total volume 12.25 per cent is gas, 10.2 per cent is solid phase No. 1, and 77.55 per cent is saturated aqueous solution, because solid phases Nos. 2 and 3 were dissolved at about 100°C. 180 ×.

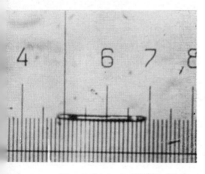

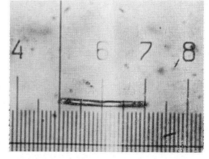

3. Same as No. 1, but at 180°C. 10 per cent gas, 8.6 per cent No. 1 solid phase, 81.4 per cent saturated aqueous solution. 180 ×.

4. Same as No. 1, but at 275°C. 2.5 per cent gas, 3.4 per cent No. 1 solid phase, 94.1 per cent saturated aqueous solution. 180 ×.

PLATE VI.

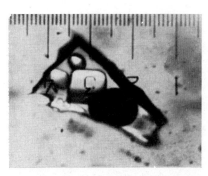

1. A large-volume inclusion of irregular shape in topaz from Volynia. This inclusion is situated in the same zone of the crystal as the inclusion shown in Plate V, 1. The following only is visible: solid phase No. 4 (hexagonal fine crystals at the lower left tip of crystal No. 1) occupying 1 per cent of the volume; solid phase No. 5, a dark overgrowth possibly an ore mineral, on the left rib of crystal No. 1; solid phase No. 6, a prismatic bluish crystal under solid phase No. 2 (solid phases Nos. 5 and 6 constitute about 1 per cent of the volume of the inclusion). Volume of the liquid phase: 54.5 per cent. 180 ×.
See also Fig. 57, p. 237 [Ed.].

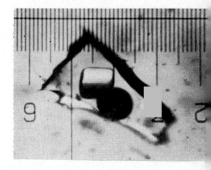

2. Same as No. 1, at 150°C. The relative volumes of the phases had changed as in Plate V, 2. 180 ×.

3. Same as No. 1, at 180°C. The relative volumes of the phases had changed as in Plate V, 3. 180 ×.

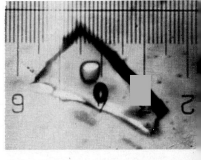

4. Same as No. 1, at 275°C. The relative volumes of the phases are the same as in Plate V, 4. Later on, the gas bubble will disappear at 300°C and a complete homogenization will take place at 310°C, as in type I, by the solution of the solid phase No. 1.

PLATE VII.

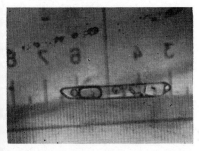

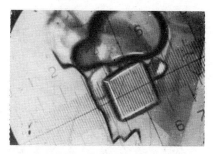

1. Flattened–tubular faceted multiphase inclusion in topaz from Volynia with a clearly defined black border(?) on the left; the gas bubble is visible. More than ten different anisotropic and isotropic 'captive' minerals. Homogenization as in type I, at 315–320°C. 100 ×. See also Fig. 57, p. 237 [Ed.].

2. A detail of a large inclusion in topaz from Volynia. "Captive" mineral No. 1 and other solid phases are under the flattened irregularly shaped gas bubble with a dark border on the left.

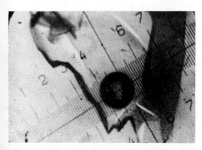

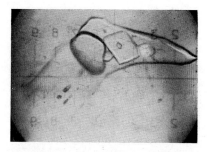

3. Same as No. 2, but at 265°, when most of the solid phases had dissolved and the gas bubble, having shrunken appreciably, had changed its position in the liquid filling the cavity. 180 ×.

4. A part of a multiphase inclusion in topaz from Volynia (the remaining part is not in the focus of the microscope). Clearly visible outlines of crystal No. 1 within which solid phase No. 5(?) proved to be included. The isotropic crystal No. 2 is on the left and crystal No. 3 is on the right. 180 ×.

PLATE VIII.

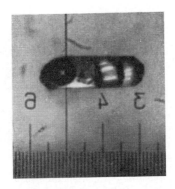

1. A multiphase inclusion in a "negative crystal" in quartz from Pamir. A round gas bubble is on the left; a large cubic "captive" crystal is on the right (halite), with another cubic crystal (sylvite) grown on its surface. An opaque ore mineral may be distinguished on top, between the two crystals. Two small crystals of a carbonate with a high birefringence are barely distinguishable on top of the large crystal. 180 ×.

2. The same paragenesis of "captive" minerals in a partially faceted multiphase inclusion in quartz from Pamir, with calcite (dark) definitely overgrowing halite. 180 ×.

3. A multiphase inclusion in quartz from Pamir. Two isotropic "captive" crystals of the isometric habit are visible. A gas bubble (dark), a very small black-ore mineral, and a small rhombohedral crystal of a carbonate are also visible. 180 ×.

4. A multiphase inclusion in quartz from Pamir. The following are clearly visible, from right to left [from bottom to top—Ed.]; a round gas bubble, a cubical "captive" crystal, and a six-face platelet of specularite orange-red in transmitted light. The rest of the cavity is filled by a saturated aqueous solution, like other multiphase inclusions. 180 ×.

PLATE IX.

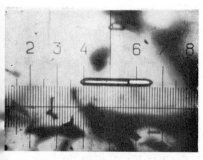

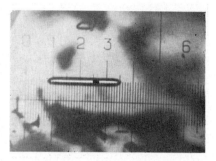

1. Same as Plate II, 2, an inclusion in topaz from Volynia, but at 150°C. The gas occupies 64 per cent of the total volume of the inclusion. 100 ×.

2. Same as No. 1, but at 290°C. Volume of the gas: 62.5 per cent. 100 ×.

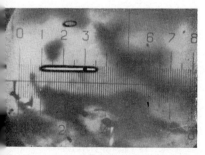

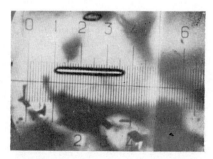

3. Same as No. 1, but at 330°C. The volume of gas has increased up to 88.8 per cent of the total, abruptly, between 300 and 330°C. 100 ×.

4. Same as No. 1, but at 335°C. The liquid phase has disappeared and a complete homogenization has taken place, as in type II, variant 2. 100 ×.

PLATE X.

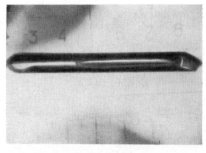

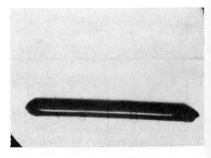

1. A rounded–tubular inclusion in topaz from Volynia. The gas occupies 53 per cent of the total volume of the inclusion at 20° C. 100 ×.

2. Same as No. 1, after the homogenization, as in variant 3, type II, with the "critical point" at 325°C. 100 ×.

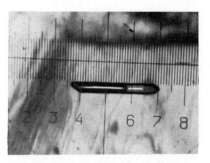

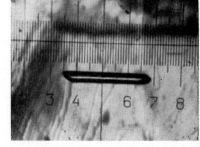

3. A rounded–tubular inclusion in topaz from Volynia. Volume of gas: 58 per cent of the total at 40°C. Homogenization as in variant 3. 180 ×.

4. Same as No. 3. Homogenized at 345°C. 180 ×.

PLATE XI.

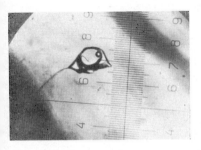

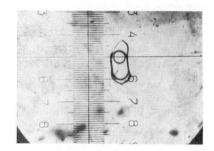

1. A complex three-phase inclusion in quartz from Middle Ural containing two immiscible liquids (aqueous solution and carbon dioxide) and a gas bubble. 180 ×.

2. A complex three-phase inclusion in quartz from Pamir (aqueous solution, liquid carbon dioxide, gaseous carbon dioxide) at 18.5°C. 180 ×.

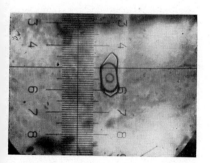

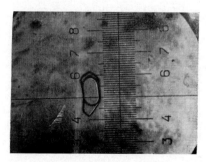

3. Same as No. 2, but at 25.5°C.

4. Same as No. 2, after its conversion, at 28.5°C, into a two-phase inclusion (the liquid carbon dioxide has disappeared).

PLATE XII.

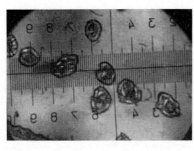

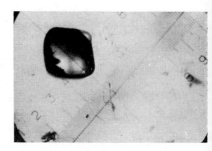

1. Exploded extremely small multiphase inclusions in topaz from Volynia. 180 ×.

2. A gaseous inclusion in calcite from trap rock, Vilyuy. 180 ×.

3. A gaseous inclusion in topaz from Volynia. 180 ×.

4. Single-phase negative crystals; liquid and solid inclusions in datolite of the latest generation. 180 ×.

PLATE XIII.

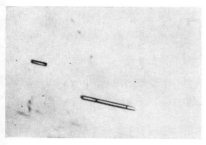

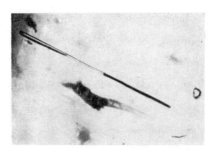

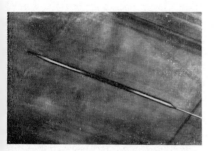

1. A regularly tubular chiefly gaseous inclusion in beryl. Homogenization, as in type II, at 300°C. The gas phase is 82 per cent of the volume at 20°C.	2. An irregularly tubular two-phase inclusion in beryl at 25°C. The inclusion is homogenized on heating to 356°C; type II.
3. A tubular two-phase inclusion at room temperature. The gas phase is 36 per cent of the volume of the cavity. Homogenizes as in type I at 362°C.	4. An inclusion in beryl at room temperature. The gas-phase constitutes 30.7 per cent of the volume. Homogenization, as in type I, at 402°C.

PLATE XIV.

1. An inclusion in beryl. Homogenization, as in type I, at 397°C. 140 ×.

2. A tubular inclusion in beryl at room temperature. Homogenization as in type I at 368°C.

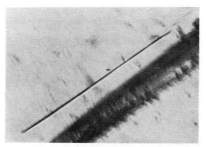

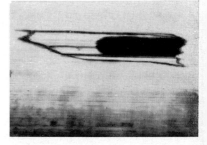

3. A very thin tubular inclusion in beryl. At 40°C the gas phase constitutes 39 per cent of the total volume of the inclusion. The inclusion becomes homogeneous (type I) at 370°C. 70 ×.

4. An irregularly tubular inclusion in beryl at 25°C. The gas bubble looks entirely black because of its complete internal reflection. The gas bubble is transparent in other positions. On heating, the inclusion becomes homogeneous, in its liquid phase, at 376°C, with an associated effervescence. 210 ×.

PLATE XV.

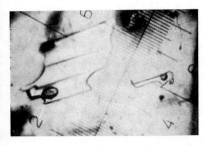

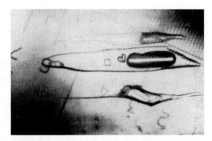

1. Two-phase secondary inclusions in aquamarine. Homogenization as in type I. The homogenization temperature: 170°C.

2. A group of multiphase inclusions in aquamarine. Homogenization as in type I at 382°C. The solid phases were incompletely dissolved.

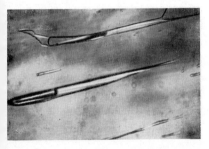

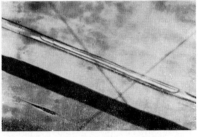

3. Irregularly tubular inclusions in beryls at 25°C. The central multiphase inclusion homogenizes at 438°C in its liquid phase.

4. A part of an extensively elongated inclusion in beryl. Presence of liquid carbon dioxide is indicated on the left of the gas bubble.

PLATE XVI.

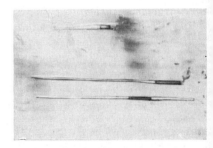

1. An irregularly shaped secondary multiphase inclusion. The solid phase is represented by acicular dendritic crystals. 240 ×.

2. Tubular secondary inclusions in beryl at 25°C. 220 ×.

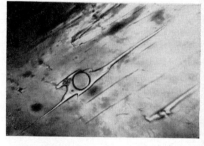

3. A multiphase inclusion in beryl. 78 ×.

4. A multiphase secondary inclusion of an irregular shape in aquamarine at 25°C. The solid phase on the left of the gas bubble has an acicular dendritic structure; a black crystal possibly of an ore mineral is under the other solid phase. 100 ×.

PLATE XVII.

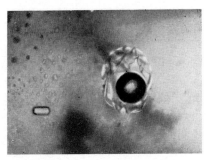

1 and 2. Two-phase inclusions in orthoclase from granites, Northern Caucasus. The outline of a cognate substance is visible on the periphery.

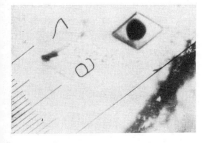

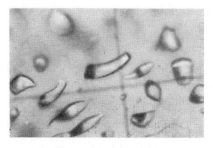

3. Two-phase inclusion (glass-gas) in garnet.

4. A group of two-phase inclusions (glass-gas) in garnet.

PLATE XVIII.

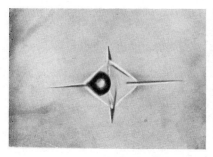

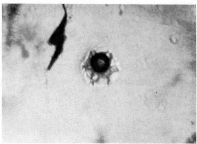

1. and 2. Two-phase inclusions (glass–gas) in garnet.

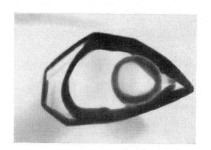

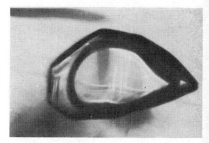

3. A mixed inclusion (aqueous solution and liquid CO_2; gas) in quartz crystal from Pamir.

4. Same as No. 3 at 28°C. The liquid CO_2 became gas.

PLATE XIX.

1 and 2. Solid inclusions of apophyllite in late calcite.

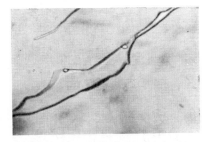

3. A single-phase inclusion of an aqueous solution in natrolite from Yukspor, Khibiny Tundra, Kola Peninsula.

4. An inclusion from the same specimen as No. 3. It consists of an aqueous phase in which several solid phases, in the form of faceted crystals, are clearly visible. There is no gas phase.

PLATE XX.

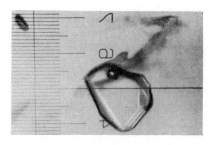

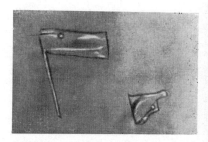

1. An ordinary two-phase secondary inclusion in quartz crystal from Pamir.

2. Two–phase inclusions in calcite from Yesaulovka, Donbass. The shape of the flat inclusion corresponds to the structure and to the cleavage of the mineral. The homogenization temperature is 70°C, type I (in the liquid phase).

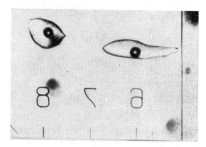

3. Typical two-phase inclusions in fluorite from Kulikolon with identical phase ratios and identical temperatures of homogenization.

4. A two-phase inclusion in sphalerite from Nagol'chik, Negol'nyi Kryazh, Donbass. The homogenization temperature, type I, is 105°C.

PLATE XXI.

1. Etch figures on walls of an inclusion in topaz after a slow homogenization and an explosion.

2. A two-phase inclusion in tourmaline from Borshchevochnyi Kryazh. The homogenization temperature, type I, is 240–250°C.

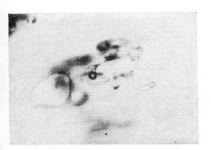

3. Two-phase primary inclusions in adularia from St. Gottard, Switzerland. Homogenization as in type I. The homogenization temperature: 130–135°C.

4. Three-phase inclusion in albite from Verkhnyaya Neyva, Nizhnyi Tagil district Ural. Homogenization as in type I. The homogenization temperature: 150°C.

PLATE XXII.

1. Gas–liquid multiphase inclusion in topaz from Volynia containing dentate crystals of a late topaz isolated from the host crystal by a narrow boundary (top and bottom). Homogenization is accompanied by an effervescence in the gas phase.

2. A liquid inclusion in topaz from Volynia containing dentate crystals of the "inner" topaz. Homogenization as in type I and is accompanied by effervescence.

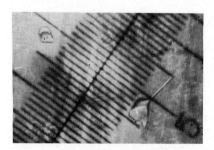

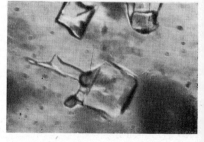

3. A single-phase inclusion (aqueous solution) in inyoite from the Inder Lake. A two-phase anomalous inclusion is visible in the lower right corner of the picture. The gas phase is a secondary phenomenon.

4. A multi-phase inclusion in quartz from Pamir. The inclusion originated on the left of the associated mineral (halite).

PART II

TRANSACTIONS OF THE ALL-UNION RESEARCH
INSTITUTE OF PIEZO-OPTICAL
MINERAL RAW MATERIALS

Translated from

Research on Mineral-forming Solutions (by inclusions)

Volume I Part 2

Ministry of Radiotechnical Industry
U. S. S. R.; Scientific-Technical Collected Papers

Editorial Board

Contents of Part II

[351]

Foreword

FOR a long time, in mineralogy in our country, in the theory of endo-genic mineral deposits, there were efforts to discover in nature the required objective data for our understanding of mineral-forming processes. The statistical approach to investigations of the mineral world had already ceased to satisfy the Russian mineralogical school a long time ago, in the unrelenting attempt, since the beginning of the twentieth century and espe-cially under the influence of V. I. Vernadskii's studies, to find the paths of the historical approach to the understnding of the phenomena of mineral genesis. Notwithstanding the appreciable successes obtained with the aid of studies of paragenesis of minerals, textures and structures of ores, as well as of details of outer and inner morphology of mineral individuals, there was a progressively growing realization that minerals themselves, as such, do not characterize reliably the depositional environments of the mineral-forming substance. These environments are determined chiefly by physico-chemical features of mineral-forming solutions and melts under-going changes in time and in space, depending on variations in the inter-dependent parameters of temperature, pressure, and concentration. Relics of these mineral-forming media are preserved in minerals as solidified, gaseous, or liquid inclusions.

It has been established during the last decade in Soviet science that experiments with such inclusions, in conjunction with geologic and min-eralogic–genetic observations and with determinations of the inner morpho-logy of crystals, offer the possibility of determining the state of aggregation of mineral-forming solutions, as well as the sequence of variations in the temperature during the process of crystallization, while analyses of inclu-sions for their constituents allow us to obtain some data on the chemical composition of mineral-forming media.

After the broad perspectives of the utilization of inclusions in science and in practice became manifest, as the result of systematic experimental studies of inclusions in minerals, a special mineralothermometric labora-tory, the first one in the U.S.S.R., was established at the Faculty of Geology of the Ivan Franko Memorial National University of L'vov and, later on, the laboratory of thermosonic analysis of minerals. This laboratory afford-ed the means for completion of the first stage of the research in relics of mineral-forming solutions by 1950.

Some of the results so obtained were presented by us in 1950, in the book *Research in Mineral-forming Solutions*.

The keys we had offered for the determination of the genesis of minerals and the types and species of homogenization discovered by us in the last five years were subjected to further verifications, in concrete geologic conditions of formation of endogenic deposits and in the laboratories of synthetic crystal growth. These verifications served to broaden and to refine the importance of inclusions in the decoding of ancient processes of formation of minerals.

Inclusions of mineral-forming solutions in pneumatolytic and hydrothermal minerals proved to be sensitive geologic witnesses of physico-chemical conditions of ancient ore-forming processes. A widest variety of compositions and phase ratios as well as the unlike course of their homogenization by heat had brought to light the characteristics of mineral genesis in different periods of time of action of mineral-forming solutions. Mineralogic–thermometric analysis of liquid inclusions makes it possible to ascertain the relative course of temperature variations during the growth of individual crystals and to develop a view of the temperature regime of the formation of many hydrothermal deposits in time and in space. The introduction of corrections for pressure and concentration of the solutions obtained for artificially grown crystals at different magnitudes of the $T-P-X^*$ and by the subsequent homogenization of artificial inclusions allowed us to come closer to a deeper knowledge of the true temperatures of the hydrothermal process whose range is from 550 to 50°C, and lower. Variations in the course of homogenization of liquid, aqueous, and gaseous inclusions are expressions of differences in the density of the parent solutions permitting us to distinguish between pneumatolytic and hydrothermal formations. Determinations of pressures at deposits of lead–zinc and gold, by inclusions in quartz, showed that these pressures are generally below 1000 atm, in the hydrothermal process. Such magnitudes do not harmonize with the actual lithostatic pressures of the overburden in view of the presence of tectonic channels and of the high macro-porosity of the surrounding rocks. It developed that the intensive alterations of these rocks did by no means invariably coincide with the main stage of the ore-formation and more often had preceded this stage. It was made possible to correlate these near-ore alterations with the vein-filling processes at the deposits, by primary inclusions in the minerals and by secondary inclusions in the rocks. The association of the hydrothermal veins with certain definite intrusions was ascertained by differences in the temperature and in the course of homogenization of the inclusions. It was established that the inclusions are exploded in the quartz crystals belonging to the early stage of the ore-formation, as the result of the entry of enstatitic porphyrites into the mineralized zone, but are preserved in auriferous quartz of the later genera

---

* The parameters of temperature, pressure, concentration [V.P.S.].

tions. Such was the broadening of the perspectives of possible utilization of inclusions in minerals in deciphering origins of post-magmatic deposits.

The methods and the techniques of the inclusion studies were improved considerably, both in regards to the qualitative investigation and to the thermosonic analysis of inclusions.

Physico-chemical interpretations of the phenomena observed in inclusions of mineral-forming solutions during the experiments served further to strengthen the theoretical premises of this research.

Extensive applications of the thermometric analysis to minerals from various endogenic deposits and the advancements in the technique and the method of the thermosonic analysis, already in 1953, provided the basis for a development of certain new methods of prospecting for mineral raw materials which will be introduced into the field practice in the nearest future.

In addition to the research staff of the Laboratory of Mineralothermal Analysis and of the Chairs of the Faculty of Geology of the University of L'vov, Ye. M. Laz'ko, Yu. A. Dolgov, V. A. Kalyuzhnyi, V. F. Lesnyak, L. I. Koltun, R. F. Sukhorskii, N. I. Myaz', several aspirants, laboratory workers, and graduate students were drawn into this research.

As the result, there developed a team in the University of L'vov, well prepared for a comprehensive research in inclusions and engaged in one common problem. Many of the members of this team were engaged in the study of deposits of crystal quartz, in the projects of the All-Union Research Institute of Piezo-optical Mineral Raw Materials (the VNIIP*). The first and the widest application of the inclusion research to genetic investigations of sources of piezo-optical mineral raw materials was undertaken in connection with that project.

G. M. Safronov and his co-workers in the VNIIP have since 1954, been conducting successfully thermometric investigations of natural and synthetic quartz that helped them particularly to arrive at [the appropriate—V.P.S.] corrections in ascertaining the absolute [true] temperatures of mineral genesis on the basis of ilquid inclusions in minerals and in determining the mechanism of formation of inclusions in quartz.

Study of inclusions, in recent years, was undertaken also by scientists of several educational and research institutions of Moscow (The National University of Moscow, Academy of Sciences of the U.S.S.R., the All-Union Institute of Mineral Raw Material), Leningrad (the All-Union Geologic Institute, the Mining Institute), Tashkent (Academy of Sciences of Uzbekistan), Alma-Ata (Academy of Sciences of Kazakhstan), Kiyev and other centers of science in the Soviet Union.

---

* Vsesoyuznyi Nauchno-issledovatel'skii Institut P'ezoopticheskogo Mineral'nogo Syr'ya [V.P.S.].

Among the Transactions of the VNIIP, special collections of scientific papers will be published once or twice a year, dealing with comprehensive investigations of mineral-forming solutions in inclusions in natural and synthetic crystals.

These publications of collected papers are intended to aid in the exchange of experience in research, in the given field, which is so essential in the understanding of origins of mineral deposits and of the synthesis of crystals.

The present publication contains the results of certain studies chiefly by the staff of the University of L'vov and of the VNIIP.

N. P. YERMAKOV

Significance of Research on Inclusions in Minerals for the Theory of Ore-formation and for the Principles of Mineral-forming Media

N. P. Yermakov

To the bright memory of S. S. Smirnov, Member of the Academy

I. LINES OF RESEARCH IN THE DEVELOPMENT OF THEORY OF ORE-FORMATION

The basis on which the theory of endogenic formation of ores is developed is itself the result of oriented research in three [different—V.P.S.] fields: (1) Geologic–petrographic; (2) Mineralogic–geochemical; (3) Laboratory–experimental. Investigations of inclusions of mineral-forming solutions and of "melts" in recent years have strengthened the findings of genetic investigations of endogenic mineral deposits by new data.

The first orientation of the research is based on comprehensive studies of geologic environments of formation of ores: facies and geochemical characteristics of ore-bearing intrusions; distances of the site of ore-deposition from the parent plutonic body and from the surface of the ground; tectonic and lithologic features of the host rocks, etc. Metallogenic research of this kind was particularly fruitful in the U.S.S.R. It brought us closer to identifications of tectonic–magmatic complexes typical of the formation of ores.

The second orientation has for its cornerstone a detailed mineralogical and geochemical study of the products of the ore-forming processes: species of minerals and their varieties; textures and structures of ores; associations of minerals; alteration of host rocks and of previously deposited minerals, etc. Such investigations made it possible for us to identify ore-formations as definite types and to prove certain orderly relationships in associations of minerals.

The aim of *the third orientation* is to synthesize, in the factory and in the laboratory, mineral products whose composition and structures would be analogous to those of natural minerals and to ascertain the ability of solutions, in different states of aggregation, to transfer non-volatile substances of which most minerals are formed. Although, as we know, environments, composition, and the state of aggregation of artificial solutions may not be identical with those operative in natural environments, they still give us an important basis for *physico-chemical interpretations of the natural mineral-forming process*. Specifically, this type of research has demonstrated the possibility of deposition of minerals from melted rock, gaseous solutions, and liquid aqueous solutions.

Notwithstanding all of these self-evident accomplishments, in 1947 Smirnov, one of the outstanding specialists in the origins of ore deposits, while summarizing the present state of our knowledge of the principles of ore-formation, had said: "All these theories are altogether too far from perfect. The keys to the problem have not been found. Our old earth will open her treasures to us when we shall find the keys" [5, p. 35]. It is evident from all this that something very important had not yet been taken into account in our former research.

Inclusions in minerals are among the principal witnesses of the ancient processes—*"the miniature autoclaves" containing relics of the solutions and "melts" from which and in the environments of which the deposition of ores and minerals was taking place*. Unfortunately, the value of inclusions was understimated for a long time and inclusions were believed to be ineffectual in any exact study of origins of mineral deposits, even in conjunction with all the other factors and methods of research. The absence of data that could be obtained by inclusion studies in the geologic research and in any attempt at constructing a theory of ore-formation, led first of all to imperfections in the classifications of endogenic mineral deposits, so that the very important group of pneumatolytic deposits was excluded from them by many foreign geologists.

In our literature too, there developed a tendency to lump together a wide variety of highly complex endogenic ore-formations under the label of "postmagmatic" deposits, developed allegedly as the result of activities entirely of hydrothermal liquid solutions. Only a few of the investigators who were employing this term had timidly in mind the pneumatolytic phenomena also as participants in the formation of such deposits.

The new classification of endogenic deposits, by groups and types, is based on mineralogic composition and tectural features of ores, on structural–lithologic environments of the formation of ores, and on morphology of ore bodies. These classifications, on one hand, are evidence of progress and development along the first two of the lines of research previously indicated, but, on the other hand, represent a partial retreat from the genetic positions in the theory of ore formation.

Despite the fact that some geologists did give some attention to the necessity of thorough mineralogic studies of alteration in rocks next to ores, the opportunities for correlations between geologic environments and products of mineral genesis remained very limited indeed. The reason for that was again in the fact that the active solutions from which the aforesaid mineral products were actually deposited remained inaccessible to direct observations. The absence of this missing link resulted, among other things, in the progressively greater deviation of mineralogy, for example, from the path of genetic science, and in its persistence merely as a descriptive science, to the point that certain textbooks of mineralogy were gradually losing their essential genetic sections and were becoming manuals of physical and crystal–chemical properties of minerals.

The theory of mineral genesis was lagging more and more, accordingly, behind a deepened insight into composition, structures, and properties of minerals themselves. As the result, the major advances in the studies of geologic environments of endogenic ore formation and of the composition of ore substance presented a certain contrast with the relatively modest successes in determinations of the other genetic characteristics of mineral deposits, fully as important.

Prospecting for endogenic deposits got off the prospector's road. This happened chiefly because of the accumulated experience in the investigation of geologic–structural environments of ore deposition, over a period of many decades, of studies of host rock alterations next to the ore, and of the solution of certain important problems, petrologic and geochemical, in the connection of intrusives with definite mineralization types. And yet it would have been possible to discover many new and important relationships by a deeper inquiry into physico-chemical conditions governing endogenic formations of minerals in nature, by the possibilities of an objective recognition of products of a given natural process that was operative in the distant past. However, the process itself, consisting of a chainwork of complicated polymorphous phenomena, cannot be adequately reconstructed in full with only the aid of its products, i.e. minerals and ores, as well as alteration of the host rocks. It is evident that one must look also for other ways that would lead to the solution of this problem, be it even to the first approximation.

The by-paths of genetic research, based on data obtainable for actual relics of mineral-forming solutions hermetically sealed and preserved until our day, in the form of solidified, gaseous, or liquid inclusions in minerals, had their early inception in the Soviet science followed by persistent development in a dynamic integration with the three lines of the research already named. Some varieties of inclusions were already known to science for a long time. However, neither with us nor abroad, until the 1950's was there any attempt at a *systematic* and comprehensive experimental study of inclusions. Nor was there any development of the procedures for studying the state of aggregation of the active solutions, of their relative and true temperatures, pressures, composition, or concentrations and also of the pH of the included natural solutions.

Soviet scientists had demonstrated in recent years that comprehensive studies of the relics of natural mineral-forming solutions are very valuable for improvements in the theory of formation of mineral deposits, serving as supplementary means, in the hands of geologists, in the successful advancement along all three of the lines of research.

In the science of ore-formation, data on the inclusions make it possible to correlate geological environments with the products of activity of post-magmatic solutions, the solutions that inevitably react with the host rocks, to a given degree. Solution and redeposition in host rocks have their expression in certain definite products deposited in the ore body by the solutions that had become enriched with new mineral substances as the result of their interactions with host rocks. At the same time, *alteration of host rocks often fail to coincide, on the chronologic scale, with processes involved in the main stage of ore deposition.*

In regards to the combinations of different substances and different states of aggregation, in the synthetic growth of minerals, much can be learned from the experience of the gigantic laboratory of nature as recorded in the hermetically sealed included systems. The theory of natural mineral-forming solutions will gain, in turn, additional opportunities for its verification and particularly for physico-chemical interpretations of phenomena observed in inclusions. Application of the laboratory data in explanations of natural phenomena of the formation of ores, *via experiments with inclusions,* will constitute a new set of premises subject to objective proof. Refinements in the present theory of ore formation are a problem of cardinal importance, scientifically and practically, that can be solved only on the comprehensive basis of all of the objective data placed at our disposal by nature.

II. UTILIZATION OF INCLUSIONS IN RECOGNITION OF GENESIS OF MINERALS AND OF ENDOGENIC DEPOSITS

The theory of the "ancient" medium of mineral genesis is based primarily on many-sided investigations of included solutions and [formerly melted and new—V.P.S.] solidified materials in minerals. It has been established by numerous observations and experiments that in the course of their crystallization, minerals are able to capture and to preserve droplets of melted substances and of solutions in which they grow. The wide range of genetic variations in mineral genesis is expressed by the observed variations in the inclusions. All inclusions in minerals fall definitely within one of the three large groups:

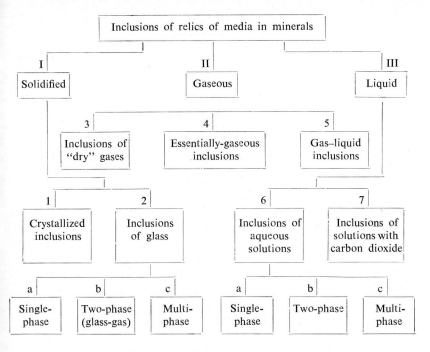

(1) *Solidified inclusions* consisting of droplets of melted substance in which a pyrogenic crystallization of their host minerals was taking place.

(2) *Gaseous inclusions,* i.e. the captured gaseous substance, often super-critical, in the form of low density solutions (not carbon dioxide*) from which the host minerals were formed.

(3) *Inclusions of liquid aqueous solutions* at relatively high densities from which their host minerals were crystallized at different temperatures.

These main groups of inclusions are clearly defined representations of distinctions in the state of aggregation of mineral-producing media: melted substance, gaseous solution, and liquid aqueous solution operative in the magmatic, the pneumatolytic, and the hydrothermal stages of mineral genesis respectively.

In the outline of the classification above every one of these three inclusion groups is subdivided into types and species that give us objective opportunities for a closer differentiation in the physico-chemical condition of mineral genesis.

---

* Unintelligible in original [V.P.S.].

(1) Genetic Importance of Solidified Inclusions

It developed, on studies of solidified inclusions in minerals of intrusive rocks, that this substance, in its present state, is characterized by a crystalline–granular structure ("crystallized inclusions") while inclusions in phenocrysts in effusive rocks consist chiefly of amorphous volcanic glass. Both of these inclusion types contain small cavities whose spherical shape is evidence of a filling with gas. Such inclusion systems consist therefore of (a) solid phases and gas; (b) solid phases only; (c) glass and gas, or (d) volcanic glass–gas [sic.].

A hermetically isolated droplet of a melted substance has been subjected to a crystallizing differentation while its was slowly cooling at depth. There was segregation of solid phases and of a gaseous phase. The volume ratios of the solid and the gas phases, in the given volume of the vacuole sealed in the host crystal, should be some function of the differences between the volume of the given liquid melt at the magmatic source and of the solidified intrusive body which took the place of the earth following an expulsion of an immense quantity of volatile substances into the surrounding rocks. The volume of the gaseous phase may be up to 20 per cent in some solidified inclusions in quartz from North-Caucasian granites and may be even greater in some crystal–gas inclusions of the residual melted substance in Volynian bodies of pegmatites.

Simple observations and measurements of phase ratios in crystallized inclusions do not allow us, of course, to make quantitative appraisals of the content of volatile and non-volatile substances in the magma.

Belyankin [1] pointed out that chemical analyses of magmatic rocks give us an idea only of the "bloodless"* composition of the magma, but not of its true composition. Only painstaking and extremely sensitive chemical analyses of solidified inclusions will enable us, in the future, to come closer to the solution of the problem of the composition of magma and to refine our experimental data on solubility of volatile substances in melted synthetic silicates.

The available and still very scarce observations on solidified inclusions in quartz from granites known to have been formed at different depths make it possible to spot certain differences in the completeness of crystallization of the included substance which may prove to be very useful in the future, in our approximate estimations of the depths of crystallization of the intrusives.

Inclusions of volcanic glass in minerals are either multiphase or two-phase (rarely single-phase). They all are typical of the phenocrysts in effusive rocks and they are evidence of differences in the rates of cooling of the liquid magma as well as of their host minerals. Multiphase inclusions

---

* "Obezkrovlennyi", adj., i.e. of a body whose blood was drained off [V.P.S.].

are formed in minerals whose crystallization began while the magma was still flowing on the surface of the ground. On the other hand, when the environment is conducive to a relatively slow cooling of the flowing magma, and of the included droplet of the melted substance, crystallization differentiation in the embedded mineral has begun but has not ended, so that there was a chance for one or for several crystalline phases to separate while the rest of the included lava was solidified as glass from which gas bubbles were parted as individuals. In the instance of two-phase and single-phase inclusions, the process of differential crystallization of the included droplet, because of the emergence of the host mineral at the surface and of the rapid cooling and solidification of the magma, was prevented by an abrupt change in the physico-chemical conditions of the existence of the droplet's host mineral.

Thus, if the entire group of solidified inclusions indicates a strictly magmatic (pyrogenic) origin of the host minerals, while the two types of inclusions here noted are indications of different environments of solidification of the magma, the species of glassy inclusions allow us, it appears, to form opinions as to a slow and quiet effusion of the lava or of its rapid expulsion to the surface of the ground.

We should point out here, that solidified inclusions differ fundamentally from solid inclusions. The latter are either accessory minerals or fragments of minerals that were formed before or contemporaneously with their host crystal, but are not relics of the crystal-forming medium.

(2) Genetic Importance of Gaseous Inclusions in Minerals

It was shown by our studies of a large number of minerals from post-magmatic deposits that, among syngenetic inclusions, one may find only either gaseous inclusions of mother liquor or liquid inclusions of aqueous solutions. In the former ones, the bulk of the volume of the vacuoles, at room temperature, is occupied by the gas phase; in the latter ones, the contents, at room temperature, is chiefly the liquid phase. In addition, one may find also inclusions of carbon dioxide as well as mixed inclusions (aqueous solution and carbon dioxide). They may be present in minerals of various origins but they are unsuited for thermometric analysis or for any conclusions in regards to the state of aggregation of the solutions. Such inclusions, like the inclusions of petroleum-like substances, are either partially or entirely alien and they present only a limited interest for the genetic conclusions.

Presence of syngenetic inclusions of gaseous solutions was found to be highly typical for the majority of minerals from skarns, greisens, pegmatitic veins, deposits situated close to the parent intrusion, and minerals produced by a simple sublimation or by complex interactions between vapors and gases and the surrounding rocks, in volcanic eruptions.

The group of gaseous inclusions may be broken down into three types, depending on the degree of filling of the vacuole with the gas, at room temperature, and on the course of their homogenization by heat (Fig. 1):

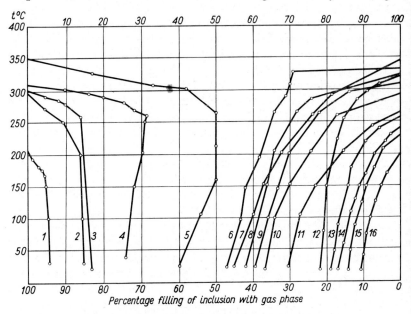

FIG. 1. The course of homogenization of gaseous and liquid inclusions in pneumatolytic and hydrothermal quartz from different sources.

1–5. Type II of homogenization; *6–16.* Type I of homogenization. Homogenization species: *4* and *5*—with the inversion point; *6* and *8*—with the boiling point; *12*—homogenization curve of a multiple phase inclusion.

(a) *inclusions of dry gases* with only small quantities of the liquid phase (the liquid phase may be absent); (b) *essentially-gaseous inclusions* with less than one quarter (by volume) of the liquid phase; and (c) *gas–liquid inclusions,* with the liquid occupying a half to one quarter of the inclusion's volume (the type III inclusions, homogenizing with the inversion point).

The relative volume of solid phases parted from the gaseous inclusions and deposited on the walls increases from inclusions of type I to type II [homogenization]. The large number of captive minerals in gas–liquid inclusions in topaz and quartz from Volynia is an indication not only of the multi-component character of the supercritical solutions but also of their appreciable capacity to redissolve and precipitate non-volatile substances whose transfer, it appears, is in the form of sodium and potassium metasilicates, chlorides, and fluorides.

The characteristic feature of the heterogeneous systems in inclusions of these types is the fact that, although they homogenize in the gas phase (type II), the course of their homogenization is not always the same (Fig. 1). The specific density of these solutions (included in the unchanging volume of the vacuoles) is below the critical density of ordinary liquid solutions. No matter how we call such solutions of relatively low density—be it fluids or supercritical solutions—they all show the same tendency on opening of the inclusions, namely, to expand indefinitely and to occupy all of the available space. Liquids have no such property. Within the gas–liquid inclusion type, the included solutions are not ideal gases with the characteristic maximum of freedom of movement of atoms, ions, or molecules of the substance. The forces of cohesion of their particles, however, do not correspond to the liquid state of substance, if we consider the relatively low density of the solution and the solution's high specific volume.

It is easy to imagine a liquid, pure water, for example, that would completely fill, at room temperature, a hermetically sealed autoclave. On heating to 374°C, and higher, its density will not decrease and its specific volume will remain low, which is not characteristic of a gaseous substance. In our discussions therefore, as to where is the gas and where is the liquid, and particularly in an objective differentiation between pneumatolytic and hydrothermal minerals, by their inclusions, we must consider, first and foremost, *the density of solutions and the specific volumes of the included solutions* rather than the temperature and the pressure as such.

Indeed, if an inclusion becomes completely filled with the liquid phase, on heating, we shall arrive, by following the appropriate isochore in the PT diagram (depending on pressure), at a point situated above the critical temperature and our liquid in the inclusion shall be in the supercritical state. Painstaking observations, in the course of heating, involving the passage through the critical temperature, showed a complete absence of any phase transformations inside the inclusions. Consequently, there is no marked difference in the properties of the liquid below and above the critical temperature, in the confined systems of this kind.

Such speculations, of course, must not be construed as the premises of a complete identity of properties of the liquid state below and above the critical temperature. It appears that the smooth variation in the temperature of the liquid phase at a constant volume leads to a gradual change in its properties. The gradual character of the process depends in all probability, in the long run, on variations in the degree of orderliness in the arrangement of the structure units of the liquid, depending on the thermodynamic conditions.

If geologists were to cease differentiating between the liquid melted substance, in which non-volatile constituents are predominant quantitatively over the volatile solvent, and liquid aqueous solutions, in which the reverse is the case, it would become impossible to differentiate between magmatic (pyrogenic) minerals and minerals of hydrothermal origins, since both were produced from liquids.

Having forfeited the opportunities of drawing boundaries between solutions and melted substances and between liquid and gas, we ought to weed out presently all genetic classifications of endogenic deposits, in the usage of science, and to abandon, in substance, the already established concepts, so fruitful in the orientation of prosecting and exploration in the field.

Nature has left us the keys to the important aspects of the origin of endogenic deposits, namely, the samples of mineral-forming media preserved as inclusions in minerals. Syngenetic ordinary inclusions of solutions, homogenizing in the gas phase and having densities lower than the critical one, while their specific volume is greater than the critical volume, constitute reliable evidence, with rare exceptions, of the crystallization of the minerals from the gas phase, i.e. of the pneumatolytic origin of the host minerals. The three types and the several species of homogenization of gaseous inclusions suggest the possibility of an objective identification of the early, the late, and even the end-stage in the development of pneumatolysis as well as their episodic manifestations in the ore-forming process. Chemical investigations of such inclusions, now under way, will enable us, in the near future, to appraise reliably the composition of gaseous emanations, given off by magmatic sources, which determine significantly the development of the economically very important greisen, pegmatites, skarns, and other mineral deposits.

(3) Genetic Importance of Liquid Inclusions in Minerals

Inclusions of liquid aqueous solutions from which minerals were crystallized or by which they were healed, in hydrothermal or in cold-water environments of mineral genesis, appear, at room temperatures, as heterogeneous or homogeneous systems. When included hydrothermal solutions with intermediate or low concentrations are heated and then cooled to such temperatures, the cooling process is conducive to a contraction of the solution's volume, to a development of a vacuum, and to a replacement of this vacuum by a gas (vapor) bubble, with the resulting formation of two-phase liquid inclusions where the gas occupies less than half of the total volume to the vacuole. If the solute concentrations, in the included solutions, are high, the cooling leads to a supersaturation, with respect to one or several of the dissolved substances, so that, in addition to the gas bubble, there is also a separation of "captive" minerals, in the vacuole's cavity, and accordingly a formation of multiphase liquid inclusions. If the included solution were tepid or cold from the start, there would be no heterogenization on its cooling down to room temperature and the inclusion would remain liquid and homogeneous.

We should distinguish therefore multiphase, two-phase, and single-phase inclusions among the inclusions of liquid aqueous solutions, as seen at room temperature. The value of these inclusions for genetic conclusions has many aspects.

Homogenization of multiphase and two-phase inclusions of this kind in the liquid phase (type I), on the application of heat, is an indication of a high density and of a low specific volume of the included solution, that is, of their liquid–hydrothermal state. Phenomena of continuous boiling are noted in some of the low-density liquid inclusions, in the vicinity of their homogenization points (Fig. 1, curves 6 and 8), the objective confirmation of the possibility of this phenomenon in the deep natural environments of hydrothermal activity. Single-phase liquid inclusions are witnesses of the formation of minerals from low-temperature solutions (below 40–50°C), as shown by artificial crystallization of various minerals from cold and tepid solutions. It should be feasible theoretically to assume the possibility that solutions included, for example, at 200°C, could endure as single-phase systems, but, if so, their preservation in the homogeneous state, at room temperature, would be contingent on a high original pressure, of the order of magnitude of 3000 atm, which is, as a rule, completely out of line with the available geologic facts.

Numerous observations show that liquid inclusions are preserved as single-phase systems in minerals that were formed on the earth's surface or in the very latest minerals in hydrothermal deposits formed at shallow depths. Normal syngenetic inclusions of aqueous solutions, homogeneous at room temperature, are indications of a tepid-water or cold-water origin of their host minerals.*

In general, syngenetic liquid inclusions that have become heterogeneous at room temperature are indications of a hydrothermal origin of their host minerals.

The key for recognizing the origin of minerals by their inclusions (Table 1) has been employed rather extensively, by this time, in studies of pegmatitic, greisen, skarn, pneumatolitic, hydrothermal, and cold-water deposits of metals and of sources of piezo-optical crystalline mineral raw materials. The utilization of this key, further elaborated in recent years, in conjunction with geologic–petrographic, mineralogic–geochemical, and mineralothermometric research procedures, has made it possible to assure

---

* Anomalous two-phase inclusions may develop in some and especially in easily soluble minerals, by leakage, since the hermetic sealing-off of the included solutions is not fully assured in such minerals.

TABLE 1

Characteristics of inclusions at room temperatures		Characteristics of inclusions at higher temperatures and in the process of heating		Genetic meaning of inclusions	
Physical state of included substance	Phases and phase–volume ratios	Types and species of homogenization	State of included substance after homogenization	Original condition of mineral-forming medium	Origin of minerals
Solidified		**I. Melting**		**Magmatic solutions**	**Magmatic**
Crystallized	C; $C+G$		Melted substance	Abyssal intrusions	Minerals of intrusives
Crystal–gas	$C > \frac{1}{2}+G < \frac{1}{2}+L$	Gradual liquefaction	Residual melted substance	Pegmatitic	Minerals of primary zones in pegmatites
Amorphous	V; $V+G$; $V+G+C$	"	Melted substance	Effusions of lava	Minerals of effusives
Gaseous		**II. Disappearance of liquid phase**		**Gaseous solutions**	**Pneumatolytic**
Dry gases	$G+L < 10\%$	Rapid conversion of liquid into gas	Gas	Gases (vapor) at very low density	Minerals of sublimations
Essentially-gaseous	$G > \frac{3}{4}+L < \frac{1}{4}$	Gradual conversion of liquid into gas	Gas	Gases at low density; more often supercritical	Early-pneumatolytic minerals and pegmatite replacements, greisens, and skarns
Gas–liquid	$G\frac{1}{2}$ to $\frac{3}{4}+L\frac{1}{2}$ to $\frac{1}{4}$	Conversions with the inversion point	Fluid (F)	Supercritical gases at moderate density	

			Fluid (F)		
Liquid–gas	$G > \frac{1}{2}+L < \frac{1}{2}+C$	Conversions with the critical point or with the boiling point		Dense gases near the critical threshold of specific volumes, temperatures, and pressures	Late-pneumatolytic minerals and pegmatite replacements, skarns, and greisens
Aqueous		**III. Disappearance of gas phase**		**Liquid solutions**	**Hydrothermal**
Multiphase	$L > \frac{1}{2}+G < \frac{1}{2}+C$	With dissolution of solid phases and disappearance of gas bubble	Liquid	High-temperature hydrotherms supersaturated with halogens	Early-hydrothermal
Two-phase	$L > \frac{1}{2}+G < \frac{1}{2}$	With gradual disappearance of gas bubble	Liquid	Dilute medium and low-temperature hydrotherms	Late-hydrothermal
Single-phase	L	—	—	Tepid and cold juvenile and meteoric waters	Cold-water minerals

Key: C—Crystals of captive minerals; V—Volcanic glass; G—Gas (vapor); L—Liquid solution; F—Fluid (densities intermediate between densities of liquid and gas).

The figures refer to phase volumes at room temperatures as of the volume of the inclusion's cavity.

the basis of the classification of postmagmatic processes in the formation of mineral deposits, to ascertain the variable course of ancient ore-forming processes as well as a whole series of fine details that must be taken into account for improvements in the theory of ore-formation.

III. IMPORTANCE OF MINERALOTHERMOMETRIC ANALYSIS AND OF DETERMINATION OF RELATIVE TEMPERATURES OF MINERAL GENESIS BY INCLUSIONS OF LIQUID SOLUTIONS

As we know, the temperature, one of the principal variables in mineral genesis, has already been employed for a long time in the genetic classification of mineral deposits. However, the classification of these deposits into high-temperature, medium-temperature, and low-temperature was founded upon the closely defined parageneses of minerals, the most approximate and conventional expressions of temperatures of the process. Attempts at determinations of the temperature by the minerals themselves had run into insuperable obstacles.

The introduction of corrections of homogenization temperatures of liquid inclusions, in order to determine the true temperatures of the original ore-forming process, is an opening of an attractive possibility of the solution of this problem. However, it is just as important to ascertain the course of variations in temperatures of mineral-forming solutions, in the coordinates of time and space. These variations are recorded in the differences between homogenization temperatures of liquid inclusions corresponding to the beginning, the middle, and the end of the process at one and the same site of mineral genesis or else to a single stage of mineral genesis at different depths.

Therein lies the essence of the thermometric analysis of hydrothermal formations, the analysis that has been successfully applied already to a series of mineral deposits. As we know, the analysis consists of a successive determination of homogenization temperatures of normal inclusions of liquid aqueous solutions in different growth zones of crystals belonging to different generations and to different paragenetic associations of minerals.

The simplest example of such studies, in relation to the coordinate of time, is given in Table 2. Here, with the aid of thermometric analysis, there is a demonstration of the progressive decrease in the temperature during the growth of a quartz crystal, within the over-all range of the minimal true temperatures.

Figure 2 represents V. F. Lesnyak's thermometric data in reference to the character of temperature variations in different stages of formation of hydrothermal lead–zinc deposits at Sadon and Zgid*.

---

* Both in Transcaucasia [V.P.S.].

Figure 3 presents our curves illustrating the rates of cooling of the ore-forming hydrothermal solutions in space, depending on their ascending migration from bottom to top, with attention to the present absolute altitude marks in the deposit's ore body* and the mean homogenization temperatures of the inclusions in sphalerite. Curve *1* refers to the deposition of the brown sphalerite in stage II of the formation of the ore; curve *2* refers to the deposition of the pale-brown sphalerite in stage III of the mineralization, in different horizons of the deposit. Curve *2* shows that the crystallization of sphalerite at the 2000 m level was taking place at the mean minimum of 177°C, while the same generation of sphalerite at the 2400 m level† was at the mean temperature of 152°. Thus the rate of cooling of the ascending solutions was about 6°C per 100 m distance.

TABLE 2. VARIATIONS IN TEMPERATURE OF SOLUTIONS DURING GROWTH OF
QUARTZ CRYSTALS

Schematic cut through growth zones of crystal	Zone No.	Sites of measurements	Homogenization temperature of primary inclusions (°C)	Homogenization type
		1	255	
		2	252	
	I	3	250	I
		4	224	
		5	215	
		6	185	
		7	168	
	II	8	168	I
		9	152	
		10	118	

These simple examples illustrate the character of application of the mineralothermometric analysis in ascertaining the course of the temperature variations in time and in space and, consequently, of variations in the other physico-chemical parameters of the ore-forming process dependent on the temperature.

The various homogenization temperatures of normal liquid inclusions are directly dependent on differences in the specific volume (density) of the

---

* Probably the lead–zinc sulfides of Sadon–Zgid [V.P.S.].
† The 2000 m and the 2400 m altitudes are as above the sea level [V.P.S.].

included solutions dependent, in turn, on variations in the fundamental parameters of the process, in an unconfined or practically unconfined system, of which the temperature is the first and foremost one.

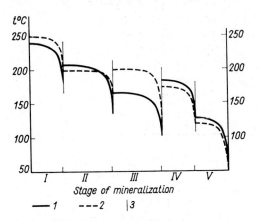

FIG. 2. Curves of the course of the temperature regime in the process of mineral genesis at polymetallic deposits.
(According to V. F. Lesnyak)

1. The temperature regime curve for mineral-forming solutions at the Sadon deposit; *2*. The temperature regime curve for mineral-forming solutions at the Zgid deposit; *3*. Tectonic dislocations

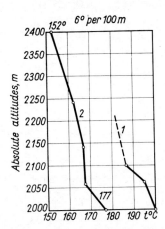

FIG. 3. Rate of cooling of ascending ore-forming hydrotherms (by sphalerites of the Sadon deposit).

1. Brown sphalerite. Stage II of the ore-formation; *2*. Pale-brown sphalerite. Stage III of the ore-formation

In the artificial hydrothermal growth of quartz and of other minerals in autoclaves, the noteworthy fact is that the homogenization temperature of liquid inclusions, in one and the same crystal, is about the same [2].

This circumstance merits a special consideration. In contrast with the ordinary conditions, we are dealing with a *hermetically confined system* in the synthetic production of minerals. The specific volume (or density) of the confined solution, the solution that fills the entire volume of the reactor, because of its thermal expansion, is already pre-determined by the coefficient of filling of the autoclave and it *remains constant* (or practically constant) *regardless of any further increase in the temperature* (and pressure). The homogenization temperature of the inclusions in crystals will be about the same and, were it to have changed since the moment of the "homogenization" of the contents of the autoclave, one should resort to the appriopriate corrections for the pressure.

In natural environments, however, the specific volume of hydrothermal solutions occupying some natural reservoir crystallizer (a quartz-bearing vug, for example) is subject to variations and is dependent mainly on the temperature, since *permeability of the surrounding rocks lowers the magnitude of the pressure factor*. One may easily visualize a natural "autoclave" of this sort filled completely by a solution at 320°C, at the beginning of the crystallization of quartz, and the same natural reservoir at 220°C, in the intermediate stage of the crystals' growth, as well as at 100°C, in the end-stage of the crystals' growth entirely filled with the solution. The densities of the solutions in all these three stages will not be the same, of course, at the identical concentrations, and the corresponding inclusions in different growth zones of the crystals or in correspondingly healed fissures of the crystals, will show different phase ratios, liquid–gas bubble, at room temperatures. These ratios will be 35 per cent, 25 per cent, and 4–5 per cent gas (vapor), in the cases as here indicated, i.e. will give us different coefficients of filling of the "natural autoclave", were we able to isolate it, in every one of the stages, and cool it. The homogenization temperatures of inclusions, in the three stages of the crystal growth, depend on the different densities that are *pre-determined mainly by the temperature state of the crystallizing solutions* and will be substantially different. Thus the homogenization will reveal the course of the temperature variations in the process of the formation of a quartz-bearing vug, i.e. *will serve to ascertain the relative temperatures* of the natural process, the most important dynamic factor in the formation of mineral deposits. For scientific and practical purposes, in determinations of the origins of post-magmatic deposits, in the present state of the theory of ore-formation, *we may confine ourselves, so far, to the minimum temperatures and to the relative temperatures* as obtained by the means of the mineralothermometric method.

The temperature scale, accepted for the earth's surface, from the melting point of ice to the boiling point of pure water, at 1 atm, cannot be easily integrated, of course, with the temperatures of the former abyssal processes of formation of minerals, on account of the radical differences in pressures and concentrations of the solutions as well as of the impossibility of direct measurements.

There will be a progressively greater discrepancy between the range of homogenization temperatures of the systems of inclusions of liquid aqueous solutions and the true temperatures, with adjustments for measurements at the earth's surface, at progressively increasing pressures and concentrations of the solutions. There is a divergence between the two temperature scales (Fig. 4).

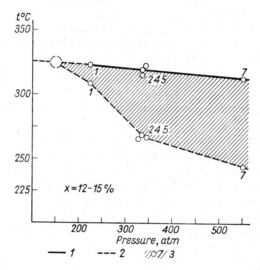

FIG. 4. Divergence between true temperatures of the hydrothermal crystallization of quartz and homogenization temperatures of inclusions in quartz, depending on pressure.

1. True temperatures; *2.* Homogenization temperatures; *3.* Points of measurements and the field of the temperature discrepancy.

The measurements of the homogenization temperatures in the same units (degrees) as at the surface have a conventional character in many instances of natural mineral genesis. Trustworthy corrections of the determined temperatures for pressure and concentration of the actual solutions sealed, as inclusions, in minerals, begin to emerge only as the result of a painstaking labor. A student of hydrothermal mineral deposits cannot help but be interested in the relative range of the crystallization temperatures of minerals and in the course of the temperature itself, for the formation of the deposit as a whole, in addition to the true temperatures. The homogenization temperatures and the true temperatures of the formation of minerals are very close to each other only in the case of medium-temperature and low-temperature ore-formations at shallow depths. We must remain reconciled with such relative meanings of the temperatures, as determined by homogenization of the included liquid aqueous solutions, at the present low level of the knowledge of physico-chemical conditions of the formation of minerals.

As we know, the biostratigraphic method of *relative chronology* had played a tremendous role in the development of geology and it was by no means in one single step that science came close to determining the true age of rocks by the methods of radio-active decomposition. The value of the method of relative geochronology has not decreased appreciably in geology, despite the emergence of the new methods of determination of *the absolute age* of rocks.

The relative age-scale is corrected to give the true age with the aid of the new methods, depending on opportunity and need. The relative temperature scale, derived by the homogenization of inclusions corresponding to different moments in the formation of minerals or of hydrothermal deposits of minerals, in reference to the theory of ore-formation, stands in need of a reduction to an absolute scale just about as much as the relative geochronologic scale needed a reduction to an absolute time basis. It looks more than peculiar therefore to see attempts made to demand absolute accuracy from thermometric analysis and regard any discrepancies between the determined and the true homogenization temperatures as errors and even as inherent defects of the method. We must not forget that *introduction of measures and numbers into abyssal geologic processes involve very serious difficulties.* We must not underrate the high significance of relative measurements indicative of the progressive development of natural endogenic processes, in contrast with the widely employed static descriptions.

The homogenization of inclusions of liquid aqueous solutions, for the purpose of determining the relative temperature of the abyssal mineral genesis, as the key to ascertaining the origin of minerals, has the place of importance in the science of ores and in genetic mineralogy, comparable to the importance of the biostratigraphic method in the determinations of the relative age of sediments in geology.

Variations in the homogenization temperatures of syngenetic inclusions allow us not only to discover variations in the course of the temperature fluctuations which is not the same for different minerals and for different deposits of minerals, but also to discover the temperature range, in degrees, of crystallization of polythermal and monothermal minerals, to ascertain the time of the appearance of a given mineral in a given deposit, and in certain difficult cases, to determine the dependence of certain physical properties and of the habit of minerals on the temperature fluctuations, as well as objectively to identify high-, medium-, and low-temperature generations of minerals and mineral deposits. The base of the scale of homogenization temperatures of inclusions of hydrothermal solutions, as a gradation of the hydrothermal process, in 150°C intervals, may be taken as follows: 500–350°C—high-temperature; 350–200°C—medium-temperature; 200–50°C—low-temperature; below 50°C—cold-water. Here too, however, one must have in mind the occasional impositions of a low-temperature mineralization on a mineralization at a higher temperature. It should be pointed out also that the mineral thermometric analysis, in some rare cases, may reveal the inverse relationship between products of early and late mineral genesis.*

IV. REMARKS ON ACTION OF MINERAL-FORMING SOLUTIONS IN TIME AND IN SPACE

The early experience we gained in the experimental studies of inclusions in minerals from endogenic deposits, situated in geologically different positions with respect to their parental magmatic intrusion and with respect to the ancient surface of the ground, allows us even now to state certain opinions as to the action of mineral-forming solutions in space and in time, the action of the "circulating juices of the earth" mentioned already by Biruni and Agricola.

The medium wherein the formation of ores takes place has been assigned to a place of importance, in the Russian as well as in the foreign literature, but the understanding of this term is still irregular. By the "medium" they generally mean only the host rocks enclosing the site of the mineralization, with all the details of their chemical composition, porosity, temperature, lithostatic pressure, etc. Meanwhile, magmatic solutions control the course of mineral genesis, solutions that remain in prolonged contact with the magmatic source, their place of origin, and parent magma, and that constitute highly active natural systems, with characteristically interrelated $T–P–X$ parameters whose variations depend on the functional relationships already indicated, solutions in a state of interaction with the surrounding rocks.

The physico-chemical parameters are changing continuously in the highly mobile solutions, and are but rarely found in a state of a sluggish equilibrium, in the relatively rare calm systems, in natural environments (a vug, a "cellar", a "nest" in pegmatites or quartz veins).

These solutions accordingly create a continuously active medium of mineral genesis and constitute the principal component of the geologic environment, in the broad sense. "*It is not possible to study a crystalline substance outside the processes by which it was formed, outside its con-*

---

* I.e., high-temperature on top of low-temperature [V.P.S.].

*nections with the liquid or the gas whose migration resulted in its formation**. The equilibrium distribution of atoms in a crystalline substance is a relative one, inasmuch as it depends on certain entirely definite physico-chemical conditions in the environment; where there is a change in these conditions (and they are not, and cannot, remain stationary), there is also a change in the character of the equilibrium or even a complete cessation of the equilibrium" [3].

Inclusions of mother liquors in minerals, inasmuch as they are hermetically sealed, constitute our records of the physico-chemical conditions at the time of the minerals' crystallization and in that sense are invaluable evidence, in their capacity as remnants of the mineral-forming medium, of the environment wherein their host minerals and the paragenetically associated minerals were crystallizing in the mineral deposits.

The former magmatic sources and their extensions, as recorded in the earth's crust by the intrusives now occupying their sites, were reservoirs chiefly of silicate magmas wherein highly complex chemical interactions of atoms and molecules were taking place at high temperatures and pressures. These processes, on one hand, were leading to the crystallization of pyrogenic minerals, formation of plutonic bodies, and of magmatic deposits, in the strict sense, while on the other hand they were conducive to a prolonged distillation of an appreciable fraction of the volatile constituents, distilled into the surrounding rocks in the form of highly mobile supercritical gaseous solutions. The mineral-forming substances in such solutions are derived either by distillation or by reactions involving formation of K and Na metasilicates as well as of easily volatile compounds of the heavy metals, such as chlorides and fluorides, or else by a solution in steam, in the form of hydrated intricate complexes. These gaseous emanations are logical products of a geochemical differentiation of the magma, of the assimilation of the intruded rocks by the magma, and, to some extent, of a borrowing from the surrounding rocks along the migration paths away from the magmatic hearth; their net effect is the creation of *the most highly reactive natural system of pneumatolytic mineral genesis*. The exceptional mobility of the magmatic secretions, the super-heated streams of gas under high pressures, leads to a thorough steaming of the mass of the surrounding rocks which is especially intensive along the main migration paths of solutions. The zones of altered rocks developed in the pneumatolytic stage of the activity of mineral-forming solutions are found to be particularly wide. Deposition from the gaseous solutions, however, is generally localized in fissures and joints, the sites of the most intensive flow of the emanations. The greatest quantity of newly formed minerals and the greatest intensity of pneumatolytic metasomatism

---

* Our italics—N. Ye.[rmakov].

occur in the passages through which the bulk of the emanations migrated (in accordance with the law of mass action).

Pneumatolytic mineral genesis had its place in a highly variable natural system, nearly always open rather than confined, changeable in time and in space. This mineral genesis depended on *the stage of development of the co-existing magmatic source and of the geologic host-environment*, i.e rocks and minerals, with their different capacities for exchange reactions

The natural physico-chemical system was characterized by its interdependent parameters: temperature–pressure–concentration, in their dynamic equilibrium, at any moment and at any reaction site. This equilibrium may be upset, with respect to any one or all of its factors, at any succeeding moment in the movement of the ascending solutions.

The continuous qualitative changes in the supercritical solutions, in time and space, bring about, as the case may be, either rapid or gradual transformations of the migrating solutions from one state of aggregation into another one, as soon as they attain a certain threshold of quantitative relationships. In the end, pneumatolytic gaseous solutions are transformed into liquid hydrothermal solutions at a certain distance from the active magmatic source and from the surface of the ground.

Such transformations in the state of aggregation of the solutions are expressed in changes in composition, paragenesis, texture, and structure of the minerals and ores deposited by the solutions. There is an appreciable decrease in the solutions' reactivity with the surrounding rocks and with the previously deposited minerals, and in the halo of corresponding alterations. Alterations of host rocks are by no means invariably syngenetic with the stage of productive ore-formation, as indicated by inclusion studies. In the course of the magmatic differentiation and of the formation of the intrusive body, there is no stable *site at which the solutions are undergoing transformations from one state of aggregation into another one*. The site itself is migrating, in the course of time, toward the upper boundary of the original magmatic reservoir (the plutonic contact) and away from the surface of the ground. Depending on the retrogression of the active part of the magmatic source (intrusion) downward and away from the intrusive contact, in the level in the earth's crust where the supercritical solutions were formerly active, thermal mineral genesis begins first of high-temperature and later of lower-temperature types. In the most common case, *polygenic* ore deposits are the result. The upper section of the ore-conducting tectonic channels, outside the reach of the fluctuating threshold at which the solutions change their state of aggregation, are characterized by purely hydrothermal deposits with a not too diversified association of minerals.

Below the maximum depth of this fluctuating threshold, closer to the magmatic source, purely pneumatolytic deposits may be found occasion lly. Their development becomes possible when the normal activity of magmatic emanations stops rapidly in the part of the lithosphere over the magmatic source. This may happen either on account of plugging of the migration paths of the solutions or because of a very rapid formation of the intrusive body and the consequent extinction of activities of the magmatic source. Occasionally, however, the ore-forming process may be so complete, in the zone of circulating endogenic solutions, that *the fluctuating threshold of transformation* in the state of aggregation may sink even into the parent intrusive itself, into its solidified upper section, i.e. below the boundary of pyrogenic formation of minerals. A hydrothermal deposition of minerals may take place therefore in the magmatic body itself, as an expression, in time, of one of the last functions of the still active part of the magmatic hearth that has receded inwards and far away from the roof of the former magmatic reservoir. Under such circumstances, skarns in the contacts, greisens in the alteration haloes, of the intrusion, pegmatites, and even pure products of pneumatolysis are subjected to transformations by the superimposed hydrothermal mineralization. For example, there is a development of polygenic pegmatitic bodies of epimagmatic, pneumatolytic, and hydrothermal origin.

It is obviously not possible to show within the limits of a short article all of the complex variability of hypogene mineral genesis, in space and time, caused by changes and transformations of the solutions from one state of aggregation into another one. We have given here only a general pattern that is often disturbed by tectonic movements, by repetitions of magmatic intrusions, and by variations of pressures in the zone of the mineral genesis. For example, a drastic reduction in pressure, as the result of an opening of new migration paths for the movement of weak hydrothermal solutions may lead to their short-term and temporary conversion into gaseous solutions and to a consequent pneumatolytic episode in the mineral genesis.

The period of magmatic activity associated with the formation of a given plutonic body that gave birth to various associations of minerals in the vicinity of the body, is subdivided in time into a series of long, medium, and short segments that may be termed stages, and sub-stages, and increments of endogenic mineralization [5]. Their visible expressions, in space and on the relative time-scale, are either the zones of the differentiated pegmatites or different ore-formations, generations, etc.

The zonal structures of pegmatitic bodies and of ore veins constitute records of variations in the mineral-forming medium. One may gain an insight into the character and the progres of these variations through studies of inclusions of the parent magma and the mineral-forming solutions.

Every one of the three stages of magmatic activity in the area of a

given mineral deposit is distinguished by a definite state of aggregation o
the mineral-forming medium: a melted siliceous residue from which pyro
genic minerals are formed; a gaseous solution which produced pneumato
lytic minerals; a hot liquid aqueous solution which yields minerals of th
hydrothermal origin.

Certain definite gradations of the mineral-forming process must b
made therefore the basis of our concepts of the genetic history of a depos
as well as of the deposit-forming process, as a whole.

*A stage of mineralization** is a major segment of mineral genesi
characterized in its entirety by *the same state of aggregation of the activ
solutions.* In a concrete geologic environment, a stage of mineralizatio
takes its course under definite physico-chemical conditions, varying† durin
a given period of time, and giving origin to specific minerals and associ:
tions of minerals that differ from products of the preceding and the su
ceeding stages qualitatively and quantitatively as well as in their structur
and textures.

A definite association of minerals produced by changes in the inte
dependent physico-chemical parameters, but without any transformatior
in the state of aggregation of the mineral-forming medium, is typical
a sub-stage of mineralization, a period of evolutionary-discontinuous d
velopment of the process within a stage. In a concrete geologic enviro
ment, a sub-stage of mineralization is represented by its products, i.e. mi
erals and ores, often cut off from the other sub-stages by tectonic di
placements.

An increment of mineralization is a part of a sub-stage and is chara
terized by a more or less abrupt change in the temperature, the pressu
or the concentration of the solutions, in either direction, producing inte
ruptions in the formation of ores and in the growth of crystals as well as
dissolution of the previously formed crystals and their subsequent r
nucleation.

The absence of objective indices for identification of the state of aggr
gation of the media from which minerals have formed had a negative effe
on the progress of the science of ore-formation and retarded discoveri
of new and genetically significant facts. The key for the recognition of t
genesis of minerals and the experiments with inclusions give us the oppc
tunity to trace the variations in the medium, within the limits of the pne
matolytic and the hydrothermal stages, and objectively to differentiate t
tween their early and late sub-stages and increments, as represented by th
sequence of mineral products. Inclusions of the mineral-forming medit

---

* The original's "etap," "stadiya," "uroven," are translated as "stage," "s
stage," and "increment" respectively [V.P.S.].

† In the original, "definite" and "varying" seem to be as inconsistent as in
translation [V.P.S.].

serve to illustrate the development of the process, by the variations in types and species of their homogenization by heat, by variations in the homogenization temperatures, composition, reaction, and concentration of the included solutions.

The stage-sequence character of the formation of mineral deposits is clearly seen against the background of the district's geologic history, on the basis of paragenetic relationships of minerals and on the basis of studies of relics of the solutions active in the geologic past preserved as inclusions in minerals.

Every transparent or semi-transparent mineral reveals its belonging to a given stage of mineral genesis through its syngenetic inclusions. Consecutive studies of the inclusions, from the earliest minerals of a hypogene deposit to the latest ones, as well as of mineral generations, enables us to make *a genetic "birth certificate"* of a deposit and trace the physicochemical history of its origin. Investigations of inclusions in newly formed minerals of the hanging wall gives us the opportunity to determine the interactions of the mineral-forming solutions and the host medium (geologic environment), in different stages of the process, and to account for the qualitative variations in composition of mineral groups in the deposit. The progressively developing research along this line helps in the evaluation of the principal factors involved in the transfer and deposition of substances from the parent solutions and will enable us in the future definitely to correlate the principal paragenetic associations of minerals and ore types with sub-stages and increments of the mineral-forming process. This, in turn, will enable us to discover orderly relationships in the distribution and in the variations of the ores, in space, so essential in prospecting for mineral deposits and for their appraisal in depth.

It is the solution of these problems, in their historical aspects, that constitutes the main substance of *the theory of the mineral-forming medium*—a part of the theory of the formation of ores.

BIBLIOGRAPHY

1. BELYANKIN, D. S., K voprosu o sovremennom sostoyanii i perspektivakh ucheniya o magmakh i magmaticheskikh gornykh porodakh. (In Reference to the Present State and the Perspectives of the Theory of Magmas and Magmatic Rocks.) *Izv. Akad. Nauk SSSR, ser. geolog.* No. 5, 1947.

2. BUTUZOV, V. P., and N. YU. IKORNIKOVA., Zhidkiye vklyucheniya v iskusstvennom kvartse. (Liquid Inclusions in Synthetic Quartz.) *Dokl. Akad. Nauk SSSR*, Vol. 104, No. 1, 1955.

3. DOLIVO-DOBROVOL'SKII, V. V., *Kurs kristallografii.* (Course in Crystalography.) ONTI, 1937.

4. YERMAKOV, N. P., *Issledovaniya mineraloobrazuyushchikh rastvorov.* (Investigations of Mineral-forming Solutions.) Izd. Khar'kov. univ. 1950.

5. SMIRNOV, S. S., O sovremennom sostoyanii teorii magmatogennykh rudnykh mestorozhdenii. (On the Present State of the Theory of Magmatogenic Ore Deposits.) *Zap. VMO*, 2nd series, 76, No. 1, 1947.

Some Characteristics of Quartz-forming Solutions

YE. M. LAZ'KO

ASCERTAINING the origins of individual minerals, association of minerals, and mineral deposits, we recognize as one of the most important and also the most difficult problems of geology. Difficulties arising in studies of accumulations of minerals whose origin is contingent on endogenic processes are particularly great. Among the series of problems facing the investigator, determinations of the character of mineral-forming solutions are highly important, that is, the determinations of their composition, state of aggregation, and of the basic physico-chemical parameters during the course of the mineral-forming process.

Comprehensive studies of the major composition of mineral accumulations and of rock alterations next to the veins, caused by interactions between the solutions and the host rocks, yield important information on the character of the mineral-forming solutions. However, the examination of liquid, essentially-gaseous, and solidified inclusions in minerals is particularly interesting, in this connection.

Sorby [22], as we know, as early as the middle of the last century laid the foundation for our deeper insight into the studies of various inclusions in minerals. The cardinal importance of inclusions was emphasized by Karpinskii, in the second half of the nineteenth century, who said: "Among the various minerals and rocks, inclusions of liquid are deemed to be, not without a reason, fractions of the same medium in which the formation of these mineral substances was taking place. Moreover, the very properties of the included liquids may yield indications of certain formerly operative conditions" [10].

Samoylov, at a later date, had also emphasized the value of inclusions, in pointing out that: "Such inclusions, gaseous, liquid, or solid, that often render the mineral's substance 'impure' for the purposes of the chemical analysis, constitute a precious material suited for the most important conclusions in regard to the origin of the mineral" [13].

As shown by these quotations, the leading Russian scientists had recognized a long time ago the immense importance of the studies of inclusions in minerals. Nevertheless, these most interesting objects were the concern of only a few investigators and, at that, merely in connection with some special problems, for a very long time, down to the early 1940's.

Systematic and purposeful examination of inclusions in minerals were begun only in 1941, by Yermakov [5, 6, 7], whose research is summarized in his well-known monograph [8].

Having no opportunity here even for a brief discussion of the main problems treated in that monograph and considering the fact that we had already done it before [11], we believe it necessary to emphasize that it was only the results of the Yermakov's research that enable us to obtain reliable data and, as it seems to us now, entirely objective data for opinions about the character of mineral-forming solutions, including quartz-forming ones.

The existence of the book by the author here cited frees us also from the necessity of reporting on the methods of determinations of the composition, concentration, state of aggregation, and temperature regime of quartz-forming solutions and permits us to discuss here only the results we obtained.

Quartz-forming solutions were studied by us in connection with the determination of the origin of the quartz crystal-bearing veins of Aldan. For that reason, our discussion will deal only with the solutions from which crystals of transparent quartz could be derived, i.e. with the solutions that were effective during the late stages of the formation of the crystal quartz-bearing veins.

Comparisons of our results obtained in the study of quartz crystals from Aldan with the not too abundant data in the available literature lead us to believe that our results have a general value in reference to the genesis of quartz crystal-bearing veins.

The inclusion studies were conducted at the Mineralothermometric Laboratory, University of L'vov, by a research team under the author's guidance. In addition, we made use of the findings of other investigators.

COMPOSITION AND CONCENTRATION OF SOLUTIONS

Detailed studies of composition and concentration of the included solutions were carried out by Vul'chin [4] who examined 19 samples prepared from 11 specimens of quartz from different sources in Aldan. Taking advantage of Vul'chin's very interesting report, we are citing here a part of his text dealing with the results of qualitative spectrographic analysis of powdered quartz samples and of dry residue of the aqueous extracts, as well as the results of semiquantitative microchemical and spectrographic analysis of the aqueous extracts:

"Qualitative analysis of the included solutions showed the following principal constituents: Na^+, K^+, Ca^{++}, Mg^{++}, Al^{+++}, Fe, and occasionally Mn, Cl^-, SO_4^{--}, BO_3^{---}.

"Qualitative analysis indicated the following relationships: $Na > K >$ Ca (rarely $K > Na$) and $Ca > Mg$. The sum of $Al + Fe + Mn$ was up to 2 per cent. Also, the estimated concentrations indicated up to 30 or 35 per cent total salts. Heavy metals: Cu, Zn, Pb, Ag were detected, in small concentrations, in hydrochloric acid extracts of the test materials.

"Qualitative and quantitative analyses showed the presence of boron (most likely BO_3^{---}) in relatively large quantities, in all samples. . . . Calculated atomic and molecular quantities of the determined constituents gave an appreciable excess of the cations. This excess is compensated probably by metasilicic anions of the type SiO_3^{--} and $Si_2O_5^{--}$, by OH^-, the hydroxyl produced by hydrolysis of the metasilicates (involving the formation of $SiO_2 + ROH$), as well as by CO_3^{--}. The calculated dissolved Si, as SiO_3^{--} (assuming its quantitative preponderance in the solution) indicates its total concentrations as high as 6–12 per cent.

"Concentrations of hydroxyl and carbonate ions should be relatively low wherever there is no precipitation of Ca, Mg, Fe, Al, Mn hydroxides." And further: "These analyses show that: (a) Na and K are conspicuosly preponderant, quantitatively, among the cations; Ca is the next one, and then Mg. Fe, Al, Mn, and others; (b) Cl^- is quantitatively preponderant among the anions; SO_4^{--} and BO_3^{---} are present in subordinate concentrations; (c) heavy metal cations, the constituents of ore minerals, are present in relatively small quantities; (d) in our particular case (two-phase inclusions), the lower limit of concentration of the quartz-forming solutions is as high as 5–6 per cent each, for K, Na and Cl^-, while the concentrations of Ca, Mg, Fe, Al, Mn, SO_4^{--}, BO_3^{---} are 1 per cent and lower."

Before we pass on to the discussion of Vul'chin's results with the quartz from Aldan, it is essential, for the sake of comparisons to quote the results obtained by different investigators in characterizing the composition of inclusions in quartz from other areas.

Sorby [22] showed, nearly one century ago, that inclusions in quartz contain up to 15 per cent K, Na, and Ca chlorides. Lindgren and Steigl [21] proved the presence of large quantities of CaO and SO_3 in inclusions in quartz from California, together with smaller but still appreciable quantities of $(K, Na)_2O$ and SiO_2 and minor quantities of Cl, MgO, Al_2O_3, and Fe_2O_3. Königsberger and Müller [20] made the following estimates of the content of different constituents in inclusions in quartz from Alpine veins: 5–9.5 per cent CO_2; 2–2.5 per cent Na; 0.7*–1.5 per cent K and Li; 0.3 per cent Ca; 1.5–1.6 per cent Cl; 0.5–0.7 per cent SO_4; 1.8–3.5 per cent CO_3.

Zakharchenko [9] published some very interesting results on the composition of some very large inclusions in piezo-quartz from different

---

* 0.9 in original reference [Ed.].

sources in Pamir. Aqueous extracts of these inclusions were subjected to chemical analysis by N. L. Lopatina, analyst, at the All-Union Geologic Institute laboratory. The results were as follows: the aqueous extract of 100 g quartz with 5–6 per cent inclusions contained 54.8 mg total salts, including 18.1 mg Cl^-, 0.7 mg SO_4^{--}, 6.1 mg HCO_3^-, 14.3 mg Na (by difference), 13.8 mg SiO_2. Quantitative spectrographic analysis of dry residue from the filtered extract gave 1–10 per cent SiO_2, 0.01–0.1 per cent Al, 0.01–0.1 per cent Mg, 1 per cent Ca, 0.05–0.1 per cent Fe, 0.001–0.01 per cent Mn. Also, the pH was determined as 8.6, i.e. the solutions were definitely alkaline, even as they were shown to be by a preliminary test with litmus paper. Solid phases, as small crystals of halite and apparently of sylvite, calcite (or dolomitic calcite), hematite, and liquid carbon dioxide were found in many high-temperature inclusions in the quartz crystals from Pamir.*

Let us return now to the discussion of our data on the quartz crystals from Aldan. It is essential here, in order to complete the picture, to supplement Vul'chin's findings on the liquid inclusions by our data on captured minerals and on accessory minerals [8] that help to characterize composition and concentration of the mineral-forming solutions. Halite and sylvite (cubical crystals that are dissolved at different temperatures within an inclusion) were among the captive minerals in the specimens from Severnoye, Kholodnoye, Kurumkan, etc., while the Severnoye specimens had also hematite (translucent red six-faced tablets). Among the accessory minerals, there were hematite (Kholodnoye, Severnoye, Dobroye, etc.), fluorite (Kurumkan, Otrada, etc.), kaolin (Kholodnoye, Khrustal'noye, Barsukchi, etc.), and chlorite (Kholodnoye, Khaptagay, Severnoye, etc.).

Fe and Si were participating accordingly in the mineral-forming solutions, in addition to the elements already enumerated. Moreover, it was demonstrated, by a study of the solid inclusions, that elements such as Fe, Mg, Ca, Al, F attained their high concentrations in the solutions only toward the end of the crystallization of quartz, since the accessory minerals here listed are found commonly and in appreciable quantities only in the outer growth zones of the quartz crystals.

Finally, we ought to mention also carbon dioxide, found in appreciable quantities in some inclusions, whose presence has been recorded in quartz crystals from many sources: Kholodnoye, Novopustynnoye, Severnoye, Kurumkan, Kilerchi, and others.

The data on composition and concentration of the solutions which were changing during the crystal growth are highly interesting. Alkali chlorides, particularly sodium chloride, are preponderant in the solution,

---

* Possibly indicating a misprint above? Extracted inclusions calculate to only 2.7 per cent salts, about 1/10th of saturation [Ed.].

as we had already seen, from the results of different investigators. According to Vul'chin's calculations, total salts in two-phase inclusions may be as high as 30–35 per cent, with a decisive preponderance of alkali chlorides. We believe that these figures are too high, in all probability. They differ rather significantly from the data obtained by Lindgren, Königsberger, and Zakharchenko. Yermakov, the greatest specialist in inclusions in minerals, also accepts the lower figures for the concentration of salts in two-phase inclusions and believes that the salts vary from 10–15 per cent [8].

An examination of the method employed by Vul'chin [4] indicates that significant errors are possible in determinations of the concentrations, caused, first of all, by the impossibility of any accurate measurements of the cavity volumes in the specimens of quartz. On the other hand, the multiphase inclusions found, on rare occasions in the Aldan quartz, indicate concentrations of the solutions even greater than the limits calculated by Vul'chin.

In any case, the first incontrovertible conclusion that may be drawn from the analyses of inclusions in quartz is to the effect that the mineral-forming solutions are primarily aqueous alkali chlorides whose concentration is subject to appreciable fluctuations, tending to be high, on the whole, and whose reaction is alkaline.

It is also a matter of considerable interest as to how the solution in what particular form affected the transfer of silica. There are two possibilities: (a) transfer as alkali metasilicates of the R_2SiO_3 or the $R_2Si_2O_5$ types followed by a deposition of the crystal-forming SiO_2 derived by hydrolysis of the metasilicates; (b) transfer and deposition of silica as free SiO_2, with the alkali chlorides functioning as catalysts. It seems as if both of these types of migration and deposition of silica are entirely probable, on a consideration of the data on inclusions obtained by different investigators. Thus Vul'chin had discovered a large excess of cations, in his conversions of the constituents to molecular and atomic quantities and made a justifiable conclusion that this excess is probably compensated by metasilicates of the type of SiO_3^{--} and $Si_2O_5^{--}$ and by other ions. This offers an easy explanation of the alkaline reaction of the included solutions, as the result of the subsequent hydrolysis of the metasilicates of the alkalies and production of hydroxide ions. On the other hand, the results of Lindgren [21] and Zakharchenko [9] show appreciable quantities of dissolved silica, apparently free, in the solutions extracted from the inclusions even at room temperatures.

An already substantial body of experimental data had been accumulated, by this time, that we feel may shed some light on the problem in question. Experiments proving an appreciable solution and transfer of silica in water at high temperatures and pressures, particularly in the field of the critical temperature of water, were performed repeatedly in the Soviet Union as well as abroad. The results and the meaning of these experiments were discussed in the articles by Belyankin [2], Khitarov [19], Syromyatnikov [16], and others. It should be pointed out that, in a series of experiments by N. I. Khitarov, additions of caustic soda to the system caused a marked increase in the solubility of silica, which, according to that author, indicates a large increase in the solvent action of water on silica in alkaline media.

Experiments with the artificial growth of piezo-quartz are especially interesting for our problem. They were conducted for a long time by different Russian and foreign investigators and were crowned with success in recent times. A recent summary of the experiments by foreign scientists is given by Buckley [1].

The first experiments with synthetic growth of quartz crystals from silica gel and glass, in the presence of water at 200–400°C, were carried out by Senarmon and Daubre as early as the middle of the last century. The size of their largest synthetic crystal was 2 mm. Early in the twentieth century G. Spezia had undertaken his newer experiments, but the crystals he produced were also small and their growth was very slow.

During the last war and shortly after its termination, experiments with artificial growth of quartz were reported by Swinnerton, Owen, and Corwin [14], Thomas, N. Wooster, and W. Wooster [17], and Van Praag [3]. The novel approach in all these experiments and their merit, in comparison with the old ones, is the authors' attention to the results on liquid inclusions in natural quartz and their endeavor to produce quartz crystals from aqueous solutions of sodium chloride at pH 10. Amorphous silica was the starting material in many experiments, because its solubility is ten times the solubility of crystalline quartz [3]. The crystals were grown in autoclaves at a practically constant temperature, by the gradient method, so that the temperature would range from 370 to 400°C, in one series of the experiments, whereupon the rate of crystal growth would increase 2.5 to 3 times, although the crystals were defective when their growth rate was highest [3, 17]. The normal rate of growth conducive to the production of crystals of good quality was about 100 $mg/cm^2/18$ hr, corresponding to 1 mm of deposition of quartz on a quartz plate which was cut parallel to the rhombohedron and was functioning as the seed. In one of the experimental series, the original solution contained Na metasilicate and a mineralizer (generally KHF_2) serving to improve the quality of the crystals [17]. The authors believe that the mineralizer's effect is merely a catalytic one, since fluosilicates are formed during the growth of the crystals.

Experiments by Walker and Buhler were particularly successful, as they were able to produce large crystals of high quality within a few weeks, with a linear growth rate of up to 2.5 mm/24 hr [18]. In contrast with the preceding experiments, they used powdered quartz as the starting material and 5–10 per cent sodium carbonate as the solution. The crystal growth was made in an autoclave at about 400°C and more than 1000 kg/cm² pressure. There was only a small temperature gradient in the experiment, only 20°C or so, by which the growth on the seed was assured. The seed was set in the upper part of the autoclave where the temperature was lower.

Thus all of the data obtained by analysis of inclusions in quartz and on the synthetic growth of quartz crystals permit us to expand the previously given conclusion in regards to the composition of quartz-forming solutions, as follows: in the majority of the cases, silica is carried by such solutions, most likely, as alkali metasilicates of the R_2SiO_3 or the $R_2Si_2O_5$ type in which sodium is generally the preponderant cation.

THE STATE OF AGGREGATION OF THE SOLUTIONS

There are substantial disagreements among geologists in regards to the state of aggregation of mineral-forming solutions. We have discussed the nature of these disagreements [12]. For that reason, we shall merely point out here that there is considerably more unanimity among the investigators in their opinions about the state of aggregation of quartz-forming solutions, inasmuch as both the experimental data and the inclusion studies show directly that quartz may grow in liquid as well as in gaseous media.

This proposition was proved experimentally by Syromyatnikov, Khitarov, Sheftal', Spezia, Van Praag, and others [3, 16, 19, etc.]. As to the proof in natural environments—this was discovered by Yermakov, who made it clear that inclusions in minerals, which includes also quartz, may be homogenized by heat either in the liquid or in the gaseous phase (homogenization types I and II respectively). We must conclude therefore that, if normal included solutions were shown to homogenize as in type I, the crystals of quartz grew in liquid solutions, whereas, if the homogenization was as in type II, they grew in gaseous solutions [8].

A systematic examination of inclusions in quartz from different sources in Aldan had demonstrated that the piezo-quartz crystals had grown from liquid solutions, in the vast majority of the cases. However, there are sections within some of the deposits (entire vein zones, frequently) where the crystal growth was in gaseous solutions, as proved by the mineralothermometric analysis. This was noted for isolated sections in the Novopustynnoye deposit, but the most valuable observations were made at the deposits of Kurumkan and Barsukchi, the ones that allow us to arrive at important conclusions regarding the origin of the quartz crystal-bearing veins of Aldan.

The articles included in this collection of papers free us from the necessity of a detailed discussion of this problem, as they present the systematic data on inclusions in quartz from the sources here enumerated. It is pertinent here merely to emphasize some of the most important conclusions of that research.

Within the boundaries of the deposits of Kurumkan and Barsukchi, there are areas of abundant quartz-bearing veins situated at various distances from the massifs of the Proterozoic granitic rocks whose evolution had led to the production of the quartz-forming solutions. Quartz crystals from veins in direct proximity to the intrusives contain inclusions that homogenize chiefly as in type II. This fact is a proof of the gaseous state of the solutions from which the quartz in these particular veins crystallized. Inclusions homogenizing chiefly as in type I are found in quartz crystals from veins situated at greater distances from the igneous rock massifs. Essentially-gaseous inclusions are found alongside primary liquid inclusions, not uncommonly, in crystals from such sources, as well as from the Novopustynnoye deposit. These facts are evidence of the evolution of the solutions, in space, from the gaseous to the liquid state, and of the pulsating character of their accession, in time, occasionally with sudden qualitative transformations in their state of aggregation. The results on crystal quartz veins of Aldan and of other districts indicate that quartz, especially high-grade quartz crystals, are rarely produced from the gaseous phase. Thus the results of the laboratory experiments with the synthetic growth of quartz are in a complete agreement with the data from nature.

TEMPERATURE REGIME OF SOLUTIONS

Large-scale mineralothermometric investigations of quartz crystals from quartz-bearing veins served to reveal similarities as well as distinctions in the temperature regimes of the solutions by which the various deposits of quartz had formed in Aldan. It is not possible here to present the specific data on such individual deposits and we shall confine ourselves accordingly to the general conclusions based on the research. The reports on the Kurumkan and the Barsukchi deposits, in the present Collected Papers, are sufficient as illustrations of these conclusions.

The highest temperatures are characteristic of the early stages of the solutions' activity, in which the vein quartz of the deposits was produced. The homogenization temperature of liquid inclusions in vein quartz not uncommonly exceeds 300°C and may be as high as 360 and even 400°C in some individual deposits.

Realizing the need of corrections for pressure and concentration, in determinations of the temperatures of the mineral-forming solutions, one may be led to believe that the formation of vein quartz in a certain part of the deposits was taking place at temperatures that were close to the critical temperature of the solutions. This supposition is supported also by the fact that numerous inclusions homogenizing as in type II (in the gaseous phase) were discovered in the vein quartz, in several instances. It is interesting here to note that the temperature range was relatively narrow, such as 25 or 30°C, in the formation of the vein quartz, judging from the bulk of our data.

There was also a formation of crystal quartz during these early stages, as for example, at the Kurumkan or the Barsukchi, although these crystals, as a rule, are only partially transparent and are low-grade materials for that reason.

We must emphasize also that there is no evidence at all that would indicate presence of several generations of quartz in one and the same vein anywhere in Aldan, while, on the other hand, zonal-structural constituents of the vein bodies showing gradual transitions from coarsely granular quartz through rod-like quartz to vugs of quartz crystals are a common phenomenon.

The foregoing facts allow us to maintain that both the vein-filling substance and the quartz crystals in the quartz-bearing veins of Aldan were produced in the course of one single process of cooling of the quartz-forming solutions, so that the early stages of the process formed the vein quartz, with the subsequent formation of the crystal quartz.

The transparent and partially transparent quartz crystals formed over a wide range of the temperature. It is possible, however, it appears, to visualize a certain optimum and a relatively narrow range, in the Aldan environments, which proved to be most favorable for the formation of the main bulk of the crystal quartz, namely, somewhere between 250 and 180°C. A significant proportion of syngenetic inclusions in crystal quartz from different sources homogenizes within that particular range. The figures here reported show that temperatures of the quartz-forming solutions were rather high during the formation of the crystal raw materials and that the main bulk of the sources of piezo-quartz in the Aldan crystal quartz district needs be classified as mesothermal.

It is of interest here to remark that thermometric studies of quartz from other quartz crystal provinces indicate that high-grade quartz crystals may be formed within a wide temperature range, from very high (about 400°C) to low (about 100°C). For the given district, however, it is possible to determine the optimum temperature regime at which the bulk of the crystal raw materials that meet the industrial specifications has been formed. This fact, as it is perfectly clear, has not only a theoretical significance but also a high practical value, inasmuch as it helps in a sound approach to the appraisal of crystal quartz veins.

In the majority of cases, the formation of the main body of crystals of industrial grade took place as the result of a gradual and apparently slow decreases in temperatures. This is indicated by the general absence of interruptions in the crystal growth, as visibly recorded by the absence of veils, of phantom crystals, etc., as well as ascertained by the mineral thermometric investigations. However, there is also evidence of a locally discontinuous growth which is demonstrable, as a rule only in certain sections of certain deposits. Such examples in the Aldan are the deposits of Kholodnoye, Severnoye, Sosedka, and others. The presence of clearly expressed phantom crystals in some "vugs" indicates that the crystals grew in solutions fed in pulses, although, as a rule, there are no abrupt variations in the temperature under such conditions, inasmuch as the homogenization temperatures of inclusions in the outer growth zones of the inner crystal and of the inner growth zones of the outer crystal are very close to each other. It was noted, on rare occasions, that there was an abrupt change during the formation of the main part of the crystal and, if so, the crystal was invariably found to be of poor quality.

The regime of the solutions becomes far more unstable and subject to recurrent variations, some of which may be rather severe, during the late stages of the activity of the quartz-forming process, when the last portions of silica are being deposited and while the crystals are acquiring their present external appearance. In very many deposits, we find crystals with zonal structures only in their outer near-surface growth zones. One, two, and, on occasions, 6–8 growth zones may be distinguished, in such instances, separated by surfaces coated by various adhering materials most often sericitic, chloritic, and kaolinitic. Analyses of inclusions in these zones indicate that the variations in the solutions took place against a general background of progressively falling temperature involving some abrupt changes, more or less clearly expressed. However, one may find also examples of an abruptly increasing temperature indicative of a rejuvenation of the solutions. The presence of adhering material on the crystal faces is evidence also of concurrent tectonic movements resulting in a peculiar kind of "paleo-earthquakes".

We must emphasize that the large-scale thermometric analyses of the crystals from large deposits has shown the possibility of abrupt variations in the temperature regime of the solutions, not only from vein to vein, in proximity of each other, but also from vug to vug, within one and the same vein. Moreover, we may observe substantial variations in the temperature regime even within one and the same vug.

Thus the temperature regime of quartz-forming solutions may be characterized only in most general terms, because of the possibility of very serious variations in its details which may be very different in different parts of the deposit and may not be identical even for the crystals in one and the same vug. This may explain why there may be such radical differences in the quality of raw crystals from different vugs of the same deposit and also of crystals from one and the same vug. The same may serve to explain such facts as the presence of cavities with large numbers of phantom crystals in some sections of a deposit and their practical absence in some other sections, or the abundance of crystals with numerous and clearly expressed growth zones, in some vugs, and their absence in some others, etc. As to the reasons for such emphatically local variations in the temperature regime of the solutions, they may be governed by variations in the rates of infiltration of the solutions, which depends on the character and the intensity of fissuring of the rock and on the character of concentrational and convection currents.

SOME DATA ON PRESSURE

We must say now a few words about the pressures that were predominant at the time of formation of quartz crystals, for the sake of a more complete characterization of the quartz-forming solutions. There is a scarcity of data on this subject and all we have is a few single determinations at the Barsukchi and at the deposits of the Sontiitskaya Group. According to Sukhorskii's investigations, some of the quartz crystals in the Novopustynnoye deposit were formed at gradually falling temperatures accompanied by decreasing pressures. Mineral thermometric examinations of one of these crystals gave the following results: the core—temperature 265–260°C; pressure 650 ± 50 atm; the middle zone—temperature 225–210°C; pressure 350 ± 40 atm [15]. So far, there are no other data on pressures at the time of the formation of the quartz-bearing veins.

The foregoing results justify an important conclusion to the effect that the formation of quartz crystals in the quartz-crystal bearing veins and, incidentally, of the veins themselves; took place not uncommonly during abrupt variations in the physico-chemical environment of the mineral formation. The composition of the solutions and their concentration, their state of aggregation, the temperature regime, and the pressure are changing, depending on their migration away from the magmatic source. The changes are indeed appreciable also in time and are clearly recognizable, not infrequently, in thermometric studies even of individual crystals.

BIBLIOGRAPHY

1. BUCKLEY, H. E., *Rost krystallov*. (Crystal Growth.) IL, 1954.
2. BELYANKIN, D. A., Naskol'ko zhe v deystvitel'nosti rastvoryayetsya kremnekislota v vodyanom pare nizhe kriticheskoi temperatury? (What is Finally the Actual Solubility of Silicic Acid in Water Vapor Below the Critical Temperature?) *Sb. Sovet. geolog.* Vol. 3, 1941.
3. VAN PRAAG, G., Gidrotermal'naya kristallizatsiya kvartsevogo stekla (vitriosila) pri postoyannoi temperature. (Hydrothermal Crystallization of Quartz Glass (vitriosil) at Constant Temperature.) *Sb. Noveyshiye issledovaniya po kristallografii i po kristallokhimii*, Vol. 1, *Rost kristallov*. (Crystal Growth.) IL, 1950.

4. VUL'CHIN, YE. I., Materialy k izucheniyu kvartsobrazuyushchikh sistem. (Materials for Studies of Quartz-Forming Systems.) *Uch. zap. L'vov. univ.* Vol. XXIII, *ser. geolog.* 6, 1953.

5. YERMAKOV, N. P., *Geologiya mestorozhdenii opticheskikh mineralov Srednei Azii i temperatury ikh obrazovaniya.* (Geology of the Deposits of Optical Minerals of Central Asia and Temperatures of their Formation.) Theses of the Candidate's Dissertation, 1943.

6. YERMAKOV, N. P., Opredeleniye temperatur obrazovaniya gidrotermal'nykh mineralov issledovaniyem zhidkikh vklyuchenii. (Determination of Temperatures of Formation of Hydrothermal Minerals by the Investigation of Liquid Inclusions.) *Dokl. Akad. Nauk SSSR*, Vol. 45, No. 5, 1944.

7. YERMAKOV, N. P., Kriterii poznaniya genezisa mineralov i sreda rudoobrazovaniya. (Criteria for a Deeper Understanding of the Origin of Minerals in Reference to the Ore-forming Medium.) *Mineralog. sb. L'vov. geolog. obshch.* No. 3, App. 1, 1949.

8. YERMAKOV, N. P., *Issledovaniya mineraloobrazuyushchikh rastvorov.* (Research in Mineral-forming Solutions.) Izd. Khar'kov. univ, 1950.

9. ZAKHARCHENKO, A. I., Rezul'taty izucheniya zhidkikh vklyuchenii v gornom khrustale. (Results of Investigation of Liquid Inclusions in Quartz Crystals.) *Mineralog. sb. L'vov. geolog. obshch.* No. 4, 1950.

10. KARPINSKII, A. P., O nakhozhdenii v mineral'nykh veshchestvakh vklyuchenii zhidkogo ugol'nogo* angidrita. (In Reference to the Presence of Liquid Carbon Dioxide in Inclusions in Mineral Substances.) *Gornyi zh.* Vol. II, No. 4–5, 1880.

11. LAZARENKO, YE. K. and YE. M. LAZ'KO, O knige N. P. Yermakova *Issledovaniye mineraloobrazuyushchikh rastvorov* (temperatury i aggregatnoye sostoyaniye). (About N. P. Yermakov's book, "Research in Mineral-forming Solutions (temperatures and the state of aggregation)".) *Mineralog. sb. L'vov. geolog. obshch.*, No. 5, 1951.

12. LAZ'KO, YE. M., Rol'pnevmatoliza v mineraloobrazovanii. (The Role of Pneumatolysis in the Formation of Minerals.) *Mineralog. sb. L'vov. geolog. obshch.* No. 5, 1951.

13. SAMOYLOV, YA. V., Mineralogiya zhil'nykh mestorozhdenii Nagol'nogo Kryazha. (Mineralogy of Vein Deposits of the Nagol'nyi Kryazh.). *Materialy dlya Geologii Rossii*, Vol. XXIII, 1908.

14. SWINNERTON, A., D. OWEN and D. CORWIN, Nekotoryye voprosy rosta kristallov kvartsa. (Certain Problems in Growth of Quartz Crystals.) *Sb. Noveyshiye issledovaniya po kristallografii i kristallokhimii.* Vol. 1, *Rost kristallov.* (Crystal Growth.) IL, 1950.

15. SUKHORSKII, R. F., Temperaturnyi rezhim obrazovanii nekotorykh khrustalenosnykh mestorozhdenii Aldana. (The Temperature Regime of Formation of Some Sources of Crystal Quartz in Aldan.) *Avtoreferat dissertatsii*, L'vov, 1954.

16. SYROMYATNIKOV, F. V., K voprosu ob opredelenii rastvorimosti kremnezyoma v vode pri vysokoi temperature i vysokom davlenii. (In Reference to the Determination of the Solubility of Silica in Water at High Temperatures and High Pressures.) *Sb. sov. geolog.* Vol. 3, 1944.

17. THOMAS, L., N. WOOSTER and W. WOOSTER, Gidrotermal'nyi sintez kvartsa. (Hydrothermal Synthesis of Quartz.) *Sb. Noveyshiye issledovaniya po kristallografii i kristallokhimii.* Vol. 2. *Rost kristallov.* IL, 1951.

18. WALKER, A. and E. BUHLER, Vyrashchivaniye krupnykh kristallov kvartsa. (Synthetic Growth of Large Quartz Crystals.) *Sb. Noveyshiye issledovaniya po kristallografii i kristallokhimii*, Vol. 3. *Kristallicheskiye struktury.* IL, 1951.

---

* Old usage of the term [V.P.S.].

19. KHITAROV, N. I., Parovaya i gazovaya fazy sistemy kremnezyom–voda. (The Vapor and the Gas Phases of the Silica–Water System.) *Sb. Sov. geolog.* Vol. 12, 1944.
20. KÖNIGSBERGER, J. and W. MÜLLER, Über die Flussigkeitseinschlüsse im Quartz Alpiner Mineralkluften. *Centr. Min.* Vol. 341, 1906.
21. LINDGREN, W. and B. STEIGL, *Geol. Surv. 17th Ann. Rept.* Vol. 2, 130, 1895–6.
22. SORBY, H., On the Microscopical Structure of Crystals Indicating the Origin of Minerals and Rocks. *Quart. J. Geol. Soc. London,* Vol. 14, 1858.

On the Possibility of Ascertaining the True Temperatures of Mineral-forming Solutions

N. P. Yermakov and Vl. A. Kalyuzhnyi

THE *multiform possibilities* of utilization of inclusions of mineral-forming solutions in shedding light on important problems of origin of endogenic deposits, particularly on the temperature regime of the crystallization of minerals and the state of aggregation of mineral-forming solutions were either resolved or posed by the middle of the present century.

It became clear at about the same time that the utilization of minerals themselves in determinations of the true or of the relative temperatures of mineral genesis is either entirely impossible or else is extremely limited, for example any objective differentation between products of pneumatolysis and of hydrothermal activity. This realization served to intensify the drive of the investigators toward a fuller and a more quantitative utilization of liquid inclusions in minerals in the capacity of self-recording thermometers and led the Soviet scientists to the creation of the thermometric analysis and of the analysis of the aggregate state of ore-forming solutions operative in the geologic past [3].

The subsequent geologic and experimental verifications of the suitability of these methods for the determination of the relative and the minimum temperatures of the formation of specific post-magmatic deposits, as well as the further development of theory of the subject, here and abroad, produced a wide discussion in the press whereby these problems advanced to a new level of understanding. At the same time, there were not only confirmations of the possibility of determining the course of the temperature variations, in time, by means of primary and pseudo-secondary liquid inclusions of solutions in different growth zones of crystals and in minerals of different generations, but also demonstrations, in space, of variations in temperature and in the state of aggregation of included mineral-forming solutions in minerals of one and the same generation collected at different depths, in the deposit, and at different distances from the source of the ore-forming solutions.

All of that has made it possible, in several test cases, to ascertain *the relative temperatures* of the hydrothermal mineralization, *in the coordinates of time and space,* and to determine objectively the boundaries of the pneumatolytic and the hydrothermal processes in polygenic deposits.

The results of the thermometric analysis of hydrothermal minerals, represented as graphs, are expressions of a temporary stability or, on the contrary, of various instabilities in the temperature and in the other physico-chemical parameters in addition to the temperature. That is, the results enable us to ascertain the dynamics of the hydrothermal process in terms of the relative magnitudes, namely, the homogenization temperatures. The latter were taken to be the minimum temperatures of formation of minerals, rather than the true temperatures, for a long time. This was the reason for a certain dissatisfaction, with the utilization of inclusions in mineralogic thermometry, on the part of several scientists who believed that the *absolute temperature* points are far more important. Some of these scientists [5, 12] attempted to ascertain the temperature corrections at different pressures and concentrations of the solutions, while some others [1, 9], for various reasons, wrote entirely about errors in the thermometric method and even about the complete unsuitability of the method, forgetting the considerable significance of the determination of relative temperatures at the beginning and at the end of the hydrothermal process or of its intermediate stages, as indicated by the homogenization temperatures of inclusions in the corresponding minerals or growth zones of the crystals.

Thus a series of articles appeared in mineralogical literature, in recent times, dealing with reliability of the fundamental premises of mineralogic thermometry based on liquid inclusions, proceeding from various facts obtained by analysis of natural materials or else by experimentation in the laboratory. These contributions undertook discussions on occasions, of facts out the broad context of the interrelated components of the process of mineral genesis as a whole, so that "new discoveries" are made, in passing, which were essentially recurrences of the old and well known special cases among the overall orderly relationships. Such a situation in the field of research on mineral genesis here discussed was the cause for the appearance of the present article whose authors endeavored to ascertain the status of mineralogic thermometry in the light of modern data.

Studies of liquid inclusions, miniature "natural autoclaves," are undertaken for the purpose of determining the main factors in the process of mineral genesis: the relative and the true temperatures, concentration, composition, state of aggregation of the solutions, etc. We shall deal here only with problems associated with the thermometry of mineral-forming solutions, although they are not the most important ones either in the theory or in the practice of the utilization of inclusions in minerals. It becomes necessary nevertheless to give the first priority to these problems in our present article, because they are the ones that had become subject to doubts, in the last five years, in the literature on inclusions, to the point of retarding the further development of all other aspects of the problem. The authors found it possible to make a tentative summary of the discussion and to try to explain away the series of premature conclusions that were the results of a sporadic or occasional interest in inclusions on the part of certain investigators.

The attempts to utilize minerals as temperature indicators of the former hydrothermal ore-forming processes give, at best, only isolated temperature points for the upper or for the lower temperature limits of formation of a given mineral, but they do not reveal the dynamics of the process whose course, as a rule, was in temperature environments undergoing variations at different rates. The only hope for a solution of this problem is related to the utilization of inclusions of liquid aqueous solutions, so widely developed in hydrothermal minerals.

The homogenization of such inclusions by heat aims to repeat the process by which the inclusions were formed, in the reverse sequence, and to restore the original parameters $(T-P-X)$ of the included system, as at the time of its isolation. A complete restoration of this original state is impossible, because of the uncertainty of the system's fundamental parameter, the temperature. As we known, the leading role of temperature is accepted because that parameter may be measured easily and without upsetting the system as a whole; as to the temperature variations in a confined system, they result in corresponding orderly variations in the other two fundamental parameters related to the temperature. The PT diagram (Fig. 1) is a good illustration of this relationship. The moment of disappearance of the gas bubble in a two-phase liquid aqueous inclusion, in the course of application of heat, corresponds to the particular lower point on the liquid–gas phase equilibrium curve *next to which* the state of the solution is to be represented by coordinates of the points on the corresponding and definite curve of equal specific volumes (the isochor). The points on the isochor *characterize the state of an already homogeneous system.* The point of the homogenization temperature is taken as the minimum temperature of origin of inclusions, since isochors are not mutually parallel but form acute angles with the pressure axis. The observed homogenization temperatures will be always lower than the true temperatures of mineral genesis.

The correction for pressure, in order to approximate the true temperature, may be applied in accordance with the appropriate PT diagrams for systems at definite solution concentrations. The diagrams for pure water may be employed, as a first approximation, for two-phase liquid inclusions.

Discrepancies between the observed and the true temperatures caused by concentrations of the cognate substance of the host minerals may be insignificant, provided such concentrations were low, at the time of formation of the mineral. The facts are ascertained generally by chemical analysis of the included solutions and by observing the deposition of the substance on the walls of the vacuole [6]. Specially designed physico-chemical experiments with the solubility of minerals (silicates, oxides, carbonates, and others) in solutions having the same composition as the included solutions would help even more in arriving at the true temperatures of mineral genesis from the observed temperatures of homogenization.

Let us consider now in brief the effects of such constituents as easily soluble salts and gas, common in the included solutions, on the accuracy of the temperature measurements by the homogenization method.

Although low concentrations of the host mineral's substance in the solution of two-phase inclusions make it possible to identify the state of the system with the diagrams of state for pure water, applications of these diagrams are not permissible, with any hope of reliability, to systems at high concentrations of easily soluble constituents. It follows therefore that, in dealing with multiphase liquid inclusions, we must employ the appropriate PT diagrams for every particular level of concentration. One of the early attempts at ascertaining the PT relationships in the H_2O–30 per cent $NaCl$ system is the research of Klevtsov [5]. On the other hand, high concentrations of salts inside inclusions broaden the range of applicability of the homogenization method as they push the critical point in the direction of higher temperature.

The effect of high concentrations of salts on the accuracy of thermometric determinations is entirely different from the effect of easily volatile constituents (CO_2, H_2S, etc.). The latter one is in the opposite direction. By lowering the critical point of water, the volatile constituents narrow the range of applicability of the method and decrease the accuracy of the method to a considerable extent. *For that reason, inclusions with carbon dioxide as well as gaseous inclusions were never recommended as test materials suited for thermometric analysis.* The diagrams of such solutions will show deviations of the gas–liquid equilibrium curves in the direction of higher pressures, as against the diagram for pure water. The isochors of the inclusions with higher proportions of easily volatile constituents will show larger angles with the pressure axis while the homogenization temperatures will show progressively greater deviations from the true temperatures of the mineral genesis (Fig. 1).

In addition to the principal variables, here enumerated, responsible for entirely definite and orderly discrepancies between the homogenization temperatures and the temperatures of formation of minerals, we must also take into account the following lesser features of mineral genesis that become manifest only in isolated cases.

As we know, the sealing of inclusions in a growing mineral takes place in a homogeneous medium, as a rule. A simultaneous entry of several different phases into an inclusion, in our view, is possible only in the following relatively rare instances:

(1) In a boiling solution, when gas bubbles adhere to the faces, of a growing crystal.

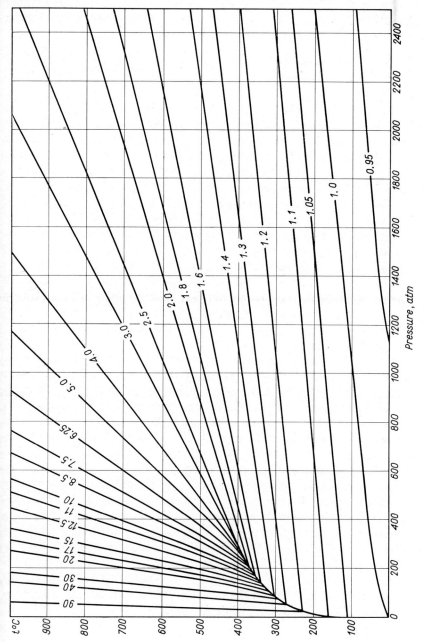

FIG. 1. PT diagram for H₂O with isolines for specific volumes. (According to Kennedy *et al.*)

(2) In a boiling solution, when easily volatile constituents are parted from the solution as bubbles (for example, in the parting of CO_2 while its solubility in an aqueous solution is decreasing).

(3) When microcrystalline associated minerals happen to settle on faces of a growing crystal, so that inclusion cavities are formed in their proximity.

It should be emphasized that the prerequisites of the crystallization involving capture and sealing of a heterogeneous system are made clear easily on detailed studies of the crystals. There are some difficulties only in the identification of inclusions produced by sealing of gas bubbles from a boiling solution [3]. Such cases are relatively rare, however (boiling is limited by the critical pressure, in a given solution).

The results of thermometric measurements in the so-called "bead-like"* inclusions, on the whole, are likewise unsuited for the determinations even of the minimum temperatures of the mineral genesis. The mechanism of the formation of such groups was first discovered by G. G. Lemmleyn and M. O. Kliya by experimentation with easily soluble salts. The "stringing-out" phenomena are undoubtedly widespread also in the case of inclusions in natural minerals, especially at rapidly falling temperatures occurring more frequently toward the end of the process.

In a rational selection of test materials for thermometric analysis it is always essential to examine carefully the inclusion groups, so as to detect any anomalous inclusions that are unsuited for thermometric determinations by virtue of their transformations in the cooling process. However, the experience of many years with the thermometric analysis of crystals from different sources shows that ordinary minerals contain an *incomparably larger number* of groups of syngenetic inclusions (on occasions, many thousand per cm³ of the crystal), with a *sustained and constant ratio of the phases*, than of inclusions that had become "bead-like" after the formation of their gas bubble. The "beading" of inclusions is a well-known exception to the rule, although certain writers, for reasons unknown, try to make this exception the rule. For example, Yakubova [9] devotes extraordinary attention to such examples, and she shows eleven photomicrographs and sketches of strung-out inclusion groups with their anomalous phase ratios. At the same time, she fails to produce even a single photomicrograph of normal liquid inclusion groups, so common in hydrothermal minerals, with their strictly consistent phase ratios and with the homogenization according to one and the same type and at one and the same temperature (with a few degrees of deviations).

---

* Presumably in reference to chains of inclusions formed from originally straight tubular inclusions [Ed.].

In her thermometric studies of inclusions in the Murzinka minerals, Yakubova, for some unaccountable reason, failed to select her test materials rationally, materials that would be suited for the purposes of geologic thermometry, with attention to the findings of Lemmleyn, Kliya, and other investigators. She ignored the need of distinguishing between primary and secondary inclusions and had obtained accordingly a set of completely unreliable and mutually contradictory data [9]. For example, Yakubova, on the basis of *obviously secondary* liquid inclusions and of complex inclusions with carbon dioxide in igneous fish-shaped phenocrysts of quartz, endeavored to determine the temperatures of formation of that quartz [9, pp. 133–134], displaying thereby a level of understanding of the problem fully comparable to the ancient ideas of the Neptunists who tried to assert a sedimentary origin for granites, using as a proof the presence of liquid inclusions in quartz grains from hydrothermally altered rocks. It is well known that only *solidified* inclusions of residual magmatic solutions are genuinely primary inclusions in α-quartz* of fish-shaped phenocrysts, while the entire varied assortment of gaseous and liquid inclusions, even without any "beading" phenomena, is merely an expression of a prolonged action of miscellaneous late solutions on graphic pegmatites at various temperatures and pressures.

The second important aspect of our problem is the question as to the extent of permissible errors caused by incomplete restoration of the original T, P, and X factors at the moment of homogenization of inclusions, i.e. what are the absolute values of the deviations. This question may be answered most fully by the PT diagrams. Unfortunately, because of the absence of sufficient experimental data, it is still impossible to construct the physico-chemical diagrams for aqueous solutions in a wide range of the concentrations, although the first data for the purpose have already been obtained for the solution of the problem of the synthesis of quartz.

On the other hand, corrections derived from the PT diagrams for pure water, in the instance of two-phase inclusions of liquid solutions, are of considerable value in the physico-chemical interpretations and enable us to come closer to the determination of the actual temperatures of mineral genesis.

Nacken [11], as early as 1921, was the first one to employ the PT diagrams for pure water in the intrepretation of the homogenization results and the subject was examined in detail by Ingerson [12] in 1947. Ostrovskii [7] and Vul'chin [2] published recently their articles on the subject involving the use of the $V–T–X$ and the $P–T–X$ diagrams. With the aid of these diagrams, these authors made several important conclusions in regards to

* Probably β-quartz of American usage [Ed.].

heterogeneous equilibria in a binary system at constant volume, filling thereby the gap in the theory of the method.

Their conclusions are entirely correct for inclusions in easily soluble minerals, but, as we know, the thermometric analysis is applicable only to sparingly soluble minerals.

Alongside the basic parameters, numerous secondary details are also expressed by the $V-T-X$ diagrams, contributing to a broad view of the phase equilibria. Some of the elements of such diagrams are still insufficiently supported by factual data, particularly for specific silicate–water systems. As the result, some of the details may obscure the substance of the problem.

Vul'chin [2], repeating the fundamental theses of Ostrovskii's study [7] and proceeding from the $V-T-X$ diagrams and from their isochoric dimensions,* believes that thermometric results obtained by homogenization of inclusions may be too low or too high, with respect to the actual temperatures of a mineral's growth. Having lost sight of the physical sense of theoretical constructions, the authors here cited arrive, in fact, at a paradox, to *the assumption that inclusions may be formed in fields in the diagram where there are no solid phases at all, i.e. in the absence of the host mineral.* Hence their erroneous assertion as to the excessively high temperatures (positive errors) obtainable by the homogenization method. In reality, homogenization temperatures of inclusions originated under ordinary conditions are always lower than the temperatures of the mineral genesis and may be even the same as the latter, in the instance of low pressures. There is no foundation whatsoever for assertions of the possibility of positive errors on the basis of the $V-T-X$ diagrams.

Positive errors in the method are possible *in the case of inclusions produced from a boiling mother liquor,* when the mineral captures a part of the system in its heterogeneous state. Positive errors of the type already discussed may develop also in careless thermometric measurements involving complex inclusions with carbon dioxide or groups of the so-called "beaded" inclusions. As we see, all these are special cases of origins and transformations of inclusions that are easily recognizable in minerals. The errors obtained in such cases are completely outside the scope of the physico-chemical diagrams presented in the works of Vul'chin and Ostrovskii and they do not correspond to the magnitudes indicated in the profiles of the $V-T-X$ diagram.

When inclusions are produced from a boiling solution, varying quantities of the gaseous phase may be captured together with the liquid phase in the inclusion's cavity. If only one of the phases is captured (either gaseous or liquid), the positive error equals zero. Since the process of

---

* "Razmer" is "dimension"; could be "scale", "reading", etc. [V.P.S.].

boiling a mineral-forming solution is limited by the magnitude of the critical pressure, the formation of inclusions of heterogeneous origin is not a common phenomenon in nature (excepting simple and complex inclusions with carbon dioxide), especially in the ore-forming environments of medium-temperature and low-temperature hydrothermal deposits [*sic*].

Certain authors [1] in recent times, in discussing the possibilities of the method of mineralogic thermometry, made erroneous assertions departing from the theoretical principles of the heterogeneous equilibria and particularly from the data of the pressure–temperature diagrams that are fundamental in thermometry. Certain experimentors, operating in the field of synthetic crystals, are especially surprised, for example, by identical homogenization temperatures of inclusions in synthetic quartz produced at identical concentrations and at the same degree of filling of the autoclave, but at different temperatures.

Liquid inclusions in crystals developed under such conditions, on their cooling to room temperature, are fairly exact expressions of the coefficient of filling of the autoclave and of the constant specific total volume of the solution and steam in the autoclave, in regards to the volume ratio of their gas bubble and liquid.

The state of the autoclave's contents is pre-determined by the coefficient of its filling and is characterized, in the given case, *by one and the same isochor of the PT diagram.* All that the authors had to do was to correct the temperature they had measured (300 ± 5°C) for *the pressure* (which is not the same for the initial, the intermediate, and the terminal stages of the growth and is not the same at different temperatures of the experiment), so that the true temperature of the crystal growth would be obtained. Butuzov and Ikornikova drew a completely erroneous general conclusion, on the basis of these special-case results, namely, that "... the homogenization temperature of gas–liquid inclusions is unrelated to the temperature of the crystal growth" [1].

It is apparent that these authors unfortunately had failed to grasp the relationship between the homogenization and the crystallization temperatures. This relationship, of course, is an indirect and not a direct one. Were it a direct relationship, all our discussions of corrections and physicochemical diagrams would be superfluous and the homogenization temperature would coincide with the true temperature of sealing of the inclusion.

As a matter of fact, the transition, *the connecting link between the two temperatures is the specific volume of the solution.* By determining the homogenization temperature, we obtain, in that very step, the specific volume of the solution at the moment of sealing of the inclusion, i.e. we locate *the corresponding and entirely definite isochor in the PT diagram.* Discovery of the absolute temperature of the former mineral genesis, even as previously stated, is contingent on our knowledge of one more unknown, namely, the pressure.

Thus, having determined the appropriate isochor on the *PT* diagram, by the means of the homogenization temperature, we are justified in the contention that there can be only one temperature corresponding to the given pressure that was determined by a given method [4]. Having found the homogenization temperature, we obtain an equation with two unknowns. This equation may be solved, particularly in the instance of synthetic crystal growth, when, at the known and constant concentration, the pressure is also known. Consequently, there is a relationship between the homogenization and the crystallization temperatures of a mineral and this relationship has and must have its expressions in diagrams, equations, and formulae.

In considering the corrections of the experimentally determined homogenization temperatures for pressure, it should be pertinent to comment on the probable pressures in natural post-magmatic processes.

High pressures of solutions are not typical for the hydrothermal process, according to geologic data, as the process takes place generally in open channels of fissures and joints. *The pressure in such channels can never compare with the lithostatic pressure, as calculated from the thickness of the overburden, and is most likely to be comparable to the pressure of a "column" of water which is about 100 atm/km depth.* Also, we should have in mind that geologic environments of the hydrothermal process *by no means correspond to hermetic conditions,* inasmuch as even undisturbed igneous rocks, as we know, have a fairly high degree of permeability for solutions. Hydrothermal and particularly pneumatolytic systems of solutions are unconfined systems, as a rule. It is just as easy to produce relatively high pressures in autoclaves as it is difficult to visualize such pressures in natural environments (outside magmatic hearths).

The experimental determinations of pressures, few as they were, with the aid of inclusions of mother liquors and of carbon dioxide of similar origin, indicated 300–500 atm, even for pegmatites, and not over 820 atm for hydrothermal polymetallic gold deposits [4]. *The pressure like the temperature, is a continuously changing variable, in the coordinates of space and time* and the range of its fluctuations is also changeable, below the 1000 atm limit, in the instance of medium-temperature and low-temperature hydrotherms (Fig. 2).

At such pressures and at the average concentrations of 12–15 per cent, the VNIIP had obtained, by this time, some very important but still tentative data on the homogenization temperatures of liquid inclusions in synthetic quartz which was produced by the hydrothermal method at known temperatures and pressures. These data are reported in the paper by Safronov and Khadzhi (Table on p. 418), in the present publication.

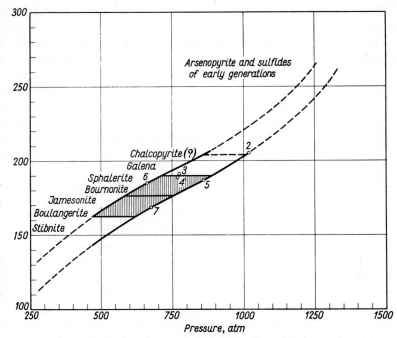

FIG. 2. The field of separation of ore minerals in Nagolnyi Kryazh; T–P coordinates; figures refer to experiment numbers.

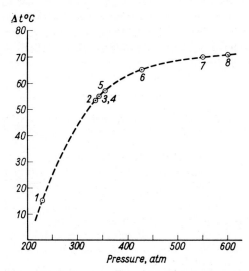

FIG. 3. Correction ($\Delta t°$) for pressure of homogenization temperatures of liquid inclusions, according to preliminary data on synthetic quartz grown in solutions at 12–15 per cent concentration; figures refer to experiment numbers.

The homogenization temperatures and their deviations from the true temperatures were determined for the 230–600 atm range of true pressures and the 316–330°C range of true temperatures. An empirical curve of corrections of the observed homogenization temperatures of two-phase inclusions for the pressure ($\Delta t°$) was drawn on the basis of these experiments (Fig. 3). Theoretically, even as it should be expected, the corrections are always positive. They *fluctuate from* 15 *to* 71°C, in the indicated range of P, T, and X, the range characteristic of medium-temperature and low-temperature products of hydrothermal mineralization and of two-phase liquid inclusions. This difference and the correction diagram (Fig. 3) refer to homogenization temperatures obtained in the commonly employed air-heated thermochambers with an insufficiently sealed inner space. In hermetic chambers with a contact heating of the test material set between two metal plates, the discrepancy between the observed and the true homogenization temperatures will be 40° lower, on the average (excepting Experiment No. 1), i.e. will be not over 30 or 31°C at 600 atm pressure.

For high pressures (up to 1600 atm) and high concentrations of NaCl (30 per cent) corresponding to multiphase liquid inclusions (with one or several solid phases), the corrections of observed homogenization temperatures were determined experimentally by Klevtsov [5]. Specifically, for the range of homogenization temperatures from 170–400°C, these corrections are 30–40°C, 60–85°C, and 110–140° at 500, 1000, and 1500 atm pressure respectively.

It is possible accordingly to come appreciably closer to the true temperatures of the natural mineral-forming process with the aid of the available methods of inclusion studies, of the evaluations of the magnitudes of densities, concentrations, and pressures of the solutions by the thermometric analysis of minerals.

BIBLIOGRAPHY

1. BUTUZOV, V. P. and N. YU. IKORNIKOV, Zhidkiye vklyucheniya v iskusstvennom kvartse. (Liquid Inclusions in Synthetic Quartz.) *Dokl. Akad. Nauk SSSR*, Vol. 104, No. 1, 1955.
2. VUL'CHIN, Ye. I., Fiziko-khimicheskaya interpretatsiya termometricheskikh izmerenii metodom gomogenizatsii vklyuchenii. (Physico-chemical Interpretation of Thermometric Measurements by the Method of Homogenization of Inclusions.) *Mineralog. Sb. L'vov. geolog. obshch.* No. 5, 1951.
3. YERMAKOV, N. P., *Issledovaniye mineraloobrazuyushchikh rastvorov.* (Research in Mineral-forming Solutions.) Izd. Khar'kov. univ. 1950.
4. KALYUZHNYI, V. A., Zhidkiye vklyucheniya v mineralakh kak geologicheskii barometr. (Liquid Inclusions in Minerals as a Geological Barometer.) *Mineralog. Sb. L'vov. obshch.* No. 9, 1955.
5. KLEVTSOV, P. V., Issledovaniye nekotorykh termodinamicheskikh svoistv kontsentrirovannykh vodnykh rastvorov solei v prilozhenii k geologicheskoi termometrii. (Research in Certain Thermodynamic Properties of Concentrated Aqueous

Solutions of Salts in its Application to Geologic Thermometry.) Avtoreferat dissertatsii, 1955.

6. LEMMLEIN, G. G. and M. O. KLIYA, Novyye dannyye ob otlozhenii veshchestv na stenkakh polosti zhidkogo vklyucheniya. (New Data on Deposition of Substances on Cavity Walls of a Liquid Inclusion.) *Dokl. Akad. Nauk SSSR*, Vol. 82, No. 5, 1952.

7. OSTROVSKII, I. A., O diagramme VTX dlya prosteyshego sluchaya v sisteme silikatov vody. (On the VTX Diagram for the Simplest Case in the Water-Silicate System.) *Izv. Akad. Nauk SSSR, ser. geolog.* No. 5, 1950.

8. SMITH, F. G., Obzor fiziko-khimicheskikh svoystv nadkriticheskikh fluidov. (Review of Physico-chemical Properties of Supercritical Fluids.) *Sb. Experimental'nyye issledovaniya v oblasti petrografii i rudoobrazovaniya.* IL, 1954.

9. YAKUBOVA, V. V., Opyt izucheniya vklyuchenii v mineralakh pegmatitov Murzinki. (An Experiment in the Study of Inclusions in Minerals from the Murzinka Pegmatites.) *Tr. mineralog. muzeya Akad. Nauk SSSR* 7, 1955.

10. KENNEDY, G. C., A portion of the system silica-water, *Economic geology*, Vol. 451, No. 7, 1950.

11. NACKEN, R., Welche Folgerungen ergeben sich aus dem Auftreten von Flüssigkeiten schlüssen in Mineralien, *Centralblatt für Mineralogie, etc.*, 1921.

12. INGERSON, E., Liquid Inclusions in Geologic Thermometry. *The American Mineralogist*, Vol. 32, No. 7/8, 1947.

Liquid Inclusions in Synthetic Quartz Crystals

G. M. SAFRONOV

IN THE studies of synthetic quartz crystals produced by the hydrothermal method, we gave most attention to liquid inclusions, the specimens of quartz-forming solutions preserved in the crystals in the course of the crystal's growth.

Two-phase liquid inclusions are defects of the synthetic crystals and are among the factors constituting evidence of the conditions of the crystallization of quartz and of the variations of these conditions in time.

Primary inclusions are particularly widespread and common. Such inclusions are formed directly in the crystal's growth zones. The so-called pseudo-secondary or primary–secondary inclusions in crystal fissures are just as common.

We are able to distinguish the following groups of syngenetic inclusions in quartz crystals.

(1) Liquid inclusions, associated genetically with aggregations of solid finely crystalline inclusions (inclusion-associates of the solid phase).

(2) Tubular inclusions, originating at the boundary of the "seed" crystal (zatravka) with the overgrowing crystal or else in individual growth zones of the crystal.

(3) Individual isolated inclusions occurring sporadically in the crystal.

(4) Inclusions due to skeletal growth.

All of these varieties of inclusions are two-phase at room temperature: the liquid occupies 75–80 per cent of the vacuole's volume and the gas bubble occupies 20–25 per cent.

Such gas–liquid ratios in the inclusions *represent* very closely *the filling coefficients of the autoclave* and they vary within a narrow range, depending on the magnitude of the temperature fluctuation [*sic*].

In the overwhelming majority of cases, inclusions formed in the process of the crystal growth have identical or almost identical phase ratios and are homogenized at the same temperature, in different growth zones or in groups of fissures synchronously healed. The per cent of the gaseous phase is higher significantly only in inclusions in a direct contact with the "solid" particles, as against the normal groups of hermetically sealed liquid inclusions, probably because of imperfections in their sealing and because of their uptake of a certain fraction of the liquid.

[408]

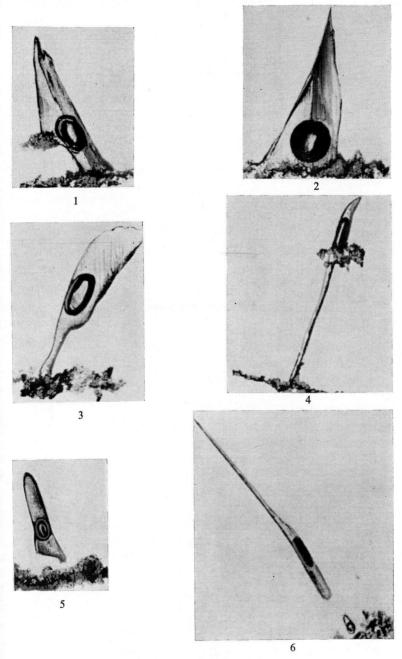

FIG. 1. Inclusions associated with solid phases in synthetic quartz crystals
100× to 150×.

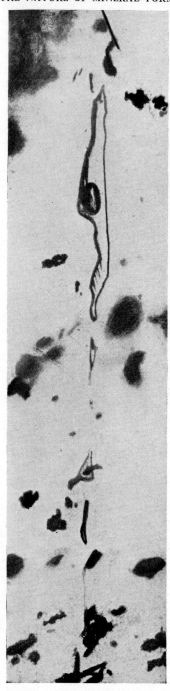

FIG. 2. (Photomicrograph). Orientation of inclusions in growth zone with respect to surface of the "seed" (at bottom.) 50×.

Inclusions associated with solid phases, investigated by E. N. Pushkina, have an average size of 0.1–0.3 mm. Some of them may be as long as 2–3 mm and are plainly visible to the naked eye. They are associated generally with the upper parts of crystals where there are accumulations of microcrystalline aggregates of solid inclusions that settled on the crystal faces during their growth.

Among these primary inclusions, one may distinguish vacuoles containing liquid together with an anomalously large gas bubble that are in direct contact with flaky solid inclusions (Fig. 1, *1, 2*), to which they are joined by a narrow channel (Fig. 1, *3, 4*), or from which they are isolated (Fig. 1, *5, 6*). The first kind often are shaped like irregular cones whose apexes are oriented toward the advancing growth of the face of the crystal.

Inclusions of the other two kinds are elongated, as a rule, and their shapes are most highly varied: globular, tubular, equant, etc.

The mechanism of formation of such inclusions is explained as follows: a solid particle fallen onto a surface of a growing crystal interferes with free access of the solution to that particular section of the crystal face. There follows a local "starvation" and the growth of the crystal becomes irregular. A small pit develops under the particle and becomes overgrown eventually by the crystal substance. The mineral-forming solution is sealed

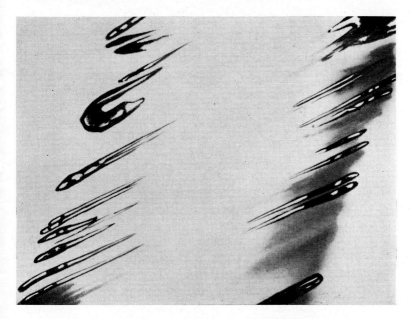

FIG. 3. (Photomicrograph.) Inclusions in zone of skeletal growth and of dissolution along the seed's surface. 56×.

in the cavity. This is how Yermakov [1] describes the process of the formation of such liquid inclusions.

Shubnikov [3] describes their formation somewhat differently. He believes that a solid particle fallen on the surface of a growing crystal may be raised during the crystal growth, with the resulting formation of a cavity in the wake of the moving particle, filled by the solution and elongated in the direction of the particle's movement. In the end, the solid particle is generally captured by the growing crystal, but at a considerable distance both from the site of its fall and from the liquid inclusion it produced (Fig. 2). Very fine particles may be captured occasionally by liquid inclusions and be sealed inside them.

FIG. 4. (Photomicrograph.) Mutual orientation of inclusions developing in the seed and in the overgrowing quartz. Some of the vacuoles pierce the entire thickness of the seed. 120×.

Both of the examples of the formation of primary inclusions here considered are probably true. This in confirmed by studies of relationships between inclusions and solid particles.

Tubular zonal inclusions are observed often in synthetic crystals, in the interspace between the seed and the overgrowing layer of quartz.

This group of inclusions differs from the ones previously described by its morphologic features, mutual orientations, and position in the crystal. The inclusions are preponderantly spindle-shaped, thinning-out toward one of the ends to yield a needle-like or a beak-like shape (Figs. 3 and 4).

The phase ratios and, consequently, the homogenization temperatures of inclusions in that group, in one and the same zone of the crystal, are constant.

The long axes of the inclusion cavities have a mutually parallel orientation and lie at different angles with respect to the seed plane, depending on the orientation of the latter. The most common range of variations in the angle of the inclusion axes with the angle of cut of the seed is 23–60°, in the crystals we examined.

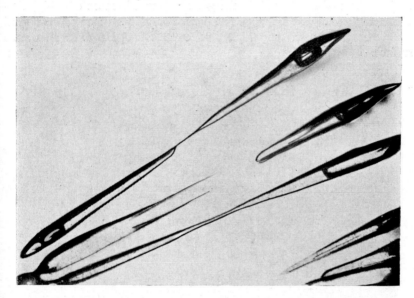

FIG. 5. (Photomicrograph.) Shapes of inclusions piercing the seed. 120×.

In the majority of cases, the liquid inclusions here described are so densely spaced as to suggest a "zone of porous, capillary, or skeletal growth" in the early stage of the formation of the crystal. This zone develops as the result of a partial solution of the seed itself, in the beginning of the experiment, accompanied by the formation of conical and needle-shaped pits in the seed's body. Later on, when the deposition of quartz begins, these pits are overgrown by the crystalline substance and the inclusions are so produced. Solution of the seed plate may go so far, on occasions, that the needle-like pits developing at opposite planes of the seed plate may join each other and may produce canals piercing the plate. In such case, there is a formation of inclusions piercing the seed plate, and coalescing with inclusions from the opposite side (Fig 5).

The vacuoles of the coalescing inclusions are nearly always symmetrical, since the micro-channels thin out toward the center of the seed plate. Gas bubbles develop occasionally at the two opposite ends of an inclusion, in the presence of a narrow connecting channel.

Inclusions of this type in natural crystals were described by Sukhorskii [2], in contact zones of morion with pale-gray quartz from the Volynian sources. Every one of the inclusions was found to be situated, in space, parallel to each other and approximately at right angles to the former faces of a phantom crystal which functioned as the seed. The author remarks that the tubular inclusions were produced as the result of a rapid growth of the crystal, in the gaseous phase, because of a high mobility of this phase at low concentrations. The growing face of the crystal could not grow sufficiently rapidly to cover the openings in all of the surface.

FIG. 6. (Photomicrograph.) Inclusions in fissures in the seed. A group of inclusions developed on healing of a fissure. 160×.

Inclusions of the same type were observed by us in quartz crystals from deposits in Southern Ural.

Inclusions produced by healing of fissures in the seed are very interesting. These inclusions are identifiable by their positions, always in the same plane of the former fissure, despite their occasionally tubular forms resembling the ones already described.

Among these inclusions, one may see individual groups consisting of several mutually parallel tubular inclusions showing the same phase ratios and homogenization temperatures and situated right next to a large inclusion of a flattened shape (Figs. 6 and 7).

As previously stated, tubular inclusions at the boundary between the seed and the overgrowing quartz are produced because of a partial solution of the seed during the initial stage of the synthetic crystal growth. The extent of the long axes of the inclusions depends directly on the extent of the solubility of the seed quartz.

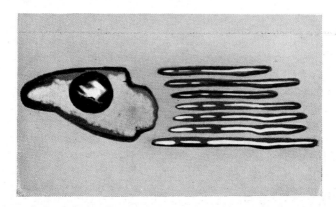

FIG. 7. (Photomicrograph.) Inclusions in the crystal's seed. 120×.

FIG. 8. (Photomicrograph.) Isolated inclusions of triangular shape. The volume of the gas phase has been increased by migration of the solution into the fissures disturbing the inclusion's cavity. 120×.

It has been observed that different sections of the seed behave differently in the process of the solution. Some of them undergo a severe etching, to the point of formation of channels through the seed. If the seed is set vertically in the autoclave, its lower sections are particularly affected by the solution. As the result, some seeds acquire the shape of a wedge.

The seed's defective sections (zones of twinning, micro-fissures, zones with mosaic structures) are especially susceptible to etching. On rare occasions, large (up to 1–2 mm) flattened inclusions were observed at the boundaries of twins.

On occasions, the seed underwent such an intensive solution that it fell off the frame in the autoclave. In cases where large apertures developed in the surface of the basal cut plane of the seed, because of solution, they would not be overgrown, on account of the slow rates of growth of the prism faces.

Etching of the seeds and the resulting formation of tubular inclusions impedes production of high-grade quartz crystals.

In order to avoid an intensive solution of the seeds, we must ascertain painstakingly the optimum conditions of operation of the reactors.

Isolated inclusions. In addition to the main varieties of inclusions produced in the crystallized quartz, one may occasionally observe isolated inclusions of highly diverse shape; triangular, equant, amoeboid, more often with irregular and wavy outlines (Fig. 8). The cavity walls of some of them have ribbed wavy surfaces and may be covered by fine striations oriented always in the same direction. The size of such inclusions varies generally from 0.3 to 0.5 mm and, rarely, up to 1 mm along the long axis of the vacuole. The volume ratios, gas bubble to aqueous mother liquor, in these inclusions at room temperature corresponds to the coefficient of filling of the autoclave (commonly 20–25 per cent gas). The inclusions are often surrounded by a network of fine fissures.

Skeletal growth inclusions appear in pyramids of irregularly grown faces. The outlines of their cavities are irregular and generally of a ribbed–angular aspect.

Some of the inclusions coalesce with each other, forming a large cavity with an unbroken configuration and producing a single common gas bubble.

The size of these inclusions is generally 0.3–0.6 mm. The largest cavities may be up to 2–3 mm long, on their long axis.

The gas bubble occupies 20–25 per cent of the cavity's volume at room temperature. Such inclusions, developing in different periods of the crystal's growth, are oriented in the direction of the crystal's face growth and are parallel to each other.

In such manner, observations on morphology and formation of ordinary inclusions of mother liquor in synthetic quartz crystals serve somewhat to increase our understanding of the mechanisms of the formation of inclusions in general and to make use of the results we obtain in interpretations of inclusions in natural crystals.

BIBLIOGRAPHY

1. YERMAKOV, N. P., *Issledovaniya mineraloobrazuyushchikh rastvorov.* (Research in Mineral-forming Solutions.) Izd. Khar'kov. univ. 1950.
2. SUKHORSKII, R. F., Vliyaniye CO_2 na temperaturu gomogenizatsii gazovykh vklyuchenii. (The Influence of CO_2 on Homogenization Temperature of Gaseous Inclusions.) *Mineralog. sb. L'vov. geolog. obshch.* No. 7, 1953.
3. SHUBNIKOV, A. V., *Kak rastut kristally.* (How Crystals Grow.) Izd. Akad. Nauk SSSR, 1940.

Thermometric Investigations of Liquid Inclusions in Synthetic Quartz

G. M. SAFRONOV and V. YE. KHADZHI

THE results of the original experiments with homogenization of liquid inclusions in synthetic quartz crystals, together with the basic physicochemical parameters of the experiments with the growth of the corresponding crystals, are summarized in the following table.

THERMOMETRIC RESULTS ON INCLUSIONS IN SYNTHETIC QUARTZ CRYSTALS

No. in sequence	No. of determinations of homogenization	Average homogenization temperature of inclusions (°C)	Per cent gaseous phase in inclusions	Average temperature in zone of crystal growth (°C)	Average pressure at which inclusions were formed (atm)	Degree of filling of autoclave with solution	Discrepancy between temperatures of homogenization (°C)
1	39	312	35–38	327	230	62	15
2	30	268	20	321	335	80	53
3	27	266	20–25	320	340	75	54
4	27	270	20–23	325	340	77	55
5	21	268	20–25	330	350	75	62
6	69	272	20–21	337	425	78.6	65
7	45	246	20–21	316	550	79	70
8	6	259	20–22	330	600	77.4	71
9	24	246	20	330	525	—	84
10	12	263	20–22	315	320	78	52

In the derivation of the average homogenization temperatures, we employed the data on tubular inclusions because they were found to be the most reliable ones, in our work.

Determinations of homogenization temperatures and the temperatures of the return to the initial state for the most common inclusions, associated genetically with the flaky finely-crystalline aggregates of a solid phase, showed an appreciable discordance, even within the boundaries of one and the same growth zone. The juxtaposition of the results made it necessary to take into account the true temperatures of crystal growth during the experiments.

Originally, the temperature of the crystallization of quartz was determined by the means of thermocouples set at two or three different places outside the reactor. It was established later that the external temperatures differ appreciably from the internal ones. Consequently, it was necessary to correct all of the earlier temperature measurements, on the basis of data obtained with the inner thermocouples and by taking into account convection currents in the solution, in every experiment.

The temperatures were measured systematically, in the later experiments, by internal thermocouples. These were the only sufficiently objective measurements in the growth zone of the crystals. It developed that the crystals exist in different temperature environments, at the gradients of the experiment. In the growth zone of the upper crystals the temperature is somewhat higher than in the central part of the autoclave, while the lower crystals grow at temperatures still higher than the upper ones. Fluctuations of temperature of the crystal growth are generally within the range of 4–8°C, under normal conditions. The external temperature gradient is greater than the internal one.

It is difficult, of course, to measure the temperature of the growth for every individual crystal with absolute accuracy, inasmuch as it depends on convection currents circulating in the solution and is subject to small variations during the cycle of the growth.

As the result of experiments with homogenization of inclusions in synthetic quartz crystals produced under hydrothermal conditions, we established the following:

(1) The homogenization temperatures of inclusions are invariably lower than the temperatures of the crystal growth. The discrepancies range from 15 to 71°C, for the solutions at one and the same initial concentration.

(2) Temperatures at the start of the heterogenization of the inclusions on cooling are generally 3–6°C lower than the corresponding homogenization temperatures.

(3) All the inclusions were homogenized in the liquid phase, with the exception of those with anomalous phase ratios whose origins were as follows:

(a) "Beading" in healed fissures;

(b) Decrepitation of quartz in proximity of inclusions brought about by fluctuations of temperatures at the time of the crystal growth; in such circumstances, a part of the solution escapes into the fine fissures and there is an increase in the volume of the gas bubble;

(c) Disturbances in the hermetic sealing of inclusions associated with solid particles, so that the liquid phase runs into interstices between the finely crystalline aggregates of solid phases; after cooling, the volume of the gaseous phase exceeds appreciably its original volume and may be as high as 80–90 per cent of the total.

(4) Homogenization temperatures of normal inclusions in different growth zones of one and the same crystal are identical or are very close to each other.

(5) During heterogenization of inclusions, the gas bubble attains rapidly 25–50 per cent of its original volume, when cooling begins. The gas phase may appear simultaneously in several places, in the inclusions, on occasions (Fig 1).

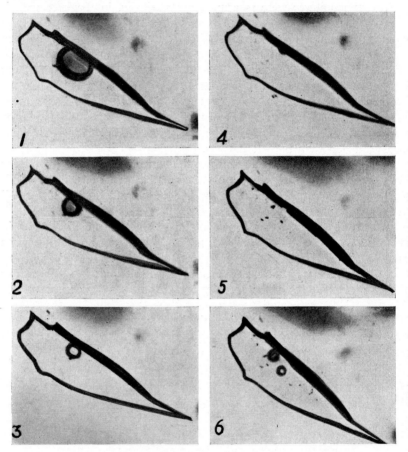

FIG. 1. Progress of homogenization of a liquid inclusion.
1. 20°C; *2*. 150°C; *3*. 185°C; *4*. 230°C; *5*. 234°C (homogenized); *6*. 229°C (the moment of heterogenization).

(6) The homogenization curves (the $T°C—F$ per cent diagram) are smooth and form a large angle with the ordinate at the moment of the homogenization. They resemble each other in all of our experiments (Figs. 2 and 3). It developed that such diagrams could be drawn only for

tubular inclusions, because it was not possible to measure exactly the volumes of the liquid and the gas in inclusions of all other shapes at the moment of their homogenization.

The results of a step-by-step survey of the homogenization process in spindle-shaped inclusions are presented in Fig. 4.

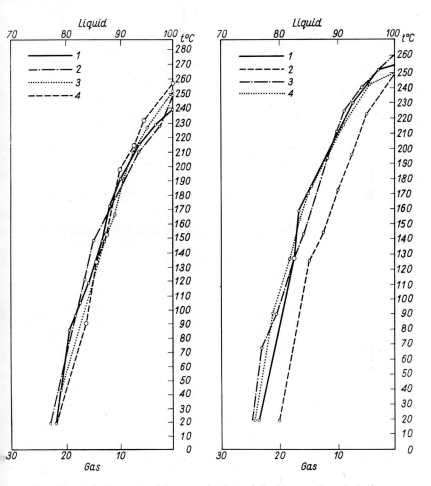

FIGS. 2 and 3. Progress of homogenization of liquid two-phase inclusions in synthetic quartz crystals.

(7) There is a noticeable difference between the homogenization temperatures of inclusions in different crystals produced in one and the same experiment, because of the temperature differences between the lower, the central, and the upper sections of the autoclave.

(8) The volume of the liquid phase in inclusions corresponds to the degree of filling of the reactor by the original solution, unless the inclusions were subjected to secondary modifications.

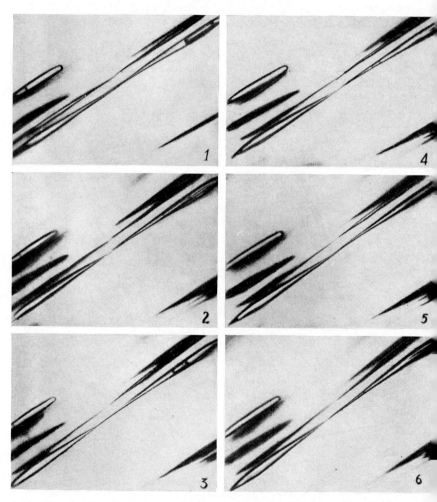

Fig. 4. Progress of homogenization of a spindle-shaped inclusion piercing the seed.

1. 20°C; *2.* 127°C; *3.* 191°C; *4.* 239°C; *5.* 253°C (homogenization); *6.* 247°C (beginning of heterogenization)

Discrepancies between the phase ratios in the inclusions and in the autoclaves are insignificant and are produced by the following variables; changes in the temperature and the solution density at different sites in the growth zone; errors in the volume measurements at the time of filling of the autoclaves and expansion of the autoclaves on heating; errors in determinations of phase ratios in the inclusions, a very difficult operation, in the instance of intricately shaped vacuoles, as previously discussed. The discrepancies vary from 1 to 3 per cent in the vast majority of cases, and do not exceed 5–6 per cent.

Measurements of the phase ratio were particularly exact in the case of tubular inclusions in the "skeletal" growth zones. The homogenization curves (Figs. 2, 3) are based on these very inclusions. The volume of the gas phase in cavities containing tubular-elongated inclusions was measured with the accuracy of up to 2 per cent.

The range of applicability of thermometric investigations in genetic mineralogy, for the purpose of determining the true temperatures, may be expanded only after we shall have found reliable correction coefficients for the homogenization temperatures and, as the matter of top priority, corrections for the pressure. Hence the thermometry and the barometry of inclusions are inseparably bound together. Until 1955, theoretical structures in microthermometric and microbarometric research in liquid and gaseous inclusions were based primarily on thermodynamic properties of pure water. For example, Ingerson made a diagram of corrections of homogenization temperatures for pressure by the means of the PT diagram for water. Such data, however, may be employed for obtaining the true temperatures only in a limited number of cases involving two-phase inclusions at low concentrations.

It has become established by this time that many inclusions contain concentrated aqueous solutions chiefly of alkali and alkaline earth chlorides. It is essential therefore to investigate the thermodynamic properties of the included solutions so as to obtain corrections for the homogenization temperatures, in order to determine the true temperatures of formation of minerals.

Research in thermodynamics of concentrated aqueous solutions was conducted at the Institute of Crystallography, Academy of Sciences of the U.S.S.R.

Successes in the progressive development of the synthesis of several minerals and, first of all, of quartz make it possible now to compare directly the thermometric results on inclusions with the temperatures of crystal growth, i.e. to make a real approach to the derivation of corrections for the pressure applicable to the homogenization temperatures.

It seemed to be essential to compare the differences between the true temperatures of crystal growth and the observed homogenization temperatures with the corresponding corrections for the pressure derived from the ratios of the thermodynamic parameters of the original solution.

The true magnitude of the correction may be determined, in every individual case, from the experimental data obtained in the synthesis of crystals under hydrothermal conditions. However, errors in the measurements of temperatures and especially of pressures during the experiment, while not interfering with the correct analysis of the characteristics of the crystal growth, preclude, so far, the construction of a PT diagram suitable for making corrections for the pressure at different temperatures.

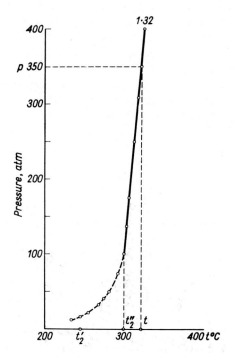

FIG. 5. Dependence of pressure on temperature in solution No. 1 at the coefficient of filling at 0.76 (Experiment No. 65).

For example, in one of the experiments, the correction of the homogenization temperature was calculated from the 1.32 isochor (with the coefficient of filling at 76 per cent (Fig. 5). The temperature ranged between 325 and 335°C in the corresponding zone of crystal growth during the experiment. The mean homogenization temperature of the inclusions in the quartz crystal was 254°C. Thus the correction may be as great as 70–80°C, more than three times as great as the theoretically derived correction for the pressure of pure water which equals 22°C under the conditions of the experiment.*

---

* In heating the inclusions, the authors used an air-heated non-hermetic thermochamber. The observed homogenization temperatures, in such chambers, are generally about 40° C too low. Thus the corrections for pressure and concentration of the included solutions should be only 30–40°C, (Editor) [N.P.Ye.].

It is not possible to make a direct comparison between these corrections, because the homogenization temperature of the solution in the autoclave cannot be exactly determined from the 1.32 isochor of the *PT* diagram (Fig. 5). One may merely remark, in general, that the isochor's field section [i.e., that part of the isochor—Ed.] in which the temperature coefficient of the pressure acquires a constant meaning, corresponding to the homogenization of the solution in the autoclave, lies in the area of temperatures exceeding the homogenization temperatures.

For the sake of a further refinement in the problem of interest, production of large-volume artificial inclusions is being undertaken, in order to carry out careful quantitative analyses of the captured mother liquor. This will make it possible, in all probability, to introduce more exactness into the corrections of temperature.

Application of Mineralothermometric Analysis in Studies of the Origins of Certain Gold Ore Deposits in Ural

L. I. KOLTUN

THE thermometric method of study of mineral-forming solutions preserved in minerals in the form of gaseous and liquid inclusions helps our orientation in certain problems in the origin of complex endogenic deposits.

The present study is one of the first attempts at a determination of genetic characteristics of two deposits of gold ore in Ural, the Berezovskoye (Berezovka) and the Kochkarskoye (Kochkar) by the thermometric method developed by Yermakov [4].

I. BEREZOVSKOYE

Paleozoic rocks of various origins occur in the geologic structures of this gold district. Sedimentary rocks, effusives with their tuffs, and intrusive bodies of diverse composition are developed extensively. The sediments and the effusives occupy about equal areas in the district. They are together in fairly steep folds and are cut by various intrusions: gabbro, quartz diorites, plagiogranites, and granites.

The earliest ultrabasic rocks—peridotites, pyroxenites, etc.—are now almost completely serpentinized. The granites, the plagiogranites, and the gabbros outcrop on the surface, as stock-like bodies, and are associated with ancient faults.

The mineralization of the district is associated with vein intrusion (dikes) or granitic rocks. These dikes are elongated rectilinearly, as slab-like bodies, 4–5 m thick, on the average; they cut through all of the rock here enumerated. The dikes are classified in four groups, depending on their age relationships, depositional features, and compositions [3].

The ore bodies are situated mainly in the granitic dikes and partially in the host rocks of the dikes in which they constitute a system of quartz veins accompanied by fairly severe alteration of the rocks in contact with the veins. Depending on their position in space and on morphologic characteristics, the veins are divided into two large groups: the first group is found only inside the granitic dikes, barely showing outside the dike

[426]

boundaries; the second group consists of the veins situated entirely in the host rocks of the dikes.

All of the veins are subdivided into two formations, on the basis of their mineralogic composition [7]; the early one—quartz–scheelite–tourmaline—and the late one—quartz–gold–pyrite. The early formation includes all of the veins in the granitic dikes and most of the veins in the host rocks. The late formation includes only some of the veins in the host rocks of the dikes.

The quartz–scheelite–tourmaline veins, in contrast with the quartz–gold–pyrite veins, are poorly developed in the district. They are found locally outside the dikes where their grouping produces independent vein fields. There is no particular variety in the mineralogic composition of the quartz–scheelite–tourmaline veins. Their principal minerals are quartz, scheelite, and tourmaline; their subordinate minerals are ankerite, muscovite, and sulfides (chiefly pyrite).

The vein-filling quartz has a platy structure whose existence is contingent on the presence of very thin inter-layers of sericite inside the veins and parallel to their contact with the host rocks. Such configuration of the quartz is typical of the veins of the early formation.

The quartz–gold–pyrite veins are the main objects of exploitation in the district. This is especially the case with veins inside the dikes. They are overflowing with a variety of ore minerals, the most prominent ones being pyrite, galena, tetrahedrite, chalcopyrite, pyrrhotite, sphalerite, magnetite, aikenite, gersdorfite, scheelite, gold, etc. In addition to quartz, the non-ore minerals include ankerite, calcite, tourmaline, muscovite, etc.

The bulk of gold in the primary ores is tied to the sulfides; some gold is present independently, as very fine veinlets in the quartz.

The character of the vein-filling is indicative of a filling of open fissures. The quartz is found growing on the fissure walls, leaving an empty space in the center, occasionally, which is filled with crystals of quartz, pyrite, galena, etc. Formation of the veins took place in several successive stages each of which is characterized by definite paragenetic complexes of minerals. According to the assertions of the investigators [7], these stages are separated from each other by shifts within the mineral-forming process.

The following stages of mineralization were identified: (1) deposition of quartz and ankerite; (2) deposition of the bulk of the sulfides; (3) the stage of finely granular pyrite and of anomalous "fibrous" quartz; (4) the calcite stage.

The vein-filling in the quartz–gold–pyrite formation was preceded by the alteration of the hanging wall which was accomplished also in four stages. It developed that the two later ones were contemporaneous with the vein-filling process.

Inclusions of the mineral-forming solutions were studied in transparent and semi-transparent minerals from the quartz-ore veins of both the late and the early formations. Quartz from different stages of the mineralization, as well as ankerite, calcite, and tourmaline were the principal test materials.

Two varieties of quartz were fairly definitely indicated in the quartz–scheelite–tourmaline veins: a milky-white "oily" one, filling the marginal parts of the veins, and a semi-transparent granular one, in the central parts of the veins where it is present together with ankerite, tourmaline, and other minerals. The quartz selvage of the vein is platy or, more rarely, massive, and is associated exclusively with fine-scaly muscovite or with greenish-gray scheelite. The layered structure of the quartz appears to be related to the layer-by-layer metasomatic replacement of the host rocks.

The milky-white "oily" quartz is filled to overflowing with an abundance of small microscopic inclusions. These inclusions show a fair variety of phase volumes and quantity*—indications of variations in the solutions *active in the deposition and the re-working of the vein quartz* during a long period of time, in the formation of the veins. Three principal inclusion types can be distinguished:

(1) Essentially-gaseous two-phase inclusions;

(2) Two-phase liquid inclusions;

(3) Three-phase mixed inclusions with carbon dioxide.

There is no visible orderly relationship in the distribution of these inclusions. They form chains, parallel to the "cleavage" of the quartz in fissures traversing the vein quartz in various directions, and they form irregularly outlined accumulations in different sections. It is extremely difficult to ascertain the genetic affilations of the inclusions of these different types.

We examined inclusions from the selvages toward the vein's center so as to obtain a view of temperatures of the later solutions which were depositing the vein quartz and reacting with the earlier quartz of the vein

A prepared section of quartz in contact with the host rock showed al of the inclusion groups here enumerated.

The essentially-gaseous inclusions were distinguished by their constant phase ratios, in that particular section 70–65 per cent of their volume is occupied by the gas and 30–35 per cent by the liquid. They are homo genized as in type II, in the gaseous phase, at 420–370°C.

There is more variety among the two-phase liquid inclusions in the quartz. Their phase ratios vary depending on variations in their homo genization temperatures: 270, 245, 225, 187°C, and lower.

---

* Probably, "number of inclusions per unit space" is meant [V.P.S.].

The essentially-gaseous inclusions are relatively scarce, more so than any other inclusion group. Accumulations of them are found chiefly in the contact zones; they could not be found in parts of the vein remote from the contact.

Liquid inclusions are observed in all parts of the quartz veins. Depending on the liquid–gas phase ratio and the homogenization temperature, these inclusions may be separated into two groups: the high temperature group, with the homogenization temperatures at 320–220°C, and the relatively low-temperature one, homogenizing between 190 and 140°C.

The low-temperature liquid inclusions (190–140°C) in the laminar "oily" quartz are definitely secondary. Most of them are found in fissures *some of which cut across several "layers" of quartz.*

The high-temperature liquid inclusions (320–220°C) appear to be primary, in certain parts of the layered vein quartz.

On a consideration of all of the inclusions in the layered quartz, one may arrive at a conclusion to the effect that this quartz was produced in two stages: by the action of gaseous solutions responsible for the deposition only of the earliest quartz layers (2 or 3 layers) and in the hydrothermal stage, in the wake of the pneumatolytic stage, when the remainder of the quartz layers was deposited, together with all of the semi-transparent granular quartz filling the cores of the veins and its associated ankerite and tourmaline.

As to the solutions from which the scheelite, the invariable associate of the vein quartz, was deposited—the problem is still obscure. Unfortunately, we could find no inclusions whatsoever in the scheelite, not in a single specimen, that could give an idea regarding the state of aggregation of the scheelite-producing solutions. True, we did find some extremely fine, entirely black pinpoint inclusions in a whole series of thin sections of the scheelite suggestive, most likely, of an essentially-gaseous filling.

The semi-transparent granular quartz and the associated ankerite are found together with the layered quartz of the veins, in the filling of the central parts of the veins. This quartz, like the layered oily one, contains an overabundance of inclusions among which we distinguish the liquid, the two-phase, and the complex three-phase ones with liquid carbon dioxide. The gaseous varieties are *absent* in the semi-transparent granular quartz.

Two-phase liquid inclusions homogenizing at 270–170°C are the primary ones, in the instance of the semi-transparent vein quartz. Its liquid inclusions, homogenizing at lower temperatures, are typical of a late stage of mineral genesis in which there was a deposition of some vein quartz, some quartz crystals (in the small cavities), and of the sulfides of Fe, Cu, Zn, Pb, etc. The inclusions with the low homogenization temperatures are secondary, in the case of the semi-transparent granular quartz. All of the three-phase inclusions with carbon dioxide are also secondary.

We succeeded in determining the homogenization temperatures only in twenty one of the thirty four inclusions. All of the determined temperatures are between 280 and 252°C. They homogenized in the liquid phase, as in type I.

It proved to be impossible to distinguish between primary and secondary inclusions in the extremely fine crystals of tourmaline. No fissuring could be detected in these crystals, so that most of the inclusions, not abundant in the mineral, are probably of primary origin.

Ankerite stands next to quartz, quantitatively, in the quartz–scheelite–tourmaline veins. It fills mainly the central parts of the veins and, more rarely, forms small independent veinlets in the hanging wall.

The ankerite forms sharp rectilinear contacts with the granular quartz and only very rarely—mutually intergrown aggregates. The ankerite is represented by crystalline masses in which the crystals are variously oriented. Some well-faceted rhombohedral crystals, slightly ferruginized on the surface, are found fairly often in the smaller cavities. Some of them have weakly expressed zonal structures.

The color of the ankerite is yellowish, yellowish gray, or, more rarely, grayish white. The mineral has an over-abundance of inclusions among which the two-phase liquid ones (the preponderant group) and the three-phase ones with carbon dioxide are distinguished. All these inclusions are characteristically small: 0.01–0.1 mm, and their shapes are highly diversified. Both the liquid inclusions of aqueous solutions and the three-phase inclusions with carbon dioxide are primary. The latter ones contain small but nearly constant proportions of liquid carbon dioxide, generally not over 5–8 per cent of the inclusion's volume. This carbon dioxide was dissolved in the hydrothermal mineral-forming solution, it appears.

The secondary inclusions are also liquid two-phase and three-phase ones with carbon dioxide.

Their shapes are the same as of the primary inclusions, in the majority of the cases, but their clear-cut association with fissures reveals their origin. There are more of the secondary than of the primary inclusions in the ankerite. The secondary inclusions homogenize within a very wide range: 200–90°C.

Short prismatic crystals of quartz may be encountered in cavities of the druses. These crystals are characteristic of the stage of mineral genesis in the course of which there was a deposition of small quantities of the sulfides (chiefly pyrite) that are found in the quartz–scheelite–tourmaline veins.

Inclusions are very common in the quartz. Its primary inclusions, the two-phase liquid ones, homogenize at 160–122°C, as in type I. Its secondary inclusions, the two-phase liquid and the three-phase ones with carbon dioxide, homogenize at 130–82°C. In addition to the primary and the secondary inclusions, some pseudo-secondary inclusions are also present, with homogenization temperatures of 132–144°C.

The quartz–scheelite–tourmaline veins are products of, first, pneumatolytic solutions and, next, of hydrothermal solutions.

In addition to quartz, the hydrothermal solutions deposited the high-temperature early tourmaline, possibly scheelite, and, after that, ankerite and the sulfides. This hydrothermal stage of mineral genesis consisted of two sub-stages: the sub-stage of finely granular semi-transparent quartz with tourmaline, and the sub-stage of ankerite with well-faceted quartz and sulfides.

The quartz–gold–pyrite veins are accompanied by halos of altered rocks. The alteration of the hanging wall cannot be considered independently from the mineralization itself, the process of the formation of the quartz-ore veins. The vein type of mineral genesis is accompanied inevitably by alteration of rocks in the hanging wall. The intensity of such alteration, next to the veins, depends on properties of the host rocks themselves as well as properties of the ore-forming solutions. The near-vein alteration, now visible, is the result of a long circulation of the ore-bearing solutions. It is for that very reason that the formation of the vein rock itself is heterochronous, so that its grains contain inclusions of different types by which the different stages of the mineralization are characterized.

We succeeded in differentiating three genetic varieties of quartz phenocrysts* in the altered rocks—the berezites—on the basis of our inclusion studies. The first and the earliest ones contain only "dry" gaseous inclusions; the second ones, intermediate in regards to the time of their formation, contain two-phase essentially-gaseous inclusions; the third and the latest ones contain two-phase liquid inclusions. Inclusions of the first two types were not detected in the quartz from the later quartz–pyrite formation.

The phenocrysts with the "dry" gaseous inclusions are the earliest ones. This is shown clearly in Fig. 1, where both varieties of the quartz are present in one and the same thin section. The quartz with the essentially-gaseous inclusions embays the earlier quartz produced by the "dry" gases and forms with the latter an uneven, tortuous, dentate contact.

The few measurements of homogenization temperatures of the two-phase essentially-gaseous inclusions, intermediate in regards to the time of their formation, show that the quartz-depositing solutions were in the gaseous state and that their temperatures were considerably above 420°C.

It is difficult to estimate the temperatures at which the quartz phenocrysts, with the earliest "dry" gases in their inclusions, were really formed.

---

* "Vkraplenniki", somewhat loosely translated here as phenocrysts [Ed.].

One may merely suppose that the temperatures of their parent solutions were higher still.

The inclusions characterizing the quartz phenocrysts of the third type—the two-phase liquid inclusions—homogenize in the liquid phase at 260–210°C. The quartz phenocrysts are closely associated with the vein quartz of the gold–pyrite formation. Complex inclusions with carbon dioxide are particularly well developed here, among the secondary inclusions, and so are the two-phase liquid inclusions that homogenize at relatively low temperatures.

FIG. 1. Inclusions in phenocrysts in altered rocks (berezites). A. The early quartz with inclusions of "dry" gases; B. The late quartz with essentially-gaseous inclusions.

Thus the process of transformation of granitic rocks into berezites, as a whole, cannot be fitted into a rigid temperature framework. This process was of a very long duration, beginning with pneumatolytic action which was succeeded by the action of hydrothermal solutions whose temperatures varied from the very high ones at the start, such as 450°C and higher, to about 100–150°C and lower still.

As pointed out by Borodayevskii [2] and confirmed by our investigations, the quartz–gold–pyrite veins were produced in four successive stages of the mineral genesis: (1) the stage of vein quartz I, pyrite I, and ankerite; (2) the stage of quartz II with the bulk of the sulfides; (3) the stage of finely granular pyrite with "fibrous" quartz; (4) the stage of calcite.

As we showed, the formation of quartz and pyrite in the first stage, in the veins, was contemporaneous with the production of the third group of quartz phenocrysts.

In the same stage, together with the quartz and the pyrite, there was a deposition of ankerite, tourmaline, muscovite, pyrrhotite, violarite, gersdorffite, hematite, etc.

Ankerite, millerite, gersdorffite, and tourmaline are absent in the veins inside the dikes, but are widespread in the veins outside the dikes.

The differences in the mineralogic composition of veins inside and outside the dikes, but belonging to one and the same quartz–gold–pyrite formation, are related to the somewhat dissimilar environments of their development. We shall consider this topic in a greater detail, in the description of inclusions in the minerals from both kinds of the veins.

Quartz of the first stage of mineralization in the veins is granular or, more rarely, massive. It accounts for the bulk of the vein. This quartz contains two main kinds of inclusions: two-phase liquid, and complex ones, with carbon dioxide. The latter ones are more abundant, but the two-phase liquid inclusions are the primary ones, for the given stage of the quartz.

The highest homogenization temperatures of the primary inclusions in the vein quartz of the first stage of mineralization did not exceed 270°C. As a whole, however, the range of these homogenizations is between 270 and 180°C. There are certain trends in the homogenization temperatures that depend on the depth.

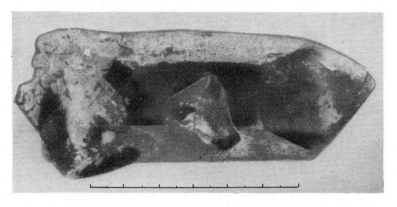

FIG. 2. Crystals of quartz from 112 m depth.

Let us consider now some concrete examples of variations in the temperature of the solutions, in the stage here discussed, as influenced by the depth of the deposition of the quartz-gold veins. Figures 2 and 3 show two crystals of quartz, geologically contemporaneous in their origin, and of about the same size, but taken from different depths: the first one (Fig. 2) at 112 m below the present surface of the ground and the second one (Fig. 3) at a depth of 165 m. Two zones, corresponding to two successive stages of mineralization, are noticeable in each crystal. The inner zone corresponds to the quartz–pyrite stage; the outer one—to the stage when the main bulk of the remaining sulfides was deposited.

FIG. 3. Crystals of quartz from 162 m depth.

The inner zone of the quartz crystal from 162 depth contains primary two-phase liquid inclusions homogenizing at 260–205°C. This one crystal, of course, cannot be taken as representative of the entire temperature range of the solutions of the first stage of mineralization, because its nucleation does not necessarily coincide with the accession of the initial portion of the solutions, especially since the crystal is growing on top of the previously formed thin layer of vein quartz belonging to the same stage of the mineralization. On the other hand, the upper temperature limit of the solutions is not particularly important here, inasmuch as it may be ascertained by examining the vein quartz. The major importance lies in the fact that the minimum temperature of the solutions, in the first stage of the mineralization and at the 162 m depth, was 205°C. Inclusions homogenizing at 205–208°C are encountered in the topmost parts of the crystal's inner zone, at its contact with the outer zone. No primary inclusions homogenizing at lower temperatures could be found by us in the inner zone of the crystal.

Two-phase liquid inclusions homogenizing at 270–275°C were discovered in the vein quartz on top of which the test crystal grew.

It is evident therefore, by inclusions in the quartz crystal and in the vein quartz, that the lowest temperature of the hydrothermal solutions in the first stage of the mineralization and at the depth of 162 m was fluctuating in the range of 275–205°C.

There is a great abundance of two-phase liquid inclusions and of complex inclusions with carbon dioxide in the gray inner zone of the quartz crystal from the 112 m depth (Fig. 2).

The primary two-phase inclusions in that zone homogenize at 235–182°C. The inclusions are generally associated with certain definite crystallographic components of the crystal, so that they are relatively easily distinguished from secondary and primary–secondary inclusions situated chiefly in fractures in the crystal. The lower temperature of the solutions, as established for the crystal's inner zone, is 182°C, in this particular crystal, i.e. 23°C lower than for the crystal from the 162 m depth.

The highest homogenization temperatures of inclusions in the vein quartz from the 112 m level were found to be 265–270°C, resembling the homogenization temperatures of inclusions in the vein quartz from the 162 m level. The difference amounts to some 5–10°C.

Thus temperatures of the solutions from which the deposition of vein quartz took place, together with the formation of some quartz crystals, fluctuated between 275 and 205°C at the 162 m depth. The solutions acting at a shallower depth (112 m) had a lower temperature during the same stage of mineralization: 270–182°C.

Homogenization temperatures of inclusions in the synchronous quartz from different depths of the deposit show only insignificant differences. However, one may be justified in the belief, on the basis of even the single example cited here, that the quartz-ore veins at still deeper levels of the deposit were produced at some still higher temperatures. By reasoning from the rate of cooling of the solutions within the examined range of depth, one may assume that the mother liquor's temperatures at the deeper levels of the deposit (212 and 262 m) were respectively 15 and 30°C higher than the temperature at the 162 m level.

The slight increase in the minimum temperatures of formation of the quartz-ore veins with depth, as indicated by inclusions, gives us every reason to believe that ores, just as rich in gold and sulfides as the ores at the shallower depths, may be discovered at deeper horizons, inasmuch as there was no drastic change in the mutually interrelated factors of the mineral genesis in the vertical direction.

The outer zones of the crystals are relatively thin: not over 1 cm in the crystals' termination.

The outer zone of the quartz crystal from the 162 m depth was formed when the solution's temperature was falling from 170 to 140°C while the outer zone of the crystal from the 112 m depth was formed from solutions whose temperature was changing from 155 to 130°C.

The succession of solution temperatures at which these two crystals were formed are represented in Fig. 4.

As shown in Fig. 4, the differences between the temperatures of the solutions, in their dependence on the depth, are clearly traceable not only in the first stage of the mineralization but also in its second stage, the stage when the quartz bearing the bulk of the sulfides was deposited. As to the quartz of the quartz–gold–pyrite formation, outside the dikes, it was formed at higher temperatures, judging by the inclusions of mineral-forming solutions. The lower temperature boundary of that quartz is between 220 and 210°, i.e. is about the same as for the veins inside the dikes.

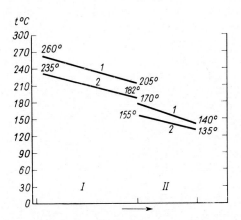

FIG. 4. Diagram of temperature regime of crystal-forming solutions at 162 m (*1*) and at 112 meters (*2*) depths.
I. Inner zones of crystals; *II*. Outer zones of crystals

As previously stated, tourmaline and ankerite are found together with quartz, alongside the ore minerals. Thin greenish fine crystals of tourmaline "pierce" the quartz and the ankerite in various directions.

We examined inclusions in the tourmaline crystals from only a single quartz vein (from the 162 m level). A few measurements of the homogenization temperatures, in inclusions in individual crystals, indicated 270–245°C as the lowest range of temperatures of formation of tourmaline, which was practically analogous to the tourmaline temperatures in the quartz–scheelite–tourmaline veins. It appears that both tourmalines were formed at about the same time.

The two-phase liquid inclusions homogenizing at 262–184°C are definitely primary for the tourmaline. The secondary inclusions in fractures in the mineral indicate much lower temperatures and even single-phase liquid inclusions are found among them.

The thermometric data show that the ankerite that fills the quartz–gold–pyrite veins was separated from hot aqueous solutions in the minimum temperature range of 262–184°C, i.e. at the same temperatures as the ankerite in the quartz–scheelite–tourmaline veins. Most likely, the ankerite in both of these formations was produced at the same time.

During the second stage, in addition to the quartz and the second generation of pyrite, there was also deposition of scheelite (insignificant quantities), tetrahedrite, galena, sphalerite, chalcopyrite, aikinite, and gold. We touched upon the inclusions in quartz of that stage in our description of the quartz crystals. We pointed out at that time that the crystals have two clearly defined growth zones, an inner and an outer one, and that the outer zone corresponds to the stage in which the separation of quartz II and of the bulk of the sulfides took place.

The second stage of mineralization is separated from the preceding one by intra-mineralization changes which cause adhesions of fragments of quartz, ankerite, and other minerals at the junction of the two growth zones of the crystals.

A fairly large quantity of inclusions is found both in the vein quartz and in the quartz crystals produced in the second stage of mineralization.

The primary inclusions belong to the two-phase liquid type. There are variations in their shape and size. Their homogenization temperatures vary from 160 to 105 or 110°C, for a given stage. This range was ascertained particularly reliably in the case of the well-faceted quartz.

The secondary and the pseudo-secondary inclusions in healed fissures in the mineral are represented by the following varieties: two-phase liquid inclusions homogenizing at 130–78°C; three-phase ones with liquid carbon dioxide; and single-phase liquid inclusions.

Before proceeding with the characteristics of the minerals of the third stage of mineralization, let us consider the pressures in the deposit at the time of deposition of the sulfides.

V. A. Kalyuzhnyi [6] undertook the work on the determination of pressures by means of combining the diagrams of state for CO_2 and water in a single plane, at the Laboratory of Thermometric Analysis of the University of L'vov.

An adjacent occurrence, in the same zone of a crystal or in the same fissure in a crystal, of two syngenetic inclusions produced under identical conditions and containing liquid carbon dioxide and an aqueous solution is an absolute prerequisite for the determination of pressure by Kalyuzhnyi's method.

Formation of such inclusions is explained by the presence of carbon dioxide as an immiscible solution. Under such circumstances, the temperature and the pressure are determined by the point of intersection of the two isochors in the field of the combined PT diagram (Fig. 5). V. A. Kalyuzhnyi made use of the data of Amagat in his construction of the diagram of state for CO_2 which made it possible for him to calculate for each isochor the specific volume, the zero-ordinate of the phase equilibrium curve, and the per cent filling with liquid CO_2 at 0°C. These results are summarized in the table accompanying Fig. 5. The diagram for water is based on the data of Smith, Keys, and Bridgeman.

We found two pairs of such inclusions in the two crystals from the deposit here described. One of each pair contained carbon dioxide and the other one an aqueous solution. On heating the inclusion with CO_2, in the first crystal (a steam bath was used), the homogenization occurred at 24°C. By such means we determined the starting point of the CO_2 isochor.

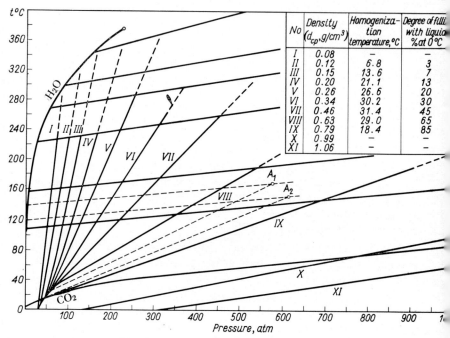

No	Density $(d_{cp}, g/cm^3)$	Homogenization temperature, °C	Degree of filling with liquid % at 0°C
I	0.08	–	
II	0.12	6.8	3
III	0.15	13.6	7
IV	0.20	21.1	13
V	0.26	26.6	20
VI	0.34	30.2	30
VII	0.46	31.4	45
VIII	0.63	29.0	65
IX	0.79	18.4	85
X	0.99	–	
XI	1.06	–	

FIG. 5. Combined PT diagram for water and CO_2.

The inclusion of an aqueous solution, next to the other one, homogenized at 138°C. The starting point of the water isochor was established accordingly. Point A_1, the intersection of the two isochors, characterizes the conditions at which both of the inclusions were formed. Hence, by the data we obtained, the healing of the fissure *took place at the true temperature of 170°C and at 585 atm pressure.* Correction for the pressure was 32°C, in this particular case.

In the second specimen, the inclusion with CO_2 homogenized in the liquid phase at 22.5°C and the liquid aqueous inclusion was homogenized at 120°C. The coordinates of the point of intersection, A_2, show accordingly the correction of 35°C for the obtained pressure of 600 atm which was effective at the time of the mineralization, i.e. about the same correction as for the first specimen. It should be pointed out, in this connection, that the inclusions of liquid aqueous solution and of carbon dioxide were in crystals taken from different parts of the deposit and at a considerable distance from each other, but from one and the same level (horizon) of mineral genesis: the first one was from the Markovskaya shaft (112 m) and the second one—from Shaft No. 13 (also the 112 m horizon).

The results obtained make it possible to introduce appropriate corrections of the temperature for the effective pressure at the time of the crystallization of the quartz and of the bulk of the sulfides. If we assume that the average correction is 34°C, *the separation of the quartz and of the associated minerals* (sulfides and gold) *took place in the range of true temperatures of 193–139°C and at pressures of the order of magnitude of 600 atm.* Undoubtedly, both the temperature and the pressure were varying with the stage of mineralization and with depth, so that our correction obtained for the sulfide stage at the 112 m level must not be applied to the long process of the mineral formation in the deposit as a whole.

The deposit has only weak expressions of the stage of finely granular pyrite with fibrous quartz and of the calcite stage, the terminal one. The stage is characterized by the formation of a small quantity of finely granular pyrite and of the anomalous "fibrous" quartz by which the pyrite is cemented. As observed by Kutyukhin and N. I. and M. B. Borodayevskii [7], small quantities of tetrahedrite, galena, chalcopyrite and the associated gold were also separated in the course of that stage.

Examinations of sections of the "fibrous" quartz showed again the common two-phase liquid, single-phase liquid, and complex (with CO_2) inclusions. The two-phase liquid inclusions are primary for the quartz. The single-phase and the three-phase inclusions with CO_2 are secondary and are situated invariably in fissures.

The primary and the primary–secondary inclusions have irregular shapes and small dimensions (0.05–0.005 mm diameter). They homogenize at 124–70°C.

Vul'chin [3], by means of microchemical analyses of aqueous extracts, examined the composition of the inclusions in vein quartz belonging probably to the first substage of the hydrothermal stage. Insofar as this quartz abounded chiefly in the low-temperature secondary inclusions characteristic of the later substages of the mineralization, we decided to cite these data in brief right here, following the discussion of inclusions in minerals of the three main stages.

Concentrations of individual constituents were calculated by the equation derived by Vul'chin.

The calculated results, based on the quantitative determination of the solutes in the aqueous extracts, are presented in Table 1.

TABLE 1. ANALYSIS OF AQUEOUS EXTRACTS (IN PER CENT)

Sample No.	Cl⁻	SO₄⁻⁻	BO₃⁻⁻⁻	Na⁺	K⁺	Mg⁺⁺	Ca⁺⁺	Al+Fe +Mn	Atomic excess of cations	SiO₃⁻⁻ +CO₃⁻⁻ +OH⁻ %	Sum of salts %	Water %
20	4.93	0.79	2.84	3.72	1.20	0.08	1.85	2.00				
21	4.92	0.91	2.85	3.70	1.21	0.07	1.90	2.00				
22	4.95	0.80	2.86	3.68	1.10	0.08	1.91	2.00				
23	4.91	0.78	2.90	3.60	1.19	0.09	1.89	2.00				
24	4.96	0.90	2.89	3.62	1.20	0.08	1.85	2.00				
25	4.97	0.89	2.88	3.64	1.20	0.08	1.80	2.00				
Average	4.94	0.85	2.87	3.66	1.20	0.08	1.85	2.00				
Molecular quantities	0.140	0.009	0.048	0.160	0.031	0.003	0.046	0.050	0.093	10.02	31.49	68.31

Editor's note: On comparison of this table with the original reference (Vul'chin, 1953, Table 7, pp. 148–149), several numerical discrepancies were found. The table is given here as originally given by Vul'chin, except for the last three numbers on the right, which Koltun has recalculated; Vul'chin's original numbers here are 7.08, 24.53, and 75.47, respectively. Both Vul'chin's original analysis and Koltun's recalculation are obscure (E.R.).

Vul'chin's calculations showed atomic excesses of the cations over the anions. He believes that the principal anions compensating the excess are metasilicates and OH^-. However, the OH^- quantities are insignificant, with respect to SiO_3^{--}, so that practically all of the cation excess needs be compensated by SiO_3^{--}. Proceeding from the excess of the cations, we calculated the weight-per cent of SiO_3^{--} required for the balance of the analysis (Table 1). The sum-total of the salts becomes 31.49 per cent accordingly (the average of the sums in all samples).

Of course, chemical analyses of aqueous extracts of a definite aliquot of pulverized quartz, abundant in inclusions, give us only an average summary composition of the solutions by which the mineral was formed, including the solutions by which it was healed after its formation. However, even the data of this sort give us some kind of an idea about chemical composition of the mineral-forming solutions and the concentrations of their constituents.

As shown by the analyses, chlorides, sulfates, and borates play important roles in the solutions and seem to be conducive to mobilization and transfers of silica and metals in true solutions.

In the calcite stage, the terminal one of the endogenic mineral genesis, calcite is closely associated with pyrite, on occasions, and appears to be crystallized together with the pyrite.

A few inclusions, among which there are two-phase and single-phase liquid ones, were discovered in sections of calcite cut parallel to its cleavage planes. No inclusions with carbon dioxide could be detected. The two-phase liquid inclusions with a very small gas bubble homogenize at 75–62–56°C regardless of the source of the specimen.

It follows therefore that the terminal stage of the mineralization is characterized by very low temperatures of the hydrothermal solutions with the upper limit not over 75–100°C. As to the lower limit of the temperatures, it is less than 50°C, as indicated by the single-phase liquid inclusions.

The highly complex structure of the deposit, the presence of quartz-ore veins of various types filling fissures in the granitic dikes and in the host rocks, variations in mineralogical composition of the veins—all of that serves to complicate the analysis of the origin of the deposit, as a whole, and particularly the time–mineralization correlations.

Nevertheless, the results of the thermometric studies of the minerals, in conjunction with the geologic–structural and the mineralogic data, lead to the belief that there was no direct connection between the deposition of the ores and the formation of the granitic dikes so abundant in the district. The dikes had no particular influence on the development of the veins outside the dikes; they functioned merely as a mechanically favorable environment for the veins inside them, inasmuch as their previously developed fissures were eventually filled with the quartz-ore materials

TABLE 2. SEQUENCE OF MINERALIZATION AND TEMPERATURE REGIME OF SOLUTIONS DURING FORMATION OF THE BEREZOVKA DEPOSIT

Stages of mineralization	Sub-stages of mineralization	Transition*	Crystallization sequence of principal minerals	Temperature of solutions by inclusions (°C)
Pneumatolytic	Alterations of hanging wall		Quartz (metasomatic in berezites)	
		×		
	"Oily" quartz		Quartz ("oily") Muscovite Cassiterite Scheelite	410–380
		×		
	Quartz (milky-white) with ankerite and pyrite I		Quartz (milky-white vein and crystals) Tourmaline Ankerite Pyrite Gersdorffite Hematite	320–170
Hydro-thermal	Quartz with the bulk of the sulfides		Quartz Pyrite II Tetrahedrite Galena Sphalerite Chalcopyrite Aikinite Gold	170
		×		
	Finely granular pyrite with "fibrous" quartz		Pyrite III Quartz ("fibrous") Tetrahedrite II Galena II Chalcopyrite II Gold	80
		×		
	Calcite		Calcite Pyrite	50 (corrected for pressure)

Temperature scale (°C): 500 470 440 410 380 350 320 290 260 230 200 170 140 110 80 50 20

derived from the circulating solutions. The source of the ore-bearing solutions was a granitic magma; the granitoid dikes themselves were derivatives of the same magma.

The deposit's formation took place against a background of tectonic adjustments by which the stages and the substages of the mineralization were separated. Every stage of the mineralization is characterized by a definite complex of minerals which is indicative of changes in the chemical composition of the solutions, from stage to stage.

The sequence of the ore-forming process and the temperature regime for every discrete stage of the mineralization are represented in Table 2. As one may see in the table, the entire process of endogenic mineral genesis is clearly divided into two stages, the pneumatolytic and the hydrothermal ones, each of which, in turn, involves a series of substages separated from each other by shifts in the character of the mineralization.

The following facts were established for the Berezovka deposit accordingly, on the basis of studies of inclusions of mineral-forming solutions in its minerals:

(1) The formation of the deposit took place by stages, first as the result of pneumatolytic and, next, as the result of hydrothermal activities. The temperature of the solutions was falling from high to relatively low. The composition of the solutions was changing, from stage to stage, with the accompanying changes in the mineral complexes laid down by the solutions.

(2) The pneumatolytic stage may be divided into two sub-stages. The veins of the quartz–scheelite–tourmaline formation began to be formed in that stage.

(3) The hydrothermal stage of the mineral genesis is typical of the veins of both of the formations but its fullest expression is to be found in the veins of the quartz–gold–pyrite formation.

(4) Homogenization temperatures of inclusions in minerals belonging to one and the same phase of mineralization are somewhat higher for the deeper horizons of the deposit than for horizons situated near the present surface of the ground.

(5) The deposition of gold took place chiefly in the second sub-stage of the hydrothermal process, the mesothermal one, together with the sulfides. However, significant quantities of gold were precipitated also during the first and the third sub-stages of the hydrothermal stage, together with the pyrite.

II. KOCHKARSKOYE

The Kochkarskoye gold deposit was found to be the product of two successive intrusions of Varrisian plagiogranites and microcline granites into the body of a Paleozoic complex.

According to Ivanov's data [5], the two intrusions made their entries during different phases of the Varissian Cycle, so that they are not merely different facies of one and the same intrusion. The intrusion of microcline granites had its origin in the later phase of the mountain building.

Both groups of intrusions have their own vein series. The vein series of the plagiogranites never cut through the microcline granites, but the latter often cut through the vein bodies belonging to the plagiogranites.

The massif of the main ore field is represented by adamellite–grandiorite, the plagioclase rocks. The massif is in contact with the intrusion of microcline granites in the west and with a body of Paleozoic, more or less metamorphosed sedimentary, tuffaceous rocks and sediments in the east.

Vein rocks (dikes) are particularly well developed in the area of the deposit, where they are represented by melanocratic varieties with porphyroblastic and lepidoblastic structures. They consist of phlogopite, hornblende, actinolite, plagioclase, epidote, carbonates; apatite, sphene, scapolite, fluorite, and tourmaline are more rarely found. The rocks are mostly foliated, but locally are massive. Their deposition was in the form of vein-like bodies extending east to west and dipping steeply (60–90°).

The distribution of the dikes outside the main ore field has not been ascertained exactly. Within the main ore field, the dikes constitute a narrow elongated zone, 3–4 km broad and 7–10 km long, along the western contact of the massif. The characteristic features of the dikes are their well sustained thickness and their considerable linear extent. The character of the rocks has not yet been fully ascertained.

The ore bodies are quartz-ore veins localized in the topmost part of the plagioclase massif. They are associated with post-magmatically altered vein rocks which they follow conformably, inside as well as outside the dikes, and in the contacts of the dikes with their host rocks. The ore-quartz veins extend almost parallel [?], a little north-east or south-east of the line. Their length is appreciable and their dip is steep to nearly vertical.

Quartz is the principal vein mineral in all veins of the deposit. The deposition of quartz took place throughout the ore-forming process, from the earliest to the latest stages. Ankerite and calcite play a subordinate role; they are not found in every vein and their deposition was a characteristic feature only some short-term segments of the ore-forming process.

Several varieties of quartz, formed in different periods of the mineral genesis, are recognizable by their structural features and by their relations to other minerals. Pokrovskii [9] differentiates two basic types of the quartz: (a) metasomatic, the product of replacement of adamellite, and (b) a filling material of open fissures. The latter type is subdivided into several groups, depending on color, structure, and form of the solid inclusions, such as: dark-gray "cast" with extremely fine disseminated arsenopyrite (particularly conspicuous); gray quartz, granular, occasionally layered, with dense dissemination of arsenopyrite, pyrite, and other sulfides. Milky-white quartz, finely crystalline quartz, and opal are less common.

We shall consider in great detail the characteristics of these quartz groups, in the description of inclusions of the mineral-forming solutions. In the meanwhile, we must point out that the metasomatic quartz is the earliest one of all; it was followed by the gray massive quartz, the milky-white quartz, and, finally, by the finely crystalline quartz and opal.

Arsenopyrite, pyrite, chalcopyrite, galena, sphalerite, "dull ores", jamesonite, gold, albite, muscovite, epidote, tourmaline, sericite, etc., were co-precipitated with quartz in different stages of the mineral genesis.

Differences in the expression of ore and vein minerals, in one and the same kind of veins, brecciated structures and replacement structures, and a large number of other variables constitute evidence of the fact that the formation of ore veins in the deposit took place in stages and against a background of fairly frequent tectonic adjustments.

Two periods of mineralization, related to a successive entry of the two intrusions, were proved by the thermometric analysis: (a) the intrusion of plagiogranites and (b) the intrusion of microcline granites. Each of these two periods, in turn, consists of two stages: the pneumatolytic and the hydrothermal one.

At the onset of the first period in the formation of the deposit, there was an intensive alteration of the host rocks (quartzification). The quartzification was effective during both of the stages of the mineralization, and not in some single one, as shown by examination of quartz crystals embedded in the plagiogranites. Two varieties of quartz grains are recognizable fairly clearly by inclusions of the mineral-forming solutions: (a) the ones with inclusions of gas and (b) quartz grains containing two-phase liquid inclusions only.

Quartz grains with inclusions of gas are the earliest ones among the secondary formations. Since their contours are uneven and "saw-tooth" also in the altered rocks of the hanging wall of the deposit previously described,* they may be regarded as evidence of a partial solvent action by the late hydrothermal solutions.

Quartz grains with the liquid inclusions contain occasionally large quantities of extremely fine disseminated sulfides, chiefly arsenopyrite. Moreover, such quartz, alongside arsenopyrite, pyrite, and other sulfides, forms small veinlets in the plagiogranite and cuts through the quartz grains that contain the inclusions of gas.

Grains of pneumatolytic quartz with inclusions of gas amount up to

---

* Berezovskoye? [V.P.S.].

70 per cent of the total number of quartz grains examined in the quartzified plagiogranites.

Depending on the degree of filling with the liquid phase, we may identify several groups of inclusions: inclusions of "dry" gases, entirely gas-filled; inclusions with a very small proportion of the liquid phase (about 4 or 8 per cent); finally, inclusions in which the liquid phase occupies up to 30 per cent of the total volume. Inclusions containing 4 or 6 per cent liquid phase homogenize at 160–170°C; inclusions with up to 30 per cent liquid phase homogenize at 390–430°C.

Hydrothermal quartz containing primary liquid inclusions fills the interstices between the previously formed grains of quartz and of other minerals composing the plagiogranites.

Depending on their gas–liquid phase ratios, inclusions in the quartz grains are most highly varied. We find inclusions in which the liquid phase is in the vicinity of 50 per cent, by volume, as well as inclusions with up to 95 per cent of the liquid phase. Every possible variation is found between these two extremes. The phenomenon is explained by a superimposition of several successive stages of hydrothermal mineral genesis on the host granites.

The homogenization temperatures vary also within a wide range, depending on the phase ratios in the inclusions. The highest ones are up to 390 or 410°C; the lowest ones, 110–100°C.

Primary inclusions are not easily identified either in the gaseous or in the liquid group. However, the absence of included gas in many individual grains of quartz is an indication that such quartz was deposited from liquid solutions; as to its relation to the other quartz grains, it points to the fact that the quartz in question is later than the quartz with the included gas. Speaking of the temperature of formation of quartz in the metasomatic replacement of the plagiogranites, in general, one must bear in mind the appreciable duration of the replacement process operative throughout the period of circulation of the pneumatolytic as well as of the hydrothermal solutions.

Inclusions containing liquid carbon dioxide, fairly common in the embedded quartz of either type, also deserve our attention. Such inclusions are almost invariably associated with fine cracks cutting across the boundaries of several quartz grains. Liquid carbon dioxide occupies a relatively small volume in these inclusions, a fairly constant one at that (about 10–15 per cent on the average). The inclusions homogenize invariably as in type I, in the liquid phase; the liquid aqueous solution in the inclusions occupies invariably more than 50 per cent of the volume. Their homogenization temperature, however, is not the same; it varies from 340 to 280°C, as indicated by relatively few measurements.

The metasomatically altered rocks are pierced by fairly large veins filled with quartz-ore materials. Quartz in such veins is often heterogeneous. Here, the gray massive variety of quartz is conspicuous, generally free from ore, and another one, also gray "layered", but with large quantities of disseminated arsenopyrite and pyrite. The ore-free gray quartz may be absent, in places, so that the entire vein may be filled with the gray quartz with the sulfides.

Both of these varieties of quartz were produced not merely at different temperatures, but also from solutions at different states of aggregation, as shown by thermometric investigations. The gray massive quartz was deposited from gaseous solutions; the layered ore-bearing quartz from hydrothermal ones.

As a rule, the gray massive quartz fills marginal sections of the veins. It is saturated with a disseminated multitude of finest inclusions of other minerals in which we recognize biotite, actinolite, hornblende, etc. Ore minerals, such as pyrite and arsenopyrite, are also conspicuous in the quartz. They are epigenetic, however, and are found invariably inside the small fissures traversing the quartz in various directions.

The gray massive quartz contains, in addition to the solid inclusions, a vast quantity of gaseous and liquid inclusions of mineral-forming solutions. Although its liquid inclusions are secondary, they are numerically preponderant over the gaseous ones.

Primary inclusions in the massive vein quartz are of the essentially-gaseous type. They occur singly and are associated generally with the accessory minerals. Their shape is highly variable. Some of them are elongated and almost tubular; others—more rarely found—are shaped like negative crystals.

The essentially-gaseous inclusions are homogenized at 360–430°C in the thermochamber. Such inclusions, if they contain up to 30 per cent liquid phase, show *a point of inversion*, in their homogenization, which is generally 15–20°C below their homogenization temperature [4].

There is no change in the character of the inclusions in the gray massive quartz that could be related to the position of the veins in space. Inclusions in specimens from the northern and the southern sections of the deposit we had examined yielded identical results.

Analogous inclusions of essentially-gaseous type are found also in the quartz grains of the quartzified plagiogranites, even as previously stated. The quartzification and the vein-filling were simultaneous processes, the results of circulation of the same magmatic solutions. However, in the plagiogranites, one also finds quartz grains with inclusions of "dry" gas which are not to be found in the massive quartz of the veins. Relationships of such quartz grains with the others is suggestive of their earlier age. It follows therefore that the quartzification began somewhat ahead of the vein-filling and that transfers of silica were accomplished by "dry" gaseous solutions, in the early stages of the process.

The secondary liquid inclusions, proponderant numerically in the gray massive quartz, homogenize as in type I, at 270°C, and lower. All of the secondary inclusions with carbon dioxide explode on heating.

The gray layered quartz, brimful of inclusions of pyrite and arseno-pyrite, is easily distinguished from the gray massive quartz. The stage in which this quartz and the sulfides were deposited is separated from the preceding stage by tectonic movements that caused a severe fragmentation of the gray massive quartz. Consequently, one may observe, in many places, a cementation of the fragmented gray quartz with sulfide–quartz materials by which every possible fissure or cavity is also filled.

Moreover, as the result of tectonic movements, there has developed an entirely new system of fissures which were subjected to filling by the quartz–pyrite–arsenopyrite materials and, to some extent, by the light-colored semi-transparent quartz belonging to a later stage of the minerali-zation.

Thermometric investigations of the gray mineralized quartz from differ-ent sites and depths of the deposit had shown that this quartz was formed from hydrothermal solutions, unlike the quartz and the other minerals of the earlier stage. The quartz is brimful of two-phase liquid inclusions, alongside negligible numbers of complex inclusions containing carbon dioxide. Depending on spatial distribution of the veins, there is some variation in the character of filling of the inclusions and of the correspond-ing homogenization temperatures. Moreover, some definitely secondary gaseous inclusions, with the gaseous phase occupying up to 75 or 80 per cent of the volume, are also found in the quartz, in certain veins. The same phenomenon is observed also in the younger quartz which was deposited together with the sulfides of Pb, Zn, Cu, Fe, etc. As we shall see later on, the gaseous inclusions belong to a much later stage of mineralization, superimposed on the earlier ones, the stage characterized by the deposition of milky-white quartz, tourmaline, and others, the stage of *repeated pneu-matolysis,* in which the activities of gaseous solutions were resumed as the result of the entry of another intrusion into the deposit.

The deposition of ore-bearing quartz, as well as of pyrite and of arseno-pyrite, its invariable associates, took place from high-temperature hydro-thermal solutions (405–290°C), as shown by the examination of its primary inclusions.

Appreciable quantities of ankerite were laid down in the veins, during the formation of the grey ore-bearing quartz, and possibly later, in parts of the deposit (the east section). Pyrite and very small quantities of other minerals were deposited together with the ankerite. No arsenopyrite could be detected in the ankerite.

We did not succeed in determining exactly the relation of the ankerite to the ore-bearing gray quartz at the site. However, since both the quartz and the ankerite are cut by fine veinlets of light-colored milky-white quartz and sulfides, it stands to reason that the ankerite was deposited particularly during the stage of the ore-bearing gray quartz or, still more likely, in the course of some later phase of that stage.

Primary inclusions in the ankerite homogenize in the liquid phase at 300–222°C, as shown by the studies of many thin sections. There are no appreciable variations in the homogenization temperatures that could be related to the territorial distribution of the veins.

Secondary inclusions in the ankerite embrace a wide range of temperatures (from 170 to 60°C). They represent the later stages of the mineralization, as we shall presently see.

Three-phase inclusions, with carbon dioxide, are also prominent, among the others, in the ankerite. Some of them were heated in the thermochamber. The determined homogenization temperatures were as follows: 272, 270, 268, 262, 260, 252, and 248°C.

The thermometric data on quartz and ankerite here cited enable us, to some extent, to appraise the temperature regime of deposition of the sulfides, chiefly of arsenopyrite and pyrite, present in close association with quartz and ankerite.

As shown by the results already cited, the crystallization of quartz was effective within the minimum temperature range of 405–290°C. The ankerite crystallized at a lower temperature: 300–222°C. Industrial quantities of arsenopyrite are found only in paragenesis with the quartz, while pyrite, on the contrary, is evenly distributed between the quartz and the ankerite.

Thus the deposition of arsenopyrite took place chiefly from high-temperature solutions, with the lowest temperature of the order of magnitude of 400–300°C. As to the pyrite, its deposition was concurrent with the deposition of quartz as well as of ankerite, i.e. within the homogenization range of 405–222°C. We must point out that appreciable quantities of pyrite were deposited also in the later stages of the mineralization, at lower temperatures.

The next stage is the richest one, in the variety of its minerals. In addition to the semi-transparent quartz, it involves the deposition of large quantities of chalcopyrite, pyrite, sphalerite, galena, boulangerite, gold, tetrahedrite, jamesonite, and many other minerals. Their deposition is always in a definite sequence. According to Pokrovskii's studies [9], as well as by our observations, sphalerite and chalcopyrite are the first sulfides that crystallized. The chalcopyrite replaces arsenopyrite and pyrite—and also sphalerite, its predecessor but still belonging to the same stage. The tetrahedrite was formed later; it replaces the arsenopyrite in fine fissures. Gold was precipitated together with tetrahedrite. The tetrahedrite was replaced, in turn, by jamesonite, boulangerite, and galena. The chalcopyrite was converted into covellite and chalcocite.

As stated by Prokrovskii, the preceding stage of quartz–arsenopyrite is separated from the succeeding one by a resumption of the tectonic movements.

The deposition of sulfide minerals was accompanied by a precipitation of appreciable quantities of quartz. The quartz, most frequently, is light-colored, transparent, or semi-transparent.

The semi-transparent vein quartz, filling the core of the vein, alongside the sulfides, contains the following varieties of inclusions; two-phase, essentially-gaseous; complex, with carbon dioxide; finally, single-phase, liquid.

The essentially-gaseous inclusions are definitely secondary. They are situated invariably in fissures that cut the quartz in various directions. Their phase ratio is fairly constant, so that the "stringing-out" phenomenon, as described by Lemmlein [8], is not a suitable explanation. The essentially-gaseous inclusions homogenize in the gaseous phase at 440–460°C.

The high-temperature two-phase liquid inclusions should be regarded as primary, in the instance of the semi-transparent quartz. We examined them also in the fine quartz crystals filling the few cavities in the veins.

As a rule, inclusions in the vein quartz are very small, so that one may succeed in seeing them only at high magnifications. Their homogenization temperature ranges from 270 to 65°C. The vein quartz and the sulfides were formed within a narrower temperature range, since it was shown by studies of the inclusions in the quartz crystals that a large proportion of the two-phase liquid inclusions, homogenizing below 130°C, is of a secondary origin. All of the single-phase liquid inclusions situated in fissures cutting across boundaries of the quartz grains are secondary, beyond any doubt.

Consequently, formation of the semi-transparent and of the transparent vein quartz, as well as the precipitation of the entire series of sulfide minerals at the site, took place from hydrothermal solutions whose minimum temperature was falling from 270 to 130°C.

The first period of the mineralization was completed in the stage of the transparent and semi-transparent quartz and of the sulfides. The second period began in connection with the intrusion of the microcline granites, in the deposit's western section. This period was radically different from the first one, in the character of its mineralization, as we shall see later.

Deposition of milky-white quartz, tourmaline, and other minerals took place in the second (the post-ore) period of the formation of the deposit. The milky-white ore-free quartz is relatively weakly developed in the deposit. It occurs in veins as feeble "layers" overgrowing quartz and other minerals of the preceding stages of the mineralization or, in places, as the sole filling of thin veins. The milky-white quartz differs from the quartz of the earlier stages by the absence of the ore minerals ((sulfides) and by the presence of small quantities of muscovite, chlorite, biotite, and sericite. In some parts of the veins, the milky-white quartz is associated with tourmaline and epidote.

We examined inclusions of mineral-forming solutions in quartz from both the eastern and the western sections of the deposit.

Essentially-gaseous inclusions, with the gaseous phase occupying about 70 or 65 per cent of the volume, were discovered in samples of quartz from the western section, the one that lies *closest to the young intrusion of microcline granites.* They are weakly elongated, and even tubular, on occasions, and their size varies from a few thousandths to 0.04 mm. These inclusions occur singly, as a rule, and rarely as groups of two or three.

The essentially-gaseous inclusions in the milky-white quartz are primary. We could not find a single one of them in a fissure. It is difficult also to speak of their "stringing-out", for all such inclusions have the same gas–liquid phase ratio and no liquid inclusions can ever be found in their proximity.

The essentially-gaseous inclusions homogenize, in the thermochamber, as in type II, in the gaseous phase, often with a recognizable inversion point. The homogenization of most of them occurs between 420 and 470°C.

Only two-phase liquid inclusions and complex inclusions with carbon dioxide were detected in the milky-white quartz of the same stage, but from the *eastern section of the deposit, at a distance from the young intrusion.*

The primary two-phase liquid inclusions homogenized at 400–360°C. This temperature range is typical of primary inclusions in the milky-white quartz from the entire eastern section of the deposit.

Thus *the formation of the milky-white quartz was taking place synchronously both from pneumatolytic solutions* (the western section, next to the intrusion) *and from hydrothermal solutions* (the eastern section, remote from the intrusion of microcline granites). Temperature of the gaseous solutions was up to 500°C, it appears, but it cannot be determined exactly by homogenization of the gaseous inclusions. As to the lowest temperature of the hydrothermal solutions, it fluctuated from 360 to 400°C (uncorrected for pressure at the time of the mineralization).

Some of the two-phase liquid and of the three-phase inclusions with carbon dioxide are definitely of a secondary origin. They are predominant locally in the milky-white quartz.

The two-phase liquid inclusions homogenize at 160–75°C. The inclusions with carbon dioxide explode on heating before they reach their homogenization temperatures. The volume of carbon dioxide in such inclusions is not constant; it may be up to 30 per cent of the inclusion's volume and may be as low as not over 5 per cent.

Negligible quantities of fine liquid inclusions are visible microscopically in the crystals of tourmaline.

The milky-white quartz and tourmaline stage must have been a short one, judging by the quantity of the materials it had produced (quartz, tourmaline, epidote, muscovite, chlorite, etc.). The gaseous solutions cooled rapidly, as they were streaming away from the intrusion of microcline granites, through fissures. They yielded their heat to the surrounding rocks and became converted into liquid hydrothermal solutions.

FIG. 6. Calcite twin from quartz-calcite vein (natural size).

The terminal stage is characterized by the formation of calcite, finely crystalline quartz, pyrite, and other sulfides. Fine calcitic veins often cut through the previously formed quartz–sulfide veins. Two varieties are recognizable among the calcite of that stage: (a) white and (b) pink, both of which were formed at identical temperatures, as indicated by the inclusion studies.

Figure 6 shows a calcite twin from a quartz–calcite vein in the "15 Years Since the October" mine (depth 263 m). The crystal has well-developed faces of scalenohedron, rhombohedron, prism, etc. Yermakov [4] described an analogous (by shape) calcite crystal from one of the lead–zinc deposits of the Soviet Far East.

On examination of the crystal shown in Fig. 6, it developed that the crystal has three rather markedly defined zones; the inner, the intermediate, and the outer, separated from each other by thin adhesions of chlorite. Primary two-phase liquid inclusions, lying parallel to the growth zones, were discovered in the inner zone. These inclusions are small and their shape is oval. They gave the following series of the homogenization temperatures, on heating: 124–118–116–109–105°C. Moreover, the crystal's inner zone was found to contain pseudo-secondary inclusions homogenizing at 94–75°C and secondary single-phase liquid inclusions. The intermediate zone, like the inner one, embraces both of the twins whose inclusions are analogous in their phase ratios and homogenization temperatures. It was shown by the analysis that the inclusions homogenize at 99–94–88–81–78–75–62°C. Finally, the outer zone contains only primary single-phase liquid inclusions.

Thermometric analyses show therefore that the crystal (twin) of calcite is a low-temperature mineral, formed when the minimum temperatures of the solutions were falling from 124°C to very low levels, about 40–30°C. The temperature regime of the solutions from which that mineral was produced is represented in Fig. 7.

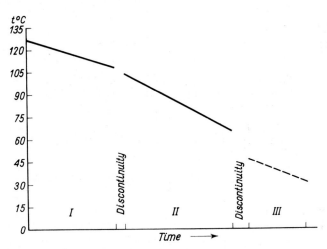

Fig. 7. Temperature regime of solutions during growth of calcite crystal.
I. Inner zone; *II.* Discontinuity; *III.* Intermediate zone; *IV.* Discontinuity;
V. Outer zone [*sic*].

One may maintain, on the basis of the data, that there was a discontinuity in the calcite growth, after the formation of each one of the growth zones. Only a thin film of the adhesions (chlorite and other minerals) were laid down during the discontinuities.

As previously stated, alongside the deposition of the calcite, there was also a deposition of finely crystalline quartz, pyrite, and other sulfides. The pyrite was found only in negligible quantities and only in association with the white calcite. Finely disseminated galena and chalcopyrite were noted among the sulfides.

In the vein calcite, where it is relatively difficult to distinguish between primary and secondary inclusions, the highest homogenization temperatures do not exceed 142°C. The lower temperature limit of the formation of calcite is characterized by the single-phase liquid inclusions (30–40°C).

Inclusions in the late fine quartz, syngenetic with the calcite, indicate, without any reservations, its low-temperature origin. The determined homogenization temperatures of its primary inclusions show that the deposition temperatures were falling from 102 to 30 or 40°C.

Gypsum and chalcedony with single-phase liquid inclusions precipitated in the very last period, from already cold and supergene solutions.

In such manner, the data of thermometric analyses of inclusions of mineral-forming solutions showed that the Kochkarskoye deposit was formed by a process operative in successive stages. The temperature of the solutions was changing abruptly. The temperature would increase somewhat at the beginning of every stage of the mineralization whereupon it would begin to fall progressively, in the course of the deposition of the substance. The abrupt variations in the temperature took place against the background of the over-all decrease.

We may draw the following conclusions from our geologic–mineralogic studies in the field and from the research on the included solutions by the method of Yermakov [4]:

(1) The Kochkarskoye deposit was formed in connection with the two intrusions and during two different periods of activity of the mineral-forming solutions.

(2) In each one of the periods, the mineralization was effective in two stages, the pneumatolytic and the hydrothermal one. Each one of the stages consisted, in turn, of several successive sub-stages of the mineral genesis (Table 3).

(3) The primary ore minerals, including gold, were deposited only from hydrothermal solutions in the earlier one of the periods.

(4) The bulk of arsenopyrite and pyrite was formed during the higher-temperature sub-stage of the hydrothermal stage.

(5) The appearance of galena, sphalerite, chalcopyrite, gold, etc., is associated with the second, the low-temperature stage of the hydrothermal process.

(6) The formation of milky-white quartz, tourmaline, and other minerals synchronous with them was related to the entry of the late ore-free intrusion of microcline granites in the western section of the deposit. The intrusion gave off fresh portions of magmatic solutions which brought about transformations and neomorphism superimposed on the previously formed deposit.

TABLE 3. SEQUENCE OF MINERALIZATION AND TEMPERATURE REGIME OF SOLUTIONS DURING FORMATION OF THE KOCHKAR DEPOSIT

Periods of mineralization	Stages of mineralization	Substages	"Intra-mineralizational shifts"	Sequence of separation of principal minerals	Temperature of solutions, by inclusions (°C) 500 470 440 410 380 350 320 290 260 230 200 170 140 110 80 50 20
I	Pneumatolytic	Quartzification of plagiogranites	×	Quartz I	
		Gray ore-free quartz		Quartz II / Albite	
	Hydrothermal	Quartz-arsenopyri-tepyrite	×	Quartz III / Arsenopyrite / Pyrite / Ankerite	
		The bulk of sulfides and gold	×	Quartz IV / Sphalerite / Chalcopyrite / Tetrahedrite / Gold / Jamesonite / Boulangerite / Galena	
II	Pneumatolytic and Hydrothermal	Milky-white quartz with tourmaline	×	Quartz (milky-white) / Tourmaline / Epidote / Chlorite	
	Hydrothermal	Calcite with finely crystalline quartz	×	Calcite / Quartz (finely crystalline) / Pyrite / Gypsum	

Studies of the inclusions show that each one of the deposits here examined had its own and fairly specific mineral genesis. This fact is closely related, of course, to differences in their geologic environments, their structures, composition of host rocks, expressions and composition of the intrusions, depths of emplacement of the intrusions, and many other factors.

The deposits here examined were previously identified as hydrothermal, in the genetic sense, with the Berezovskoye regarded as typically "meso-thermal" and the Kochkarskoye as typically "hypothermal."

The research on inclusions of mineral-forming solutions in different mineral complexes of these two deposits indicates that the deposits were developed in two stages, pneumatolytic and hydrothermal. Each one of those, of course, has its own specific features. There is no basis whatsoever for ascribing a purely hydrothermal origin to these deposits, and even less reason to tag them as "hypo-", "meso-", or "epithermal".

It is perfectly natural that a close coordination of the geologic–mineralogic research with the thermometric research is essential for the correct explanation of processes involved in the formation of hypogene deposits, since the thermometry allows direct determinations of the state, the minimum temperature, and the composition of mineral-forming solutions. This is the only way toward an orientation in the most highly involved problems of the formation of ores and toward the right paths in research and in prospecting.

BIBLIOGRAPHY

1. BORODAYEVSKII, N. I., *Berezovskoye rudnoye pole*. (The Ore Field of Berezovo.) Metallurgizdat, 1947.
2. BORODAYEVSKAYA, M. B. and N. I. BORODAYEVSKII, Dorudnyye struktury bere-zovskogo mestorozhdeniya. (Pre-ore Structures of the Berezovo Deposit.) *Sb. Sovet. geolog.* No. 29, 1948.
3. VUL'CHIN, Ye. I., Materialy k izucheniyu kvartsoobrazuyushchikh sistem. (Data Pertinent to Study of Quartz-forming Systems.) *Uch. zap. L'vov. univ.* Vol. 23, *ser. geolog.* No. 6, 1953.
4. YERMAKOV, N. P., *Issledovaniya mineraloobrazuyushchikh rastvorov*. (Research in Mineral-forming Solutions.) Izd. Khar'kov. univ. 1950.
5. IVANOV, A. A., Geologiya korennykh mestorozhdenii zolota na Urale. (Geology of Primary Deposits of Gold in Ural.) *Tr. geolog. inst. ural'sk. filiala Akad. Nauk SSSR*, No. 16, 1948.
6. KALYUZHNYI, V. A. and L. I. KOLTUN, Nekotoryye dannyye o davlenii i tempe-raturakh pri obrazovanii polimetallicheskikh mestorozhdenii Nagol'nogo Kryazha. (Some Data on Pressure and Temperatures during Formation of Polymetallic Deposits in Nagol'nyy Kryazh.) *Mineralog. sb.* No. 7, 1953.
7. KUTYUKHIN, P. N., N. I. BORODAYEVSKII and M. B. BORODAYEVSKAYA, O sostave i okolozhil'nykh izmeneniyakh na berezovskom rudnom tele. (On Composition and Near-vein Alterations in the Berezovo Ore Body.) *Sb. Sovet. geolog.* No. 14/15, 1947.

8. LEMMLEIN, G. G., Osobennosti zalezhivaniya treshchin v kristalle v rezhime sni-zhayushcheysya temperatury. (Special Features of Healing of Fissures in Crystal in the Environment of Decreasing Temperature.). *Dokl. Akad. Nauk SSSR*, Vol. 97, No. 6, 1952.

9. POKROVSKII, P. V., Morfologiya i mineralogiya zhily zelyonoy Kochkarskogo Rayona. (Morphology and Mineralogy of the Green Vein, the Kochkar District.) *Sb. Sovet. geolog.* No. 2, 1939.

Mineralothermometric Research at the Tyrny-Auz Skarn-ore Complex, North Caucasus

V. F. LESNYAK

SKARN rocks and the associated ores are among the most highly involved hypogene developments in the earth's crust. Economic accumulations of mineral raw materials, particularly copper, iron, tungsten, molybdenum, tin, and other ores are often associated with skarn rocks. It is for that reason that there exists an abundant literature on skarns, both in the U.S.S.R. and abroad. It ought to be pointed out, however, that origins of skarn-ore deposits and especially the course of variations in the state of aggregation and in the temperature regime of mineral-forming solutions in the process of their formation are still relatively obscure.

In determinations of conditions responsible for the formation of hypogene deposits, many investigators, even at this time, are still basing their conclusions entirely on the mineral composition of the deposits, i.e. on the end-products of the mineral-forming environment. As to the medium of the mineral genesis (the mineral-forming solutions), it somehow escapes their attention.

It has been reliably established, by this time, that, on occasions, large inclusions in minerals and, more often, small and even ultra-microscopic inclusions are preserved relics of the medium (with its special physico-chemical features) from which the minerals themselves and, consequently, the deposits of minerals had been produced.

As shown by Yermakov, the original conditions of mineral genesis, temperature, pressure, state of aggregation, composition, and concentration of the solutions operative millions of years ago may be restored with the aid of microscopic, spectrographic, and chemical studies of the inclusions, as well as by their thermometric analysis [5].

In recent years, Soviet scientists, by the means of thermometric analysis of inclusions, obtained highly valuable data on the temperatures of formation of individual minerals and of associations of minerals for many deposits of metallic and non-metallic ores. Very interesting results were published quite recently: Grushkin, on the results of the inclusion studies in quartz and fluorite crystals from pegmatitic veins of Central Asia [2, 3], Zakharchenko, on quartz and pegmatite veins of Pamir [6], and others [4, 5, 7, 8, 9].

Proceeding from the attainments of the Soviet scientists, we attempted, by means of thermometric analysis of inclusions in minerals, to ascertain variations in the state of aggregation and in the temperature regime of mineral-forming solutions in some of the skarn deposits of Northern Caucasus and Central Asia and to determine the role of inclusions as criteria in prospecting for ore minerals.

A large-scale thermometric investigation of inclusions in transparent and semi-transparent minerals, with attention to the sequence of their appearance, enabled us to establish a series of orderly relationships in the formation of a whole series of mineral deposits. The present report deals with one of those.

The contact-metasomatic skarn-ore complex, the object of our detailed thermometric studies, is localized amidst Paleozoic clayey sandstones and carbonate sediments and it consists of hornfels and limy ore-bearing skarns, quartz–silicate and quartz ore-bearing veins cutting the skarn, with the sulfide mineralization imposed on the skarns and on the quartz–silicate ore-bearing veins. This intricate hypogene complex is associated with a major zone of tectonic disturbance and is in contact with an intrusion of biotitic porphyritic granites that were the principal source of the ore-forming solutions. Geologic history of the skarn-ore complex here discussed is represented by the following sequence of events, by the majority of the investigators:

(1) Oscillating movements of the region's mobile zone were conducive to the entry of a granitic intrusion into the body of the Lower Carboniferous limestones and clayey sandstones, along a large fissure. Under the influence of high temperature and pressure, the clayey sandstones in the contact zone were altered into pyroxene and biotite hornfels while the underlying limestones were altered into marble.

(2) The overlying rocks and the solidified part of the intrusion were subjected to an intensive fragmentation under the pressure of the ascending magma. As the result of a horst-like uplift of the limestone block, there was a development of two relatively powerful brecciation zones descending to great depths.

(3) Along these brecciation zones, the ore-forming solutions streamed outward from the magmatic hearth and it was these solutions that were responsible for the conversion to skarn of the tectonic breccia, consisting of fragments of hornfels and limestone. As the result, there developed two genetic varieties of skarns; the hornfels and the limestone kinds, produced by alteration of hornfels and limestone respectively. Fragmentation of the solidified peripheral part of the intrusion and of the host rocks continued throughout the entire period of the stabilization of the skarn-ore complex.

(4) Toward the end of the main stage of the skarn formation, there was an intrusion of vein rocks into the fissures, of the so-called leucocratic

granitoids: granite porphyries, granite aplites, etc., derivations of the same magma, but contaminated by the carbonate rocks. The granitoid intrusion gave a new impulse to the solutions by which the succeeding stages of the skarn formation were brought about.

(5) Formation of margins of the skarns, next to the granitoids, and development of the network of quartz–silicate and quartz-ore veins and veinlets belong to the succeeding stages of the skarn formation.

(6) In a still later stage of the formation of the deposit, there was a pulsation of ore-forming solutions in the fissures resulting in the sulfide mineralization (the garnet–sulfide skarns).

It has been established, on the basis of structural relationships of different components of the ore body (presence of fissures, brecciated textures, intersections of veins, etc.), that the mineral-forming process was effective against the background of many recurrent tectonic movements accompanied by fragmentation of the host rocks and of the previously formed complexes of minerals and by their recrystallization and cementation by the younger materials.

Omitting here a detailed analysis of the former ideas regarding the origin of this intricate ore complex, it ought to be pointed out that neither the state of aggregation nor the temperature regime of the mineral-forming solutions had been ascertained. The entire process of the development of the skarn-ore complex was viewed by the preceding investigators tentatively as a hydrothermal or a hydrothermal–pneumatolytic one.

The problem of the time when the quartz in the deposit was formed and of the genetic relation of the rare-metal ores to that quartz is the cardinal one and yet controversial at the same time.

Some of the investigators believe that the quartz formed both in the early and in the late stages of the formation of the deposit and that the molybdenite is related genetically both to the garnet and to the quartz. Some others maintain that the quartz is one of the latest minerals in the deposit (the eighth and the ninth stages of mineralization) and that it has no genetic relationship to the molybdenite. Such mutually contradictory opinions are produced simply because there were no studies of the inclusions of mineral-forming solutions in this deposit, by which the genetic character of the deposit's minerals could be determined.

According to the literature [1], more than hundred species of minerals are known in the deposit. In order to ascertain the state of aggregation of the mineral-forming solutions and the variations in the temperature regime under which the very intricate mineral complex formed, we examined inclusions of mineral-forming solutions in different minerals, in the sequence of their crystallization, namely:

(1) In quartz and feldspars from granites and from leucocratic granitoids;

(2) In pyroxenes, garnets, scheelites, quartz, and fluorite from the skarns;

(3) In quartz, scheelite, and fluorite from the quartz–silicate and quartz veinlets cutting the skarns;

(4) In quartz, fluorite, and calcite filling, alongside the sulfides, fissures and cavities in skarns and in marmorized limestones;

(5) In quartz from the antimony deposit, 3 to 5 km from the skarn body to which it is related genetically.

Our results on the inclusions of mineral-forming magmatic "melts" and solutions, in the minerals here enumerated, are reported in the following pages.

(1) INCLUSIONS IN MINERALS OF MAGMATIC ROCKS

Young granitoids, the principal ones of which are porphyroid biotite granites, granite–porphyries, and granite–aplites, belong with the magmatic rocks of the complex here examined. A brief characterization of these rocks, together with the conditions of their formation and a detailed description of the inclusions in their minerals, have already been reported by the author [9] and, for that reason, only general remarks on the subject are to be made here.

The primary inclusions in quartz, the latest mineral in the listed granitoids, are represented by relics of a solidified melt. The melting temperature of these inclusions is far outside the limits of our technical facilities (600–700°C) and cannot be determined accordingly. These inclusions constitute evidence to the effect that the intrusion of the porphyritic biotite granite and its derivatives (granite porphyries and granite aplites) were produced from a molten magma that had solidified at relatively shallow depths. The active portion of the magmatic hearth, at a greater depth, was highly impregnated with volatile constituents (gases and vapors). That may be surmised from the abundant multiphase gaseous inclusions and of two-phase liquid secondary inclusions in the granitoid minerals constituting a record of the frequently recurrent action of gaseous and liquid solutions on the rocks, in association with the tectonic movements during and after their development. The relation of the skarn ores to the intrusion of the porphyritic biotite granites has been established by the composition and the state of aggregation of the solutions in secondary inclusions [9].

(2) INCLUSIONS OF MINERAL-FORMING SOLUTIONS
IN SKARN MINERALS

Pyroxenes, garnets, wollastonite, and quartz are the principal rock-forming minerals of skarns in the complex we examined. Vesuvianite, fluorite, calcite, and others are present in subordinate quantities. Scheelite is among the ore minerals in which we examined the inclusions of mineral-forming solutions.

Quartz, fluorite, and calcite were especially well suited for the inclusion studies. They are common in the skarns themselves as well as in the high-temperature and the low-temperature vein formations of the skarn complex. We succeeded in tracing the sequence of variations in the state of aggregation and composition of the solutions, as well as in the temperature of the mineral genesis, by the inclusions in anhydrous silicates, scheelite, quartz, fluorite, and calcite.

(a) Inclusions in Anhydrous Silicates

Inclusions of mineral-forming solutions were discovered in pyroxenes, garnets, and, to some extent, in vesuvianite.

Inclusions in pyroxenes. The earlier investigators recognized two generations of pyroxene in hornfels and limestone skarns: (1) an earlier finely crystalline pale green one whose composition corresponds to that of diopside–hedenbergite and (2) a later coarsely crystalline, dark green one, which is rarely pure hedenbergite.

It has been established that the pale green finely crystalline pyroxene crystallized at the very beginning of the formation of the skarn body, ahead of all other minerals, where it is found chiefly in skarns that were formed on the hornfels base. In view of these considerations the inclusions we found in the pyroxene ought to be representative of the state of aggregation of the mineral-forming medium at the earliest stage of the skarn formation. The inclusions we detected in that variety of pyroxene were extremely small, from the vanishing size to 0.002 mm in diameter. They were single-phase and apparently gaseous, dark, rounded. They were freely disseminated throughout the pyroxene grains, unrelated to fissures in the mineral, and, for these reasons were assumed to be primary.

Very small inclusions, of the same general appearance as the ones just described, were observed in fissures within the pyroxene grains, as chainworks conformable to the fissures. Their positions were taken as evidence of their late origin, i.e. of their belonging to the secondary type.

The coarsely crystalline pyroxene has a dark green color, but appears ordinary green in thin fragments. It cuts through the pale-green pyroxene and plagioclase, in the veinlets of the hornfels skarns, but functions as one of the main rock-forming minerals in the limestone skarns, complex skarn veinlets, and quartz veins with molybdenite. Its grains may be as large as 5–6 mm, in places. Large crystals of hedenbergite, up to 15 cm long, are found in the northern section of the ore field. It has been established that the mineral crystallized after the bulk of garnet, vesuvianite, and wollastonite, but still in the early stage of the skarn formation.

It was proved by microscopic examination of thin fragments of the pyroxene here described, cut from the crystals along the cleavage planes, that the inclusions unrelated to healed fissures as well as the inclusions that are definitely secondary, are of the "dry" gas variety, it appears. Their shapes are rounded or elongated, their sizes are not larger than 0.01 mm in diameter, their color is black. The poor translucence of the mineral makes it difficult to recognize these inclusions.

Inclusions in the pyroxenes were not heated in the thermochamber, because it was not possible to find any with the liquid phase and also because of technical difficulties.

No two-phase liquid inclusions could be detected in the pyroxenes despite our painstaking and repeated search. One may conclude therefore that, since only gaseous inclusions are found in the pyroxenes, the evidence is to the effect that the transfers of elements from which the pyroxenes were formed within the skarn body took place with the active participation of a gaseous medium.

Inclusions in garnets. Garnets are the principal rock-forming minerals in the skarns and, for that reason, they have a cardinal importance in ascertaining conditions of origin of the skarns.

The preceding investigators [1] had recognized four varieties of garnets, in the sequence of their separation from the solution, and on the basis of their chemical composition.

I. Red-brown garnet, with a composition corresponding to that of grossularite–andradite. This garnet is isotropic under the microscope and it often contains particles of diopside–hedenbergite. In the skarns, it forms structureless agglomerations and vein-like masses in hornfels and marble. This garnet is the main rock-forming mineral of the pyroxene and the garnet skarns. It is found in large quantities throughout the skarn body. It is easily distinguished from the other garnets by its optical properties, color, and widespread occurrence in the deposit.

II. Pale-brown garnet, occasionally greenish. Is found chiefly in marble–skarn contacts. Consists chiefly of fairly large well-formed weakly zonally-anisotropic crystals. Obviously anisotropic. Composition: up to 94 per cent andradite molecule. Macroscopically easily distinguished from the other varieties.

III. Brick-red garnet. Chiefly veinlets: more rarely, irregular agglomerations. Aggregates of fairly large well-formed crystals of it often fiill cavities. Definitely anisotropic. Composition: 30 per cent andradite; 63 per cent grossularite.

IV. Dark-red garnet. Represented generally by large well-formed crystals. Found mainly in the garnet–sulfide skarns. Radically anisotropic. Composition: practically pure andradite.

Specimens with garnets were taken from different parts of the ore body, for investigations of inclusions of mineral-forming solutions. In his selection of the garnet varieties, the author was guided by the earlier investigators, in their indications of the sequence of separation of the garnets and of the paragenesis.

Inclusions of mineral-forming medium of our interest are detectable in every variety of garnet (Fig. 1).

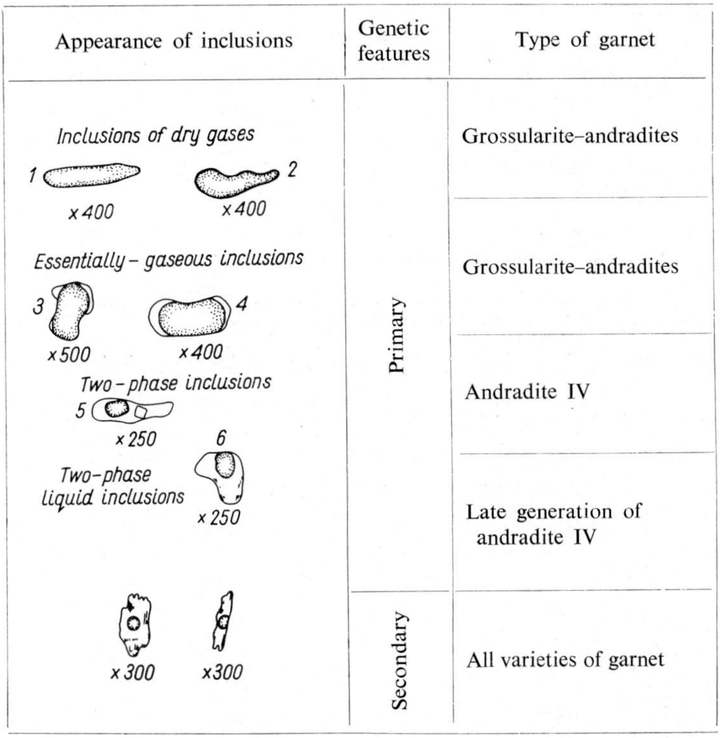

Appearance of inclusions	Genetic features	Type of garnet
Inclusions of dry gases		Grossularite–andradites
Essentially – gaseous inclusions	Primary	Grossularite–andradites
Two-phase inclusions		Andradite IV
Two-phase liquid inclusions		Late generation of andradite IV
	Secondary	All varieties of garnet

FIG. 1. Gaseous and liquid inclusions in garnets.

In the red-brown garnet (garnet I), whose specimens were taken from the footwall of the ore body, in the mine workings, both primary and secondary inclusions are represented by various "dry gases" and by essentially-gaseous inclusions. After microscopic examination of a large number of thin sections, at high magnifications ($300-500\times$), it was shown that, in garnet I, secondary liquid two-phase inclusions, produced during the late stages of the mineralization, are found only occasionally in healed fissures. Thermometric analytical results on the inclusions were as follows: gaseous inclusions, with 5–15 per cent, by volume, of the liquid phase, homogenize at 380–420°C in the gaseous phase, as in type II. Liquid inclusions in the fissures homogenize in the liquid phase, as in type I, at 280–340°C.

Thin sections of garnet II, for the inclusion studies, were cut from specimens of the limestone skarn collected from mining workings in various parts of the deposit. Inclusions in garnet II, as in garnet I, are of the gaseous type and most of them are inclusions of "dry gases," in the sense of the Yermakov's classification [5]. Essentially-gaseous inclusions, with the gas phase occupying more than 50 per cent of the volume, are found in smaller numbers. Secondary liquid inclusions, with the gaseous phase at 20–45 per cent of the volume, are noted occasionally, in healed fissures.

The inclusions of "dry" gases remain unchanged on heating, so that all that can be said of them is that they indicate a gaseous state of the solutions sealed and preserved in that variety of garnet.

The essentially-gaseous inclusions homogenize in the gaseous phase, as in type II, at 360–400°C, with an inversion, the temperature of which is generally 20–40°C below the homogenization temperature of a given inclusion. The secondary liquid inclusions homogenize at 280–230°C.

The brick-red garnet III is the main rock-forming mineral both in the limestone skarns and in the complex skarn veinlets. Microscopically, this garnet is seen either as veinlets or again as irregularly shaped areas. The garnet in quartz veinlets cutting the skarns and the hornfels is mainly of the same type. That garnet often produces accumulations of fairly large crystals, chiefly in the skarn–marble contacts.

Gaseous inclusions were detected in a large number of thin sections of garnet III scattered disorderly throughout the mineral, in some places, or else are arranged in streamers along fissures. Moreover, inclusions of dry gases are definitely preponderant, while essentially-gaseous inclusions are encountered only in insignificant numbers. The latter homogenize in the gaseous phase at 360–420°C, with a point of inversion, whose temperature is 10–40°C below the homogenization temperature.

Garnet IV is the representative garnet in the garnet–sulfide skarns. It is practically a pure andradite, as shown by the earlier investigators [1]. The color of garnet IV ranges from dark brown to light brown. This garnet often forms accumulations of fairly large crystals 3 cm in diameter, and larger. The crystals are zoned, with well-developed rhombohedral faces. Garnet IV is easily distinguished from the other varieties by its dark brown color.

Fluorite is associated with garnet IV crystals, as a rule, and so is quartz, calcite, and copper and iron sulfides. Small octahedral crystals of magnetite are often observed on the faces of the quartz. The large garnet crystals are overgrown by small light-brown crystals of garnet IVa (a later generation) that also have well-developed rhombohedral faces. The coarse variety of the garnet contains essentially-gaseous inclusions, in the majority of the cases; liquid inclusions are rarer. Garnet IVa crystals, overgrowing the crystals of garnet IV, contain only liquid inclusions. Three-phase liquid inclusions with a small cubic crystal of solid phase are found occasionally.

Homogenization temperatures of the essentially-gaseous inclusions in garnet IV, on heating in the thermochamber, range from 370 to 380°C. The cube-shaped captive crystals dissolve at 180°C.

We may draw the following general conclusion regarding crystallization of the garnets, from the foregoing considerations:

Garnets I, II, III, and the early generation of garnet IV crystallized from supercritical gas-like solutions apparently at a very high pressure. Garnet IVa, the late generation, with associated fluorite, quartz, calcite, and the ore minerals of the sulfide complex, crystallized from hot liquid aqueous solutions. The subsequent alteration and solution of the garnets took place probably at fairly low temperatures, as evidenced by the two-phase and even single-phase liquid inclusions detectable in healed fissures of the crystals.

Thus garnets I, II, III, IV may be regarded as indications of a pneumatolytic mineral genesis and garnet IVa as a product of a hydrothermal activity.

Inclusions in vesuvianite. Vesuvianite in the deposit plays a minor role in the structure of the skarn body and cannot be regarded as a rock-forming mineral. It is a constituent of the limestone skarns and of the complex skarn veinlets in the marble.

Vesuvianite is an early mineral, judging by morphologic indications. Its grains are corroded and are distributed next to the contact zones of the complex skarn veinlets, in an association with pyroxene and wollastonite. Its crystallization began ahead of the hedenbergite, apparently, but continued concurrently with the latter.

The vesuvianite grains vary from 0.5 to 1.5 mm in size. Their shape is prismatic and their colors range from honey-yellow to light-buff.

Extremely small black inclusions of the mineral-forming medium are visible microscopically in thin sections of the mineral at high magnifications. Their content is probably gas, because no discrete phases are detectable in them and because the intensive scattering of light, on which their "black color" depends, indicates a low density of included solutions.

The vesuvianite is associated with garnets I, II, III, wollastonite, pyroxene II, scheelite, and molybdenite. Inclusions of the mineral-forming medium in the garnets and in the scheelite consist of gas. This constitutes evidence of a crystallization from gaseous solutions and there can be no doubt therefore that the vesuvianite was crystallized under the same conditions as the previously enumerated minerals, i.e. pneumatolytically.

(b) Inclusions in Scheelite

The main bulk of scheelite in the deposit here considered is accumulated in the limestone skarns and in the quartz–silicate veinlets cutting the marbles as well as the skarns.

The scheelite in the skarns and the skarn veinlets is associated chiefly with the dark-green coarse-grained pyroxene (hedenbergite–diopside) and, more rarely, with garnet, wollastonite, and quartz [1]. Its deposition occurred in two phases: the main phase of the skarnization and the ore

Appearance of inclusions		Gaseous phase (approx.)(%)	Homogenization temperature (°C)	Type of homogenization
Inclusions of dry gases  1 ×200 2 ×200	Primary	100	—	—
Essentially–gaseous inclusions 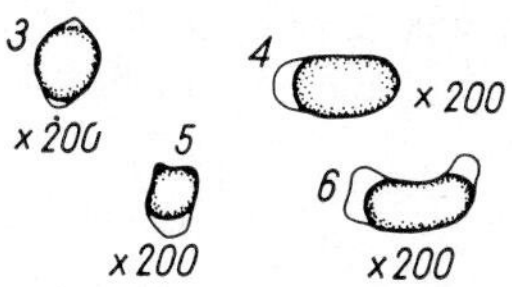 3 ×200 4 ×200 5 ×200 6 ×200	Primary	80–95	280–300	in gaseous phase II
		65–70	340–400	
Liquid two–phase inclusions 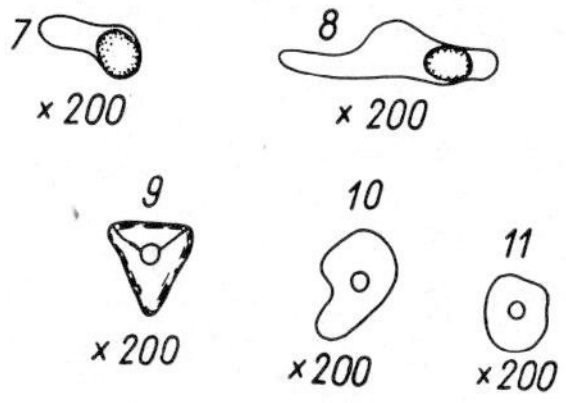 7 ×200 8 ×200 9 ×200 10 ×200 11 ×200	Secondary	20–40	280–320	in liquid phase I
		5–10	175–250	

FIG. 2. Gaseous and liquid inclusions in scheelite from skarns.

veinlet phase in which it is found together with pyroxene and garnet. The scheelite is easily recognized microscopically by its high relief, clearly visible cleavage, and the high index of refraction: $\gamma = 1.936 \pm 0.002$, $\beta = 1.921 \pm 0.002$.

We succeeded in finding several pieces of pyroxene skarn with agglomerations of scheelite grains as large as 5 mm for examination of their inclusions of mineral-forming medium. The inclusions were studied microscopically in thin fragments of the mineral placed in an immersion liquid with the refraction index very close to that of the mineral. Vast quantities of inclusions of the mineral-forming solutions were discovered in many of the mineral fragments examined. The most typical ones, by appearance, are represented in Fig. 2.

The vast multitude of inclusions in the scheelite consists definitely of gas, with the preponderance of "dry" gases, and of a smaller number of essentially-gaseous inclusions with the gaseous phase at 60–90 per cent of the volume. The number of gaseous inclusions is so large that it cannot be counted in the microscopic field, in many fragments. Some other fragments of the mineral contain fewer inclusions, but even then still hundreds and thousands.

The maximum size of the inclusions does not exceed 0.02 mm. They are chiefly oval, lentil-shaped, or pear-shaped, and occasionally elongated. Both the inclusions of "dry" gases and the essentially-gaseous inclusions are generally scattered throughout the microscopic field; more rarely, they are seen as swarm-like congestions or as streamlets (secondary inclusions).

On heating of the essentially-gaseous inclusions, we obtained the following results: the irregularly shaped inclusions with about 90 per cent gaseous phase homogenize at 280–320°C in the gaseous phase; pear-shaped inclusions with about 85–90 per cent gaseous phase homogenize at 340–370°C, also in the gaseous phase.

The gaseous character of a very large number of inclusions in the scheelite we examined convinces us that the mineral was crystallized from gaseous solutions. In other words, the bulk of scheelite was crystallized pneumatolytically, under the same conditions as the pyroxenes, garnets, vesuvianite, the early wollastonite, some of the molybdenite, and a portion of the early quartz (see below). As to the temperature at the time of crystallization of scheelite, it was apparently considerably higher than the critical temperature of water.

Inclusions of the hydrothermal type in thin sections of the scheelite we examined, with the gaseous phase not over 50 per cent of the volume, are distributed as swarm-like groups or else as chains extending along fissures in the mineral, in one direction. They homogenize as in type I, i.e in the liquid phase, at 180–320°C.

Among the associates of the scheelite, one often finds molybdenite and transparent minerals whose particles are barely visible in the microscope at high magnifications. The associated minerals are found throughout the scheelite; their distribution may be uniform or in groups. Molybdenite as a rule, fills fine fissures in the scheelite and, more rarely, is found also in the form of isolated scales. The scales are not larger than 0.05 mm.

It follows therefore, from the foregoing considerations, that the scheelite of the deposit is mainly a mineral of pneumatolytic origin. A smaller quantity of scheelite crystallized during the hydrothermal stage of the mineral genesis. This latter crystallization is evidenced by the liquid inclusions in the mineral homogenizing at 180–320°C.

The crystallization of scheelite from gaseous solutions took place after the crystallization of the bulk of garnets (grossularite–andradites) and pyroxenes, but before the abundant quartzification of the pneumatolytic stage and the subsequent sulfide–carbonate mineralization of the hydrothermal stage. It was in connection with that particular process that the largest accumulations of scheelite are found, in areas rich in hedenbergite, grossularite–andradite, and in the highest-temperature pneumatolytic quartz with molybdenite, in the deposit in question.

(c) Inclusions of Mineral-forming Medium in Fluorite

Fluorite is fairly common in the deposit. It is present chiefly in the limestone and the garnet–sulfide skarns.

It has been taken to be even a rock-forming mineral, in some sections of the skarn body, which is indicative of an appreciable quantity of fluorine in the magmatic solutions responsible for the skarnization. The highest concentrations of fluorite are observed in the limestone–skarn contacts.

The hornfels skarns rarely contain fluorite. Quartz is associated with the fluorite in the limestone skarns. Fluorite often fills interstices between grains of pyroxene, garnet, and scheelite. Its color is white. The size of fluorite grains in polished sections is 0.1–0.2 mm and, occasionally, 1 mm. The crystal faces are generally frosted. In the sulfide complex imposed on the skarns, fluorite with quartz or with calcite is found as well-formed cubical crystals 1–2 mm in size.

Thin sections of fluorite, 0.5–0.6 mm thick, were cut for the inclusion studies. They were examined under the polarizing microscope at 250–500× magnifications.

Three types of inclusions were found in fluorite from the skarns: gaseous, multiphase, and two-phase liquid.

The gaseous inclusions are represented by the essentially-gaseous variety, with the gaseous phase occupying 60–70 per cent of the volume. Such inclusions have regular hexagonal shapes and their sizes range from a few thousandths to 0.02 mm. Their boundaries with the host mineral are sharply defined. The inclusions are situated parallel to the growth faces of the crystals and there can be no doubt that they are primary, in the genetic sense. On heating in the thermochamber, the essentially-gaseous inclusions homogenize in the gaseous phase (as in type II), with a clearly indicated point of inversion. Their homogenization is brought about at 400–410°C. The temperature of the inversion varies from 370 to 375°C.

Thus the earliest generation of fluorite crystallized from gaseous solutions, i.e. pneumatolytically.

The multiphase inclusions in fluorite from the skarns are not common. Most of them consist of three phases, i.e. contain a captive crystal; four, five- six-, and seven-phase inclusions are still more rare. In one of the seven-phase inclusions, ellipsoidal in shape, there is a black cubical crystal, apparently an ore mineral [pyrite?]. There are cubes and discs of light-colored non-ore minerals in the same inclusion. In three-phase and four-phase inclusions, captive minerals are cubic; disc-shaped and hexagonal ones are rarer. The hexagonal crystals are greenish-gray.

It is a matter of interest that, in many of the flat multiphase inclusions of rectangular or irregular shapes, the boundaries are almost invisible before the heating, i.e. that the index of refraction of the included liquid is nearly the same as the optical constant of fluorite. In the course of heating, when captive minerals begin to dissolve, the inclusion's boundaries become visible rapidly. All captive minerals in the fluorite's multiphase inclusions are isotropic. These minerals are apparently sylvite, halite, and other chlorides crystallizing in the isometric system.

Homogenization temperatures of the multiphase inclusions are reported in the table, Fig. 3. It is evident from the table that, the more of the solid phases in an inclusion, the higher is its homogenization temperature, i.e. the greater the chloride concentrations in the solutions, the higher the temperature of the solutions.

The gaseous phase disappears at 505–510°C, in strongly supersaturated solutions subjected to heat. It reappears at 480°C, on slow cooling. Dendritic growth of the solid phases arises suddenly at 380°C. Further cooling produces their differentiation into particles of rounded shapes. Such behavior of the captive crystals, on heating, is observed also in the multiphase inclusions in quartz from the skarns and in quartz veinlets cutting through the skarns. It follows therefore that the captive crystals in the fluorite's inclusions are probably essentially the same in their composition as the captive crystals in the inclusions in quartz presently to be described.

The two-phase liquid inclusions in fluorite from the skarns are localized in healed fissures and are secondary. In a number of specimens collected at the skarn–limestone contacts, in paragenetic association with quartz, calcite, and sulfides of copper, iron, and zinc, fine grains of fluorite were found whose primary inclusions were represented by the liquid two-phase varieties. Such inclusions homogenized at 270–275°C. Extremely small

Appearance of inclusions	No. phases	Phases	Temperature of disappearance of phases (°C)
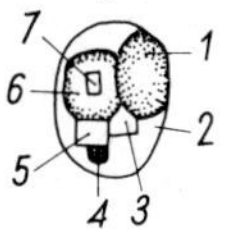	1	Gas	505–510
	2	Liquid	—
I	3	?	420
	4	Pyrite	?
	5	Sylvite	105
	6	Halite	390
	7	?	400
II 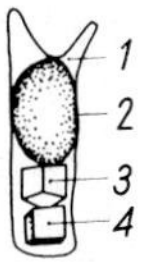	1	Liquid	—
	2	Gas	480
	3	Halite	320
	4	Sylvite	80–90
III 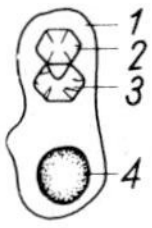	1	Liquid	—
	2	?	140
	3	?	310
	4	Gas	475
IV 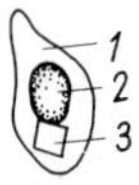	1	Liquid	—
	2	Gas	370
	3	Halite	325

FIG. 3. Multiphase liquid inclusions in fluorite from limestone skarns.

liquid inclusions in the still more recent fluorite contained barely visible gas bubbles disappearing at 90–80°C.

Consequently, one may believe, on the basis of the inclusions of mineral-forming solutions, that fluorite, in the deposit here examined, crystallized from gaseous as well as from liquid solutions and that its crystallization coincided, in the main, with the formation of pneumatolytic and hydrothermal quartz, as evidenced by the state of aggregation and the homogenization temperatures of the inclusions.

(d) Inclusions in Quartz

Three morphologic varieties of quartz are recognized in the deposit: (a) quartz, a constituent of the skarns; (b) vein quartz; (c) comb quartz, cavity-filling.

Quartz forms aggregations of granules, in the skarns, in interstices between granules of pyroxene, vesuvianite, and garnet. This is an indication that it separated after these minerals.

Appearance of inclusions		Approximate phase ratios, percentages	Homogenization temperature of gaseous phase (°C)	Type of homogenization
Accessory minerals 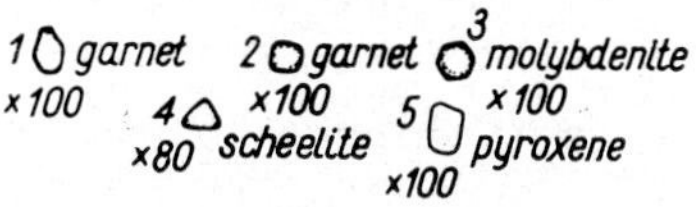 1 garnet ×100; 2 garnet ×100; 3 molybdenite ×100; 4 scheelite ×80; 5 pyroxene ×100		—	—	—
Inclusions of dry gases 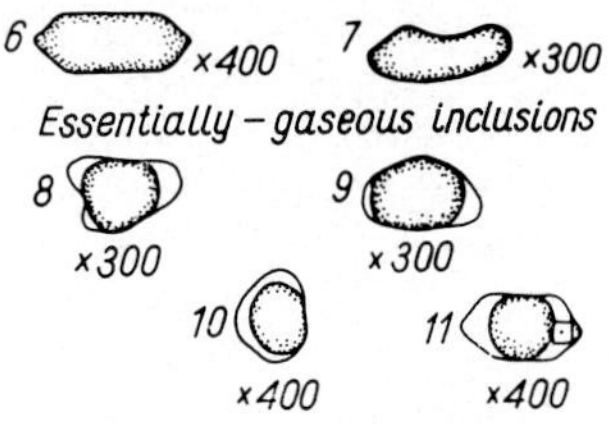 6 ×400; 7 ×300	Primary	100 : 0 : 0	—	II
Essentially-gaseous inclusions 8 ×300; 9 ×300; 10 ×400; 11 ×400		(80–85) : (15–20) : 0	300–340	
		(60–70) : (30–40) : (0–05)	360–480	
Multiphase inclusions 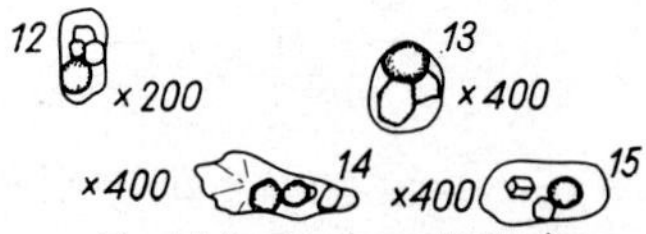 12 ×200; 13 ×400; 14 ×400; 15 ×400	Pseudo-secondary	(20–25) : (40–50) : (30–35)	320–360	I
		(15–20) : (60–70) : (15–20)	270–300	
Liquid two-phase inclusions 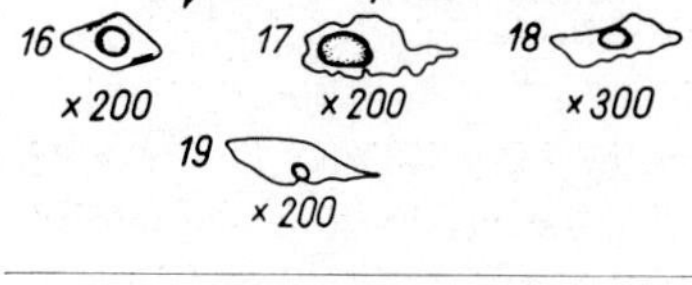 16 ×200; 17 ×200; 18 ×300; 19 ×200	Secondary	(30–40) : (60–70) : 0	240–270	
		(5–10) : (90–95) : 0	130–170	

FIG. 4. Inclusions in quartz from skarns.

Two varieties of quartz are distinguished in the abundant quartz veinlets cutting the skarn body and the host rocks: (a) light-gray quartz of a coarsely crystalline aspect with molybdenite and scheelite, similar to the quartz of the skarns; (b) finely granular quartz, of equant shape, with undulant extinction; strongly contaminated locally with foreign inclusions; generally associated with chalcopyrite, pyrrhotite, epidote, and carbonates.

The author made a detailed study of the inclusions of mineral-forming media in quartz belonging to different mineral associations of the skarn-ore complex and in the early quartz from the quartz veins, both of which are essentially analogous. Inclusions of dry gases and essentially-gaseous inclusions are preponderant in both. Multiphase and two-phase liquid inclusions are seen in smaller numbers. Figure 4 represents the most typical appearances of gaseous and liquid inclusions in quartz from the skarns and from the early quartz veinlets. Inclusions of dry gases and essentially-gaseous inclusions pierce right through the quartz and their distribution is uniform. Multiphase and two-phase liquid inclusions are localized in healed fissures. All types of the inclusions are characteristically small.

Many of the dry gas and essentially-gaseous inclusions are apparently primary. Their numbers cannot be counted. There are hundreds and thousands of such inclusions per mm^2, even in inclusion-poor sections of the quartz. In places their distribution resembles a sieve-like mass, and elsewhere, swarm-like aggregations or, again, mutually intersecting streams.

The essentially-gaseous inclusions, on heating in the thermochamber, homogenize as in type II, with inversion, in the gaseous phase, at 320–570°C.

Judging by spectrographic analytical data, the inclusions homogenizing at 570°C contain solutions saturated chiefly with chlorides and also fluorides of Ca, Na, K, Al, Fe.

Multiphase liquid inclusions, widespread as they are in the quartz, are still not as abundant as the two types of gaseous inclusions just described. Their common distribution is in small narrow bands and it looks as if these bands are bundled together rather frequently into irregular shaped accumulations. Among them one may see three-, four-, five-, and six-phase inclusions. The captive crystals have shapes of small cubes, disc-like bodies, parallelepipeds, hexagons, shuttle shapes, and irregular platelets.

On heating in the thermochamber, the multiphase inclusions homogenize in the liquid phase, i.e. as in type I, at 300–575°C. Also, the temperature at which their gas bubble disappears depends significantly on the degree of their saturation with solid phases: the more of the captive crystals in an inclusion, the higher is the inclusion's homogenization temperature.

The captive crystals dissolve at different temperatures: the cubes at 60, 105, and 185°C; the rhombohedra at 260, 270, and 295°C; the parallele-pipeds at 155 and 160°C; the discs at 235–315°C; the hexagons at 360, 380, 385°C; the irregular platelets at 350, 370°C, etc.

The foregoing data indicate that the captive crystals include several different minerals. Some of them are easily soluble even at low tempera-tures, while some others require both high temperatures and high pressures.

The liquid two-phase inclusions in quartz from the skarns and in the early quartz from the veinlets are obviously secondary, on account of their positions in healed fissures. Their shapes are generally irregular; oval shapes are rare. They are generally larger than the gaseous and the multi-phase inclusions and may be as large as 0.07 mm. Their gas–liquid percent-age phase ratio varies from 1:8 to 1:3. Such inclusions homogenize from 120 to 300–380°C.

As previously stated, the skarns and their host rocks (sandstones, hornfelses, granitoids, etc.) are pierced by many quartz veinlets the sum total of which constitutes about 5 or 6 per cent of the ore body, as a whole. Their width varies from 0.5 to 10 cm, with the most common range of 1–3 cm; they are rarely 10 cm wide and 20 cm is rarer still. Most of the quartz veinlets contain silicates and rare-metal ores and it is for that reason that they are classified as different types depending on their com-position: (1) quartz–pyroxene; (2) quartz–garnet; (3) quartz–plagioclase; (4) quartz; (5) quartz–carbonate. The most common ones are of the quartz–garnet type nearly all of which contain molybdenite in their contact zones. The quartz–plagioclase veinlets are relatively rare; the quartz–carbonate ones are found chiefly in the foot-wall of the ore body, and not too often at that.

The mutual intersections of the veinlets and their piercing of different rocks indicate that they were not formed at one and the same time. Forma-tion of the veinlets depended on tectonic movements that occurred after the main stage of skarn formation.

Quartz from the molybdenum-bearing veinlets and the ore-free quartz veinlets contain chiefly gaseous inclusions (dry gases and essentially-gaseous); multiphase liquid inclusions and secondary liquid two-phase inclusions are more rare.

The large equant kernels of the early quartz composing the veinlets are generally brim-full with gaseous and multiphase inclusions whose ap-pearance does not differ in any respect from the previously described inclusions in quartz from the skarns (Figs. 4 and 5). The two-phase liquid inclusions are obviously secondary in this quartz. The liquid two-phase inclusions are typical of the finely-granular quartz of the veinlets.

Thus three characteristic types of inclusions were established for quartz of the skarns and of the numerous quartz–silicate and quartz veinlets: the gaseous, the multiphase, and the liquid two-phase. Their distribution in quartz is indicative of sequences in the state of aggregation of the solutions in the process of formation of the molybdenum-bearing quartz veinlets piercing the ore body. The solutions were gaseous, in the earliest stage of formation of the veinlets, and their temperature was not lower than 380°C and probably higher than 500°C. The gaseous solutions were saturated with chlorides of K, Na, and other elements.

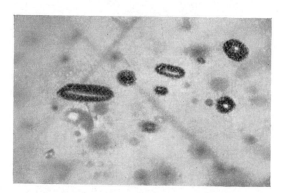

FIG. 5. Inclusions of dry gases in quartz from the skarns.

The chloride-supersaturated solutions were pulsating at lower temperatures. The multiphase inclusions in the minerals constitute records
of these solutions as they were at the time of mineralization. Judging by
the paragenesis of the minerals, that stage of the process produced the
bulk of quartz, fluorite, molybdenite, and scheelite. The initial temperature
of the chloride-supersaturated solutions was at least 400–570°C, as indicated by the homogenization temperatures of the multiphase inclusions.

At 280–300°C, the solutions were already not too saturated with the
chlorides and for that reason, they gave rise to three-phase, rarely four-
phase inclusions with small cubes of apparently halite and sylvite.

The secondary two-phase inclusions in the early quartz of the veinlets
were described homogenize at 120–360°C and represent the later stages
of the mineralizing process.

(e) Inclusions in Crested Quartz and Calcite

Let us consider now the characteristics of inclusions in quartz and
calcite, the fissure-filling and cavity-filling minerals of the skarns.

As a rule, fissures and cavities in the skarns, particularly in the skarn-
limestone contacts, are filled by an assortment of minerals including most
commonly the dark-brown generally coarsely crystalline garnet (andradite),

quartz, fluorite, calcite, epidote, prehnite, ilvaite, and some ore minerals: magnetite, pyrite, arsenopyrite, chalcopyrite, sphalerite, pyrrhotite, galena, and others.

FIG. 6a. Photograph of sectioned zoned crystal. 1.5×.

Section of zoned quartz. 3×	Zone No.	State of aggregation of inclusions by zones		% gas primary inclusions	Homogenization temperature (°C)
		Primary	Secondary		
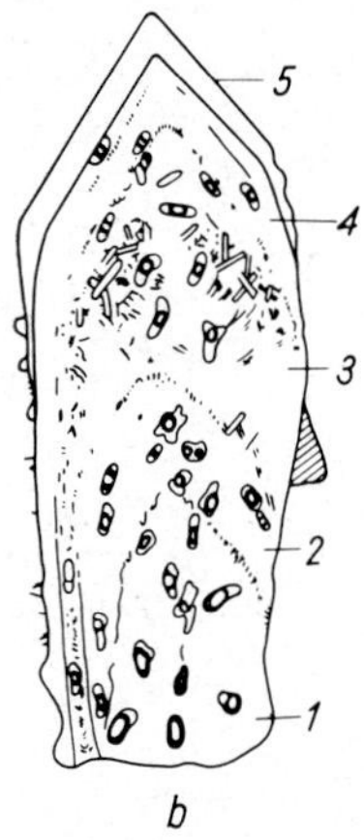	1	Gaseous	Liquid multi-phase and two-phase	70–50	325–340
	2	Liquid multi-phase and two-phase	Liquid two-phase	35–40	265–280
	3	Liquid two-phase	Liquid two-phase	30–35	245–270
	4	Liquid two-phase	Liquid two-phase	23–25	215–220
	5	Liquid two-phase	Liquid two-phase	13–15	175–190

FIG. 6b. Inclusions in zoned quartz crystal and their homogenization temperatures.

Cavities containing the minerals here enumerated may be up to 1.5 n in diameter, and larger. We established the following sequence of the associations of minerals, for the deposit we examined:

The "cast" vein quartz and garnet are overgrown by zoned quartz crystals, assembled into druses up to 4 or 5 cm long and up to 1.5 or 2 cm broad with severely eroded crystal terminations. On top of quartz with the corroded crystal terminations and in interstices between them we find rhombohedral calcite, copper and iron sulfides, fluorite, and other minerals. Prismatic calcite is the latest mineral in such cavities.

We will now proceed with a discussion of inclusions in quartz and calcite in these cavities, in the sequence of crystallization of the minerals.

Inclusions in zoned quartz. Figure 6b shows a cut through a crystal of zoned quartz and a diagrammatic pattern of the distribution of inclusions of mineral-forming media. On the right of the figure, the gas–liquid phase ratios are shown, in correspondence to the different growth zones and homogenization temperatures of the inclusions. One may also see that the zoned quartz crystals grow on top of the earlier molybdenum-bearing massive quartz.

There is a substantial difference between the inclusions of mineral-forming media in the "cast" vein quartz and in the growth zones of the crystals overgrowing that quartz.

The vast majority of inclusions in the massive quartz which supports the growth of the zoned crystals is of the gaseous and the multiphase types. Their character is about the same as that of the already described inclusions in quartz of the quartz–silicate veins piercing the skarn body.

It follows therefore that the massive quartz crystallized during the pneumatolytic stage of formation of the deposit.

The first zone composing the base of a zoned crystal, over which the next zones were later developed, is also brimful of gaseous inclusions. They go right through the zone and are undoubtedly primary, in many instances. These inclusions homogenize in the gaseous phase at 325–340°C. Occasionally, one finds among them some multiphase inclusions (four- and five-phase). The latter are probably secondary, since most of them are definitely localized in healed fissures, alongside two-phase liquid inclusions.

The maximum amount of multiphase inclusions is concentrated at the boundary between the first and the second zone, where one may see that the growth was interrupted, as recorded by microscopic nuclei of quartz crystals growing into the second zone of the main crystal. Thus the first zone belongs still to the pneumatolytic stage, but the second zone ushers in a new stage of mineral genesis (hydrothermal). The transition from the pneumatolytic to the hydrothermal stage is characterized by solutions highly supersaturated with chlorides and it is these solutions that are recorded as captive crystals in the multiphase inclusions.

The second zone consists of transparent quartz. It has no gaseous inclusions and only negligible quantities of multiphase inclusions. Primary two-phase liquid inclusions are in positions parallel to the zonation of the crystal (Fig. 7); they homogenize at 265–280°C.

The zone contains solid inclusions of the associated crystals, representatives of previously crystallized minerals that settled down from the solution and were captured by quartz in the course of its growth. These minerals could not be identified, on account of their small size.

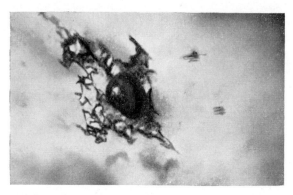

FIG. 7. Primary inclusions in the second zone of the quartz crystal (see Fig. 5).

The upper boundary of the second zone represents an interruption in the crystal's growth, as evidenced by the roughness of its edge caused by solution, in all probability.

The third zone characterizes a new period in the quartz crystal growth; also, the temperature rises somewhat at the beginning of this zone's growth. The quartz of the zone is turbid, because of the huge number of needles of a light-colored mineral, probably wollastonite, and of two-phase liquid inclusions. The needles of wollastonite are concentrated chiefly in the upper and in the lower parts of the zone. They are often assembled into sheaf-like aggregates. This particular period of the mineralization is clearly represented in the deposit and is well marked by wollastonite needles in the zoned crystals of quartz. The finely acicular wollastonite is found in large quantities also in the quartz filling the centers of the complex skarn veinlets, as already described. This quartz filling the central part of the complex skarn veinlets apparently belongs to the same level of mineralization.

Homogenization temperatures of the inclusions in the zone with the needles of wollastonite vary between 270 and 245°C.

The fourth zone consists of transparent quartz and it is evident that its growth also began after some pause in the formation of the mineral and after a partial solution of the previous crystal faces. The evidence consists of a rough and uneven boundary with the third zone.

The needles of wollastonite are very rarely found in the fourth zone. This zone contains fewer inclusions of the mineral-forming media than the preceding zones. All this is indicative of a relatively more quiet growth environment for the zone. Its primary as well as its secondary inclusions are of the two-phase liquid type. The primary ones homogenize at 215–220°C; the secondary ones at 170–160°C.

The *fifth* and the last zone is relatively broad, in some crystals, but is narrow in some others. It contains relatively few inclusions. The zone displays six cycles of successive crystal growth expressed by vaguely outlined narrow sub-zones. It appears that the formation of these sub-zones was accompanied by a decrease in the temperature and by a slowing of the crystal growth. Primary inclusions in the fifth zone homogenize at 190–175°C.

Thus the stage of the hydrothermal process in which the zoned quartz crystallized was characterized by hot liquid aqueous solutions with an abrupt drop of temperatures from 280–275°C to 190–170°C (uncorrected for pressure).

Judging from the paragenesis of the association of the minerals, the zoned quartz here described crystallized at the same time as the low-temperature generation of garnet (andradite), fluorite, scheelite, magnetite, pyrrhotite, part of the pyrite, zinc blende (marmatite), and galena.

It is easy to establish, from the paragenetic associations, that the coarsely crystalline rhombohedral calcite crystallized immediately after the zoned quartz. Coarsely crystalline calcite of rhombohedral habit is widespread in the deposit, particularly in the northern part of the ore field, in the skarn–limestone contact. It is a major constituent of the sulfide complex, alongside andradite, quartz, fluorite, and copper and iron sulfides. The calcite fills fissures and cavities in the form of massive aggregates, in places, or in the form of regularly shaped crystals elsewhere. Calcite with a platy habit is also present in many fissures and cavities, where it crystallized somewhat later than the rhombohedral calcite, but still during the same stage. The platy calcite is apparently an expression of another epoch of mineralization. Quartz and sulfides belonging to later epochs of mineralization are associated with the platy calcite. Crystallization of the rhombohedral and platy calcite signifies a rather abrupt beginning of a change in the composition of the solutions, a shift toward a higher carbonate content, while inclusions in the rhombohedral calcite are indicative of an increase in the temperature at the onset of that stage in the hydrothermal process.

Primary inclusions of the mineral-forming media in the coarsely crystalline rhombohedral calcite are represented entirely by two-phase liquid types with the gaseous phase occupying 20–30 per cent of the volume (Fig. 8).

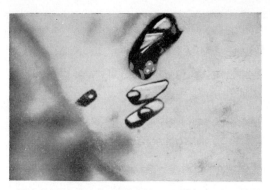

FIG. 8. Primary inclusions in rhombohedral calcite.

Measurements of the homogenization temperatures for many of the inclusions showed that the coarsely crystalline rhombohedral calcite, in fillings of cavities and fissures in the limestone skarns, and in the sulfide complex, was formed from hot liquid solutions at 260–195°C, and even lower. Epidote, chlorites, zinc blende, fluorite, chalcopyrite, quartz, galena, and some other minerals are associated with the rhombohedral calcite.

Consequently, the separation of the coarsely crystalline calcite coincided with a most intensive process of epidotization, chloritization, and carbonatization of the previously-formed silicate minerals. This may be observed at the skarn–limestone contacts, where large accumulations of hedenbergite are intensely replaced by calcite.

One may observe in many cavities exposed by the mine workings in the limestone skarns and in the marmorized limestones that well-faceted crystals of quartz of prismatic habit, with well-developed rhombohedral faces, so different from the previously described crystals of zoned quartz with ragged terminations, had grown between platelets of the rhombohedral calcite.

Individual crystals of that variety of quartz, in vugs, may be up to 2 cm in length and up to 0.8 cm in width. Two growth zones are clearly visible in thin sections of such crystals. The inner zone is a small crystal with easily noticeable faces and a poorly outlined formation, partially dissolved. The outer zone is much broader. Small calcite crystals are visible embedded in its periphery. The rhombohedral faces of the outer zone are appreciably corroded and, in the pits, one may see inserted crystals of calcite and of the younger quartz. Remnants of the mineral-forming solutions in both of the zones are represented by liquid two-phase inclusions whose distribution pattern and homogenization temperatures are shown in Fig. 9.

The pattern indicates that the crystal's inner zone was formed at a minimum temperature of 180–230°C. After that, the crystallization was

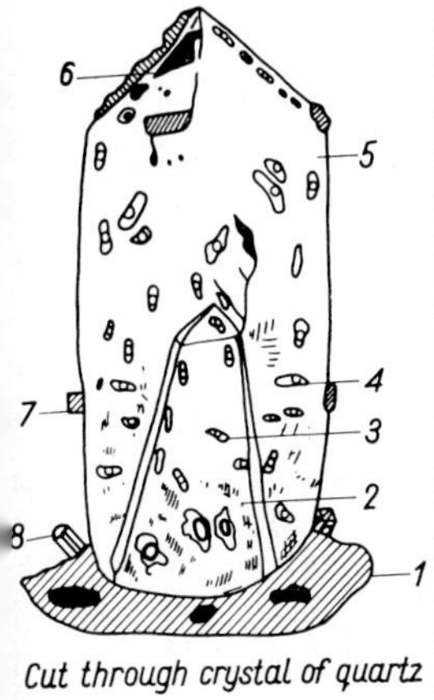

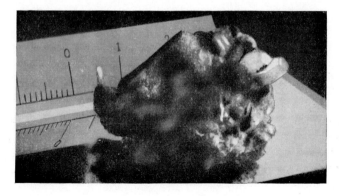

Cut through crystal of quartz

Name of zone	Gas-liquid ratio in in-clusions by zones (%)	Homogenization temperature (°C)
1. Massive quartz with garnet	—	—
2. Turbid zone of crystal with primary inclusions	35 : 65	225–230
3. Transparent zone of inner crystal with primary inclusions	25 : 75	180–205
4. Turbid zone of outer crystal with primary inclusions	25 : 75	200–205
5. Transparent zone of outer crystal with primary inclusions	15 : 85	150–160
6. Anomalous inclu-sions in fissures	—	—
7. Calcite	—	—
8. Crystals of quartz	—	—

FIG. 9. Pattern of distribution of inclusions in quartz crystals with well-developed rhombohedral faces and homogenization temperatures of the inclusions.

interrupted. After the interruption, the temperature rose abruptly, so that effective growth of the outer zone occurred at 205–160°C.

In many druse cavities of the skarns in our area, quartz crystals with well-developed rhombohedral faces are overgrown by small crystals of

FIG. 10a. Crystals of prismatic calcite (white) on quartz.

prismatic calcite (Fig. 10a). Moreover, this calcite includes several morphologic varieties, the most common ones of which are as follows:

1. Prismatic calcite with thickened terminations; crystal faces of this variety are often encased in a coating of pyrolusite.
2. Prismatic calcite without thickened terminations.
3. Scalenohedral calcite.

Every one of the varieties of calcite crystals has a zoned structure. Figure 10b illustrates cut sections through calcite crystals and reports the homogenization temperatures of their inclusions as well as inclusions in minerals associated with calcite.

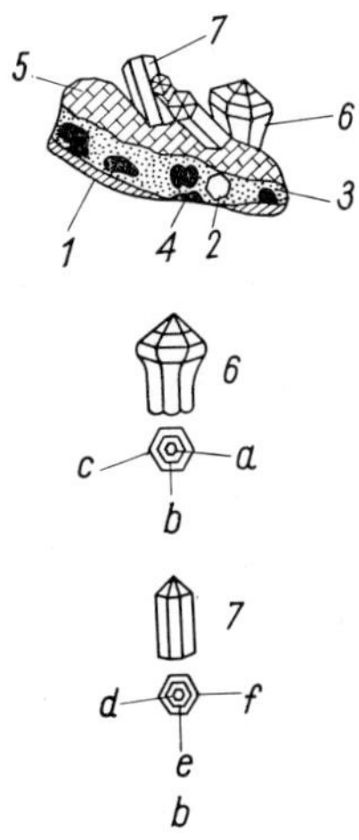

1. Skarn with disseminated sulfides	—
2. Quartz crystals	220–180
3. Massive quartz	220–180
4. Brown iron oxides	—
5. Crust of finely crystalline calcite	—
6. Calcite crystal with a black coating	162–75
a. Central zone	162–160
b. Intermediate zone	82
c. Peripheral zone	76–75
7. White calcite crystals	97–70
d. Central zone	97
e. Intermediate zone	88–87
f. Peripheral zone	78–70

FIG. 10b.

Three clearly defined growth zones are present in the pyrolusite-coated calcite crystals with thickened terminations as well as in the calcite crystals without such terminations.

Judging from homogenization temperatures of inclusions in the calcite with thick terminations, it grew at low temperatures, 162–75°C. Calcite crystals without the thick terminations were growing at still lower minimum temperatures: 97–70°C.

Crystals of quartz, with elongated-prismatic habit, are found in association with the prismatic calcite. Their size varies from 1 cm to very small. They are often assembled into druses of microscopic dimensions. The quartz crystals are transparent and their inclusions of mineral-forming solutions are easily detectable.

The quartz contains primary two-phase inclusions with the gaseous phase occupying about 10 per cent of the volume. These primary inclusions homogenize at 120–130°C. A large number of secondary single-phase liquid inclusions occurs in healed fissures of the crystals.

It follows that the small quartz crystals associated with the prismatic calcite crystallized under the same conditions as the calcite, i.e. at low temperatures.

It appears that the crystallization of the prismatic calcite with the finely crystalline quartz, in the main, was a completion of the hypogene process that gave rise to the deposit here discussed.

The scalenohedral calcite is widely represented in the northern part of the ore field, in the skarn–marble contact, where it produces beautiful druses in the vugs. Its crystals are like obelisks and may be as long as 7 cm and up to 3 cm across. Faces of the larger crystals support growth of smaller ones forming steeple-like agglomerations. The bases of the larger crystals are finely-zoned; the crystal tops are massive transparent calcite.

We could not detect any two-phase inclusions in the calcite here described. All of its inclusions are single-phase liquid ones, which is an indication of its having been crystallized from cold or tepid solutions at the very end of the hydrothermal process.

The following conclusions can be made, in regards to the formation of the skarn complex we examined, on the premises of the thermometric analysis of inclusions developed by Yermakov [5].

The structure of the ore body, the variations in the state of aggregation and in the temperatures of the solutions in the inclusions, and morphologic features of the paragenetic associations of the minerals—all indicate that the mineral genesis in the deposit here discussed occurred in stages. Moreover, the endogenic mineral genesis is clearly divisible into two stages: the pneumatolytic and the hydrothermal ones (Fig. 11).

The pneumatolytic stage took its course against the background of tectonic movements producing large fissures and fragmentation zones in the solid rocks overlying the magmatic source which consisted, by that time, of the already solidified part of the intrusion itself as well as of the limestones and the hornfelses penetrated by the intrusion. The pent-up mineral-forming solutions, in the molten body under the solidified shell, were streaming outwards, as gases and vapors, through the finest fissures and pores of the rocks, toward the lower pressure zones. These solutions were chiefly water vapor, oxygen, hydrogen, sulfur, carbon dioxide, fluorides and chlorides of aluminium, iron, magnesium, alkali earths, and other easily volatile constituents. They brought about an intensive reactional–metasomatic mineral genesis in the limestone–hornfels contacts and, to some extent, also in the solidified upper part of the intrusion, with the resulting development of hornfels and the limestone skarns. These

Stages of mineral genesis

Stages of mineral genesis	Character of mineralization	Stages of mineralization	Curves of the temperature regime of the mineral genesis / Sequence of separation of minerals
		Tectonic movements	
		Interruptions of growth	
Pneumatolytic	Rare–metal	The main stage of skarn formation (I) and the stage of complex skarn veinlets (II)	Plagioclase; pyroxene I *Garnet I* *Garnet II* Vesuvianite; wollastonite Pyroxene II *Scheelite* Molybdenite *Quartz* *Fluorite* Pyroxene II
Hydrothermal	Rare–metal	The stage of quartz–molybdenite–scheelite veins	*Scheelite* *Garnet III* Molybdenite *Quartz* *Fluorite* Scheelite
Hydrothermal	Rare–metal	The stage of silicate solutions supersaturated with chlorides	*Molybdenite, quartz* *Fluorite* *Magnetite; garnet IV* *Magnetite*
Hydrothermal	Sulfide	The stage of zoned quartz	Scheelite *Zoned quartz* Chlorites; albite Lievrite [ilvaite] Epidote-zoisite Cu Fe sulfides (small quantities) Rhombohedral calcite
Hydrothermal	Sulfide	The stage of rhombohedral calcite	*Quartz* Chlorites Sulfides of Zn, Pb, Cu, Fe Quartz
Hydrothermal	Sulfide	The stage of quartz–chalcopyrite	Platy calcite Sulfides of Cu, Fe, Zn Quartz
Hydrothermal	Sulfide	The stage of prismatic calcite	*Prismatic calcite* Sulfides of Sb, Cu, Fe Quartz
Hydrothermal	Sulfide	The stage of formation of antimony ores	Calcite, ankerite pyrite, antimonite chalcopyrite chalcedony opal-braganite

FIG. 11. Pattern of variation in the temperature regime

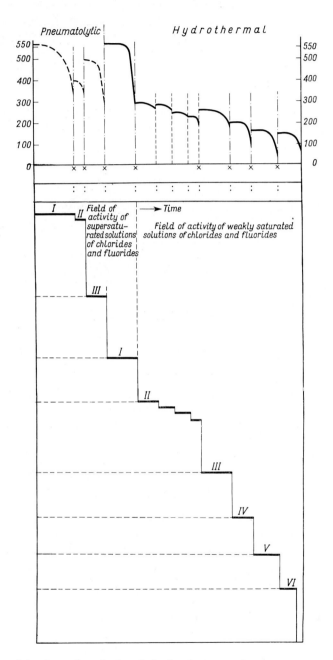

sequence of the formation of minerals in the skarn complex.

solutions had very high temperatures, considerably above the critical temperature of water (in the range of 500–700°C). These solutions were captured, as gaseous inclusions, by several minerals: pyroxenes, garnets, vesuvianite, scheelite, the early quartz, and fluorite.

The transition from the pneumatolytic to the *hydrothermal stage was* a consequence of a decreased temperature throughout the system of the magmatic hearth in the process of cooling.

The first portions of the hydrothermal solutions were highly super-charged with chlorides and fluorides of Na, K, Ca, and others and seemed to have had, at the start, temperatures exceeding appreciably the critical temperature of water.

The temperature regime, pressure, composition and concentration of the solutions—all were changing abruptly or gradually, in certain definite periods of time, within the hydrothermal stage of the mineralization, depending on the positions of their sources and on the geological environ-ment. Sudden increases in the temperature of the solutions generally coincided with tectonic adjustments opening new migration paths to fresh portions of the solutions originating in the depths of the cooling magmatic hearth and permitting access of these solutions to the sites of the mineralization.

Changes in the physico-chemical environments were registered by the formation of certain definite associations of minerals containing remnants of the mineral-forming media in the form of liquid inclusions we have already described in detail.

The following stages and epochs of mineralization embraced in the hydrothermal process are suggested by inclusions of the mineral-forming solutions and by paragenetic associations of the minerals:

(1) The stage of high-temperature liquid solutions highly super-saturated with chlorides and fluorides. Quartz, fluorite, molybdenite, scheelite, magnetite, andradite, and a fraction of copper and iron sulfides crystallized from these solutions. The supersaturated solutions had an initial temperature of about 600°C; they cooled gradually to 280–300°C. The minerals were deposited essentially in the same fissures and cavities as the minerals of the last two stages of the pneumatolytic mineral genesis. In other words, the transition from gaseous to liquid solutions was brought about by a lowering of the temperature. This particular stage of the mineralization is marked by immense numbers of multiphase inclusions in quartz and in fluorite, in magmatic rocks as well as in the skarn complex, supersaturated with solid phases.

(2) After the entire system became sufficiently cool, there was an incidence of new tectonic movements by which new zones of disruption were produced. Hot aqueous solutions streamed into these zones. They carried metals, sulfur, and other constituents on which the next stage of

the hydrothermal mineralization depended, the stage characterized by relatively weak concentrations of chlorides and fluorides of the alkali metals. This second stage of the hydrothermal process was marked by intensive deposition of zoned quartz and fluorite in fissures and cavities of the skarns and skarn veinlets as well as in the skarn–limestone contacts. The separation of minerals during the second stage took place under the temperature regime of 275–150°C (uncorrected for pressure). The redeposition of garnets (as hydrothermal andradite in the sulfide complex) took place during the same stage, alongside the crystallization of epidote, chlorite, fluorite, hydrothermal scheelite, magnetite, zoned quartz, marmatite, and a negligible fraction of the sulfides: pyrrhotite, pyrite, arsenopyrite, chalcopyrite, and others. This particular stage of the hydrothermal mineralization is easily recognized by the zoned quartz with needles of wollastonite. The growth zones of the quartz are expressions of the abrupt drop in the temperature, of solution, and of renewed growth at different levels of the mineralization.

Two-phase liquid inclusions are typical of the second stage of the mineralization, even as they are of all of the subsequent stages.

(3) The third stage of the hydrothermal process, the stage of carbonates–sulfides, was the leading one in the sulfide mineralization. Its minerals constitute the bulk of the sulfide complex. The mineral genesis was given a new impulse, during that period of time, by tectonic movements which opened the paths to the hot sulfide-saturated bicarbonate solutions ascending from the depths. A sudden abrupt increase in the temperature, from 150 to 260°C, is noted for the first level of the mineralization. The further growth of the minerals was at progressively falling temperatures, from 260 to 195°C and down to 160°C. The "typomorphic" mineral of that stage is the coarsely crystalline calcite of rhombohedral habit with which the other minerals are associated. The bulk of pyrrhotite, arsenopyrite, pyrite, and polymetallics (galena and sphalerite), now reached by the shafts in the north-eastern part of the ore field, was separated during that stage.

(4) The fourth stage of the hydrothermal process may be called the quartz–chalcopyrite stage. As the temperature rose up to 250°C, a fresh portion of hydrothermal solutions entered the fissures and cavities. The stage was characterized by the deposition chiefly of quartz, but also of small quantities of calcite, chalcopyrite, and chlorite. Within the same period of time, there was a deposition of very small crystals of cleiophane, arsenopyrite, and pyrite, in the contact zones around the fissures and cavities. The mineral complex of the fourth stage of the mineralization was deposited chiefly in fissures and cavities at the skarn–limestone contacts and also in fissures in the biotite porphyritic granite. Copper ores in the

neighboring sections of the ore field belong apparently to the same stage of mineralization.

Toward the end of the fourth stage, the temperature of the solutions fell down to 120°C (uncorrected for pressure). There was a gradual change in composition of the solutions; an increase in the concentrations of calcium and iron bicarbonates.

(5) The stage of prismatic calcite should be regarded as the fifth and the coolest stage of the hydrothermal process. It signifies the end of activities of the hydrothermal solutions, and its expressions, within the skarn body's boundaries, are much weaker than of any of the preceding stages. At that time, the carbonate–silica solutions seeping through fissures and pores of the previously formed mineral zones had temperatures in the vicinity of 162 to 70°C. Calcite of prismatic habit and the latest generation of quartz crystallized from these solutions. As to the ore minerals, there was a separation of small quantities of marcasite, melnikovite, cleiophane, etc., caused by redeposition of minerals in the earlier stages of the process. The minerals of the fifth stage are found often in the shape of well-formed crystals, as cavity-fillings in the limestone skarns and in the accumulations of minerals of the sulfide complex.

It is established accordingly, by the data of the thermometric analysis of inclusions of the mineral-forming solutions, that the temperature regime in the formation of the skarn-ore complex here discussed evolved by abrupt changes, against an overall background of temperature decrease for the system as a whole. Such variations in the temperature of the solutions were caused by tectonic movements accompanied by periodic reopenings of old fissures and by developments of new fissures in the zones undergoing the mineralization.

Formation of the skarn-ore complex took place in an environment of both continuous and discontinuous change in temperature and in composition of the solutions. From gaseous solutions, with temperatures exceeding the critical temperature of water, to liquid solutions, with temperatures barely above the temperatures of surface processes—that was the wide range of mineral genesis in our highly complex polygenetic skarn-ore complex.

BIBLIOGRAPHY

1. *Geologiya i rudnyye mestorozhdeniya Tsentral'nogo Kavkaza.* (Geology and Mineral Deposits of Central Caucasus.) Izd. Akad. Nauk SSSR, 1948.
2. GRUSHKIN, G. G., Nekotoryye voprosy genezisa mineralov. (Certain Problems in Origins of Minerals.) *Mineralog. sb. L'vov. geolog. obshch.* No. 4, 1950.
3. GRUSHKIN, G. G., O meste flyuoritno-rtutno-sur'myanoi formatsii v sovremennykh klassifikatsiyakh rudnykh mestorozhdenii. (In Regards to Position of the Fluorite–Mercury–Antimony Formation in Modern Classification of Ore Deposits.) *Tr. inst. geolog. Akad. Nauk Uzbek. SSR*, No. 11, 1954.

4. YERMAKOV, N. P., Temperatura obrazovaniya gidrotermal'nykh opticheskikh mineralov Sredney Azii. (The Temperature of Formation of Hydrothermal Optical Minerals of Central Asia.) *Sb. Sovet. geolog.* No. 1, 1944.
5. YERMAKOV, N. P., *Issledovaniya mineraloobrazuyushchikh rastvorov.* (Research in Mineral-Forming Solutions.) Izd. Khar'kov. univ., 1950.
6. ZAKHARCHENKO, A. I., *Mineraloobrazuyushchiye rastvory i genezis kvartsevykh zhil.* (Mineral-forming Solutions and Origins of Quartz Veins.) Gosgeoltekhizdat, 1955.
7. KALYUZHNYI, V. A. and L. I. KOLTUN, Nekotoryye dannyye o davleniyakh i temperaturakh pri obrazovanii mineralov Nagol'nogo Kryazha (Donbas). (Some Data on Pressures and Temperatures in the Formation of Minerals of the Nagol'nyy Kryazh, Donets Basin.) *Mineralog. sb. L'vov. geolog. obshch.* No. 7, 1953.
8. LESNYAK, V. F., Temperaturnye usloviya obrazovaniya odnogo svintsovo-tsinkovogo mestorozhdeniya Kavkaza. (Temperature Conditions in the Formation of a Lead–Zinc Deposit in the Caucasus.) *Mineralog. sb. L'vov. geolog. obshch.* No. 8, 1954.
9. LESNYAK, V. F., O nekotorykh geneticheskikh osobennostyakh granitoidov odnogo iz rayonov Severnogo Kavkaza, ustanovlennykh po vklyucheniyam mineraloobrazuyushchey sredy. (About Certain Genetic Features of Granitoids in one of the Districts of the Northern Caucasus, as Determined by Inclusions of the Mineral-forming Medium.) *Uch. zap. L'vov. univ.* Vol. XXXV, *ser. geolog.* No. 8, 1955.

Results of Mineralothermometric Studies
of Certain Crystals of Morion* from Volynia

N. P. YERMAKOV, V. A. KALYUZHNYI
and N. I. MYAZ'

CRYSTALS of morion are found occasionally together with topaz, in large cavities of natural "crystallizers" in certain pegmatitic bodies of Volynia. Zonal structures of these crystals are indications of variations in the environment wherein the crystals were formed. Since 1949, the authors had carried out more than 1500 thermometric analyses and analyses of the state of aggregation of relict solutions, sealed as inclusions inside the crystals, in order to determine the character of variations in the solutions from which the morion crystallized. The present article gives the results of these investigations for the ten largest crystals of quartz collected from different pegmatitic bodies. They show that different zones in individual crystals may be produced from solutions with different states of aggregation: from supercritical gaseous as well as from liquid hydrothermal solutions.

Thermometric analyses of gaseous inclusions do not give us, of course, temperatures sufficiently close to the true temperatures of mineral genesis, but they are interesting for comparisons between different crystals and their growth zones.

The temperature series of liquid inclusions reported below showing type I homogenization, occasionally involving boiling points, are more or less near the true crystallization temperatures of the morions and are important also in relative comparisons of crystals. Some of these figures are typical of the temperatures of simultaneous homogenization of series or groups of inclusions belonging to some particular moment of crystal-face growth or of healing of some particular fissure in the crystal. The occasionally noted instances of homogenization at unlike temperatures, for inclusions in the same healed fissure, are qualified in the text, in every case.

---

* Morion is a dark variety of smoky quartz [Ed.].

[490]

GIANT CRYSTAL No. 1

The outer transparent 16 cm zone of this giant consists of morion; its inner zone is gray; its center is a reticulate quartz with a vast quantity of essentially-gaseous inclusions. The broken surfaces of the crystal were found to be regenerated by a transparent crystal quartz.

It was established, in the sample of the crystal at 41 cm from the prism face, that its primary inclusions homogenize as in type II at 305°C (without inversion). Among the fissure-healing secondary inclusions, it was possible to recognize groups that homogenize at 240–280°C and at 145–195°C, both as in type I.

In another sample, from the central part of the crystal, taken at 28 cm from the outer face of the prism, the homogenization of primary inclusions was also as in type II (without inversion), at 320°C. Rare secondary liquid inclusions in the crystal's fissures, in contrast with the abundant primary ones, homogenized at the same temperatures as the secondary inclusions in the sample just described.

A sample of the crystal's gray zone, 24 cm away from the surface, was found to have an abundance of primary gas–liquid inclusions homogenizing as in type II, *with inversion,* at 310–330°C. Secondary inclusions in that sample homogenized as in type I and at the same temperatures as reported for the preceding samples.

The type II homogenization at 340–350°C, *with inversion* at 270°C, was ascertained in inclusions in the gray quartz 1 cm away from its boundary with the morion and 17 cm from the surface of the prism. In the morion sample from the contact zone (15 cm from the crystal's surface) the course of the homogenization was the same [i.e. type II, with inversion —V.P.S.], but at 330°C.

In the morion's outer zone, the homogenization was at 325–275–240°C, with inversion and with a criticial point. Also, the zone was found to contain essentially-liquid secondary inclusions representing different temperatures of fissure-healing: from 215 to 275°C and from 55 to 90°C, alongside pseudo-secondary inclusions homogenizing at 310–327°C.

It should be noted that, in the sample cut off from the surface of the prism (down to 1 cm depth), we discovered isolated multiphase liquid inclusions, *situated outside the fissures,* homogenizing at 302–310–320°C as in type I. An extremely rapid disappearance of the gas bubble, with boiling, several degrees below the homogenization temperature, was the special feature of the homogenization of these inclusions.

Definitely secondary inclusions were seen in fissures, in the zone right next to the crystal's surface, with homogenization temperatures at 55–90°C and at 140–190°C. The fissures' systems were healed probably concurrently with the very late formation of amethyst, chalcedony, and opal.

The crystal's inner part, broken in places, was regenerated by transparent quartz, with inclusions typical of the part of the crystal next to the surface (type II homogenization at 260–257–240°C and type I at 300–307°C).

Our study of the giant crystal here discussed proved to be very useful in the orientation of our subsequent work. For the first time we had the opportunity to track the sequence of types and species of homogenization of inclusions in quartz caused by variations in the solutions during the growth of a single crystal. These variations, tracked from the crystal's center to its outer morion zone, were reasonably clear-cut.

Essentially-gaseous inclusions (88–84.7 per cent gas; homogenization type II) were found in the inner part of the crystal (deeper than 25 cm from the prism surface). In the 25–16 cm span, below the surface, the inclusions were gas–liquid, with proportions of the liquid (at room temperature) increasing progressively toward the periphery of the crystal. This trend was accompanied, in our experiments, with a *progressive increase in the homogenization temperatures* (type II, with inversion) from 310–312°C to 350°C.

The zone of morion was formed mainly in the terminal stage of pneumatolysis (at the very beginning of hydrothermal activity), marked by a lowering of the homogenization temperatures of *the gas–liquid inclusions, found together,* it appears, with *the primary essentially liquid inclusions* homogenizing in the *liquid phase, but with boiling ahead of the homogenization.* We could definitely see, in one case, in a healed fissure, in the same zone of a different crystal, *the most highly varied homogenization temperatures and phase ratios.* That was typical, in our opinion, of *the crystallization and healing of minerals in boiling aqueous solutions freshly arisen from supercritical solutions.*

CRYSTAL No. 2

A similar pattern of variations, from the center to the periphery, is seen in a quartz crystal 25 cm between the prism faces. The crystal's marginal zone also consists of transparent morion and its interior is gray quartz. Primary inclusions in the crystal's inner zone homogenize, *with inversion,* at 310–305–290–285–280–270°C, but at 335–340°C, at its contact with the outer zone. In the outer morion zone, we again observe a radical decrease in the homogenization temperatures of the gas–liquid inclusions, down to 305–205°C. Moreover, that zone contains also some essentially-liquid inclusions whose positions in the crystal are such that it is not always possible to place them as secondary, with respect to the zone. Their homogenization temperatures (type I) were found to be as follows: 303–252–247–240–230–228–203°C, i.e. the same as in the former instance of homogenization in the gaseous phase.

A thought occurs here that the simultaneous presence of both gas–liquid and liquid inclusions homogenizing within one and the same range of the temperature may be explained only by a boiling of the solution during the growth of the crystal's outer zone.

Comparisons of the results for the first and for the second crystal lead us to the conclusion that the second crystal is *younger* than the first one. Its growth began when the inner part of the giant crystal was already formed, from gaseous solution, and had attained already appreciable dimensions. The giant's zone at 28–17 cm distance from the present faces of the prism is synchronous with the inner part of the second crystal. Both crystals completed their growth at the same time, in the last phase of the mineralization, at the border-line between pneumatolysis and hydro-thermal activity, when the mineral-forming solutions were boiling.

CRYSTAL No. 3

A crystal of morion with two well-preserved prism faces was examined thermometrically. The third face was severely corroded and was overgrown by crystals of smoky and transparent quartz. The other faces of the crystal were not preserved.

The examination was in the following sequence: the overgrowing crystals, beginning with the smallest ones, were studied first and the main crystal afterwards.

The small crystals of the overgrowth, "d", "e", and "f", showed the following:

(1) Inclusions of aqueous solutions with 10–20 per cent gaseous phase were more abundant than the others. They were often found in healed fissures extending not quite to the outer surfaces of the crystal.

(2) Obviously secondary gaseous inclusions with 100–99 per cent gas, in healed fissures extending definitely to the outer faces of the crystals. Among them there were a few inclusions with intermediate phase ratios.

In medium-sized crystals in the overgrowth on the main crystal (crystal "a"), the following was noted:

(1) Liquid–gas inclusions, more abundant than the rest, with a maximum of 40–50 per cent gas phase.

(2) Inclusions with 95–98 per cent gas phase were rarely found. Bands of regularly shaped tubular inclusions were conspicuous. Their included contents were at considerable distances from each other* and were oriented in the same direction.

Flattened and perfectly flat inclusions were also seen.

All of the inclusion types here enumerated were found also in the main crystal.

---

* Original obscure [V.P.S.].

The following was shown by the analytical results:

(1) In the small crystal "f" (7 × 2 mm), from the overgrowth, all syngenetic inclusions homogenize in the liquid phase at 112–119–130–135–185–198–260–264–280°C.

(2) The small crystals "e" (crystal's termination) and "d" also display homogenization as in type I and in the following range of the temperatures: 150–152–158–170–171–180–184–244–249–251°C.

(3) Crystal "a" proved to be very similar to the large, main crystal. Its syngenetic inclusions homogenized in the liquid phase at 292–310–309–312°C or else at 320–324–327°C, also in the liquid phase, but occasionally in the gaseous phase, *with boiling* of the included solutions 5–8°C below the homogenization temperatures.

(4) The abundant inclusions in the main crystal homogenize generally in the liquid phase, but with boiling. The following series of homogenization temperatures was established, which is probably very close to the true temperatures of crystallization, in view of the boiling of the included solutions: 283–285–290–292–300–307–312–315–316–317–320–322°C.

Also, we discovered inclusions homogenizing in the gaseous phase at 332°C, with boiling, and inclusions homogenizing with a critical point at 327°C.

A series of progressively decreasing temperatures of the once active solutions was established for liquid inclusions, secondary with respect to the main crystal, but representing the process of growth of the small crystals, and homogenizing in the liquid phase, *without boiling*: 262–261–244–240–215–200–197–177–172–167–165–162–158–155–153–152–148–145 143–142–110–103–102°C.

Some new and interesting phenomena were discovered in the inclusions of the boiling solutions.

One of the tubular inclusions contained 46 per cent gas phase at room temperature. This inclusion behaved normally on heating up to about 230°C, i.e. the volume of its gaseous phase contracted gradually. *A second phase boundary* appeared at 230°C, separating a liquid of rather high index of refraction which occupied one end of the inclusion. The volume of that liquid continued to increase on further heating, while the volume of the gaseous phase still decreased. The aqueous solution began to boil at 325°C and continued to boil until the end of the homogenization. The gas phase disappeared at 327°C, but the liquid of high index of refraction remained in one end of the inclusion where it occupied 8 per cent of the inclusion's volume.

In order to save the inclusions, it was not heated above its homogenization temperature. On cooling the heterogenization took place in the reverse sequence.

It follows that the liquid solution, in the inclusion here described, contained *a substance easily soluble at low temperatures, but sparingly soluble at high temperatures.* The presence of that substance was apparently conducive to a lowering of the critical temperature as well as of the homogenization temperature. The stratification of the liquids was connected possibly with certain definite ratios of the inclusion's solutes, $Na_2O-SiO_2-H_2O$, as in the phenomena that take place in experiments with the system of this composition.

More detailed and exact investigation of the behavior of the inclusions here described, in the course of their homogenization, reflected so clearly in the homogenization curves, in addition to the chemical analyses of the included mother liquors and the diagrammatic physico-chemical comparisons, may give us the key to the phase transformations in remnants of the parent solutions imprisoned in minerals.

Detailed studies of this crystal allow us to believe that:

(a) crystallization of the morion took place at the threshold between the pneumatolytic and the hydrothermal processes, from liquid solutions near their boiling points and their critical points;

(b) the overgrowing small crystals of crystal-quartz grew slowly from ordinary hydrothermal solutions, seemingly at low concentrations, at an appreciable drop of temperatures of the quartz-forming solutions;

(c) toward the end of the hydrothermal mineral genesis, probably because of a radical decrease of the pressure brought about by tectonic factors, there was a superimposition of a pneumatolytic phase in the course of which there was a healing of fissures in the small crystals as well as in the main crystal.

CRYSTAL No. 4

This small crystal has a zonal structure: (1) The crystal's center is smoky quartz. (2) The part next to the rhombohedral surfaces is morion, 9–10 mm thick. (3) A pale gray thin siliceous opal–chalcedony crust over the rhombohedral faces and present also, as irregular spots, on the faces of the prism.

There is a striking difference between the first and the second zones, in quantities of their inclusions. The light smoky zone has abundant inclusions of various sorts, while there are only a few of them in the morion.

The following was identified in the crystal:

(1) Gas–liquid inclusions with large proportions of the gas phase (50–60 per cent). It was proved that they occur to within 1 or 2 mm of the outer faces of the prism.

(2) Liquid inclusions of aqueous solutions—obviously primary—in the thin upper morion zone of the crystal. Large full-volume inclusions (occasionally 1 by 1.15 mm) with irregular shapes, are plainly visible in this group.

(3) Multiphase liquid inclusions, extremely small, not susceptible to measurements.

(4) Single-phase liquid inclusions, obviously primary, in the opal-chalcedony crusty overgrowth. Such inclusions constitute evidence of the growth of such crusts from tepid and cold-water solutions.

Only liquid inclusions, homogenizing at 163–187–190–200°C, could be found in the crystal's thin outer morion zone.

The interior of the crystal consists of a gray (smoky) quartz and contains gas–liquid inclusions homogenizing, with inversion, at 299–306–308–312–314°C.

Pseudo-secondary inclusions were also observed in that zone, in its fissures, synchronous with the formation of the crystal's outer morion zone. The following homogenization temperatures were established, with homogenizations in the liquid phase: section from the crystal's base—160–173–184–186–189–195–200°C; section under the morion termination of the crystal—113–117–168–170–172–175–176–180–184–188–190–192–193–196°C.

Consequently, the crystal here described grew mainly from pneumato-lytic solutions and only its morion termination and its thin outer zone crystallized from low-temperature hydrothermal solutions.

CRYSTAL No. 5B

The following zones were identified in this thermometrically examined crystal of morion, with poorly preserved faces and with evidence of a mechanical fragmentation:

(1) The top zone, consisting of amethyst spread as islands over the entire surface of the main crystal faces, and growing also as a crystalline filling in the crystal's fissures. One such large fissure runs through the entire body of the crystal. This fissure is *completely filled with crystalline amethyst* in one side of the main crystal, but ist left open and gaping on the other side. An opal–chalcedony crust was laid down in places on the surface of the amethyst.

(2) A more or less continuous zone of a transparent light-colored crystal quartz.

(3) The morion zone.

The amethyst has an abundance of radiating ray-like fine-needle crystals of goethite with rounded aggregations of hydrohematite. Inclusions of mineral-forming solutions are rarely found. They proved to be chiefly low-temperature hydrothermal and secondary single-phase liquid inclusions. The primary liquid inclusions each contain a gas bubble occupying up to 10 or 15 per cent of the cavity's volume. Such inclusions were formed inside or around the accumulations of the finest needles of goethite and are isolated from each other. Their homogenization temperatures range from 130 to 150°C.

Inclusions of liquid aqueous solutions are abundant in the zone of the light-colored crystal quartz and in the morion of the inner part of the crystal.

They homogenize, as in type I, at the following temperatures: in crystal quartz—175–178–182–184–187–192–200–202–208–210°C; in morion—200 –204–210–212°C.

However, both of the zones contain some very minute gaseous inclusions, probably of a secondary origin, with homogenization temperatures of 300–340°C.

CRYSTAL No. 6A

This crystal is a large one, with a large number of defects. The crystal is a gray honeycomb quartz with morion, 25 cm along the c axis, and 12 cm broad at the base. The crystal was probably broken off and the resulting rough surface was overgrown by transparent multinucleated growth. The boundary between the rough base and the transparent overgrowth is sharply defined, but no inclusions could be detected in it. To a lesser extent, there was also a deposition of light-colored transparent quartz on the principal faces of the main crystal. The crystal's termination is disjointed; the main terminations is recognizable, and so is the other one, weakly developed, which belongs to the second individual. The outer faces of the crystal are rough, definitely mosaic, with ample relics of a multinucleated growth.

The crystal, in the main, is of morion; its growth was completed by light-colored quartz whose thickness ranges from a few mm to 1–1.5 cm.

The multinucleated growth zone of the quartz contains inclusions of an associated mineral, with an acicular habit. The mineral is probably goethite which is so often found in gaseous macro- and micro-inclusions. It occurs in zones often parallel to the crystal-growth faces, and the bundles of radially diverging crystals always point toward the crystal's face. It needs be assumed that, in the case here described, goethite crystallized concurrently with quartz from pneumatolytic gaseous solutions, during a certain stage (goethite in the inclusions continued to crystallize until the vacuoles were finally sealed and it does not dissolve completely on homogenization).

Inclusions of the parent solution were found to be chiefly gaseous (90–97 per cent gas phase) and they nearly always contained liquid carbon dioxide (about 2–3 per cent). They were situated in healed fissures. Liquid inclusions with 95–97 per cent liquid phase were extremely rare. They were found in healed fissures as well as in isolated positions.

The crystal's inner zone contained inclusions of "dry" gases with 10 to 1 per cent liquid phase. Such inclusions were more abundant than the others. They were situated in healed fissures running through the crystal in all directions.

Obviously pseudo-secondary inclusions were found among the gaseous ones. They were situated in reticulate fissures, sharply conspicuous against the background of smoky quartz that had undergone the $\alpha–\beta$-transformation. Such inclusions represent undoubtedly the first moments of the pneumatolytic growth of the morion. Gaseous solutions were functioning as the mother liquor, in that stage, as indicated by the inclusions with very small quantities of liquid (up to 2–3 per cent).

The homogenization temperatures of the various gaseous inclusion groups were as follows: 142–184–220–224–232–280°C.

Large gaseous inclusions, generally with carbon dioxide, are of considerable interest. The walls of their vacuoles are coated with a very thin film appearing as an irregular tortuous honeycomb. This roughness would vanish slowly on heating and would reappear on cooling, but in different positions. These inclusions give us the opportunity to appraise the concentrations of the gaseous mineral-forming solution which may acquire a real significance in an appreciable degree of transfer of substances.

Liquid inclusions with various phase ratios are found in every part of the morion zone. As a rule, they are situated in fissures of various ages. Their homogenization temperatures, by analysis, were as follows: 182–202–214–255 and 261°C. Among these heterochronous inclusions, we must call attention to some very rare large ones, obviously secondary, with 1 to 5 per cent gas phase and homogenization temperatures of 60–70°C. Very fine scales of an iron mica were common inside these inclusions. Their origin belongs to the very last stage of activity of the liquid solution which were apparently also depositing chalcedony.

Liquid three-phase inclusions are also rare. In addition to liquid and gas, they each contain a small cubic crystal. The crystal remains unchanged despite an appreciable overheating of the inclusions, over and above their homogenization temperatures. Such inclusions homogenize at 216–217–218–225°C.

The multiphase crystal–gas inclusions, the bulk of whose volume is occupied by solid phases and the rest by liquid and gas, are generally very small and are to be found in the gray quartz. As many as five captive crystals could be distinguished in such inclusions at high magnifications.

The first two of the five (apparently sylvite and halite) dissolved at 40–60°C and 170–260°C respectively. On the whole, such inclusions are distinguished by their very high homogenization temperatures, type I, involving, it appears, a fusion of parts of the captive crystals at 540–585–600°C.

A light-colored associated mineral of a rounded shape, indicative of a strong solvent action, was found at the crystal's base, 1.5 cm from the surface of the face. This crystal was shown to be topaz by optical measurements, and contained gaseous inclusions. It was not possible to investigate the inclusions further.

It developed, in this manner, that the growth of the crystal here examined was complicated and confused by recurrent alterations in the physico-chemical environment of the mineral genesis. One may be certain only in the fact that the crystal's transparent outer zone was deposited during repeated superimpositions of pneumatolysis involving solutions containing carbon dioxide and other substances. Highly concentrated fused solutes with brine, as well as both gaseous and liquid solutions at different temperatures and concentrations took part in the mineral genesis. It appears that the rapidly changing conditions of crystallization that produced the kaleidoscopic assortment of inclusions were also responsible for the many defects of that disorganized crystal.

LARGE CRYSTAL No. 7

This crystal has a strong morion zone overgrowing the turbid gray quartz comprising the inner core of the crystal. The boundary between the morion and the turbid honeycomb quartz was found to be sharply defined. The crystal's thickness was about 0.5 m, from face to face of the prism, and its length was 1 m. The lower part of the crystal was regenerated by a very thin layer of light-colored quartz. There were very many solid inclusions in that part of the crystal—associated crystals with very high indices of refraction. The crystal was traversed by fissures, healed by pneumatolytic solutions, judging from the character of their gaseous inclusions, the solutions from which the thin layer of transparent quartz was laid down. Inclusions with 40 to 90 per cent gas were predominant in the crystal; inclusions with CO_2 were also present. The crystal's inner part had abundant faceted essentially-gaseous inclusions homogenizing as in type II at 351–341–335–330–321–320–302–295°C. Typical temperatures for the crystal's center were 351–330–320°C.

One side of the boundary between the honeycomb gray quartz and the morion had gaseous inclusions homogenizing as in type II at 310–278–270–262°C, while the other one had inclusions of liquid aqueous solutions with type I homogenization at 274–272–251–248–243–241–217–206°C. The morion zone itself contained scarce and isolated definitely primary inclusions of liquid aqueous solutions homogenizing at 257–230–216°C. Along the fractures inclusions were developed with homogenization temperatures of 193–186–135°C, typical of the crystal's transparent outer zone. In that zone, liquid inclusions were encountered which yielded the following series of homogenization temperatures: 203–201–195–192–189–182–178–177–176–173–172–169–166–163–161–160–131°C.

Every zone of the crystal here described is traversed by fissures of various ages carrying groups of gaseous inclusions homogenizing as in type II at 341, 332, 328, 325, 320, 315, 302, 298, 289, 268, and even 215°C.

The following homogenization temperatures were established for groups of gaseous inclusions in the various fissures cutting through the morion zone: 352, 348, 333, 241, 240, and 234°C.

The core of the thermometrically examined crystal was formed at high temperatures, as α^* quartz, which was later transformed into the honeycomb β-quartz. The numerous honeycomb fissures, resulting from the α–β-transformation, were healed at once with the essentially-gaseous solutions. Deposition of the morion zone began toward the end of their activity and proceeded under the stabilized regime of liquid aqueous hydrothermal solutions whose temperature fluctuated between 275 and 215°C (uncorrected for pressure). Later, on the growth faces of the morion, there was deposition of transparent and grayish crystal quartz, at 200–130°C, from liquid solutions.

These solutions, while active, healed the heterochronous fissures in the morion zone. Afterwards, possibly by some tectonic movements, the crystal was broken from the place where it grew and was pierced by fissures of a later origin. Tectonic movements of that kind brought about a decrease in the pressure at the site of the mineralization and a fresh outburst of pneumatolysis, in which the initial dissolution was followed by a regeneration of the crystal's broken surface by transparent quartz accompanied by the healing of its later fissures by gaseous solutions.

CRYSTALS Nos. 8 and 9

Fragments of crystals of morion, with well-preserved faces of their steepest rhombohedron and partially preserved faces of the prism, were examined thermometrically. The crystal faces are covered by well-defined striations. There are traces of solution on the edges of the rhombohedral faces. One of the prismatic faces is striated at a 45° angle.

Transverse cut sections through the crystal show plainly two zones: the inner one, of morion and the outer, of light-colored crystal quartz.

---

* Note usage of α and β here is the reverse of U.S. usage [Ed.].

The thickness of the light-colored quartz varies from 0.5 to 0.7 cm, on the average, on different faces of the crystals. The crystals have very abundant liquid inclusions. There are several primary tubular inclusions in the morion zone, deep in the crystal, oriented parallel to the faces of the prism. There are some tubular inclusions also in the light-colored outer zone of the crystal. Their shapes are somewhat irregular and they contain carbon dioxide.

Structural resemblances between the two crystals and the thermometric data lead us to believe that both crystals were taken from one and the same vug. Gas–liquid inclusions, homogenizing as in type II with inversion, at 350–338–278°C, were discovered in the interior of both crystals. The relative scarcity of such inclusions, by comparison with their numbers in the other crystals examined by us, leads to the conclusion that the pneumatolytic stage was relatively unimportant in the crystallization of these two crystals.

There is a multitude of liquid inclusions of hydrothermal solutions in the morion zone. They homogenize as in type I at the following series of temperatures: 383–343–338–334–333–300– 289–279–247–236–225–214°C.

Typical homogenization temperatures, 203–194–193–192–191–177°C, were established definitely for inclusions in the transitional zone of crystal No. 8. This temperature range is narrowed down to 205–190°C, in the analogous zone of crystal No. 9. The outer zone of light-colored quartz contains successive series of inclusions homogenizing at 193–190–183–177– 175–164–152–141°C. The same zone has some inclusions in its fissures homogenizing between 118 and 99°C. That zone, in crystal No. 9, shows the following temperatures: 195–193–184–183–173–164–152–141°C. Homogenization temperatures of pseudo-secondary and secondary inclusions in heterochronously healed fissures could be established also for the morion central zone. Specifically, the measured temperatures for the central zone of morion were 195–193–184–166– 161–118°C.

CRYSTAL No. 10

Crystal No. 10 was found to differ somewhat in its structure from Nos. 8 and 9, as shown by thermometric studies.

Two zones of light-colored quartz are clearly visible in the outer envelope of the transparent quartz crystal, in addition to the inner morion zone.

Presence of a few gas–liquid inclusions was established in the inner part of morion, homogenizing as in type II, with the inversion, at 377–361– 358 and 388°C; these are absent in the outer zones.

A series of liquid inclusions, very abundant in the morion and the morion–quartz inter-zone section, homogenizes as in type I and at the following temperatures, in decreasing order: 359–338–303–280–230–227–

225–224–219–215°C. Temperatures of 209–206–203–198–195 and 187°C were recorded for the morion at its boundary with the inner zone of light-colored quartz.

A series of higher homogenization temperatures of liquid inclusions was discovered in that quartz: 224–220–213–205–203–197°C. At its boundary with the outer zone of light-colored quartz, the numerous inclusions manifested a stable homogenization temperature of 185°C. Liquid inclusions in the outer zone of that second variety homogenized as in type I at 179–175–142–129°C.

Pseudo-secondary inclusions were found, of course, also in crystal No. 10, in fissures within its inner zone, with their homogenization temperatures falling within the range of homogenization temperatures of the corresponding outer zones. Despite the differences in the structure of this crystal and the structures of the previously described crystals 8 and 9, we must acknowledge also some features of their resemblance in the structures as well as in the homogenization temperatures. Only the abrupt change in the temperature at the onset of deposition of the first variety of light-colored quartz merits our attention.

With the last three examples of quartz crystals we examined, from the pegmatites of Paromovka, it was illustrated how studies of inclusions may give a clue to a syngenetic character of the crystals or to a close resemblance of the environments wherein the crystals were formed. The typical feature of the Paromovka crystals is *the very rapid decrease in the pulse of the temperatures of the mineral genesis.* Not in a single stage, not at any single level of the crystallization was there a period of time of steady and balanced temperatures and of functionally related variables. Even relatively small crystals display evidence of a striking decrease of the temperatures of the solutions within a range in the vicinity of 180°C. This served as a stimulus for a rapid and hurried crystallization, for a capture of a vast number of liquid inclusions, and for the appearance of many defects (mosaic, etc.) in the crystals.

It had already been demonstrated in 1944* that monothermal crystallization proceeding within a relative short range of fluctuation of temperature and of the related factors is conducive to formation of the most perfect crystals. Such relatively balanced stages of post-pneumatolytic and hydrothermal mineral genesis have their expressions in many large vugs of Volynia, as shown by the thermometric studies of many crystals. However, there are certain individual features of different large vugs alongside the common over-all characteristics of the mineral genesis. Even in one and the same large vugs, depending on the positions of the crystals, certain nuances in the crystallization are detectable thermometrically

---

* *Sovet. geolog.,* No. 1, 1944.

together with the genetic reasons for material differences in the appearance and structure of individual crystals, against the background of general features typical of one and the same large vug. The stages of post-pneumatolytic early-hydrothermal crystallization that are characterized by homogenization of the inclusions in the liquid phase, involving the point of inversion, the critical point, and boiling, were favorable for the crystallization of morion, in a relatively slowly changing temperature environment.

Both in the north of Volynia and in the Paromovka area, we find great contrasts both for crystal growth and the formation of large vugs containing the crystals.

Certain Genetic Features of the Kurumkan Deposit Ascertained by Means of Mineralothermometric Analysis

YE. M. LAZ'KO

THE crystal quartz deposit of Kurumkan is one of the most interesting bodies in the Upper Aldan crystal quartz district. Its geologic structure, however, will be reported here only in a most general way, inasmuch as our paper deals with a specific problem. Rocks of the Archaean complex: various quartzites with quartzite–gneisses, garnet–, sillimanite–, and cordierite–gneisses, basic crystalline schists and quartz–feldspar–gneisses participate in the geologic structures of the district, together with the Proterozoic granitoids already described [4]. In addition to the rocks here enumerated, the Archaean complex includes granite–gneisses, small massifs of granitoid rocks, alaskite granites, granite–pegmatites, and migmatites of various kinds.

Primary sedimentary rocks of the Archaean complex are assembled in a series of anticlinal and arm-like synclinal folds, complicating the apron of a large anticlinal structure of the first order. The deposit's fracture pattern is intricate. Combinations of different systems of fissures and fractures produce local accumulations, in different parts of the deposit, in which most of the occurrences of the veins and most of the large vugs and "nests" of crystal quartz are segregated. Four parts of the deposit are differentiated, the four vein zones, the confines of which contain the basic occurrences of the veins in which the great majority of crystal-quartz-bearing cavities is found. These cavities are associated with different systems of fissures, with their intersections, with the contact zone of pegmatitic or quartz veins, or else the cavities are found inside the latter.

Processes of near-vein alteration are expressed with a particular intensity wherever there is an abundance of fissures in which there is an appreciable accumulation of quartz veins as well as of crystal-quartz-bearing cavities. Pegmatitic and pegmatoid formations especially are radically altered by hydrothermal metamorphism and are generally transformed into clayey materials.

Quartz crystals from Kurumkan are characterized by their moderate size, hexagonal habit, and, as a rule, a smoky color of variable intensity.

Liquid and essentially-gaseous inclusions are common in the crystals. Among their solid inclusions, kaolin, hematite, fluorite, calcite, and chlorite were observed.

A high degree of scattering of the indications of crystal quartz over a wide area, at the Kurumkan, made that deposit a promising field for systematic mineral thermometric investigation, an undertaking that enabled us to draw several important conclusions regarding the origin of the deposit.

Two zones, the inner one of morion and the outer one of a lucid crystal quartz, show plainly in transverse cuts through the crystals. Thickness of the lucid quartz, the outer zone, varies from 0.5 to 0.7 cm, on the average. The crystals are literally filled to overflowing with liquid hydrothermal inclusions, generally with irregular shapes. Several primary tubular inclusions were encountered in the morion zone. They are situated deep in the crystal parallel to the prism faces. The lucid zone also contains tubular inclusions, of a rather irregular shape, with carbon dioxide.

Crystals from the southern part of the deposit, from trenches Nos. 73, 77, X-3, 113, 114, from the south-eastern part of opencut No. 1, and other sites, contain large numbers of essentially-gaseous inclusions homogenizing in the gaseous phase within a relatively narrow range of the temperature: 500–470°C. The southern part of the deposit is characterized also by an abundance of primary inclusions and of inclusions whose origin is uncertain homogenizing at high temperatures: (a)* 400–390–370–360–350–340°C; (b) 300–290–280–270–260–250–240°C, the typical homogenization series established for the inclusions. In addition, large numbers of secondary inclusions are also present that homogenize within a wide temperature range: 230–60°C. Many of these secondary inclusions contain a solid phase, a little cube of halite, or liquid carbon dioxide.

In the central part of the deposit, in the vicinity of shaft No. 6, the crystals chosen for the analysis were taken from the upper and the lower horizons of the mineralized zone. Analysis of the primary inclusions of uncertain origin served to establish the following typical homogenization series for early crystals: (a) 230–225–220–210–205–200–190°C; (b) 180–170–165–160–155–145–140°C. For later crystals, the series were found to be: 135–130–125–120–115–110–100°C. Essentially-gaseous, liquid, and multiphase inclusions with halite or carbon dioxide were discovered among the secondary inclusions. It should be pointed out that the essentially-gaseous inclusions are less abundant than the liquid ones. There is a smaller number of multiphase inclusions, especially of inclusions with solid phase.

---

* (a) presumably refers to the primary inclusions and (b) to the doubtful ones [V.P.S.].

Crystals from the northern part of the deposit, taken from large vugs, "nests", and small vugs in opencuts Nos. 3 and 4 and from nearby trenches contain inclusions (primary and uncertain ones) that homogenize at relatively low temperatures: (a) 170–160–165–160–150°C and (b) 140–135–130–120–115–110°C.

Secondary inclusions belong to various types and homogenize within a wide temperature range, although both essentially-gaseous and multiphase ones, with halite, are rarely found among them and, at that, only in certain crystals. Graphs of the temperature regime for such inclusions are shown in Fig. 1.

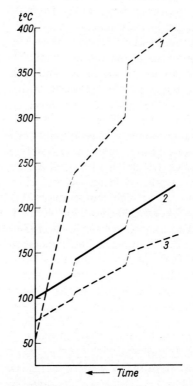

FIG. 1. Temperature regime of solutions (as indicated by inclusions in quartz).
1. Vugs in the southern part of the deposit; *2.* Vugs in the central part; *3.* Vugs in the northern part.

It should be of interest here to consider the data obtained by Koltun [3] for liquid inclusions in fluorite crystals, a mineral often found associated with quartz in the vicinity of opencut No. 4. The inclusions in fluorite crystals situated with a clearly defined growth zone of the quartz showed a homogenization temperature of 158°C. Primary inclusions in the quartz itself, in the same growth zone, showed the same homogenization temperature which is undoubtedly an indication of a syngenetic origin of the host mineral and of its associate, the fluorite, which grew within a definite range of temperature, concurrently with the quartz, and from the same solution.

In addition to crystal quartz, the columnar and massive vein quartz, as well as the hydrothermally altered quartzites within the mineralized zone were subjected to mineralothermometric investigation.

Various kinds of secondary inclusions were discovered in the quartzite grains: essentially-gaseous, liquid, and multiphase, with carbon dioxide and with solid phases. Their homogenization was within a wide range: 440–65°C.

Essentially-gaseous inclusions are predominant in the massive vein quartz, with homogenization temperatures of 470–360°C, as well as high-temperature liquid inclusions homogenizing at 390–270°C. Inclusions in the columnar vein quartz are chieflly high-temperature liquid ones homogenizing at 335–240°C. Homogenization temperatures of the inclusions vary, depending on the spatial position of the vein quartz: the highest temperatures were recorded for the deposit's southern part, in opencut No. 1—335–315°C.

Moreover there is an interest also in data on the temperature regime of the solutions from which the vein quartz formed, at every concrete site: the maximum drop in the temperature does not exceed 30°C, as determined for the vein quartz crystals from different sites.

The foregoing results of the large-scale mineralothermometric analyses enable us to make a series of conclusions the most important ones of which are the following:

(1) Within the boundaries of the Kurumkan deposit, there is no observable orderly relationship between variations in the homogenization temperatures of inclusions in transparent crystal quartz or columnar vein quartz and distances from the powerful pegmatitic bodies. This is particularly clearly shown by the examples of opencut No. 3 and especially of the center of opencut No. 2 where crystal quartz is found in direct proximity to a large pegmatitic body traversing the entire territory of the deposit in the north-easterly direction. Inclusions in crystals from these two sources homogenize at significantly lower [sic] temperatures than inclusions in crystals from the southern part of the deposit.

(2) Presence of large numbers of inclusions was noted in the crystals, with homogenization in the gaseous phase, which is an incontrovertible evidence of proximity of a magmatic source of the solutions.

(3) The number of inclusions in quartz decreases gradually, as one goes from south to north, which leads to the belief that the crystal quartz-bearing veins of the deposit are connected genetically with the intrusion

of granodiorites situated to the south of the deposit. This view is confirmed by the gradual decrease in the temperatures, as recorded on homogenization of the inclusions in the crystals of both primary and uncertain origin, as one moves away from the intrusion (Fig. 2), and as evidenced by the progressively decreasing numbers of multiphase inclusions with halite.

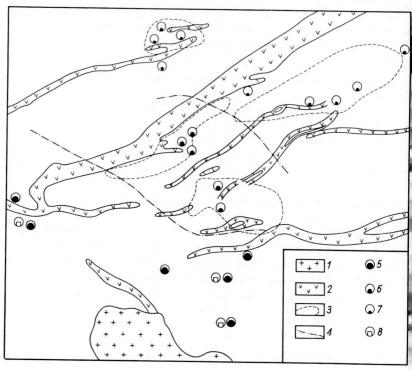

FIG. 2. Distribution pattern of various inclusion types in quartz of different vein zones.

1. Proterozoic granitoids; *2*. Archaean pegmatites; *3*. Vein zone boundaries; *4*. Boundaries of concenters of heterotypic and heterothermal inclusions; *5*. Essentially-gaseous and high-temperature liquid inclusions (homogenization temperatures of liquid inclusions 400-240°C); *6*. Medium-temperature liquid inclusions (homogenization temperatures 230-140°C); *7*. Low-temperature liquid inclusions (homogenization temperatures 170-110°C); *8*. Multiphase inclusions (with halite and carbon dioxide)

(4) Quartz, both as a vein filling and as quartz crystals, was deposited from liquid and gaseous solutions. The role of the gaseous solutions decreased progressively with distance from the magmatic source. This is shown especially clearly in the examples of crystal quartz and vein quartz. The relationship is not observed in the instance of the earliest massive vein quartz, however. That variety, it appears, was formed in the early stages of stabilization of the intrusion, during accessions of the hottest

gaseous and liquid solutions, when the distance from the intrusion was not the decisive factor in the abrupt transitions from one state of aggregation to another or in the temperatures of the solutions.

(5) Hydrothermal metamorphism of the quartzites proceeded under the influence of the same solutions by which the quartz crystals were formed. This is evidenced by the great variety of secondary inclusions in quartz grains in the quartzites, analogous to inclusions of the same type but of primary origin in crystal quartz from different parts of the deposit.

(6) There is probably a definite connection between the quality of the crystals and the character of the solutions. The best grade of raw crystal materials is extracted from cavities in the northern and the central parts of the deposit, while the raw materials from its southern section are distinguished by their low quality.

BIBLIOGRAPHY

1. GRIGOR'EV, D. P., Generatsiya i zarozhdeniye mineralov. (Generation and Beginnings of Minerals.) *Mineralog. sb. L'vov. geolog. obshch.* No. 3, 1949.
2. YERMAKOV, N. P., *Issledovaniya mineraloobrazuyushchikh rastvorov.* (Research in Mineral-forming Solutions.) Izd. Khar'kov. univ., 1950.
3. KOLTUN, L. I., Opyt geneticheskogo issledovaniya nekotorykh endogennykh mesto-rozhdenii po vklyucheniyam v mineralakh. (An Experiment in Genetic Investigations of Certain Endogenic Deposits by the Means of Inclusions in their Minerals.) *Avtoreferat dissertatsii.* L'vov, 1953.
4. LAVRENKO, E. I. and E. M. LAZ'KO, O porodakh granodioritovogo ryada iz verkhov'ev reki Aldana. (On Rocks of the Granodiorite Series from Headwaters of the Aldan River.) *Dokl. Akad. Nauk SSSR*, Vol. 89, No. 6, 1953.

Genetic Relation of Quartz Veins in the Barsukchi Deposit and Granitic Intrusions as Indicated by Inclusions in Minerals

A. V. Piznyur

THE crystal-quartz-bearing veins of Barsukchi are associated with quartzites. Macroscopically, they are medium-grained and rarely coarse-grained rocks, pale gray to white and locally blue with a brownish tinge.

Granoblastic kernels, many of which are fragmented, are visible microscopically in the quartzites. Sillimanite needles, often piercing quartz grains, are situated in fissures as well as between grains of quartz, alongside platelets of mica. Large grains of potassium feldspar, isolated scales of sericite, and films of iron hydroxides are also found rather often. Among the ore minerals, the rocks contain substantial quantities of magnetite.

In addition to these admixtures, the quartz grains composing the quartzites also contain secondary impurities of mineral-forming solutions with carbon dioxide. The quartzites are severely altered at their contacts with the quartz veins. The contacts are clearly defined or, in places, vague. The quartzites were particularly well altered also in the fissured zones which contain the crystal-quartz-bearing cavities for that reason.

The near-vein alterations are especially well defined within the fourth and the first vein zones (Fig. 1). The quartzites, in these areas, are of characteristically dense textures and their colors are red-brown or green, depending on the presence of hydromica, iron hydroxides, sericite, and chlorite. Thickness of the near-vein alterations, in the zones, is 1 or 2 m, decreasing gradually at increasing distances from the veins. Solution of the quartzites is also noticeable.

The near-vein alteration in the third vein zone is associated, in all probability, with the fracture that runs directly across the zone and extends toward the fourth vein zone. As the result of the alteration, there is a development of rocks that have lost the normal appearance of the quartzites. They have acquired a dark brown color, the characteristic microfolding, and came to resemble metamorphic mica schists. Only an occasional presence of large relict grains of quartzite tells us about the original composition of these rocks.

[510]

There is appreciably less alteration in the quartzites of the second vein zone at their contact with quartz veins. The near-vein alteration has a somewhat different character in that area. The foremost processes were as follows: leaching, secondary quartzification, and, locally, feldspatization and limonitization. In places, the quantities of silica leached out of the quartz were so great that the zone's rocks failed to preserve even their skeletal forms and were converted into a friable rubble. The secondary quartz does not cement the quartzites but is formed in the pores of the rocks in the form of a free growth of finest crystals.

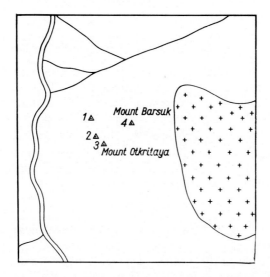

FIG. 1. Distribution pattern of vein zones in the Barsukchi deposit.

In order to determine the character of the near-vein alteration in the quartz grains composing the quartzites, we examined their secondary inclusions of mineral-forming solutions. The size of the grains was 0.2 to 5–7 mm; their form was equant; their color pale gray to dark blue. There is an abundance of secondary inclusions in various states of aggregation and composition, in thin sections cut from the quartzites.

1. INCLUSIONS IN GRAINS OF QUARTZITE

Transparent quartz grains composing the quartzites near the fourth vein zone contain, in addition to their solid inclusions, very small gaseous and liquid inclusions with different phase ratios as well as inclusions with carbon dioxide. All of them are secondary and their forms are irregularly equant. Inclusions of the essentially-gaseous type are predominant (the gas bubble occupies 75–90 per cent of the inclusion's volume). They homogenize as in type II, at 458, 437, 412, 400°C. The liquid inclusions homogenize as in type I in the following range of the temperatures: 373, 368, 360, 348, 317, 305, 300°C.

The inclusions with carbon dioxide have highly varied phase ratios: $G < CO_2 > L$; $G > CO_2 > L$; $G < CO_2 < L$; $G > CO_2 < L$. On heating, the inclusions with CO_2 homogenize at the following temperatures: 29.8, 30.2, 30.4, 30.78, 30.8, 30.88°C.

The liquid inclusions, right next to the inclusions with CO_2, homogenize as in type I at 130, 128, 125°C.

Proceeding from the foregoing minimum temperatures, the minimum pressures of 210–190 atm are indicated by Kalyuzhnyi's curves [2].

Extremely small liquid inclusions are situated in fine fissures which cut across the quartzite grains and also at boundaries between the grains. They yield a continuous series of homogenization temperatures from 373 to 30°C, as a reflection, it appears, of multiple repetitions of superimpositions of individual stages of mineralization. This in indicated also by the fact that all inclusions in a given fissure have nearly the same homogenization temperatures and have nothing in common with any other fissure that has its own range of homogenization temperatures. It is possible to break down the previously cited temperature series into groups each of which is associated with a single fissure: 340–320, 300–295, 270–255, 195–160°C, etc.

From these results, we may conclude that the alteration of quartzites near the fourth vein zone, the closest one to the granitic intrusion, was the result of activities of pneumatolytic as well as of hydrothermal solutions highly saturated with CO_2. Metasomatism played an essential part in the transformation of the quartzites.

Inclusions in quartzite grains near the first vein zone, the most distant one from the granitic intrusion, differ from the ones described. Their forms are irregular and their sizes are also small, but their composition is different. There are practically no gaseous inclusions among them, none of the very type that is so preponderant in quartzites of the fourth vein zone. However, even in the vicinity of the first zone, there are very many inclusions with CO_2 with different phase ratios, as well as liquid inclusions whose presence also aids us in drawing certain conclusions in regards to the minimum pressure effective in the area at the time of the formation of the deposit.

The homogenization data on the inclusions with CO_2 give us the following temperatures: 27.2; 24.3; 24.2; 21.2°C. Homogenization temperatures of the liquid inclusions are: 125, 120, 110, 105°C. This allows us to assume that the minimum pressure range was 140–120 atm.

Some of the inclusions in quartzite grains of the area homogenize at lower temperatures: down to 90°C. They too can be grouped by their fissures, each with its own definite range of homogenization temperatures.

Secondary inclusions in the quartzites enable us to establish the minimum temperature conditions as well as the pressures of the solutions in the host rocks during the formation of the deposit.

The foregoing discussion permits us to draw the following conclusions:

(1) The district was subjected to tectonic movements in the course of the formation of the deposit whereby the migration of solutions was facilitated.

(2) The corresponding pressures were not uniform. The pressure was high in the vicinity of the fourth vein zone, near the intrusion, and low in the vicinity of the first vein zone.

(3) In the vicinity of the fourth vein zone, the initial pneumatolytic solutions were succeeded by hydrothermal ones, with intensive metasomatism accompanying the alteration of the rocks.

(4) In the vicinity of the first vein zone, the solutions had only a hydrothermal character and their action on the host rocks consisted of leaching and withdrawal of minerals, with the production of the friable quartz rubble.

(5) The solutions were highly saturated with carbon dioxide in both areas.

(6) The absence of essentially-gaseous inclusions in the vicinity of the first vein zone and their radical preponderance in the vicinity of the fourth vein zone shows that the granitic intrusion was the source of the mineral-forming solutions.

2. INCLUSIONS IN VEIN QUARTZ

The deposit's vein quartz is represented by two varieties: (1) massive sugary dense fine-grained vein quartz (the first vein zone) and (2) columnar vein quartz, including large and giant-sized crystals (the fourth vein zone).

The vein quartz in quartzites is a fissure filling. As a rule, the more severely fissured areas and the zones of fragmentation are richer in vein quartz. In most of the cases, the coarse columnar quartz aggregates grow directly on top of the altered quartzite. More rarely, the quartzite is covered by a thin layer (0.5–5 mm) of a sugary milky-white vein quartz. Contacts of the vein quartz with the quartzites are generally sharp, and occasionally vague. The vein quartz contains practically no impurities, although small quantities of hematite, rutile, muscovite, sericite, and—more rarely—anatase and sphene are visible locally. In addition to these minerals, the vein quartz contains an abundance of essentially-gaseous and liquid inclusions of aqueous solutions.

A. Inclusions in massive vein quartz

The massive vein quartz within the first vein zone boundaries is severely fissured and has an abundance of small inclusions. Their forms and sizes vary over a wide range, from barely visible under the microscope to 0.05 mm. The inclusions' phase ratios are variable. This indicates a frequently repeated imposition of the mineralization stages during the formation of the deposit and of the healing of fissures by fresh accessions of solutions.

Thermometric analysis of inclusions of mineral-forming solutions in small crystals encountered in the sugary quartz that seem to be from some later stage, as against the sugary vein quartz wherein they are contained, gave the following temperatures: 325, 295, 289, 270, 269°C; the inclusions homogenized as in type I.

The absence of gaseous inclusions in the milky-white vein quartz was due apparently to its long distance from the intrusion functioning as the source of the mineral-forming solutions.

B. Inclusions in columnar vein quartz

The columnar vein quartz in the fourth vein zone is a loosely growth-joined columnar crested aggregate of crystals of various sizes, of a few centimeters' order of magnitute, and occasionally even up to tens of centimeters. Distribution of the crystals in the vein quartz is, on the whole, perpendicular to the plane of their growth. In the majority of the cases, the quartz grows directly on top of the quartzite; more rarely, the quartz is underlain by a thin layer (up to 5 mm) of a fine-grained vein quartz. The quartzite-quartz contacts are sharp. The columnar vein quartz is often represented by a brush-like growth of well crystallized semitransparent vein quartz and of transparent crystals. Some of these brushes, judging by their transparency and the orientation of crystals, indicate crystallization in an open space.

As a rule, the columnar crystals of quartz have growth zones. Their primary inclusions are easily identified for that reason. Growth zones of the crystals are separated by adhesions of solid inclusions of hematite, quartz fragments, and platelets of mica. They contain essentially-gaseous and, more rarely, liquid primary inclusions, as well as some very small inclusions with carbon dioxide. Their forms are equant and their sizes are small (up to 0.03 mm).

The minimum range of temperatures of the columnar quartz crystal growth was 515 to 115°C, as indicated by the determined homogenization temperatures of its primary inclusions, against the background of a general lowering of the temperatures and of the successive states of aggregation of the mineral-forming solutions.

The cores of the columnar vein quartz crystals were growing in pneumatolytic solutions (homogenization of the inclusions at 515–470°C, as in type II). Inclusions in all of the other growth zones homogenize as in type I, in the liquid phase. There is a suggestion of a discontinuous crystal growth (breaks between the ranges of the temperatures and separations of the growth zones by adhesions of solid inclusions).

The data here reported lead us to the following conclusions:

(1) The vein quartz in quartz-crystal-bearing veins in proximity to the intrusion has mainly essentially-gaseous inclusions, while vein quartz at a distance from the intrusion has liquid inclusions of the mineral-forming solutions.

(2) Inclusions in both varieties of vein quartz contain relatively small quantities of liquid carbon dioxide.

(3) Formation of vein quartz in areas of the fourth and of the first vein zones took place at relatively high temperatures, as compared with temperatures of the solutions that produced hydrothermal alteration of the quartzites.

(4) The state of aggregation of the mineral-forming solutions was changing together with the decrease in the temperatures from the central parts of the crystals to the peripheral growth zones of the columnar vein quartz.

(5) Accessions of mineral-forming solutions had a pulsating character, as confirmed by the discontinuous growth of the columnar quartz crystals and by healing of the fissures.

3. INCLUSIONS IN CRYSTAL QUARTZ

A. Inclusions in crystal quartz of the fourth vein zone

We are reporting here the results on the two most representative crystals, in a characterization of the temperature regime of the zone.

One of these crystals is 3 cm long, along its main axis, and its prismatic faces are 1 cm apart. The thin section used in the analysis was cut through the entire crystal parallel to the main axis. The crystal consists of two parts: a turbid one, from the base to about one half of the crystal's length, and a perfectly transparent one composing the rest of the crystal. Essentially-gaseous inclusions are predominant at the very base of the crystal. They homogenize as in type II at 362, 336, 312°C. The quantity of the essentially-gaseous inclusions decreased with distance from the crystal's base, so that essentially-liquid inclusions, homogenizing as in type I at 294, 289, 269°C, already become predominant halfway up the crystal.

The crystal's upper part is tinted brown and is perfectly transparent, with the zone's boundary marked by the color. Pseudo-secondary inclusions in fissures infesting that part of the crystal gave the following homogenization temperatures: 133, 110, 100, 90, 80°C, with the homogenization as in type I.

There are adhesions of solid inclusions, hematite and rutile [3], near the outer faces of the crystal separating the crystal's central zone from its thin outer zone. In the midst of these solid inclusions, liquid inclusions are also found, with homogenization temperatures at 110, 105°C.

The crystal also has inclusions with liquid carbon dioxide; their determined homogenization temperatures are analogous to those of inclusions in the quartzites, the host rocks of the zone.

Crystal quartz of industrial grade was crystallized in a hydrothermal environment, at the minimum temperatures of 240–200°C. The crystal growth was concluded at 150–100°C. The crystal-quartz-forming process in the fourth vein zone is represented in Fig. 2, where the lower curve refers mainly to crystals of industrial grade.

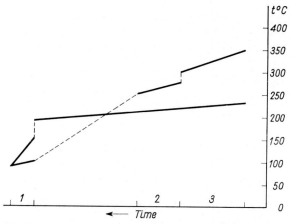

FIG. 2. Temperature regime during formation of crystal quartz in the fourth vein zone.

1. The outer zone of the crystal; homogenization as in type I; 2. The middle zone of the crystal; homogenization as in type I; 3. Base of the crystal; homogenization as in type II.

Our investigations showed that crystal quartz in the fourth vein zone was formed first by pneumatolytic solutions succeeded later by the hydrotherms. Formation of the outer parts of the crystals, the ones that meet industrial specifications, was brought about by the action of the hydrotherms. Formation of the columnar vein quartz and of the vein zone's crystal quartz, on the whole, was apparently a result of one single process associated with an appreciable lowering of the temperature. In the vicinity of the fourth vein zone, in addition to the solution of a pneumato-lytic character, there were accessions also of solutions highly enriched with carbon dioxide.

B. Inclusions in crystal quartz of the first vein zone

Crystals of the first vein zone have a transparent termination, with a slightly pink tinge, and are generally turbid at their base. Their length is 12–13 cm, along the main axis, and their prismatic faces are 1.5–2 cm apart. The crystals' habit is medium- or long-columnar, prismatic, with the development of main rhombohedral and pyramidal [*sic*] faces, with an abundance of hemihedral faces, ones that are absent or nearly absent in crystals of the other vein zones.

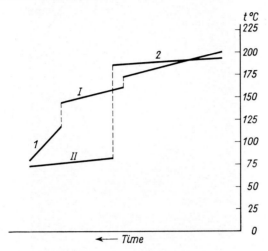

FIG. 3. Temperature regime during formation of crystal quartz in the first vein zone.

I—Crystal No. 1; *II*—Crystal No. 2 (*1*—transparent section, "the cap"; *2*—central part of the crystal.

For a characterization of this zone, sections were cut from crystals, along the main axis as well as at right angles to the main axis. Examination of thin sections showed an extreme scarcity of gaseous inclusions homo-genizing as in type II. Among the solid inclusions, hematite, magnetite, quartz fragments, and sericite are common. All of the solid inclusions are situated between growth zones that occur in every crystal. Liquid inclusions are common, generally of irregular shapes and up to 0.2 mm in size. The transparent terminations of crystals in this vein zone generally have no growth zones, but their basal parts do have such zones.

The results of our study of two representative crystals indicated the sequence of temperatures during their growth, as represented in Fig. 3.

One may see that the central part of crystal No. 1 was growing at a minimum temperature of 195–170°C. Later on, the temperature fell to 160–140°C. The crystal ended its growth at 115–80°C.

Crystals with "caps", i.e. with transparent terminations of a color different from the tint of the rest of the crystal (Fig. 4), were formed under a rather different temperature regime, although the temperature of the beginnings of crystallization of both parts were the same. The turbid part

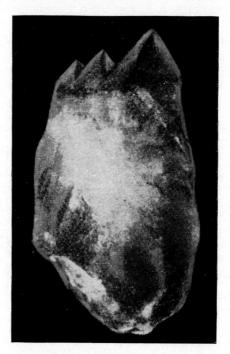

FIG. 4. Crystal quartz with a transparent termination ("the cap").

of the crystal grew at the minimum temperatures of 190–180°C. This temperature range was sustained until the transparent pink termination began to grow. At that time, the temperature of the solutions was 80–75°C. Thus the growth of crystals in the first vein zone began at a gradually falling temperature and continued, with interruptions, at repeated and drastic drops in the temperature of the solutions.

Omitting here the descriptions of crystal quartz from the third and the second vein zones, together with their thermometry, we shall present a tabular summary of our results and a general diagram of relative temperatures for the deposit as a whole (Fig. 5).

The data here reported, from our thermometric investigations by Yermakov's method [1], have led us to certain conclusions that are worth-

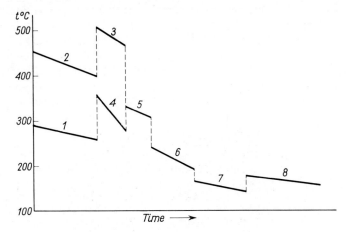

FIG. 5. Summary diagram of relative temperatures of solutions at the Barsukchi deposit.

1. Quartzites in vicinity of the first vein zone (away from the intrusion); *2.* Quartzites in the vicinity of the fourth vein zone (next to the intrusion); *3.* Columnar vein quartz of the fourth vein zone; *4.* Massive vein quartz of the first vein zone; *5.* The fourth vein zone *6.* The third vein zone; *7.* The second vein zone; *8.* The first vein zone.

while in regards to evidence of the origin of the deposit. The principal conclusions are as follows:

(1) At increasing distances from the granitic intrusion the source of the quartz-forming solutions, the temperature fell from 515°C in a quartz vein near the intrusion to 80°C in one far away from the intrusion.

(2) There was a parallel change in the state of aggregation of the solutions (pneumatolytic to hydrothermal). Inclusions in the altered quartzites, the vein quartz, and crystal quartz of the fourth vein zone in the vicinity of the intrusion homogenize as in type II, while inclusions in quartzites, vein quartz, and crystal quartz in the first, the second, and the third vein zones, at some distances from the intrusion, homogenize as in type I.

(3) The temperature regime in the host quartzites, in the course of the hydrothermal metamorphism, differed from the temperature regime at which the vein quartz was formed. The determined temperatures for secondary inclusions in hair-like fissures in the quartzite grains were 27–52°C lower than the temperatures for inclusions locked in the vein quartz which was deposited in open fissures.

(4) Processes of wall rock alteration, next to the intrusion of granites (vicinity of the fourth vein zone), were chiefly replacements of minerals by minerals, but, at a distance from the contact (site of the second vein zone), it was the leaching that was of most importance. The pressure of mineral-forming solutions by which the quartzites were altered was higher next to the intrusion than at some distance away.

RESULTS OF THERMOMETRIC INVESTIGATIONS

Test material	Range of minimum temperature (°C)	Type of homoge-nization	Minimum pressure, atm	Abundance of gaseous inclusions
Quartzite, near intrusion	458–400	II	210–190	very high
Quartzite away from intrusion	286–263	I	140–120	low
Vein quartz near intrusion (vicinity of the fourth vein zone)	515–470	II	—	very high
Vein quartz away from intrusion (vicinity of the first vein zone)	362–290	I	—	low
Crystal quartz (the fourth vein zone)	336–312	II	—	very high
Crystal quartz (the third vein zone)	240–199	I	—	low
Crystal quartz (the second vein zone)	160–140	I	—	isolated inculsions
Crystal quartz (the first vein zone)	190–160	I	—	nearly none

BIBLIOGRAPHY

1. YERMAKOV, N. P., *Issledovaniya mineraloobrazuyushchikh rastvorov*. (Research in Mineral-forming Solutions.) Izd. Khar'kov. univ., 1950.
2. KALYUZHNYI, V. L., Zhidkiye vklyucheniya v mineralakh kak geologicheskii barometr. (Liquid Inclusions in Minerals as a Geological Barometer.) *Mineralog. sb. L'vov. geolog. obshch.*, No. 9, 1955.

Inclusions in Reticulate Quartz of Volynian Pegmatites and the Results of Thermosonic Analysis

YU. A. DOLGOV

As a rule, reticulate quartz occupies the central zone of morion crystals where it represents the first, highest-temperature stages of quartz growth in cavities within pegmatites. Reticulate quartz is situated in the centers of large and small crystals. It has well-defined faces resembling the outlines of a hexagonal pyramid; the prism faces are generally absent. There is a clearly defined boundary between the reticulate quartz and the later zones of the overgrowing morion, with an occasional distortion of rectilinear contact.

The color of reticulate quartz in the central zone of the crystals varies within a wide range, from a deep morion to colorless. Such quartz is not transparent in large lumps, on account of a multitude of inclusions. In thin sections, not thicker than 2 mm, the main body of the reticulate quartz (outside the healed fissures) is transparent regardless of its color.

The reticulate configuration of the healed fissures may be recognized in lump specimens, against its contrasting background, by an experienced eye. The configuration is plainly visible in thin sections. Size of the cells in the healed reticulate fissures varies from 1 to 3 mm and may be up to 8 mm, in exceptional cases. Extremely fine cells (much smaller than 1 mm) may be found occasionally.

The cells often resemble distorted hexagons, but, still more often, depart appreciably even from that from (Fig. 1).

Our microscopic studies of reticulate quartz were made in thin sections and at different magnifications. We prepared and examined more than 300 such sections, some of which had areas larger than 10 cm².

Configuration of the network of healed fissures was studied at low magnifications against a black background, in reflected light. High magnifications were employed in the examination of inclusions in healed fissures and in the zones between them. The data so obtained enabled us to recognize resemblances and dissimilarities in the configurations of sealed fissures, in forms and sizes of the inclusions, in the states of aggregation, and in the phase ratios of the inclusions.

Inclusions in the quartz are situated mainly in healed reticulate fissures. The reticulate pattern of fissures is produced only by transformation of

[521]

FIG. 1. Microphotograph of reticulate quartz.

the high-temperature α-quartz into the β-quartz involving a rapid cooling. Inclusions are found not only in healed reticulate fissures but also in healed rectilinear fissures. Both of these inclusion categories are pseudo-secondary, inasmuch as they were developed synchronously with the overgrowth of the post-reticulate quartz, while the fissures were still healing. The recti-linear fissures also contain pseudo-secondary inclusions that are syngenetic with inclusions in the zones whose growth was synchronous with healing of the fissures by the same mineral-forming solutions.

There are also rectilinear fissures with secondary inclusions that were healed by solutions epigenetic with respect to the already-formed quartz. Thus the pseudo-secondary and the secondary inclusions are not repre-sentative of the state of aggregation of the solutions from which the reticulate α-quartz had grown.

Primary inclusions, characterizing the mineral-forming medium by which the pre-inversion α-quartz was formed were sought in the spaces between the healed reticulate fissures. The search was a difficult one and required a large number of preparations.

Presence of the primary inclusions was established in the spaces between the fissures. They proved to be ordinary solidified inclusions represented by crystals with gas or, very rarely, without gas, indicative

---

* I.e., crystal–gas, crystal–liquid–gas or crystal only [V.P.S.].

of certain $C–G$, $C–L–G$ ratios or else just plain C.* All of that is typical of the state of aggregation of the mineral-forming solutions from which the pre-inversion α quartz was formed, as a melt.

A category of primary inclusions was discovered, with immense quantities of the solid phase densely packed in the inclusion, but showing no clearly faceted forms. Interstices in that solid phase contained small quantities of liquid with a gas bubble of an appreciable size. Such a state of aggregation of the included mineral-forming solution, as evidence of the state of aggregation of the original mineral-forming solution, depicts the later as a highly supersaturated melt-solution tending toward a melt. Such inclusions could be heated successfully up to 450–500°C. These are the temperature limits withstood by two of our preparations before their destruction.

Attainment of these temperatures failed to produce homogenization; there was merely an increase in the liquid phase and a decrease in the solid and the gaseous phases.

A third category of inclusions discovered in the inter-fissure spaces could be considered a primary one only tentatively. It consists of large inclusions of irregular shapes with solid phases and with non-spherical gas bubbles. Origins and environments of the formation of such inclusions are still obscure, although there is no doubt as to their $C–G$ ratios.

Pseudo-secondary inclusions in reticulate fissures have their own characteristic forms and phase ratios. Most of them have nearly balanced forms. Exceptions are rare. These inclusions generally appear as negative crystals with a short prism. Very often their forms appear distorted, by the position of the thin section and the inclusions contained therein, with respect to the axis of observation. The inclusions marked-off* as hexagonal ones lie in the plane perpendicular to the sixfold axis and show only the nearly hexagonal forms, but it is difficult to appraise the length of the prism with their aid. Variations in sharpness of the outlines, with depth, suggest a negligible length of the prism.

Examination of many thin sections of reticulate quartz served to establish the presence of deviations toward an unbalance in shapes of the inclusions and variations in the length of the prism.

As to the state of aggregation—we found a consistent preponderance of essentially-gaseous inclusions and of inclusions of "dry" gases.

In regards to the phase ratios, we observed essentially-gaseous inclusions containing up to 25 per cent liquid phase, inclusions of "dry" gases with not over 5 per cent of liquid, and complex multiphase inclusions with two liquids (solution and liquid CO_2) and gas. More rarely, we saw inclusions with a liquid, a gas, and a solid phase or with two immiscible

---

* As in the standard practice prescribed by Yermakov in his book [V.P.S.].

liquids, a gas, and a solid phase. The gaseous phase was preponderant over the solid and the liquid phases in the latter two instances.

After our studies of the main features of the majority of pseudo-secondary inclusions, we may point out that inclusions with appreciably more gas than liquid are the preponderant type by far in the group. However, the liquid content of inclusions may vary up to its maximum, when the liquid begins to exceed the gas. Pseudo-secondary inclusions in rectilinear and in curved fissures are of a later origin than inclusions in the reticulate fissures. They were produced in the post-inversion period of quartz growth. They cut across the reticulate quartz and the overgrowth zones of the crystal (Fig. 1), and carry inclusions with more gas than liquid. Their form is nearly balanced, in the majority of cases. As shown by Tsinzerling's experiments and by our studies, fissures of that sort are formed in the temperature range from the inversion point to 200°C and only as the result of a contractional compression caused by a general cooling of the host rocks, particularly during rapid cooling against a background of slowly decreasing temperatures.

Inclusions in the rectilinear and in the curved fissures, as against inclusions in the reticulate quartz, are of a later age and are indicative of low temperatures, but they resemble inclusions in the reticulate quartz in their form, state of aggregation, and the phase ratios.

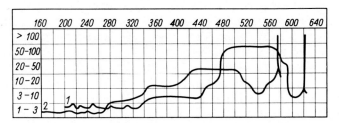

FIG. 2. Thermosonogram of reticulate quartz.

1. Curve with a drastic decrease in frequency preceding the dense inversion maximum; *2.* Curve with a less clearly expressed decrease in frequency preceding the dense inversion maximum. The temperature difference preceding the dense inversion constitutes 50°C (the ordinate shows the frequency of explosions).

Low density of mineral-forming solutions is a common feature of pseudo-secondary inclusions, healed reticulate fissures, as well as of straight and curved fissures. This fact "runs like a red thread" through the entire history of the crystal's growth. The formation of the contraction fissures is related evidently to an abrupt cooling of the crystal and to a decrease in the density of the mineral-forming solution in the cavity of the vug. Fissures with obviously secondary inclusions are a great rarity in reticulate quartz. Such fissures developed in, and were healed by, the very last portions of already cooled liquid mineral-forming solutions. The fissures appear to be of a mechanical origin, the results of tectonic movements and of falls from the cavity's walls. They were healed concurrently with the growth of the regenerated zones. Inclusions in such fissures are more often flat and are rarely "three-dimensional." The majority of them contain only small quantities of gas. The homogenization temperatures are low: from 30–40 to 100–120°C.

More than 50 thermosonic analyses were made on the reticulate quartz. The reticulate quartz stands out conspicuously in the thermosonograms we obtained (Fig. 2).

Explosion of low-temperature secondary inclusions may or may not occur in the low-temperature stages, from 30 to 120–150°C. Occasional explosions at low frequency may take place within the range of 150–300°C. Explosions with high and ultra-high frequency begin at 300–500°C, ± 50°C. The frequency of explosions is diminished from 500°C to the inversion point. The inversion point is confined to a 5–6°C span of temperature, after 500°C, where it occurs at various temperatures and with appreciable displacements. Displacements of the inversion point take place on changes in the pressure and in the presence of impurities. Experiments with thermosonic recording are done only at 1 atm pressure and, for that reason, displacements of the inversion point cannot be affected by the pressure. Displacements of the inversion point in our experiments were up to 40°C (and higher, on occasions).

Explosions of inclusions at the inversion point are facilitated by the structural rearrangements with the accompanying increase in volume. There are no explosions at the inversion point in pure quartz which is inclusion-free. Reticulate quartz, within the narrow range of polymorphic transformations, produces a very large number of explosions called by us "the density maximum". There are density maxima in all thermosonograms of reticulate quartz, without exceptions. This fact allows us unmistakably to identify presence of reticulate quartz, in cores and placers, which is important in prospecting for pegmatites of the chamber type.

Influence of Liquid and Gaseous Inclusions on Magnitudes of Losses on Ignition of Minerals

N. P. Yermakov and N. I. Myaz'

EXISTENCE of liquid and gaseous inclusions must be taken into account in descriptive mineralogy, in studies of the properties and composition of minerals.

Inclusions of liquid aqueous solutions, so widespread in hydrothermal minerals, and of gaseous inclusions, common in minerals of pneumatolytic origin, affect both the chemical composition of seemingly identical crystals, and their specific gravity, losses on ignition, and a whole series of physical and chemical properties of minerals. Neglect of inclusions of mineral-forming solutions in crystals has led and is still leading to many perplexities in the interpretation of results even of the most reliable and painstaking determinations. The necessity of taking into account the included mother liquors in determination of the losses on ignition will be presently demonstrated.

As we know, water is present in many minerals where it plays an exceptional role in mineral genesis and in metamorphism. So far, only three types of such water were recognized: water of constitution, crystallization, and adsorption. Our research showed that large quantities of water are locked in primary, pseudo-secondary, and secondary liquid and gaseous inclusions in many pneumatolytic, hydrothermal, and cold-water minerals and also in metamorphosed–hydrothermal minerals. The total quantities of such inclusions are so great, on occasions, that their aqueous solutions may occupy up to 10 per cent of the crystal's volume, and more. Expulsion of all this water by overheating and exploding the liquid inclusions [1] leads naturally to appreciable losses on ignition of minerals.

Microscopic studies of a whole series of crystal-hydrates, such as inyoite, gypsum, alunite, etc., show that such minerals may contain very large numbers of inclusions of mother liquor and not merely the water of crystallization, as it was heretofore believed [2, 3]. Up to this time, liquid inclusions are omitted from consideration in tensiometric [vapor pressure?] studies and in interpretation of the results on dehydration of minerals. Some of the hydrous borates, such as inderborite and hydroboracite, of a very close or identical composition, differ from each other only by their water content which is calculated entirely to water of crystallization. It is possible that a number of crystal-hydrate minerals, differentiated from each other only by their water content will require a special investigation in the future, in order to find out what particular kind of water was really responsible for their separate identifications.

Proceeding from the established fact that primary, pseudo-secondary, and secondary inclusions of mother liquors (liquid and gaseous) are common phenomena in practically all minerals and that the included water is liberated on heating, by rupture of the vacuoles, we desire here to show the need of accounting for such water in the thermal studies of certain minerals.

Specifically, in the classification of water in crystals and solid colloids, in addition to the three known types, the waters of constitution, hydration, and adsorption, we must recognize the fourth one, captive or *parental,* locked hermetically, or nearly so, in the pores of minerals.

While examining fluorites, as early as in 1943, one of us had proved that "the more liquid inclusions in fluorite, the greater is the loss on ignition. Ruptures of such inclusions are easily brought about by ignition (by overheating above the homogenization temperature) resulting in losses of volatile constituents, chiefly water" [1, p. 301]. For example, 1.35 per cent of the weight of a greenish fluorspar from a hydrothermal source in Tadzhikistan was lost on ignition, from a specimen containing an abundance of aqueous inclusions; a colorless optical-grade fluorite, with very few inclusions, lost 0.06 per cent, while a perfectly transparent bluish fluorite, practically free from inclusions, showed no losses, even after ignition up to 500°C.

For our continuing experimentation along that line, we used the most common "anhydrous" mineral, crystal quartz from Volynia, Aldan, Nagol'nyi Kryazh, and Altai, in view of the difficulties involved in the calculations of relative quantities of the captive and of the other three types of water, in hydrous minerals. None of the latter three types could be reasonably expected to be present in quartz. Quartz has an additional convenience, as a test mineral, because it affords the basis for comparisons between the losses on ignition from crystals of pneumatolytic vs. hydrothermal origin containing approximately equal quantities of inclusions.

Determinations of the losses on ignition are made at temperatures up to 1200°C, in a muffle furnace or over a gas burner. The test materials are sections cut from crystals or fragments of quartz so that the number of inclusions can be counted approximately in the previously measured area of the section. It is desirable to have the sections as uniform in size as possible (1 cm² and 1.6 mm thick; rarely 1.5 mm). The inclusions are counted at 120× magnification, under the microscope, and their character is identified. The average count* is made per one division of the micrometer grid with an area of 1.6 mm². The section is weighed then on an analytical balance. After weighing, the section is placed in a platinum crucible, with a lid, in order to prevent mechanical losses of the test material on explosion and spattering of the inclusions which is accompanied by loud crackling. The section is ignited for 30–90 min.

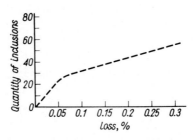

Graph of dependence of ignition losses on quantity of inclusions
in pneumatolytic quartz from Volynia.

After ignition, the section is placed in a desiccator. After cooling, the section is weighed repeatedly. The difference between the weights before and after the ignition is the loss due to the mechanical removal and evaporation of the inclusions' water.

Repeated microscopic examinations of the sections had shown that extremely fine liquid inclusions and the larger gaseous inclusions withstand a considerable overheating and remain unexploded, by virtue of the strength of the vacuole walls in which they are sealed. Consequently, the figures on the loss on ignition, cited below, need be regarded as the minimum.

A closer approximation to the true magnitude of the losses could be attained by an extremely fine grinding of the quartz. Such grinding leads to losses in weight even before the ignition, because of the mechanical breakage and of the evaporation of volatile substances. The subsequent ignition of the quartz powder assures a more complete explosion of the inclusions with aqueous solutions than is the case of thin sections. The general total of losses of water and of other volatile substances contained in inclusions is the sum of the losses caused by the mechanical fragmentation and of the losses occasioned by explosions of the inclusions by heating the powdered mineral. This fact served to explain, for the first time, the cause of the losses on ignition of anhydrous minerals that do not undergo dissociation.

---

* I.e., the number of inclusions in a cube of 1.6 mm edge length [i.e., in a volume of (1.6 mm)³—Ed.] in the section is multiplied by the appropriate number to give the total number for the entire section, it appears [V.P.S.].

As shown by observations, after the evaporation of the included liquid, the mineral solutes deposit as a precipitate, forming thin films on the surface of the crystal fragments, and dendritic coatings inside fissures through which the volatile substances, released by the explosions, had escaped. The losses on ignition of minerals are greater, for that reason, the lower the concentrations of the captive solutions, all other things being the same.

The losses on ignition were the lowest, under identical experimental conditions, in the instance of pneumatolytic quartz containing single-phase gaseous inclusions. At equal numbers and size of inclusions per unit volume of the mineral, the losses on ignition of high-temperature quartz with two-phase and multiphase inclusions of solutions with a large gas bubble were smaller than from low-temperature quartz with inclusions of liquid aqueous solutions containing a small gas bubble.

The diagram represents the average results obtained on 14 fragments of a crystal quartz from Volynia containing primary gaseous inclusions. These inclusions, in the pneumatolytic quartz, have an approximately equal size and a fairly uniform distribution in the mineral. With approximately 50 inclusions in a square of side 1.6 mm, the average ignition loss was 0.210 per cent. The ignition loss was 0.165 per cent and 0.090 per cent respectively for nearly 40 and ca. 30 inclusions. There were no ignition losses for the outer zone of a morion, a transparent crystal quartz containing few or no inclusions. These findings indicate a direct relationship between the magnitude of the ignition loss and the quantity of the inclusions.

A similar dependence was found for a hydrothermal crystal quartz from Aldan, as the result of 17 tests. The ignition losses varied from 0.07 per cent to 1.60 per cent, at 10 to nearly 200 inclusions respectively, per square of side 1.6 mm.

Five experiments with crystal quartz from hydrothermal polymetallic sources in the Nagol'nyi Kryazh gave ignition losses of 0.57 per cent at 40 inclusions and 0.64 per cent at 50 inclusions per unit area of the sections we employed.

One may see from the example of the crystal quartz from a hydrothermal source in Altai we examined that the ignition losses from different parts of one and the same crystal are not the same. This fact depends again on the quantity of inclusions per unit volume of the mineral. The losses were 0.24 per cent, 0.49 per cent, and 0.75 per cent respectively at the lowest, intermediate, and the maximum densities of the inclusion population.

There should be further investigations along this line. One may conclude, however, even on the basis of our preliminary results, that volatile substances, chiefly parental water, contained in the inclusions in minerals, must be taken into account in interpretations of the dehydration curves of such minerals and in ascertaining magnitudes of the losses on ignition of minerals.

BIBLIOGRAPHY

1. YERMAKOV, N. P., *Issledovaniya mineraloobrazuyushchikh rastvorov.* (Research in Mineral-forming Solutions.) Izd. Khar'kov. univ., 1950.
2. FEDOT'EV, K. M., In *Trudy inst. geolog. nauk, Akad. Nauk SSSR,* No. 120, 1949.
3. NIKOLAYEV, A. V., In *Izv. sektora fiz. khim. analiza,* No. 15, 1947.

On the Morphology of Liquid Inclusions in Crystals of Quartz from Pamir

G. M. Safronov

Milky-white varieties of quartz are the common type in the quartz-bearing veins of Pamir; water-clear crystals of quartz are relatively rare.

Turbidity is one of the most common defects of quartz crystals. This defect may be either syngenetic or epigenetic and, in either case, it is due to the presence of liquid inclusions in the crystals. It is such inclusions of microscopic size that cause the pale-gray and the milky-white coloration of the crystals.

It should be pointed out at the same time that liquid inclusions are one of the principal defects of the industrial grade of the crystals and that an inquiry into the morphological characteristics of such inclusions is a matter of some interest accordingly.

Our studies dealt with the inclusions in quartz crystals from five different sources in the Pamir. We examined crystals containing remnants of the mineral-forming solutions, i.e. liquid inclusions. Most of such inclusions are to be found, as a rule, in the base of the crystals (in the crystals' "beard"), while the terminations of the crystals are transparent, as a rule, and may contain only isolated single inclusions.

Primary and also primary–secondary liquid inclusions are especially important in the determination of the lowest temperatures of the crystallization of quartz.

Primary inclusions are relatively rare [1]. Primary–secondary inclusions are far more common. They are situated in the healed fissures across the crystal or in some definite zones of the crystal. These are the inclusions that produce the bulk of the turbidity in the quartz.

Primary liquid inclusions are formed generally during the skeletal and the subparallel growth of the crystal (especially when the growth is rapid). Primary liquid inclusions may be often found also on faces of phantom crystals where adhesions of different minerals (hematite, carbonate, chlorite, sericite, and others) may also be found occasionally. The primary character of such inclusions is definitely indicated by their association with the former component sections of the crystal growth.

Primary–secondary inclusions develop in healed fissures which do not outcrop on the surface of the crystal. The development of such inclusions

[531]

during the fissure-healing process, at different stages of the crystallization, takes place concurrently with the accession of the layers of new growth on the faces of the crystal. Inclusions of this type had been termed pseudo-secondary [2], as distinct from the secondary inclusions [3, 5] formed during the healing of fissures after the growth of the crystal has stopped.

Primary and pseudo-secondary inclusions may be found in any part of the crystal. Thermometric studies of these syngenetic inclusions enable us to appraise the relative temperatures at different stages of the mineral genesis and also the true temperatures, after the appropriate corrections have been made. The homogenization temperature of primary–secondary inclusions is the temperature at which the next outer zone of the crystal began to grow [2]. Fissures formed in quartz in the course of growth of the crystals are healed by fresh portions of the solutions (in the subsequent stages of the crystallization) which serve to complete their growth. The homogenization temperature of primary inclusions in the outer zone of the crystal is generally the same as the homogenization temperature of primary–secondary inclusions in the healed fissures cutting through all of the inner zones of the crystal and encased in its outer zone.

Although, since the beginning of the nineteenth century, morphology of inclusions had been described by numerous investigators, many of the morphologic–genetic types of the shape of cavities of the inclusions in quartz from Pamir have remained so far unreported in the literature.

A brief morphological description of liquid inclusions examined by us in crystals of quartz from Pamir is presented on the following pages.

The primary and pseudo-secondary inclusions here examined are two-phase, three-phase, or multiphase, in regard to their state, as observed at room temperature. Some of these inclusions contain as many as four captive minerals [2], among which we have identified halite, sylvite, carbonate, fluorite (?), and hematite. The latter is also a captive mineral, in all probability. The captive minerals were identified by their crystallographic form, index of refraction, color, the temperature coefficient of their solubility, and by injections of immersion liquids [i.e., by their index of refraction].

Primary inclusions occasionally may have the balanced shape of negative crystals, and they are of the multiphase type. The bulk of their volume is occupied by a gas bubble (1 in Fig. 1). Such primary inclusions were found to be of the highest temperature kind, homogenizing at 400°C and higher.

It needs to be pointed out that diverse forms of faceted and semi-faceted negative crystals may be observed in one and the same zone or fissure (2 and 3 in Fig. 1).

The ones that come closest to being at equilibrium have only the faces of a rhombohedron, but none of a prism (Fig. 1, 4).

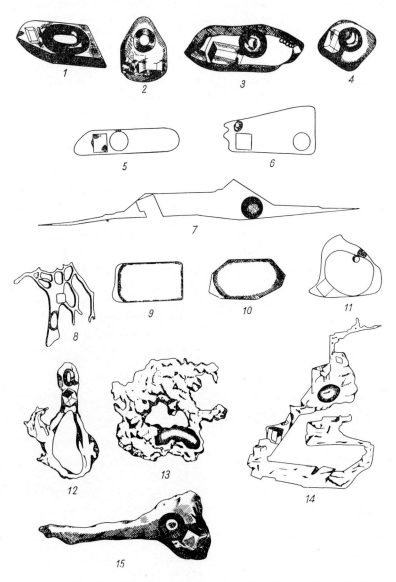

FIG. 1. Shapes of liquid inclusions in crystals of quartz from Pamir.

1. An inclusion most of which consists of a gas bubble; *2*, and *3*. Different shapes of fully developed and half-developed faces of negative crystals; *4*. An inclusion in a cavity enclosed entirely by rhombohedral crystal faces; *5*. A tubular-flat inclusion; *6*. A rectangular-trapezoid inclusion; *7*. A spear-shaped inclusion; *8*. A reticulate inclusion; *9*, *10* and *11*. Inclusions of liquid carbon dioxide; *12* and *13*. Annular inclusions; *14*. A "semi-annular" inclusion; *15*. A multiphase club-like inclusion.

Flat inclusions are found chiefly in healed fissures. The most conspicuous varieties of this type are the flattened–tubular (Fig. 1, 5), the rectangular–trapezoid (Fig. 1, 6), and spear-like. The latter variety is straight-sided, with acute angles, and generally contains halite as a captive mineral (Fig. 1, 7).

In addition to these morphological types of the shape of inclusions, we also found *reticulate inclusions* (Fig. 1, 8) which look as if they were made of a network of channels intersecting each other and which contain in common one gaseous phase and one solid phase. Such inclusions are especially interesting as examples of the dendritic character of fissure healing.

In the inclusions of carbon dioxide (Fig. 1, 9, 10 and 11), the carbon dioxide gas and the vapor of the liquid form one single large gas bubble inside of which, occasionally (Fig. 1, 11), one may see a spherical drop of liquid carbon dioxide disappearing rapidly on a gentle heating. The periphery of this inclusion is occupied by the aqueous mother liquor from which two different solid phases are formed upon a subsequent cooling: one small cubic crystal of halite and one crystal of carbonate.

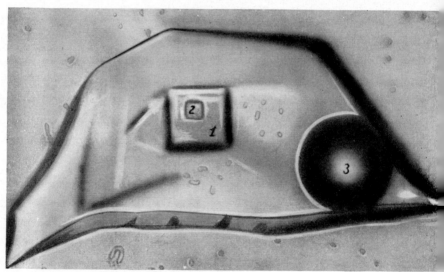

FIG. 2. A compressed multiphase inclusion in quartz from Pamir.
1. A captive mineral; *2.* A liquid inclusion; *3.* A gas bubble. 900×.

The boundaries of the inclusion containing carbon dioxide have the shapes of negative crystals in their planar view. Characteristically, gaseous carbon dioxide occupies more than 80 per cent of the total volume of the inclusion. Liquid carbon dioxide separates from the gaseous phase after even a very slight cooling of the inclusion.

Annular inclusions of the isometric forms as in Fig 1, *12* and *13*. A crystal of quartz is on the inside, surrounded completely by the liquid phase like an island. Such annular inclusions belong to the primary–secondary type and are found in healed fissures. Distances between the walls are often unequal, in the course of the healing of fine fissures, and, for that reason, accessions of the healing solutions and sealing of the fissures take place at unequal rates.

As the result, "bridges" develop across the fissures, in places, with the parallel development of isolated "islands" surrounded by the asymmetrical annular inclusions.

A semi-annular inclusion is visible in Fig. 1, *14*, an example of an unbalanced shape of this morphologically complex group of liquid inclusions. Club-shaped multiphase inclusions were observed by us on several occasions (Fig. 1, *15*).

Also, a large polygonal three-phase inclusion measuring 0.12 by 0.05 mm is shown in Fig. 2. The captive mineral in this inclusion is halite. The length of edge of its crystal is 0.017 mm. This captive mineral, in turn, contains a liquid inclusion with a continuously moving gas bubble. The cavity of this latter liquid inclusion has the shape of perfect cube whose edge measures 0.005 mm. The continuously moving gas bubble has the diameter of 0.0015 mm. The bubble oscillates in a circular path, at the rate of 4–6 mm per second* at 18–20°C. This phenomenon is due to the Brownian movement of the molecules in the liquid [4].

Thus two new morphological forms, the reticulate and the annular, were discovered as the result of examination of numerous inclusions in the quartz from Pamir. Presence of liquid inclusions in captive minerals was also demonstrated, together with the continuous Brownian movement of the gaseous bubble compressed therein.

BIBLIOGRAPHY

1. GRIGOR'EV, D. P., K voprosu o razlichenii pervichnykh i vtorichnykh zhidkikh vklyuchenii v mineralakh. (On the Subject of Distinctions between Primary and Secondary Liquid Inclusions in Minerals.) *Mineral. sb. L'vov. geolog. obshch.* No. 2, 1948.
2. YERMAKOV, N. P., *Issledovaniya mineraloobrazuyushchikh rastvorov.* (Studies of Mineral-forming Solutions). Izd. Khar'kov. univ. 1950.
3. LEMMLEIN, G. G., *Zeit. Krist.,* B. 71, H. 3, 1929.
4. ALLING, H. L., *Petrologiya.* (Petrology.) (Translated from English.) 1941.
5. SORBY, H. C., On the Microscopical Structure of Crystals, *Quart. J. Geol. Soc.* (London) vol. 14, pp. 453–500, 1858.

---

* Probably microns and not millimeters [V.P.S.].

Brief Communications

On the Composition of Liquid Inclusions of Quartz Crystals from Southern Ural

A. Ye. Lisitsyn and S. V. Malinko

IN THE summer of 1955 the authors were engaged in studies of crystal quartz veins on the eastern slopes of Southern Ural. Their studies covered a fairly large territory with a large number of evidences of the presence of crystal quartz in a wide variety of geologic environments.

Crystal quartz veins in the area are associated with internal and external contacts of Harz granitoid massifs piercing Ordovician and Carboniferous metamorphosed bodies of sedimentary and effusive rocks. The greatest accumulation of crystal quartz formations is observed in leukocratic granites, quartz porphyries, and mica–quartz schists. In these rocks the areas with the crystal quartz veins are associated with zones of intensive disjunctive and plicative disturbances.

Examinations of the composition of liquid inclusions in crystal quartz from different sites were done by microscopic, microchemical, and spectrographic methods at the All-Union Institute of Mineral Raw Materials laboratories.

At the vast majority of the sites, in the area we examined, crystal quartz contains an abundance of inclusions characterized by the presence of only two phases: liquid solution and gas (Fig. 1). Moreover, many inclusions contain liquid carbon dioxide, immiscible with aqueous solutions at room temperatures (Fig. 2). We call such inclusions "three-phase complex", following Yermakov's terminology [2]. In three-phase inclusions, the gaseous phase occupies, on the average, about 20 per cent of the inclusion's volume. There is a high degree of variation, in three-phase inclusions, in the volume ratios of gas, solution, and liquid carbon dioxide. It is enough to mention that liquid carbon dioxide occupies from 3–5 to 85–90 per cent of the total volume of such inclusions. Inclusions of carbon dioxide, without any aqueous solution, were observed locally.

Crystal quartz in some parts of the district contains occasionally also three-phase and multiphase inclusions, in addition to the ones just described. In addition to aqueous solution and gas, they have also a solid

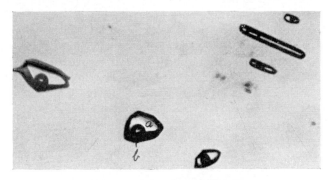

FIG. 1. Two-phase inclusions. 90×.
(a) Aqueous solution; (b) Gas bubble.

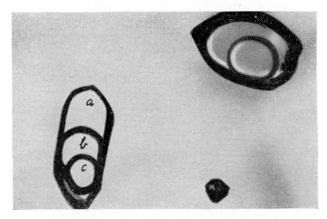

FIG. 2. Complex two-phase inclusions. 220×.
(a) Aqueous solution; (b) Liquid carbonic acid; (c) Gas bubble.

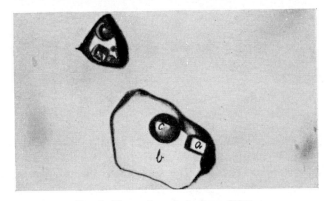

FIG. 3. Three-phase inclusions. 220×.
(a) Halite; (b) Aqueous solution; (c) Gas bubble.

phase represented by one or several minerals. Among the latter, isotropic small cubes of halite and sylvite and aggregations of platelets of a carbonate are clearly distinguished. Halite and sylvite were identified by the character of their dissolution on the application of heat to quartz thin sections in the thermochamber of Yermakov's design. The fine crystals of sylvite dissolve completely at 75–90°C, by virtue of their high thermal coefficient of solubility. There is no external change in the halite crystals at that

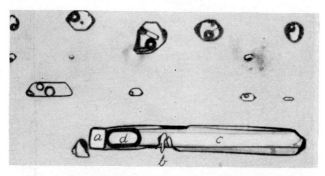

FIG. 4. Multiphase inclusions. 220×.
(a) Halite; (b) Carbonate; (c) Aqueous solution; (d) Gas bubble.

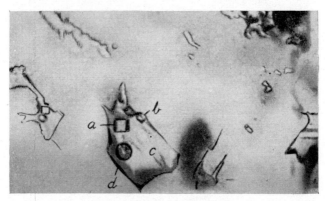

FIG. 5. A multiphase inclusion. 220×.
(a) Halite; (b) Sylvite; (c) Aqueous solution; (d) Gas bubble.

temperature. They dissolve completely only at 180–200°C. The carbonate platelets are easily identified in crossed nicols, by the interference coloration typical of calcite and dolomite. The solid phase in multiphase inclusions is generally represented by one single mineral, halite (Fig. 3), or else by the carbonate, or, again by two minerals, halite and carbonate, simultaneously (Fig. 4). Inclusions with sylvite are more rare (Fig. 5). Occasionally, inclusions with the solid phase contain also liquid carbon dioxide (Fig. 6).

Presence of the following major elements in the inclusions was established spectrographically, at the VIMS laboratory, by analysis of dry residues of filtered aqueous extracts of crystal quartz from different sites: Na, K, Ca, Mg, and Si. The following were detected, in negligible quantities: Al, Fe, Mn, Ni, Cu, Pb, Zn, Sn, and Sr. The alkalies and the alkaline earths showed the following relationships: $Na \geqslant K \geqslant Ca \geqslant Mg$. The Si content is equal to or smaller than the K content, as a rule.

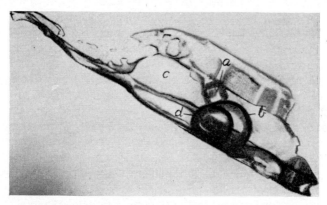

FIG. 6. A complex multiphase inclusion. 220×.
(a) Halite; (b) Liquid carbon dioxide; (c) Aqueous solution; (d) Gas bubble.

Microchemical analyses of the aqueous extracts at the VIMS microchemical laboratory confirmed the spectrographic findings. They showed that the sum of the alkali cations, Na + K, generally exceeds the sum of Ca + Mg. The sums of the alkalies and the alkaline earths were equal, in isolated cases. Ca is definitely predominant among the alkaline earths. Examination of the aqueous extracts in the flame photometer, at the VIMS spectrographic laboratory, served to differentiate the alkali metals. It showed that Na and K are present in different proportions, in crystals from different sites and that Na is generally predominant.

Microchemical analyses had also demonstrated the presence of the anions, Cl^-, HCO_3^-, and SO_4^{--}, and their varied proportions in different specimens, so that $C \leqslant SO_4^{--} \leqslant HCO_3^- \leqslant Cl^-$. Moreover, the analyses showed that the silica content of the aqueous extracts is about one half to one third the combined sum of anions and cations. We should consider, in this connection, that a part of the silica was derived from the quartz, in the course of the extraction. Consequently, the quantities of silica deposited as fine linings on the inclusions' walls, after the inclusions were sealed, should be somewhat smaller still. On the contrary, the true HCO_3^-

content of the inclusions should be higher than was indicated by the chemical analysis, inasmuch as the gaseous phase, consisting mainly of CO_2, is inevitably lost in the extraction.

Thus the identifications of minerals present as solid phases are fully confirmed by the spectrographic and by the microchemical analyses.

Microchemical analyses of aqueous extracts of the crystals having inclusions of supersaturated solutions with the solid phase (halite, sylvite, carbonate) gave the highest results for the constituents. Recalculations of the results, in terms of the most probable combinations, show the likelihood of the following easily soluble salts in the aqueous phase of the inclusions: $NaCl$, KCl, $CaCl_2$, $MgCl_2$, $Ca(HCO_3)_2$, $CaSO_4$, $MgSO_4$, and the alkali silicates: Na_2SiO_3 and K_2SiO_3.

Thus the chemical composition of inclusions in crystal quartz is identical for the various sites and sources of the district's crystal quartz. Nonetheless one of the sites shows a strikingly different phase composition because of its supersaturated solutions. The crystals from that site have abundant three-phase and multiphase inclusions with one or several minerals precipitated from the solution as a solid phase. By way of contrast, there is less carbon dioxide in the inclusions in crystals from that site than in the other test materials. Such circumstances are evidence to the effect that the crystal quartz deposits of Southern Ural were produced in rather different environments.

The presence of supersaturated solutions is definitely an indication that the crystal growth at the site in question took place from more highly concentrated solutions than elsewhere. The mineral-forming solutions acting at that site were also hotter. The latter is indicated by the relatively small quantities of carbon dioxide included in the crystals. Carbon dioxide, an easily volatile substance, would naturally rise to the higher levels where the temperatures would be lower. This would be facilitated further by the intensive tectonic activity at the site, as evidenced by the multitude of fissured zones.

The foregoing conclusion is sustained by the data on homogenization temperatures of liquid inclusions in the crystal quartz from different sources in the district. Indeed, the homogenization temperatures of the inclusions in crystals from the site characterized by the high concentrations are 30–50°C higher than in inclusions in crystals from other sources.

BIBLIOGRAPHY

1. GRUSHKIN, G. G. and P. L. PRIKHID'KO, Ob izmenenii khimicheskogo sostava, kontsentratsii i pH gazovo-zhidkikh vklyuchenii v ryade posledovatel'nykh generatsii fluorita. (On Alterations in Chemical Composition, Concentration, and pH of Gas–Liquid Inclusions in Series of Successive Generations of Fluorite.) *Zap. vsesoyuz. mineralog. obshch.* Pt. 81, No. 2, 1952.

2. YERMAKOV, N. P., *Issledovaniya mineraloobrazuyushchikh rastvorov.* (Research in Mineral-forming Solutions.) Izd. Khar'kov. univ. 1950.
3. ZAKHARCHENKO, A. I., Rezul'taty izucheniya zhidkikh vklyuchenii v gornom khrustale. (Results of Studies of Liquid Inclusions in Crystal Quartz.) *Mineralog. sb. L'vov. geolog. obshch.* No. 4, 1950.
4. KLEVTSOV, P. V., Issledovaniye nekotorykh termodinamicheskikh svoystv kontsentrirovannykh vodnykh rastvorov v prilozhenii k geologicheskoi termometrii. (Investigation of Certain Thermodynamic Properties of Concentrated Aqueous Solutions in Application to Geologic Thermometry.) *Avtoreferat dissertatsii*, 1955.

On the Problem of Fissure Healing in Synthetic Quartz Crystals

G. M. SAFRONOV and V. YE. KHADZHI

HEALED fissures and mirror fissures [flat fractures showing total reflection?—Ed.] are produced in synthetic quartz crystals on disturbances in the optimum conditions of crystal growth.

The healing of fissures, with the accompanying formation of many liquid inclusions, takes place both during the crystallization and after completion of the cycle, for a short time, during the lowering of the temperature of the original solution. In the latter case, there is a recrystallization of the fissures outcropping at the surface of the crystal.

It was established by microscopic studies that the morphology and the phase ratios of such inclusions vary within a wide range, depending on the degree of the recrystallization of the fissures. It may be sufficient here

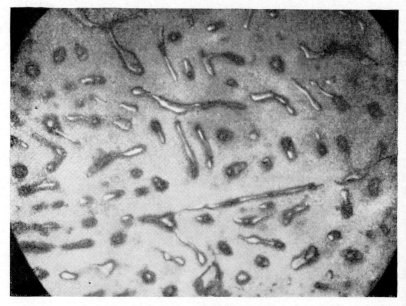

FIG. 1. Anomalous "strung-out" inclusions in cavity of a rapidly healed fissure. 120×.

[542]

FIG. 2. Skeletal type overgrowth of fissure with inclusions of residual cooled solution. The earlier two-phase inclusions are visible in the cells of the skeleton. 80×.

to comment on some features of liquid inclusions in partially healed fissures without considerations of the nature of mirror fissures and inclusions in completely healed fissures since the latter were already discussed in the literature, in ample detail.

As previously stated, that type of fissure originates in the end stage of crystal growth. The fissures are healed accordingly by solutions whose activity is being exhausted. The process is accompanied by the development of highly involved forms of "skeletal" deposition of the substance in the fissures, with creation of associations of anomalous inclusions out of equilibrium, which are distinguished by a wide variety of phase ratios (Fig. 1) and by frequent "stringing-out" phenomena.

Alongside inclusions of an equant rounded shape, one may find also irregularly elongated inclusions and, more rarely, amoeba-like shapes. There is no orderly relationship whatsoever in the mutual orientations. One may plainly see occasionally, however, how chain-works of inclusions with anomalous phase ratios are produced by "stringing-out" of a tubular inclusion in the fissure's plane, etc.

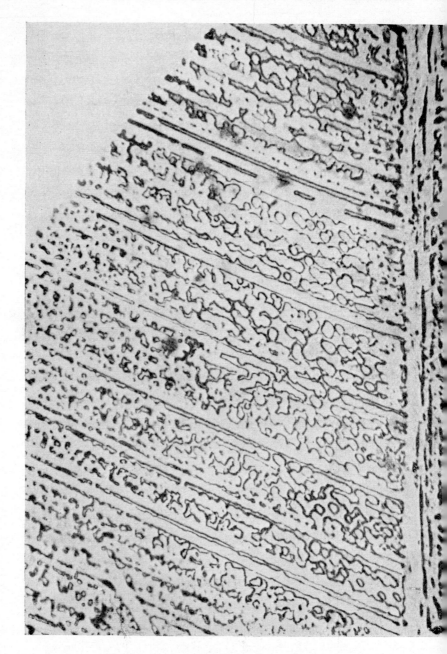

FIG. 3. Pattern of skeletal growth in a half-healed fissure with inclusions of residual cooled solution. 90×.

The fissure-healing mechanism was investigated in detail by Lemmlein [2] and Kliya [3]. These investigators made clear the relationships in the dendritic skeletal overgrowth of fissures by the cognate substance and ascertained the causes of the formation of balanced and unbalanced inclusions in equilibrium and non-equilibrium, of "frozen" shapes, etc.

Our studies of synthetic quartz crystals provide supplementary illustrations of such phenomena and show also that, in sparingly soluble crystals, the solution loses its activity on rapid cooling of the autoclave and becomes incapable of healing the youngest fissures. Such fissures, with their highly diversified inclusions, we call *half-healed*. Their inclusions, as a matter of fact, were not able to part from each other during the rapid skeletal healing of the fissures. They formed a skeletal carcass of a peculiar configuration (Fig. 2). Small two-phase inclusions are present inside the cells in the quartz. They antedate somewhat the network of the residual single-phase inclusions of cooled solution.

These inclusions are particularly well represented by the frozen forms in Fig. 3, where the pattern of the skeletal growth is clearly shown in the plane of a half-healed fissure. It occurs in association with such amoeba-like areas (containing the solution) with parallel rows. As one may see, such skeletal growth forms vary depending on changes in the orientation of fissures in the crystal and the boundaries of the zones of the different generations of quartz (the seed versus the overgrowth).

In isolated cases of synthetic quartz growth, one may observe a stratification in the material overgrowing the seed plate involving the formation of a large inclusion of residual solution at the boundary.

The observations here reported supplement our concepts of the mechanism of formation of inclusions in fissures, in an environment of rapidly falling temperature, and help also in a rational selection of test materials suited for mineral thermometric investigations.

BIBLIOGRAPHY

1. YERMAKOV, N. P., *Issledovaniya mineraloobrazuyushchikh rastvorov.* (Research in Mineral-forming Solutions.) Izd. Khar'kov. univ. 1950.
2. LEMMLEIN, G. G., Protsess zalechivaniya treshchin v kristalle i preobrazovaniye formy polostei vtorichnykh zhidkikh vklyuchenii. (The Fissure-healing Process in Crystals and Transformations in Shapes of Cavities with Secondary Liquid Inclusions.) *Dokl. Akad. Nauk SSSR*, Vol. 78, No. 4, 1951.
3. LEMMLEIN, G. G. and M. O. KLIVA. Osobennosti zalechivaniya treshchin v kristalle v rezhime snizhayushcheysya temperatury. (Characteristics of Fissure-healing in Crystals at Falling Temperatures.) *Dokl. Akad. Nauk SSSR*, Vol. 87, No. 6, 1952.

On Inclusions in Gypsum from the Hydrothermal Deposit of Alaverdy

V. F. LESNYAK

IN 1949, the author visited the Alaverdy Group of mineral deposits where he made a moderate collection of minerals a part of which was examined thermometrically.

Despite the fact that the Alaverdy mine-fields are among the most ancient ones in Transcaucasia (mined since the eighth or the ninth century) the environments under which they were formed are still not entirely clear and, specifically, the origin of their gypsum is still an unresolved controversy. Some of the investigators are inclined to believe that gypsum is exogenic in the Alaverdy, produced by weathering of sulfides. A hypogene origin of the gypsum was proposed by V. G. Grushevoi, I. G. Magak'yan also refers the gypsum to a hydrothermal origin and assigns it the last place in his sequence of crystallization for the deposit. Magak'yan believes that the Alaverdy deposit was formed at a shallow depth and at a low temperature, as evidenced by the fine-grain character of the ores and the widespread occurrence of colloform textures. He reports the following sequence of crystallization for the Alaverdy minerals: ilvaite and sericite; quartz I; pyrite; arsenopyrite; fluorite; chalcopyrite; barite; bornite; stannite; native gold; bismuthite; tennanite; galena; quartz II; calcite; anhydrite and gypsum [2].

The Alaverdy ore bodies are chiefly lenses and vugs composed of the enumerated minerals among which gypsum is very prominent. Gypsum is especially widespread in the hanging wall of ore bodies and is closely associated also with the sulfides.

Using Yermakov's method [1] we made microthermometric examinations of fluorite, calcite, and gypsum from different sites in the Alaverdy. Homogenization temperatures were determined for inclusions of the mineral-forming solutions.

These inclusions proved to be two-phase, in fluorite and calcite, with a very small gas bubble. The homogenization temperatures of inclusions in fluorite did not exceed 100–120°C, on heating in the Yermakov microthermochamber. All of the inclusions homogenized in the liquid phase, i.e. as in type I [1]. The inclusions in calcite were extremely small and were difficult to photograph, on account of turbidity in the calcite itself. Fig. 1 is a sketch of the inclusions in calcite. The liquid occupies more than 95 per cent of the inclusions' total volume. The homogenization temperatures of the inclusions in calcite do not exceed 80°C.

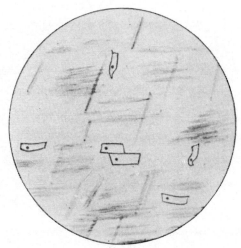

FIG. 1. Two-phase liquid inclusions of minera-forming solutions in calcite. 160×.

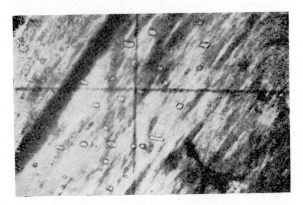

FIG. 2. Single-phase liquid inclusions in gypsum from the Alaverdy deposit. 120×.

Crystals of gypsum for the inclusion studies were taken from different places in the deposit. The inclusions observed in thin sections of gypsum cut from the crystal were mainly of the single-phase liquid type situated in crystal growth zones and in the plane of the cleavage. Their habit is that of negative crystals (Fig. 2). Isolated two-phase inclusions with various liquid–gas phase ratios are fairly common among the multitude of primary single-phase inclusions. One may notice, on a careful examination, that such inclusions are anomalous and that their gas bubbles are caused by leakages of the liquid along small fissures in the cleavage planes (Fig. 3).

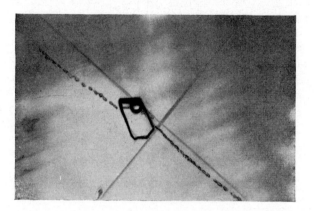

FIG. 3. Anomalous two-phase inclusions in gypsum from the Alaverdy deposit. 120×.

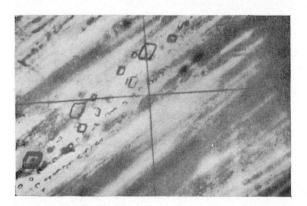

FIG. 4. Single-phase liquid inclusions in gypsum from the Shchiretskoye deposit. 120×.

Gypsum from other sources was also examined, for the sake of comparison. Figure 4 is a photograph of inclusions of mineral-forming solutions from the Shchiretskoye deposit situated in limestones and having definitely a sedimentary origin. As one may see in Figs. 3 and 4, there is a great deal of resemblance in the shape of the single-phase liquid inclusions from the Alaverdy and the Shchiretskoye. Liquid inclusions in gypsum from the Kalushskoye deposit of potassium salts are also single-phase.

One may believe therefore that the Alaverdy gypsum needs be classified with the cold-water formations whose temperature of crystallization does not exceed 50°C [1].

The bulk of the minerals in the hypogene Alaverdy ore complex precipitated from low-temperature and cold-water hydrothermal solutions, in the range of minimum temperatures from 100–120 to 50°C, and lower. Gypsum in the Alaverdy ore bodies is the product of the end-stage of the hydrothermal process.

Additional thermometric studies are required, however, for an appraisal of the temperature environment wherein the deposit was formed, as a whole.

BIBLIOGRAPHY

1. YERMAKOV, N. P., *Issledovaniya mineraloobrazuyushchikh rastvorov.* (Research in Mineral-forming Solutions.) Izd. Khar'kov. univ. 1950.
2. MAGAK'YAN, I. G., *Alaverdskii tip orudeneniya i yego rudy.* (The Alaverdy Type of Mineralization and its Ores.) Izd. Akad. Nauk Armyansk. SSR, 1947.

Thermometric Investigations of Inclusions in a Zoned Quartz Crystal from Pamir

E. N. PUSHKINA and G. YA. YAKOVLEVA

AMONG crystals of quartz in the Pamir Collection, we discovered several specimens with clearly defined zonal structures which were subsequently subjected to thermometric studies. Subsequent examinations of these crystals, by growth zones, using the methods of thermometric analysis, made it possible to ascertain the general features of the temperature variations during the growth of a typical crystal.

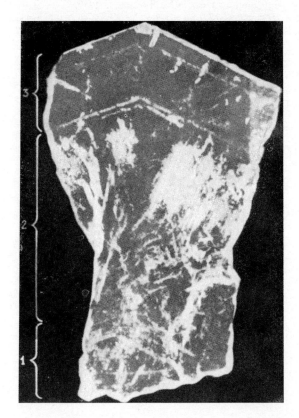

FIG. 1. Section cut from termination of a zoned quartz crystal from Pamir at 30° angle to the *c* axis; zones *1*, *2* and *3*. ×2.

[550]

Figure 1 is a section cut from a zoned quartz crystal from a deposit in the Pamir crystal-quartz province. Three differently colored zones (gray to pale-gray) are plainly visible in the crystal. Solid inclusions (hematite) are visible at the zone boundaries. The thicknesses of the inner, the middle, and the outer zones are 10, 26, and 12 mm respectively.

Several sub-zones in the crystal were revealed by microscopic studies, with liquid, multiphase, and two-phase primary and pseudo-secondary liquid inclusions.

The homogenization data on the inclusions in the sub-zones are summarized in Table 1 and are represented in Fig. 2.

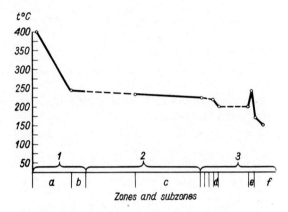

Fig. 2. Temperature growth regime of zoned quartz crystal from Pamir. *1, 2, 3,* zones; *a, b, c, d, e, f,* sub-zones.

On the basis of the thermometric investigations performed, it is possible, in a general way, to shed some light on the course of formation of the crystal and to suggest the lower temperature limits of crystallization.

TABLE 1. HOMOGENIZATION DATA ON INCLUSIONS IN ZONED CRYSTAL OF QUARTZ

No. in sequence	Growth zones	Growth sub-zones	Homogenization temperature (°C)	Correction for pressure (°C)	Crystallization temperature corrected for pressure
1	Inner	a	400	30	430
	Inner	b	242	45	287
2	Middle	c	236–225	44–43	280–268
3	Outer	d	219–200	43–42	262–242
	Outer	e	236	44	280
	Outer	f	167–152	41–40	207–192

Note: In correcting the homogenization temperatures for pressures, P. V. Klevtsov's data were employed.

The initial crystallization of the quartz occurred at a minimum temperature of 400°C and from chloride-saturated solutions. The temperature dropped to 242°C while the inner zone was being formed. The "b" sub-zone of the inner zone was crystallizing at about the same minimum temperature [242°C?—V.P.S.]. The temperature dropped to 225°C, gradually, during the crystallization of the middle zone. There was an intensive precipitation of hematite at 225–219°C, contemporaneous with the beginning of the crystallization of the outer zone. Later on, toward the end of the formation of that zone (sub-zone "e"), up to 236°C, there were accessions of hotter solutions associated with the healing of the fissures and the precipitation of hematite and calcite on the crystal faces. The last sub-zone grew at a minimum temperature of 167–152°C.

As it should be expected, the zonal structure of the quartz crystal is somehow related to the temperature fluctuations. The determined temperature regime is represented in Fig. 2. Approximations to the true temperatures of the quartz crystal growth were attained by corrections for pressure amounting to 30–45°C (see table). The temperatures of crystal growth fluctuated from 430 to 190°C.

A Note on Crystal Quartz from Aktas I Deposit, Kazakhstan

N. I. MYAZ'

MORE than one hundred crystals from several veins of the area were scanned by us. We must report, first of all, the low quality of these crystals. Their random clustering is typical and it is evidence of unfavorable conditions of crystal growth.

Two habit types, the long prismatic and the short prismatic, may be distinguished among crystals from the area. Crystals flattened along the threefold axis are common but doubly terminated crystals are practically never found.

The surface of crystal faces is shiny, as a rule, with many vicinal faces, chiefly on the rhombohedral faces. Prismatic faces are often clearly striated. Hemihedral faces may be found (generally one or two faces of bipyramid).

Twinning may be noted on the crystals, by the Dauphiné law, but the twins are generally small and are found chiefly on prismatic faces. Brazilian twins are rare.

Most of the crystals are colorless, although smoky crystals may be found fairly often; their hue is fairly dense.

Among defects of the crystals, we should mention the abundance of two-phase liquid inclusions responsible occasionally for the milky-white color, fine fissures and "veils", frequent twinning and interpenetration of crystals, and inclusions of epidote and chlorite throughout the body of the crystals. The terminations of the crystals have fewest defects, in nearly all instances; appreciably fewer inclusions, even if the crystal itself has very many of them.

Planes of fracture in the bottom of some crystals and of some crystal clusters are often regenerated and the regenerated surfaces are often overgrown by numerous very fine short prismatic crystals.

We used the most representative crystals for thermometric investigations. Their sections were cut, most frequently, parallel to the threefold axis. The examinations showed that the shape of the inclusions is nearly always irregular, with tortuous outlines; a triangular shape is extremely rare (a triangular primary inclusion was found only once, in the core of the crystal at its base). The inclusions are small, as a rule; no large ones could be found; their distribution is disorderly and they pervade sometimes the entire body of the crystal. The inclusions are often associated with various networks of fissures crossing the crystals. Such inclusions are mainly primary–secondary two-phase liquid ones. Single-phase liquid inclusions are more rarely found; three-phase liquid inclusions with a gas bubble and a "captive" mineral are also rare. No inclusions with carbon dioxide could be discovered.

All of the inclusions of mineral-forming solutions homogenize in the liquid phase, as shown by thermometric analysis. Homogenization temperatures of the latest inclusions in fissures are 40–80°C, while most of the primary–secondary inclusions homogenize at 60–105°C. A single primary inclusion had a homogenization temperature of 115°C, the maximum for crystals from its area.

As shown by the results of the thermometric analyses, crystal growth in the given area took place from low-temperature hydrothermal solutions, while the temperature was decreasing gradually, and, it appears, took place from the latest accessions of these solutions. It was this, in all probability, that caused the poor quality of the crystals. The absence of traces of any natural etching of the crystal quartz faces indicates that, even if some part of the solutions were able to enter the vein cavity, they were not able to change the original appearance of the crystals, but could merely produce a partial healing of the fissures. The regeneration of the fractured surfaces at the bottoms was brought about apparently by the last portions of the hydrothermal solutions, since the maximum homogenization temperature of inclusions in the regenerated parts of the crystals amounts to 70°C.

Abstracts of Addresses

Inclusions of Mother Liquors in Minerals and Their Significance in Theory and Practice*

N. P. Yermakov

(1) Inclusions of melts and solutions—a sensitive geologic witness of physico-chemical environments of former processes of mineral genesis

A clear understanding of inclusions as preserved "juices of the Earth" (Al-Biruni), taken as "parts of the medium in which the formation... of mineral substances took place" (A. P. Karpinskii) and representing "a precious material for the most important conclusions regarding origins of minerals" (Ya. V. Samoylov). Attainments of the Soviet scientists in their studies of inclusions in the last decade.

Modern classification of inclusions by their composition, phase state, type, variety, and species of homogenization. Inclusions as direct indicators of magmatic, pneumatolytic, hydrothermal, or cold-water origin of minerals.

(2) Taking account of solutions included in crystals is essential in descriptive mineralogy

Composition of included solutions has an appreciable effect on the total chemical composition of minerals. Observed variations in the specific gravity of a mineral are often related to variations in the quantities of inclusions it contains. Differences in the content of liquid and gaseous inclusions that explode on overheating cause variations in the loss on ignition, in one and the same mineral. Even "anhydrous" minerals contain appreciable quantities of water, in the included mother liquor (sometimes with carbon dioxide), in addition to the waters of constitution, crystallization, and adsorption.

---

* Proceedings of the All–Union Conference on Mineralogy and Geochemistry, April 5–11, 1954.

[555]

(3) Analyses of natural included systems yield direct information on composition, concentration, and pH of mineral-forming solutions that were operative in the geologic past

Direct and indirect methods of qualitative studies of inclusions. Multiphase liquid inclusions as indicators of multicomponent highly concentrated mother liquors. Cardinal importance of chlorides as carriers of metals in true solutions and the "hydrothermal brines".

Initial analytical findings on solutions and investigations of captive minerals in confined systems of inclusions. Variations in the number of captive minerals and in their relative volumes in crystals of different generations are a self-evident record of qualitative and quantitative changes in dissolved substances in the course of mineral genesis.

Studies of inclusions may offer geochemistry some new data on migration and behavior of elements in mineral-forming processes of distant geologic past.

(4) Syngenetic inclusions of carbon dioxide and of dilute aqueous solutions make it possible, in certain cases, to make appraisals of pressures during endogenic mineral genesis

Examples of calculation of pressures from measurements of density of included carbon dioxide and of the homogenization temperatures of syngenetic liquid inclusions... possibility of determination of pressures by the H_2O and CO_2 diagrams of state superimposed in the first plane, by determining the point of origin of the isochors with the aid of homogenization temperatures of dilute aqueous solutions and of the syngenetic carbon dioxide.

Examples of calculation of pressures in polymetallic deposits and at different levels of a deposit of gold.

Attempts at calculation of pressures in included liquid systems by determination of the mutually related parameters, with an example of a fluorite deposit.

(5) Mineral thermometric analysis as the means of ascertaining the course of the temperature variations during growth of individual crystals and the temperature regime of formation of hydrothermal deposits

Essence of the analysis and examples of individual monothermal and polythermal minerals. Determination of the causes of interruptions in their growth and of the pulsations in the growth of zoned crystals.

Examples of mineral thermometric studies of hydrothermal lead–zinc deposits and of deposits of piezo-optic minerals. Temperature diagrams and graphs of temperature variations in the process of formation of a hydrothermal deposit. Rates of cooling of the solutions in their ascending movement. The degree of proximity of the determined to the true homogenization temperatures of liquid inclusions in hydrothermal mineral genesis.

(6) Ascertaining the state of aggregation of the solutions effective in the geologic past as the means of deciphering processes in the formation of complex polygenic deposits

The place of minerals containing gaseous and gas–liquid inclusions in geology.

Examples of multistage growth of individual crystals in pegmatites and in skarns. Succession of variations in types and species of homogenization of primary inclusions in different growth zones of crystals. Investigations of inclusions in different paragenetic groups of minerals in ore formations in certain deposits of rare metals and gold ores. Determinations of stages, sub-stages, and levels of the physico-chemical environments in the formation of complex polygenic deposits and graphs of the stages of mineralization. Proofs of pneumatolysis. Possibilities of a genetic diagnosis of different ore-deposition types with the aid of inclusions in vein minerals.

"Stratigraphy" of the deposition of minerals and discovery of favorable as well as of unfavorable sub-stages for the deposition of minerals.

Insight into the dynamics of endogenic ore-depositing processes and of discontinuities in their course with the aid of inclusions of mineral-forming solutions.

(7) Investigations of inclusions may be conducive occasionally to ascertaining relationships between endogenic ore-deposition and intrusive activities

Examples of variations in the temperature range and the species of homogenization of inclusions in quartz of one and the same generation, traced throughout the extent of the vein, as indicators of a genetic connection with a definite intrusion. The probability of destruction of liquid inclusions in vein minerals in proximity to a post-ore intrusion. The case of the association of a primary and a superimposed mineralization with two periods of magmatic activity in the district, in the instance of a gold-ore deposit in Ural.

(8) Comparisons of primary and pseudo-secondary inclusions in ore-vein minerals with secondary inclusions in minerals of host rocks opens the possibility of a coordination of the near-ore alterations with the vein-filling processes

Possibilities of a discovery of a paragenetic synchronization of minerals, within ore-field boundaries, and of bodies and veins, on the basis of primary and pseudo-secondary inclusions. The method of synchronization of endo-mineralizational tectonic movements with the formation of secondary inclusions in hair-like fissures in minerals. Contemporaneous formation of primary and pseudo-secondary inclusions with secondary inclusions of solutions in minerals of host rocks (specific examples).

The widespread process of steam-cooking of host rocks by pneumatolytic solutions and the near-vein rock alterations under the influence of hydrothermal solutions. Mineralogically visible and invisible alterations. Cases of non-coincidence of visible alteration in host rocks with the ore-forming sub-stages of the mineralization.

(9) **Investigations of inclusions in differentiated pegmatites of the chamber type offer the possibility of tracing the intricate process of their development, from the sub-stage of the residual magma solutions to the excretion of the tepid-water hydrothermal solutions**

Distinctions in the pegmatite-forming process resulting in the formation of the exo-intrusive or of the endo-intrusive chamber-type pegmatites, with the example of Volynia. Geologic environments of the deposits. The mechanism of the formation of vugs and caverns; conditions of their nourishment by mineral-crystallizing solutions. Character of visible and invisible alteration of granites next to the pegmatites; causes of kaolinization and of the formation of placers.

(10) **Mineral thermometric and thermosonic analyses of inclusions in minerals provide a foundation for new methods of prospecting in soil-covered flat terrains**

Substance and premises of thermosonic analysis. Production of an automatic thermosonic recorder. Examples of thermosonograms for minerals of different origins. Utilization of wide halos of dispersed quartz rubble and sand surrounding the pegmatites of Volynia in prospecting for morion placers. Utilization of secondary inclusions in quartz from altered and from macroscopically unaltered host granites in discovery of ore lodes and of pegmatitic bodies. "Sonant" and "non-sonant" granites and possibilities of appraising expressions of pneumatolytic and hydrothermal stages of mineralization on the basis of thermosonograms. Limitations of the methods and possibilities of their further development.

January 18, 1954. Moscow

PART III

TRANSACTIONS OF THE ALL-UNION RESEARCH
INSTITUTE OF PIEZO-OPTICAL
MINERAL RAW MATERIALS

Translated from

Research on Mineral-forming Solutions (by inclusions)

Volume II Part 2

*Ministry of Radiotechnical Industry,
U.S.S.R.; Scientific-Technical Collected Papers*

Editorial Board

Contents of Part III

The present sequential issue of the topical collected papers, *Transactions of the All-Union Research Institute of Piezo-optical Mineral Raw Materials,* as with Part 2, Volume I, deals entirely with research in mineral-forming solutions. It represents mainly the work completed in 1957 at the All-Union Research Institute of Piezo-optical Mineral Raw Materials (VNIIP), the All-Union Institute of Mineral Raw Materials (VIMS), the All-Union Institute of Geology (VSEGEI), the Institutes of the Academies of Sciences of the USSR, Ukr. SSR, Uzb. SSR, and of the Universities of Moscow and L'vov.

Several articles in this issue of *Collected Papers* deal with the methods and techniques of research, namely, with the apparatus for thermosonic analysis of inclusions. Most of the articles bring to light various aspects of applications of previously developed methods in the examination of deposits and of crystals of piezo-quartz, tourmaline, optical calcite, fluorite, and synthetic quartz.

The Homogenization Curves in Mineralogical Thermometry and their Construction

V. A. KALYUZHNYI

LIQUID inclusions in minerals are relics of mineral-forming solutions and, from the physico-chemical point of view, are systems of equilibrium, under constant conditions and not subject to qualitative alterations. In surficial environments, the inclusions are heterogeneous systems that almost invariably pass into the homogeneous state on heating. The homogenization curves, with coordinates of temperature and phase ratio, provide an objective view of the course of the homogenization process.

The character of the homogenization curves, as records of changes in the phase ratio resulting from heating, depends on many factors among which the prime one is the original state of aggregation of the mineral-forming media.

Let us consider the inclusions's state in a mineral, as a two-phase single-component system, water plus vapor, at equilibrium, under given constant conditions.

Let us introduce now the following designations:

W—total volume of the inclusion;
L—volume of water in the inclusion;
G—volume of water vapor [in the inclusion—V.P.S.];
M—total mass of water and water vapor;
M_L—mass of water; M_G—mass of water vapor;
V_L—specific volume of water; V_G—specific volume of water vapor.

The following system of equations will be applicable to inclusions of such type:

$$L+G = W; \quad M_L+M_G = M.$$

Substituting $M_L = \dfrac{L}{V_L}$ and $M_G = \dfrac{G}{V_G}$ into the second equation and solving the equation for L, we have:

$$L = \frac{MV_LV_G-WV_L}{V_G-V_L}. \tag{I}$$

The relationship here obtained applies not only to the system water plus vapor but to any two-phase confined saturated system. By employing the general equation, (I), it is possible to construct homogenization curves for inclusions in minerals with different phase ratios, starting at any temperature at which the given system may exist. It is essential to know only the specific volumes of the phases and the changes in the inclusion's total volume at changing temperatures. The first two quantities in the system water plus saturated vapor are sufficiently well known from the literature [1, p. 198]; the thermal volume expansion of some minerals is also known [1]. True, all of these data were determined only for points more or less far apart (for example, for 10° or 20°C intervals on the water plus vapor saturation curve). The curves built on such a basis allow us, nevertheless, to determine V_L, V_G, and W also for the intermediate points, with a sufficient degree of accuracy.

Consider now an example. Assume that we must build a homogenization curve for an inclusion whose phase ratio is 90:10 (water:vapor) at room temperature (20°C). For the sake of simplicity, let us assume that the inclusion's volume remains constant at increasing temperatures.

(1) Under such conditions, at 20°C, eqn. (I) will be valid, and may be written as follows in order to facilitate the calculations:

$$M = \frac{L(V_G - V_L) + WV_L}{V_G \times V_L}. \tag{I a}$$

Substituting the known values of (I) in the right part of this equation, we calculate the mass which is constant as long as the given inclusion continues to exist as a confined system:

$$M = \frac{90(57824 - 1.002) + (100 \times 1.002)}{57824 \times 1.002} = 89.82.$$

(2) Calculation of the specific volume at the inclusion's homogenization temperature:

$$V = \frac{W}{M}; \quad V = \frac{100}{89.82} = 1.133.$$

(3) From Table 1 or from a nomogram derived from that table, we find the temperature at which the inclusion will be filled completely by either one of the phases. This temperature is 169°C, in our particular case.

(4) Substituting the values for V_L and V_G, for temperatures from 0°C to the homogenization temperature, we find the per cent of filling of the inclusion with water at each of these temperatures, thus determining points on the homogenization curve on the phase ratio–temperature diagram. The values of M and W remain constant, under the circumstances. Thus the

inclusion will contain the following volume of water:

at 40°C:

$$L = \frac{(89.82 \times 19543 \times 1.008) - (100.1 \times 1.008)}{(19543 - 1.008)} = 90.53,$$

at 60°C:

$$L = \frac{(89.82 \times 7678.3 \times 1.017) - (100 \times 1.017)}{(7678.3 - 1.017)} = 91.34, \text{ etc.}$$

Twenty homogenization curves shown in Fig. 1 were built in such manner. The initial phase ratio for these curves was taken at 20°C, the room temperature; the inclusion's per cent of filling with water at 0°C was calculated from eqn. (I).*

The calculated percentages of filling of inclusions with water at different temperatures, in the course of the homogenization, are summarized in Tables 1 and 2.

It is not difficult to determine the critical phase ratio for a closed system water + vapor by means of eqn. (I). This requires the determination of the mass from the known critical specific volume ($M = W : V_{crit}$) and the substitution of this datum and the values for the specific volumes of water and of vapor at the temperature at which we wish to determine the phase ratio by eqn. (I). We find accordingly that the critical volume of water, at room temperature, in a closed saturated system, at constant volume of the cavity, is 31.335 per cent. [*sic.*]

We may shorten the calculation of homogenization curves somewhat by taking the initial phase ratio at 0°C and not at room temperature. The total mass of the inclusion becomes then practically the same as the volume of the liquid phase at 0°C, in its absolute magnitude. For example, if the inclusion contains 90 per cent water at 0°C, the total mass equals 90.000005; when the inclusion is 10 per cent liquid phase, the total mass becomes 10.00004. Thus the M in eqn. (I) may be replaced by the absolute value of the volume of water at 0°C, with a sufficient degree of accuracy.

But the simplest procedure for construction of systems of homogenization curves is derived from one of their features. This feature may be formulated as follows: if the initial volumes of water in a series of inclusions, at one and the same temperature, differ from each other by some constant magnitude (in per cent), the differences between the volumes of the liquid phase in any two inclusions next to each other will be the same also at any other temperature. In other words, straight lines drawn parallel to the

---

* The first curves of this type were built by V. S. Sobolev jointly with N. P. Yermakov, in 1951. Editor [N.P.Ye.].

TABLE 1. PHASE RATIOS IN INCLUSIONS OF WATER DURING THE PROCESS OF HOMOGENIZATION (AT CONSTANT VOLUME)

Filling of inclusions with water (%)

°C	4.99	9.98	14.97	19.97	24.96	29.95	31.28	34.94	39.93	44.92	49.91	54.90	59.89	64.88	69.88	74.87	79.85	84.85	89.84	94.83	99.82
0	4.99	9.98	14.97	19.97	24.96	29.95	31.28	34.94	39.93	44.92	49.91	54.90	59.89	64.88	69.88	74.87	79.85	84.85	89.84	94.83	99.82
20	5.00	10.00	15.00	20.00	25.00	30.00	31.34	35.00	40.00	45.00	50.00	55.00	60.00	65.00	70.00	75.00	80.00	85.00	90.00	95.00	100.0
40	5.03	10.06	15.08	20.12	25.15	30.17	31.48	35.20	40.28	45.26	50.29	55.32	60.35	65.38	70.41	75.44	80.47	85.50	90.53	95.56	—
60	5.06	10.14	15.21	20.29	25.37	30.44	31.80	35.52	40.59	45.67	50.74	55.82	60.90	65.97	71.05	76.12	81.20	86.27	91.34	96.42	—
80	5.11	10.24	14.38	20.51	25.65	30.79	32.16	35.92	41.06	46.19	51.33	56.46	61.60	66.73	71.87	77.01	82.14	87.28	92.42	97.56	—
100	5.15	10.36	15.57	20.78	25.99	31.20	32.56	36.41	41.61	46.83	52.04	57.24	62.46	67.66	72.88	78.08	83.30	88.51	93.67	98.92	—
120	5.18	10.48	15.77	21.07	26.37	31.67	33.08	36.96	42.26	47.56	52.85	58.15	63.44	68.74	74.04	79.34	84.64	89.94	95.20	—	—
140	5.19	10.59	15.99	21.39	26.79	32.19	33.53	37.58	42.99	48.39	53.79	59.19	64.59	69.98	75.37	80.78	86.18	91.53	96.99	—	—
160	5.16	10.68	16.20	21.72	27.24	32.76	34.23	38.28	43.80	49.31	54.84	60.35	65.87	71.39	76.92	82.43	87.95	93.47	98.97	—	—
180	5.07	10.73	16.39	22.05	27.71	33.37	34.88	39.03	44.67	50.34	56.00	61.66	67.32	72.97	78.64	84.29	89.95	95.61	—	—	—
200	4.91	10.73	16.56	22.38	28.20	34.03	35.58	39.85	45.68	51.50	57.32	63.15	68.97	74.80	80.62	86.45	92.26	98.10	—	—	—
220	4.62	10.64	16.66	22.69	28.71	34.73	36.34	40.75	46.77	52.79	58.81	64.83	70.86	76.88	82.90	88.92	94.94	—	—	—	—
240	4.16	10.42	16.69	22.95	29.21	35.47	37.15	41.74	48.00	54.26	60.52	66.78	73.05	79.30	85.57	91.83	98.10	—	—	—	—
260	3.45	10.01	16.57	23.14	29.70	36.26	38.01	42.81	49.39	55.95	62.51	69.08	75.64	82.20	88.77	95.33	—	—	—	—	—
280	2.33	9.29	16.24	23.19	30.12	37.10	38.96	44.09	51.01	57.97	64.92	71.88	78.83	85.78	92.74	99.70	—	—	—	—	—
300	0.55	8.04	15.53	23.02	30.51	38.00	40.00	45.50	52.98	60.47	67.96	75.45	82.94	90.43	97.92	—	—	—	—	—	—
320	—	5.82	14.10	22.39	30.63	38.96	41.17	47.25	55.53	63.82	72.10	80.39	88.67	96.96	—	—	—	—	—	—	—
340	—	1.30	10.97	20.64	30.30	39.96	42.54	49.63	59.29	68.95	78.62	88.28	97.95	—	—	—	—	—	—	—	—
360	—	—	1.71	14.80	27.89	40.97	44.47	54.06	67.14	80.23	93.32	—	—	—	—	—	—	—	—	—	—
—	—	—	—	5.68	30.58	37.23	—	55.46	80.35	—	—	—	—	—	—	—	—	—	—	—	—

abscissa (Fig. 1) are cut by the homogenization curves of such inclusions into equal sections.
Let us prove this relationship.

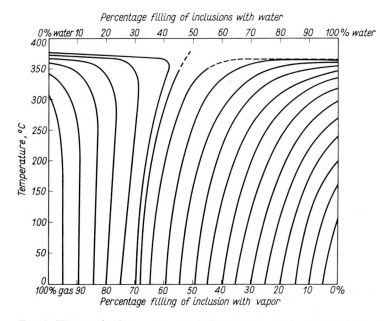

FIG. 1. Homogenization curves for inclusions of water calculated from empirical data for saturated system water-vapor (at constant volume).

It is perfectly clear, in the instance of inclusions of pure water, in thermostable volumes, that the process and the temperature of their homogenization depend only on the phase ratios, by volume, and not on the shape or the size of the inclusion, i.e. that inclusions with the same phase ratios homogenize by the same type and at the same temperatures. Hence, the proof requires a series of inclusions 1, 2, 3 ..., n of the same volumes and forms. At $T°$ temperature, the liquid phase will occupy then L, $(L—x)$, $(L—2x)$ ..., $L—(n—1)x$ per cent of inclusions' volume respectively, i.e. the volume differences in the liquid phase of any two consecutive members of the series will be x per cent. It is easily seen that the total masses of these inclusions (i.e. of any two consecutive members of the series) differ also by one and the same magnitude. Hence, at $T_1°$ temperature, the liquid phase of the inclusions in the 1, 2, 3, ..., n series will occupy the following volumes respectively:

$$L' = \frac{M'V_L V_G - WV_L}{V_G - V_L}, \qquad L'' = \frac{M''V_L V_G - WV_L}{V_G - V_L},$$

$$L''' = \frac{M'''V_l V_G - WV_L}{V_G - V_L} , ..., \text{etc.}$$

The volume-differences for water in adjacent inclusions, at $T_1{}^\circ$, will be:

$$L' - L'' = \frac{V_L V_G (M' - M'')}{V_G - V_L} , \quad L'' - L''' = \frac{V_L V_G (M'' - M''')}{V_G - V_L} , ... \quad \text{(II)}$$

All of these expressions are evidently identical with the $L' - L'' = L'' - L''' ...$, since the specific volumes of water and of vapor are equal at equal temperatures and at equal mass-differences, $M' - M'' = M'' - M''' ...$, i.e. the volume differences in the liquid phase of any two consecutive inclusions in the series are equal, at $T_1{}^\circ$, which completes its proof.

Proceeding from the relationship we have proved, we may propose the following very simple nomographic method for construction of systems of homogenization curves.

(1) A single homogenization curve is drawn with the aid of eqn. (I), e.g. for an inclusion with 30 per cent liquid phase at 20°C.

(2) The mass of the next inclusion, e.g. with 25 per cent liquid phase at 20°C, is calculated from eqn. (I a).

(3) The volume difference for water in these two inclusions, for a series, of temperatures, is calculated from eqn. (II).

(4) Along [straight—V.P.S.] lines drawn parallel to the abscissa, at distances corresponding to the temperature intervals, we mark off sections equal to the calculated differences [in per cent of filling?—V.P.S.].

(5) The points so located are joined by smooth curves.

Numerical expressions for the degree of filling, at a given temperature may be now discovered, provided that the calculations were sufficiently exact, by adding or subtracting the calculated differences to or from the appropriate values of the abscissae of the points situated on the neighboring calculated homogenization curves. The homogenization temperatures can be found graphically or may be determined by the method already outlined (items 2 and 3).

Let us consider now the character of homogenization of inclusions of pure water in certain minerals. Systems of homogenization curves are easily built, for different minerals, from data on the volume coefficient of thermal expansion [1]. Such curves do not differ appreciably from the ones already discussed. Variations in the homogenization temperatures are also not very significant (Table 2).

The greatest difference between the homogenization temperatures of inclusions of water in a thermostable* volume and of quartz and topaz

---

* "Termoneizmenyayemyi" (a Greek–Slavic hybrid term), i.e. "unaffected by temperature" in the abstract sense [V.P.S.].

TABLE 2. COMPARISON OF HOMOGENIZATION TEMPERATURES OF WATER INCLUSIONS
IN MINERALS AND IN THERMOSTABLE VOLUMES

Nos. in sequence	Filling with water at 20°C (%)	Theoretical homogenization temperatures of inclusions		
		in thermostable environment	in topaz	in quartz
1	100.0	20.0	20.0	20.0
2	95.0	114.0	115.0	118.0
3	90.0	169.0	171.0	175.0
4	85.0	214.0	216.0	219.5
5	80.0	250.0	252.5	256.0
6	75.0	281.0	283.0	286.0
7	70.0	306.5	308.0	310.5
8	65.0	327.0	328.0	330.0
9	60.0	343.0	344.0	345.0
10	55.0	355.0	355.5	357.0
11	50.0	364.0	365.0	365.5
12	45.0	369.0	369.5	370.0
13	40.0	372.0	372.0	372.0
14	35.0	373.5	373.5	373.0
15	31.871			374.1*
16	31.524		374.1*	
17	31.335	374.1*		
18	30.0	373.8	373.8	373.8
19	25.0	372.5	372.5	372.0
20	20.0	368.5	368.5	368.0
21	15.0	362.0	362.0	361.0
22	10.0	344.0	344.0	343.0
23	5.0	304.5	304.0	303.5
24	0.0	20.0	20.0	20.0

* Critical temperature.

is 6 and 4°C respectively, as shown by the data in the table. The differences between the critical phase ratios are insignificant. Thus the critical volume of water in the thermostable volume of the inclusion is 31.335 at 20°C and is 31.524 and 31.871 respectively for inclusions in quartz and topaz, all other things being the same (Table 2), i.e. there is only a barely noticeable change in the critical phase ratio resulting from the increase in the volume of the liquid phase.

Because of the widespread and common occurrence of inclusions with liquid carbon dioxide and because of the potential interest in this phenomenon, in science, we calculated a system of homogenization curves for inclusions with CO_2.

Amagat's empirical results [6] were used by us in that operation, namely, the specific gravity of liquid (d_L) and of gaseous (d_G) CO_2

(Table 3). Equation (I) was employed in its following form, in order to simplify the calculations:

$$L = \frac{M - Wd_G}{d_L - d_G} .$$

TABLE 3. THE GAS–LIQUID SATURATION FOR CARBONDIOXIDE (ACCORDING TO AMAGAT)

Tem. (°C)	Density of liquid CO_2 g/cm³	Density of gaseous CO_2 g/cm³	Pressure	Tem. (°C)	Density of liquid CO_2 g/cm³	Density of gaseous CO_2 g/cm³	Pressure
0	0.914	0.096	34.3	18	0.786	0.176	53.8
1	0.910	0.099	35.2	19	0.776	0.183	55.0
2	0.906	0.103	36.1	20	0.766	0.190	56.3
3	0.900	0.106	37.0	21	0.755	0.199	57.6
4	0.894	0.110	38.0	22	0.743	0.208	59.0
5	0.888	0.114	39.0	23	0.731	0.217	60.4
6	0.882	0.117	40.0	24	0.717	0.228	61.8
7	0.876	0.121	41.0	25	0.703	0.240	63.3
8	0.869	0.125	42.0	26	0.688	0.252	64.7
9	0.863	0.129	43.1	27	0.671	0.266	66.2
10	0.856	0.133	44.2	28	0.653	0.282	67.7
11	0.848	0.137	45.3	29	0.630	0.303	69.2
12	0.851*	0.142	46.4	30	0.598	0.334	70.7
13	0.831	0.147	47.5	30.5	0.574	0.356	71.5
14	0.822	0.152	48.7	31.0	0.536	0.392	72.3
15	0.814	0.158	50.0	31.25	0.497	0.422	72.8
16	0.804	0.164	51.2	31.35	0.464	0.464	72.9
17	0.796	0.170	52.4				

* Misprint for 0.841? [Ed.].

The results are summarized in Tables 4 and 5 and are represented diagrammatically in Fig. 2.

Twenty-seven additional curves were drawn, by the graphic–analytical method, based on the already proved characteristics of systems of homogenization curves, for inclusions with CO_2, with the initial phase ratio at —50°C (Fig. 3). We used data from the manual [4, vol. 1, p. 820] in calculating the basic curves.

The character of our calculated curves resembles the character of Yermakov's empirical curves for inclusions of aqueous solutions [2]. The possibility of homogenization in the gaseous or in the liquid phase is confirmed, for inclusions in minerals. The homogenization curve with a point of inversion [2] is entirely regular. Moreover, in the instance of inclusions homogenizing in the gaseous phase, all homogenization curves, without exception, have inversion points, as a matter of fact. We understand that it is practically impossible to prove their presence experimentally for inclusions with very small degrees of filling with water. The

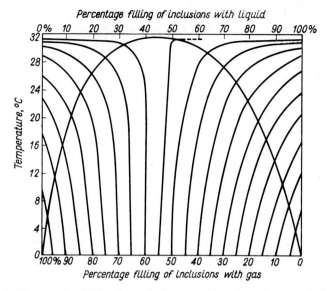

FIG. 2. Homogenization curves for inclusions with carbon dioxide calculated from experimental data of Amagat (at constant volume).

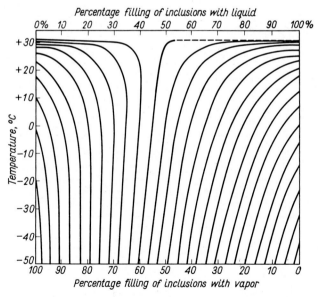

FIG. 3. Homogenization curves for inclusions with carbon dioxide calculated by the graphic-analytical method from experimental data.

TABLE 4. CALCULATED PHASE RATIOS FOR INCLUSIONS WITH CARBON DIOXIDE IN THE PROCESS OF HOMOGENIZATION (AT CONSTANT VOLUME)

Temp. (°C)	Filling with CO₂ (%)																			
	5.00	10.00	15.00	20.00	25.00	30.00	35.00	40.00	44.99	50.00	55.00	60.00	65.00	70.00	75.00	80.00	85.00	90.00	95.00	100.0
0	4.67	9.72	14.76	19.80	24.85	29.89	34.93	39.98	45.01	50.08	55.11	60.15	65.19	70.23	75.28	80.32	85.36	90.41	95.45	—
1	4.22	9.32	14.41	19.50	24.60	29.69	34.78	39.88	44.96	50.06	55.16	60.25	65.34	70.44	75.53	80.62	85.72	90.81	95.90	—
2	3.89	9.04	14.19	19.35	24.50	29.65	43.80	39.95	45.09	50.25	55.40	60.55	65.71	70.86	76.01	81.16	86.31	91.46	96.61	—
3	3.43	8.65	13.87	19.08	24.30	29.52	34.73	39.95	45.15	50.38	55.60	60.82	66.03	71.25	76.47	81.68	86.90	92.12	97.33	—
4	2.60	7.95	13.29	18.64	23.99	29.33	34.68	40.03	45.36	50.72	56.07	61.41	66.76	72.11	77.45	82.80	88.14	93.49	98.84	—
6	1.60	7.10	12.59	18.09	23.59	29.09	34.58	40.08	45.57	51.08	56.57	62.07	67.57	73.07	78.56	84.06	89.56	95.05	—	—
8	0.54	6.20	11.85	17.51	23.17	28.82	34.48	40.14	45.78	51.45	57.11	62.77	68.42	74.08	79.74	85.39	91.05	96.71	1	—
10	—	5.12	10.97	16.82	22.68	28.53	34.38	40.23	46.07	51.93	57.78	63.63	69.49	75.34	81.19	87.04	92.89	98.74	—	—
12	—	3.85	9.96	16.06	22.16	28.27	34.37	40.48	46.57	52.69	58.79	64.90	71.00	77.10	83.21	89.31	95.42	—	—	—
14	—	2.16	8.55	14.94	21.33	27.72	34.11	40.50	46.88	53.28	59.67	66.06	72.45	78.84	85.23	91.63	98.02	—	—	—
16	—	0.30	7.00	13.71	20.41	27.12	33.82	40.53	47.21	53.93	60.64	67.34	74.05	80.75	87.46	94.16	—	—	—	—
18	—	—	4.98	12.08	19.18	26.29	33.39	40.49	47.57	54.69	61.79	68.89	75.99	83.09	90.19	97.29	—	—	—	—
20	—	—	2.00	9.65	17.29	24.94	32.58	40.22	47.85	55.51	63.16	70.80	78.45	86.09	93.74	—	—	—	—	—
22	—	—	—	6.46	14.83	23.19	31.55	39.92	48.26	56.65	65.61	73.37	81.74	90.10	98.47	—	—	—	—	—
24	—	—	—	1.74	11.12	20.51	29.89	39.27	48.62	58.03	67.41	76.79	86.17	95.55	—	—	—	—	—	—
26	—	—	—	—	4.99	16.01	27.04	38.06	49.06	60.11	71.13	82.16	93.18	—	—	—	—	—	—	—
28	—	—	—	—	—	2.80	18.30	33.79	49.24	64.77	80.27	95.76	—	—	—	—	—	—	—	—
30	—	—	—	—	—	—	12.06	30.83	49.54	68.35	87.11	—	—	—	—	—	—	—	—	—
30.5	—	—	—	—	—	—	—	21.67	50.00	78.47	—	—	—	—	—	—	—	—	—	—
31.0	—	—	—	—	—	—	—	1.60	56.00	—	—	—	—	—	—	—	—	—	—	—
31.25	—	—	—	—	—	—	—	—	—	—	—	—	—	—	—	—	—	—	—	—

TABLE 5. HOMOGENIZATION TEMPERATURE OF INCLUSIONS WITH CARBON DIOXIDE
AT THERMOSTABLE VOLUMES

Nos. in sequence	Filling with liquid CO_2 at 0°C (%)	Theoretical homogenizaion temperatures of inclusions	Nos. in sequence	Filling with liquid CO_2 at 0°C (%)	Theoretical homogenzation temperatures of inclusions
1	100	0	12	44.99	31.35*
2	95	7.3	13	40	31.3
3	90	13.0	14	35	30.9
4	85	17.5	15	30	30.2
5	80	21.3	16	25	28.9
6	75	24.5	17	20	26.5
7	70	27.1	18	15	23.2
8	65	29.0	19	10	18.3
9	60	30.2	20	5	11.0
10	55	30.8	21	0	0
11	50	31.2			

* Critical temperature

determined homogenization temperatures of natural inclusions always exceed the calculated ones, because natural inclusions are mineral solutions almost invariably.

There are wide discrepancies between the observed and the calculated critical phase ratios, H_2O-vapor. In the most perfect tubular inclusions, where the error in the determined phase ratios cannot exceed 2 per cent, the critical filling with aqueous solutions varies between 44 and 46 per cent. Hence the difference between the determined and the calculated results equals 13–15 per cent. It is difficult to explain such divergencies by the experimental data directly*. Thus there is no essential difference in the homogenization of an inclusion that contains 44 per cent H_2O and 56 per cent liquid CO_2 at room temperature (quartz from the Donets Basin) and the other one, with 44 per cent aqueous solution and 56 per cent gas phase (topaz from Volynia). Homogenization of both of them is "with a critical point", although it is true that their homogenization temperatures differ appreciably; the first one homogenizes at 262°C and the second one at 360°C.

A special case is presented by tubular inclusions in a morion crystal whose homogenization also involves critical phenomena. One of them, for example, contains 54 per cent aqueous solution and 46 per cent gas, at room temperature, and becomes homogeneous at 332°C. The prepared section, with that particular inclusion, was cooled at —4°C before its

* I.e., ascribed to errors in the measurements? [V.P.S.].

thermometric analysis, but no liquid CO_2 could be detected in it. The homogenization's course included the critical point, despite the radically different phase ratio, as against the ratios in the preceding cases. In this latter case, however, at temperatures exceeding 200°C, there was a stratification of the aqueous solution into two immiscible liquids. The volume of the second liquid, with the high refraction, was up to 7 or 10 per cent of the inclusion's volume at the homogenization temperature [3].

The great scarcity of the observed critical phenomena did not allow us to assemble a set of inclusions at various concentrations of relatively easily soluble salts. Test materials of this sort could yield certain additional data pertinent to the effect of salt concentrations on the critical phase ratios. Possibly it is the very presence of salts in the included solutions that leads to the discrepancies between the calculated and the determined data. This supposition is based on the calculations derived from certain general thermodynamic relationships and confirmed by direct results obtained by certain investigators in their studies of the critical state of solutions.

Van der Waals' equation is an equation of the third order and its roots are the same at the critical ratio of the parameters [5].

By a further elaboration of the equation of state, we obtain:

$$\frac{RT_{\text{crit.}}}{P_{\text{crit.}} V_{\text{crit.}}} = \frac{8}{3} = 2.67, \tag{III}$$

valid for any substance. This is the critical coefficient [5].

Equation (III) may be written also as:

$$V_{\text{crit.}} = \frac{R}{2.67} \times \frac{T_{\text{crit.}}}{P_{\text{crit.}}}.$$

If R remains constant at the critical point of water and of dilute aqueous solutions, we may find the critical volume for H_2O from the data of Ölander and Liander [7] for the critical state of the 5 per cent aqueous solution of NaCl ($P_{\text{crit.}} = 354$ kg/cm^2 and $T_{\text{crit.}} = 424$°C), namely:

$$V_{\text{crit.}} = \frac{R}{2.67} \times \frac{647}{224} = \frac{R}{2.67} \times 2.8,$$

and also for the 5 per cent solution:

$$V_{\text{crit.}} = \frac{R}{2.67} \times \frac{697}{354} = \frac{R}{2.67} \times 1.9.$$

By calculations, $V_{\text{crit.}}$ for $H_2O > V_{\text{crit.}}$ for the NaCl solution.

Hence we may conclude that the critical volume decreases at increasing concentrations of easily soluble salts, i.e. that an increase of easily soluble salts in aqueous solutions is conductive to an increase in the critical filling of inclusions with aqueous solutions.

Schröer's measurements of the critical filling for solutions at different concentrations [8], however, are the most convincing proof of our conclusions. His diagram's curves represent different concentrations of NaCl, KCl, KBr, etc. Segment of these curves, parallel to the ordinate, correspond to the critical phenomena observed in the solutions during the experiment.

It follows directly from that diagram that the degree of critical filling, at increasing concentrations of NaCl and KCl, increases approximately as follows (Table 6).

TABLE 6. DEPENDENCE OF CRITICAL FILLING ON CONCENTRATION OF SOLUTIONS
OF NaCl AND KCl

NaCl		KCl	
Concentration moles/l.	Limits of filling	Concentration moles/l.	Limits of filling
0.0342	0.33–0.36	0.0342	0.33–0.37
0.0855	0.35–0.38	0.171	0.36–0.38
0.171	0.36–0.40	0.342	0.39–0.40

BIBLIOGRAPHY

1. BERCH, F., D. SHERER and G. SPAYCER [F. Birch, J. F. Schairer, H. Spicer], *Spravochnik dlya geologov po fizicheskim konstantam.* (Geologist's Manual of Physical Constants.) 1949.
2. YERMAKOV, N. P., *Issledovaniya mineraloobrazuyushchikh̄ rastvorov.* (Research on Mineral-forming Solutions.) Izd. Khar'kov. univ. 1950.
3. KALYUZHNYI, V. A., Novyye nablyudeniya fazovykh prevrashchenii vnutri zhidkikh vklyuchenii. (New Observations on Transformations of Phases inside Liquid Inclusions). *Mineralog. sb. L'vov. geolog. obshch.* No. 10, 1956.
4. *Spravochnik khimika.* (Chemist's Manual.) Vol. I, Goskhimizdat, 1951.
5. SHTRAUF, Ye. A., *Molekulyarnaya fizika.* (Molecular Physics.) Gostekhizdat. 1949.
6. AMAGAT, E. H., Sur la détermination de la densité des gaz liquéfiés et de leurs vapeurs saturées. *Compt. rend.* t. 114, pp. 1093–98, 1322–26, 1892.
7. ÖLANDER, A. and H. LIANDER, The Phase Diagram of Sodium Chloride and Steam Above the Critical Point. *Acta chem. Scand.*, vol. 4, No. 9, 1950.
8. SCHRÖER, E., Untersuchungen über den kritischen Zustand. *Zeit. Phys. Chem.* Bd. 129, 1927.

Studies of the Decrepitation of Quartz
and the Universal Decrepitation Amplifier-Recorder*

YE. YE. KOSTYLEVA and V. A. LABUNTSOV

As WE know, the descrepitation method is employed in mineralogical thermometry and is based on rupturing the walls of gas–liquid inclusions resulting from a radical increase in pressure, in the liquid phase, after it fills the entire inclusion on heating.

The decrepitation method, like the homogenization method, is based on Sorby's thesis that a fluid or a liquid solution captured by a growing mineral was a single phase and that the subsequent cooling of the inclusion sealed in the mineral caused a decrease in the pressure resulting in segregation of the gas phase, as a gas bubble, and occasionally also of a solid phase, as a crystal. This differentiation process is reversed by heat applied to the inclusion, so that the crystal is dissolved, the gaseous phase disappears, and the inclusion is filled with the liquid phase only. The temperature at which a single homogeneous phase is produced in the inclusion is taken to be the minimum temperature at which the mineral was formed [3, 7]. Further heating leads to a rapid build-up of pressure and to rupture of the inclusion's walls. The temperature of such decrepitation is taken to be, provisionally, the temperature of formation of the mineral. Thus the decrepitation method represents a kind of a record of the homogenization phenomena employed by Yermakov and his school [3] as the basis for determining temperatures of the formation of minerals.

As noted in Yermakov's contributions [4] and in the critical studies by other investigators, the homogenization method is particularly well suited for determining the temperatures of liquid, aqueous, and low concentration mineral-forming solutions, but only if the required corrections for pressure and concentration are insignificant. The decrepitation method also requires corrections for the resistance to rupture of the inclusion's walls, a function of the physical properties of the mineral. There can be no doubt, however, that the course of the decrepitation of a mineral

---

* The work was done with the participation of T. K. Sukhushina (mineralogical and chemical tests) and A. L. Dmitrik (decrepitation curves) of the staff of Division of Mineralogy, Institute of Geology of Ore Deposits, Petrography, Mineralogy, and Geochemistry, Academy of Sciences of the U.S.S.R.

reflects some specific features in its formation and serves possibly to characterize mineral deposits according to type.

In our search for the most reliable criteria for typing the various deposits of vein quartz, for comparisons between quartz veins or different generations of quartz, and for comparisons of the temperature intervals in the formation of quartz, our set objective was to ascertain relationships in the decrepitation of quartz from different sources.

The decrepitation method is not popular. It was first proposed by Scott, in 1948, with his primitive apparatus, and was in use since that time chiefly for orientation on the temperatures of formation of minerals. The method's most extensive applications were in the U.S.A. In the U.S.S.R., Dolgov at L'vov [1] had used this method successfully. The decrepitation and the temperatures were recorded, in his apparatus, by an automatic thermosonic recorder, autographically, on film, by the oscillographic method. In addition to determinations of the temperatures, Dolgov used the method, for the first time, in his differentiation of the Neogene sediments in Transcarpathia [2]. The method was used also in Japan, alongside the electron-microscopic studies of micropores in quartz, in determining the properties of quartzites [6].

Our research in the decrepitation of minerals requires construction of appropriate apparatus. We present here a brief description of the set-up we had built that permits an evaluation of the decrepitation effects by the numbers of the explosions, while providing a graphic record of the dependence of the course of the decrepitation on temperature.

* * *
*

The installation consists of an amplifier–recorder of the sounds of the decrepitation, with a microphone feeder, and an electrical furnace with a thermocouple and a pyrometer (Fig. 1).

The feeder is a quartz tube (24×275 mm); the test material is set in the bottom of the tube. The tube's open end is connected with the electromagnetic microphone (type MED) inserted into an ebonite chamber. The tube's closed end is placed inside a horizontal electrical furnace; the temperature of the furnace is raised automatically, by means of an adjustable autotransformer, type LATR. A platinum–rhodium thermocouple is introduced into the furnace through the latter's opposite end, so that the thermocouple almost touches the tube; the thermocouple is connected with the millivoltmeter (pyrometer). The furnace with the feeder is placed inside the screening box. Sonic impulses of the decrepitation, produced by heating the mineral, are converted into electrical impulses by the microphone and are sent to the amplifier–recorder of the decrepitation.

The electronic amplifier–recorder, whose circuit is shown in Fig. 2, performs the following functions: (a) amplification of the decrepitation

FIG. 1. The decrepitation apparatus.

a—feeder with microphone; *b*—electrical furnace; *c*—screening box;
d—millivoltmeter (pyrometer); *e*—amplifier recorder; *f*—source block.

signals received from the microphone feeder; (b) conversion of these
signals into standard impulses suited for recording by the electromechanical
counter; (c) integration of the impulses, so as to record their frequency;
(d) recording of the impulses. The apparatus affords the following record:
(1) unconverted amplified decrepitation signals received from the feeder
as electrical impulses of different amplitudes; this kind of the record is
called procedure I; (2) standard "normalized" impulses, i.e. impulses with
equal amplitudes and duration, obtained by conversion of the impulses
received from the feeder directly; this kind of the record is called procedure II; the count of the normalized impulses is made by the electromechanical counter; (3) frequency of incidence of the impulses or their
number per unit time; this kind of record is called procedure III, or
recording by integration. The procedures are set by the switch [relay?—
V.P.S.].

Recording of impulses by the apparatus (Fig. 1, *e*) is done by: (a) the
electromagnetic counter set in the front panel, with a pointer which
advances by the same number of divisions with every normalized impulse
it receives; the counter records every impulse, regardless of the position
of the switch controlling the procedure; (b) the indicator: under procedure I,

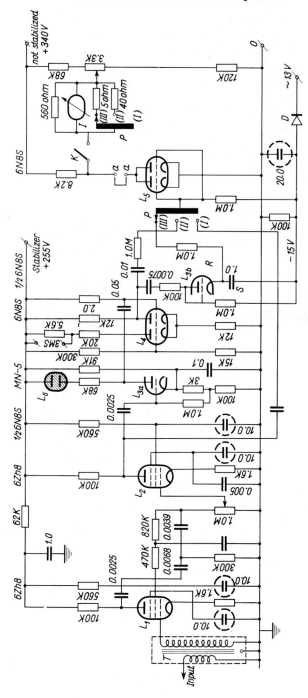

Fig. 2. Circuit of the electronic amplifier-recorder (without the feeder block).

* *Note:* The printing in the original is not sufficiently clear to avoid ambiguity in the identification of all Components [Ed.].

this instrument responds to every impulse it receives by an abrupt deflection of the pointer, in proportion to the amplitude of the impulse; under procedure II, the instrument receives normalized impulses, so that equal deflections of the pointer are produced, regardless of the amplitude of the impulse; under procedure III, the pointer's deflections are smooth and they represent the frequency of incidence of the impulses; (c) regardless of the procedure, the neon lamp in the front panel flashes every time an impulse is received.

The process of decrepitation, together with the temperature log may be recorded automatically on photographic film by the oscilloscope trailing device. There are sockets for that purpose in the front panel of the instrument. The manner of the automatic recording by the oscilloscope depends on the procedure of operation and is analogous to the deflections of the indicator. The record may be made simultaneously, by means of all of the facilities here named (the counter, the indicator, the neon lamp, the oscilloscope). Thus the operator may count decrepitations with the counter concurrently with the autographic logging by the oscilloscope. A minor rearrangement in the output stage makes it possible to keep an autographic record of the decrepitation also by the means of an autographic electronic potentiometer.

Figure 2 is the circuit of the electronic amplifier-recorder (without the feeder block) that assures the efficiency of all of the logging methods of the decrepitation here enumerated. This instrument has the following components: a—a two-stage amplifier employing tubes L_1 and L_2, with a filter interposed between the stages which serves to weaken the induction in the amplifier from the 50 cycle circuit; b—a delayed multivibrator, on the double triode L_4 and the buffer tube L_3 through which the multivibrator is activated; c—an integrating network to which the normalized impulses are fed by the multivibrator through the diode L_{3b}; d—the terminal stage, on tube L_5. The two-stage amplifier has an amplifying coefficient of 6000, with the frequency of 1000 cycles; the impulses from the microphone are sent to the amplifier input, through an insulated cable (about 2 m long) and through the harmonizing transformer, with a transformation coefficient of 1 : 16. The sensitivity is regulated by the potentiometer in the L_2 grid circuit. The delayed multivibrator "normalizes" the impulses, which is required for their subsequent integration and also for the correct functioning of the electromechanical impulse counter. The multivibrator performs a complete oscillation cycle and delivers an impulse of an entirely definite amplitude and duration per every impulse, with positive polarity, fed by the second stage of the L_2 amplifier to the grid of the L_{3b} tube. The electromechanical counter EMC and the neon lamp L_6, functioning as an optical indicator of the impulses, are included into the anode grid of the left (as in the circuit in Fig. 2) triode of the multivibrator. The switch II, in its three different positions, makes it possible to maintain any one of the three logging procedures. When set at I, the grid of the tube L_5 of the terminal stage is receiving amplified impulses directly from the second stage of the L_2 amplifier; in position II, it receives normalized impulses from the multivibrator; in position III—voltages from the integrating circuit proportional to the frequency of the impulses to be recorded. The tail of the electromagnetic oscilloscope may be put into the anode circuit of the terminal stage (instead of the bridge a–a). The measuring device I is connected to the L_6 lamp, so that its pointer may be set at zero, in the absence of impulses.* By the means of the second section of the relay II, operating under procedures II and III, the appropriate resistance shunts are put into the circuit, in parallel with the instrument M. The feeder block operates independently off an ordinary two-half wave rectifier, on the 5Ts4C Kenotron producing a direct 320 : 340 V current at 60 mA. This voltage is used directly to feed the terminal stage. The two-stage amplifier and the multivibrator are fed 255 V from two gas-discharge stabilizers, in series, types SG-4 and SG-3, to the rectifier through the 3000 Ω resistance. The negative displacement voltage of —15 V, served to the L_5 grid, is obtained from an ordinary single-half-way rectifier on the DGTs germanium diode, with a smoothing condenser of 20.0 μF. The filaments of all tubes are fed by alternating current. The amplifier is mounted on a duraluminum chasis and is set in a duraluminum case. The wiring of the components and of the entire apparatus offers no particular difficulties, on the whole. One must merely give particular care to the insulation of the microphone, the input transformer, and the grids of tubes L_1 and L_2. It is also necessary to make the voltage fluctuations of the 225 V feeding the amplifier and the multivibrator sufficiently small.

We found it possible to use the apparatus in ordinary laboratories and to feed alternating current to the entire set-up, because of the following provisions: (a) insulation of the furnace, the microphone feeder, the input transformer, and the amplifier itself; (b) the use of the independent feeder block with the gas-discharge stabilizers; (c) the use of a filter in the amplifier circuit, so as to minimize induction from the fifty-cycle grid.

In practice, the decrepitation counts are made by the electromechanical counter, by recording their numbers at predetermined temperature intervals (20° or 10°C), i.e. the increments in the total number of explosions, as against the count for the preceding temperature interval. Concurrently, the counter keeps the sum-total of the explosions. The decrepitation record is represented graphically, on completion of the experiment: the tempera-

---

* We began a modernization of the integrating component and of the amplifier's output stage; it is proposed to replace them by an integrating circuit, with a feed-out condenser and with a parallel-balanced stage respectively.

ture intervals are marked off on the abscissa and the corresponding decrepitation increments on the ordinate. Thus the decrepitation analysis of a test mineral by the counter may be expressed by a curve and by the number of impulses for the entire experiment as well as for a given temperature interval.

Decrepitation analysis with the use of the oscillograph may be conducted with the counter. Because of the slowness of the process itself and because of its discontinuities, the oscilloscope must be put into the circuit only when the frequency of the explosions begins to increase, i.e. for the temperature intervals corresponding to the frequency maxima; when the intensity of decrepitations becomes very high, the oscilloscopic log may be maintained best under procedure III.

*   *
*

All of the decrepitation curves here reported were obtained under identical conditions; the optimum grain size of quartz used in the analyses was determined empirically as 1 mm. Smaller sizes of the grains weaken the expression of the decrepitation, but yield analogous curves. The weight of the test aliquot was set at 3 g, to suit quartz samples showing medium intensities of decrepitation. The aliquot had to be doubled, where the decrepitation was weak or absent. The temperature range in all experiments was 0–600°C and the heat was applied at the rate of 10–12°C per minute. The record of the decrepitation was taken at 20°C intervals. The absence of errors in the apparatus was attested by replicate experiments which showed a good reproducibility of the results.

The inclusion–decrepitation dependence was tested on a well-formed quartz from the Astaf'evo deposit, Southern Ural. The milky-white basal part of the crystal showed a high degree of decrepitation, with a typical curve and the frequency maxima at 240–260°C. The crystal's termination, a perfectly pure optically transparent smoky quartz, showed no decrepitation at all.

In some cases, the decrepitation may be caused by other factors operative during the application of heat. For example, an amethyst-quartz from the Podol'skoye limestones, Moscow area, gave a decrepitation curve with several sharp peaks, unlike the other decrepitation curves (Fig. 3). The anomalous nature of that curve was proved at a slower rate of heating when no decrepitation whatsoever could be detected. In the case of a normal decrepitation, caused by inclusions, the curves can be repeated invariably. Decrepitation of quartz samples we had tested was checked repeatedly by heating at slower rates (Fig. 4).

The decrepitation record at smaller temperature intervals, e.g. every 10°C, results in greater irregularity of the curve, so that the frequency maxima may be somewhat displaced, in comparison with that shown by

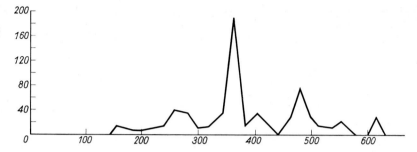

FIG. 3. Anomalous decrepitation of quartz from a deposit at Podol'skoye, Moscow area.

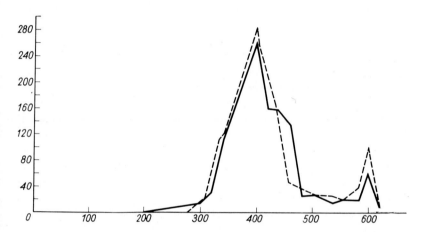

FIG. 4. Normal decrepitation curves at ordinary and at slower rates of heating.

a count at every 20°C. The irregular rate of the process, with the counts at every 10°C, indicates a discontinuous decrepitation, on account of irregularities in the composition of inclusions, due probably to the character of their origin. The more uniform the conditions under which the inclusions were formed, and the more regular was the growth of the crystal, the fewer irregularities in the decrepitation curve. Thus the decrepitation curves for a well-formed semi-transparent quartz crystal from the Mikoyan deposit, taken at 10° and at 20°C intervals, are very similar. The decrepitation curves for a massive ore-bearing quartz, based on readings at 10°C intervals, differ, by their irregularities, in many instances, from the curve based on readings at 20°C intervals, so that it is necessary to smooth the curve for the sake of comparison.

The decrepitation tests were performed for quartz samples from deposits of various types: the pegmatites of Volynia, Karelia, and Mama;

the quartz–wolframite–molybdenite and cassiterite veins of Kazakhstan, Transbaykalia, and the Maritime Region (the Far East); the "crystal quartz" veins of Southern Ural, Aldan, and the Maritime Region; the "blank" conformable and cross-cutting veins of Arctic Ural. In all, we made about 300 tests.

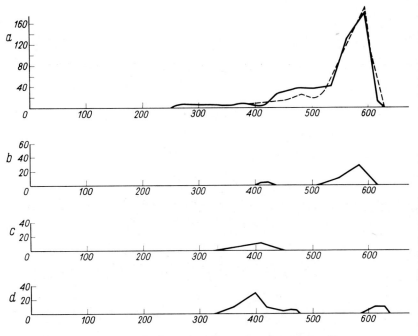

FIG. 5. Decrepitation curves for quartz from pegmatites.

a—Volynia; *b*—Karelia (blocky quartz); *c*—Mama, Eastern Siberia; *d*—Mama (quartz-muscovite complex).

The decrepitation curves shown later in the text belong to quartz of different origins (Fig. 5, 6 and 7) and illustrate the wide variations in the intensity of the phenomenon, and in the form as well as in the course of the curves. The greatest decrepitation intensity was displayed by the quartz from the Batystau tungsten deposit in Kazakhstan (Fig. 6, *a*, 7507 impulses), by the quartz–cassiterite from the Shumilovo deposit, Transbaykalia (4425 impulses), quartz from the Astaf'evskoye, Southern Ural (Fig. 7, *a*, 3700 impulses), and quartz from the pegmatites of Volynia (Fig. 5, *a*, 1207 impulses). The decrepitation effects were small or insignificant in the quartz from Mama, Eastern Siberia (Fig. 5, *c* and *d*, 20 and 40 impulses), the quartz–cassiterite from Khrustal'noye (30 impulses) and from Voznesenskoye (14 impulses), both in the Maritime Region. Many

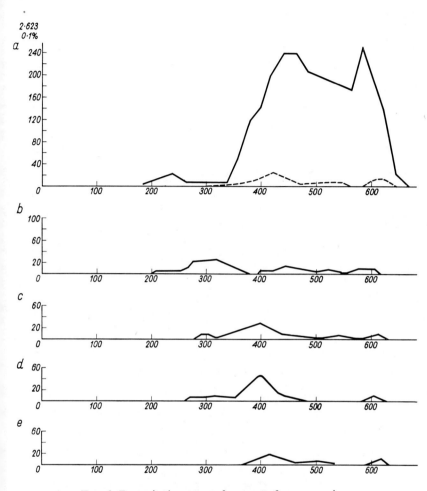

FIG. 6. Decrepitation curves for quartz from ore veins.

a—Batystau, Kazakhstan (gray quartz; the dotted line represented a crust of milky-white quartz); *b*—Dzhida, Transbaykalia (quartz from cavity in a wolframite vein); *c*—Dzhida, Transbaykalia (quartz with beryl and biotite); *d*—Tetyukhe, the Far East (long prismatic quartz); *e*—Tetyukhe, the Far East (bipyramidal quartz).

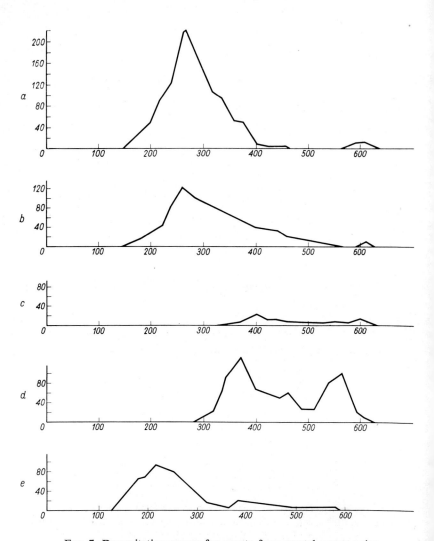

FIG. 7. Decrepitation curves for quartz from crystal quartz veins.
a—Astaf'evskoye, Southern Ural (vein quartz); *b*—Astaf'evskoye, Southern Ural (the basal milky-white part of the crystal); *c* and *d*—Aldan; *e*—Polar Ural.

quartz specimens show several up-swings or peaks of decrepitation, such as the quartz from Dzhida, Transbaykalia (Fig. 6, b). Supplementary decrepitation peaks are common at 500–600°C, as, for example, for specimens from Bukuka, Miloyan, Tetyukhe, and Mama (Fig. 5, d; Fig. 6, b, c, and e).

Different generations of quartz may be identified by the decrepitation method. Thus the curve yielded by the milky-white crust over the smoky quartz from Batystau was markedly different in its intensity as well as in its temperature of decrepitation (Fig. 6, a).

*   *
*

For interpretations of the decrepitation effects, we made microscopic studies of transparent thin sections and grains of quartz before and after the experiments. Also, by way of orientation, we examined the over-all composition of the inclusions by determining specific gravity of the quartz, the losses on ignition, and the water plus distilled volatile fractions produced from quartz on ignition in a tube. The test materials, in all cases, were 1 mm quartz grains selected under the binocular microscope.

The loss on ignition was determined by igniting 1 g aliquots of quartz, in an electrical furnace, or on a gas burner, to constant weight. The required time was determined empirically: about 1 hr in the furnace; about half an hour on the burner [5]. Aqueous and fluid emanations of quartz were studied in a test tube of a refractory glass, 0.5 cm in diameter, using 0.5 g aliquots. A thermocouple was set inside the tube and was connected to a millivoltmeter. The open end of the tube was cooled by a strip of filter paper or cotton soaked in water. The tip of the thermocouple was inserted into the test quartz; the heating over the gas burner was begun at a distance from the flame and continued at progressively decreasing distances with 100°C temperature increments: 200–250, 300–350, 400–450, and 500–600°C. The sample was kept inside each of the heat zones for 5–8 min. Water was given off by the quartz samples at different temperatures (condensed as droplets or films at the open end of the tube); the volatile gases formed distillation rings at various distances from the sample. The temperatures of the evolution of water and gases generally coincided with the decrepitation effects, as shown in Fig. 8.

Such comparisons help to interpret decrepitation curves and lead to the following conclusions:

(1) Variations in the decrepitation intensities depend on the numbers and the size of the exploded inclusions. Many of the ore-bearing quartz crystals contain extremely small single-phase apparently gaseous inclusions, one micron or fractions of one micron in size, that fail to explode even on heating even up to 1000–1200°C. Inclusions larger than 1 μ do not always explode on heating to 600°C.

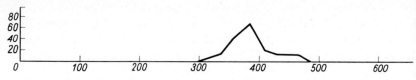

FIG. 8. Decrepitation curve for quartz from Aldan and temperatures of separation of water and of distilled fluids.

Decrepitation is intensified by increasing quantities of two-phase inclusions larger than 1 μ. This conclusion is based on the ratio of inclusions per 1 mm², counted under the microscope, to the number of the recorded decrepitations:

Source	Total number of inclusions, 0.0001–0.001 mm	Number of two-phase inclusions	Number of decrepitations
Mama, Eastern Siberia	2900	100	45
Mama, quartz–muscovite complex	13,100	500	225
Bukuka	24,000	810	375
Voznesenskoye, Maritime Region	39,000	—	14

(2) The supplementary peaks at 580–620°C, and higher, are caused by a delayed decrepitation of gaseous inclusions. Non-aqueous distillates are generally observed in the test-tube experiments at such temperatures.

(3) The evolution of H_2O in the test-tube experiments is not recorded in the decrepitation tests, on many occasions. This water probably does not belong to liquid inclusions but is held in the capillary interstices of hydrothermal quartz.

(4) A prolonged and gently sloping ascent of the curves is caused by decrepitation of secondary gas–liquid inclusions which do not yield high decrepitation frequencies, but produce relatively sparse and random impulses. A steep rise of curves, ending in a peak corresponding to the maximum decrepitation frequency, is caused by primary gas–liquid inclusions. The more homogeneous is the composition of primary inclusions, the steeper is the slope and the sharper and the clearer defined is the peak of the curve—and the steeper is its descent. Curves of such type are observed in the instance of some well-formed quartz crystals. A prolonged gently sloping descent of the curves is due to inclusions with heterogeneous compositions and phase ratios.

(5) The genetic type of a quartz is characterized by the temperature field wherein the frequency maxima of the decrepitation of primary inclusions are to be found. For example, quartz from the pegmatites of Volynia and Karelia and the ore-bearing quartz of the pegmatoid section of the Batystau deposit (Fig. 5 *a*, *b*; Fig. 6, *a*) are characterized by the high-temperature field (500–600°) of their decrepitation frequency maxima; ore-bearing quartz of a hypothermal origin has a decrepitation frequency maximum in vicinity of 400°C, and higher, and supplementary peaks at 500–600°C caused by its gaseous inclusions. The frequency maxima of the decrepitation of quartz of the "crystal-quartz type" veins are not the same: 220–250°C for quartz from Southern Ural and 400°C for quartz from Aldan, in harmony with the different genetic environments of the formation of these two deposits. The "blank" [barren?] quartz veins of Arctic Ural also yield different maximum temperatures of decrepitation and require further studies.

On the whole, the decrepitation features of quartz may be useful in comparisons and correlations of quartz veins of different origin. Also, the decrepitation curves may be used tentatively, as indications of the genetic type of quartz, of quantities and size of its inclusions, their character, of the presence of gaseous inclusions, etc.

Further work needs be directed toward deepening and refining of the decrepitation method, development of autographic oscilloscopic logging, a more detailed location of the maxima of the decrepitation frequencies, applications of the method to quartz crystals of different habits and generations, and its application to other minerals.

BIBLIOGRAPHY

1. DOLGOV, YU. A. and L. D. RAYKHER, Avtomaticheskii termozvukoregistrator. (The Automatic Thermosonic Recorder.) *Mineralog. sb. L'vov. geolog. obshch.* No. 7, 1953.
2. DOLGOV, YU. A., Raschleneniye termozvukovym metodom osadochnykh terrigennykh kvartssoderzhashchikh tolshch neogena Zakarpat'ya. (Differentiation of Sedimentary Terrigenic Quartz-bearing Neogene Horizons of Transcarpathia.) *Geolog. sb. L'vov. geolog. obshch.* No. 1, 1954.
3. YERMAKOV, N. P., *Issledovaniya mineraloobrazuyushchikh rastvorov.* (Research in Mineral-forming Solutions.) Izd. Khar'kov. univ. 1950.
4. YERMAKOV, N. P. and V. A. KALYUZHNYI, O vozmozhnosti vyyavleniya istinnykh temperatur mineraloobrazuyushchikh rastvorov. (On the Possibility of Ascertaining the True Temperatures of Mineral-forming Solutions.) *Tr. VNIIP* Vol. I, pt. 2, 1957.
5. YERMAKOV, N. P. and N. I. MYAZ', Vliyaniye zhidkikh i gazovykh vklyuchenii na velichinu poter' pri prokalivanii mineralov. (The Influence of Liquid and Gaseous Inclusions on the Magnitudes of Loss on Ignition of Minerals.) *Tr. VNIIP* Vol. I, pt. 2, 1957.
6. IVAO, AKABORI, KONDZUMI and MINATO, Elektronnaya mikrografiya nekotorykh kremnyevykh porod so spetsial'nym izucheniyem mikropor s flyuidnymi vklyuche-

niyami. (The Electronic Micrograph of Certain Siliceous Rocks with a Particular Study of Micropores Containing Fluid Inclusions.) *J. Japan Assoc. Mineral. Petrol. and Econ. Geol.* Vol. 37, No. 5, 1953 (in Japanese and in English). *Ref. zh. geologiya* Vol. I, pt. 2, 1956.

7. SMIT [Smith?], F. G., *Geologicheskaya termometriya po vklyucheniyam v mineralakh.* (Geologic Thermometry on the Basis of Inclusions in Minerals), 1956.

A Simplified Automatic Thermosonic Recorder

A. I. Zakharchenko N. S. Lazarevich, G. I. Moskalyuk
and A. A. Moskalyuk

DETERMINATION of the temperatures of endogenic formation of minerals was and is a very real problem in the analysis of the origins of mineral deposits as well as in the solution of basic and practical problems in In 1948, H. S. Scott proposed the decrepitation method for determining temperatures of formation of minerals by exploding their liquid inclusions by heat. The method is based on the relatively slow and gradual increase in pressure in liquid inclusions while they are being heated up to their homogenization temperature. However, immediately after disappearance of the gas phase, even a small increase in the temperature causes a drastic increase in pressure inside the inclusions. The inclusions' walls are unable to withstand this increase and the host mineral begins to rupture, i.e. becomes subject to decrepitation. This is evident from diagrams of the specific volume of water, as a function of temperature and pressure, frequently cited in various publications [2, 3, 4, 5]. The major explosions of liquid inclusions begin at about their homogenization temperatures.

The basic advantages of the method are its simplicity and suitability for non-transparent minerals.

In the beginning, the ruptures of liquid inclusions were counted with the aid of a medical stethoscope, as the number of pops (ruptures) per unit time. The scope of such method of counting the explosions is limited, however. Only clearly defined, i.e. isolated, and generally anomalous explosions can be so counted, per unit time (one minute), which leads to errors and introduces a subjective element into the research.

P. Peach, in 1949, proposed the first automatic thermosonic recorder as an instrument for objective counting of the explosions. He offered only a brief description of the main components of the apparatus, without any circuits that would make its construction possible, and he used complicated and expensive instruments outside the reach of most research workers.

Yu. A. Dolgov and L. D. Raykher (of the National University of L'vov), in 1950, built a better automatic thermosonic recorder, but also based on complicated and costly instruments (oscillographs, seismographs*).

---

* Presumably a variety of sensitive microphone? [Ed.].

The All-Union Geologic Institute (VSEGEI) began to work with thermometric methods of research in 1949. The homogenization method was adapted first and, in 1952, also the decrepitation method, with the use of the medical stethoscope. Later on, it was decided to develop an automatic recorder of relatively simple construction that could be recommended for a mass-production and a widespread use in the research.

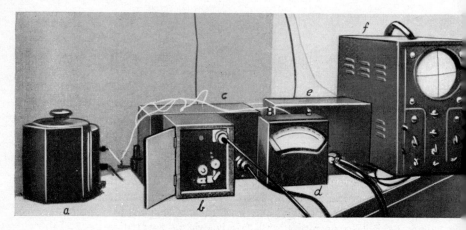

FIG. 1. The main instruments of the set-up for thermosonic recording.
a—the furnace thermo-regulator, type LATR; *b*—the electromagnetic autograph; *c*—the amplifier; *d*—the galvanometer; *e*—the rectifier; *f*—the electronic oscilloscope (for visual observations).

The basic technical difficulties with the design of the automatic thermosonic recorder were as follows:

(1) The sound effect produced by the decrepitation of minerals is so weak that a highly sensitive microphone is required for the conversion of the acoustic signals into electrical ones.

(2) The microphone must tolerate heating of the test materials up to 800°C, i.e. up to the highest temperatures of inclusions of natural mineral-forming fluids.

(3) The charge-chamber and the microphone inside it must be impermeable to sounds from the outside.

(4) The apparatus, as a whole, must be reliable, simple, and must not require highly qualified personnel for its operation.

Particular attention was given to standard instruments made in our country on a large scale, in the development of the various units of the apparatus.

A blueprint and an installed model of the automatic thermosonic recorder, with the autographic tracer and the electronic oscilloscope (but without the seismograph) attachments were developed with attention to the available instruments of domestic and foreign designs. The thermosonic recorder was used for making hundreds of measurements, as well as in the analysis of the temperatures of formation and alteration of many hydrothermal minerals. The results proved to be entirely satisfactory.

After the first apparatus was developed, we began to receive many requests from organizations and individuals and also from Czechoslovakia, Bulgaria, China, and other countries, for determinations of the temperatures of mineral genesis on a large scale, and for aid in the construction of simplified automatic thermosonic recorders. In 1957, at the VSEGEI, a simplified model of the automatic installation, suited for mass-production, was quickly designed and built.

That thermosonic recorder consists of the following units, as shown in Figs. 1 and 2:

(1) *Thermofurnace* (Fig. 2) is a hollow cylinder *a* wound by a heating coil. The quartz tube *b* is set inside the furnace. The tube's diameter is 25–50 mm; one end of the tube is sealed, the end in which the ground test mineral is placed. The microphone is set over the open end of the tube.

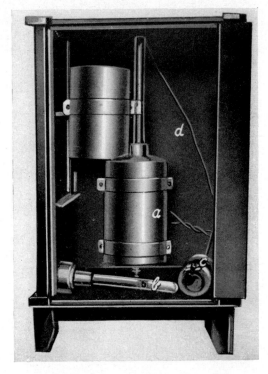

FIG. 2. The furnace with its charge.

a—the furnace's cylinder, in wrappings; *b*—the quartz tube; *c*—the microphone with the insulator; *d*—the sound-proof case.

A thermocouple, connected to a galvanometer graduated in degrees centigrade, is placed in the tube in direct proximity to the test mineral. The furnace is capable of heating the test mineral up to 800°C. The furnace is placed inside a sound-proof case, in order to shield the microphone from interferences.

(2) *Electronic amplifier* (Fig. 3) of the sounds of rupture received by the microphone assures the normal functioning of the logging device. The amplifier is of the three-stage low-frequency kind; it transmits the 100 to 3000 cycle band. The amplification coefficient $K = 30,000$. The 6Zh4 tubes are used in the hook-up.

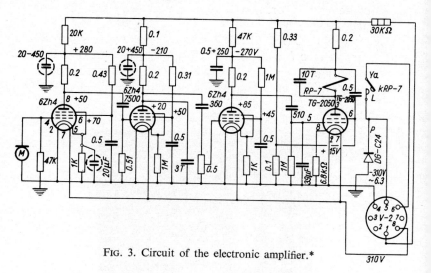

FIG. 3. Circuit of the electronic amplifier.*

The thyratron TG-2050 functions as a load on the output of the amplifier, with the RP-7 polarized relay in its anode circuit. On activation of the thyratron, the relay governs the electromagnets of the recording device through its own contacts. The amplifier receives its electrical energy from the alternating current grid through a separate rectifier.

(3) *The recording device* is a writing attachment for plotting the numbers of the ruptures in relation to the temperature of the mineral and the temperature in the recorder.

Instead of the expensive and intricate oscilloscopes and seismographs, we designed and made a very simple autograph for the impulses whose electrical circuit is shown as Fig. 4.

The autograph has an electric motor of the SD-2 type on whose axle the receiving casette is set. The dispensing cassette, with 10 m of wax

---

* Note: The printing in the original is not sufficiently clear to avoid ambiguity in the identification of all components [Ed.].

paper tape, is in the front panel. Two pens of the autograph are connected to the electromagnet's bases and are off-set with respect to the long axle. For manual marking the temperature on the tape, the front panel has a button which, on pressing, makes a thin line on the tape.

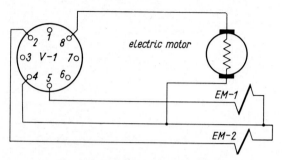

FIG. 4. Circuit of the autograph.

The electric motor is fed from the special wiring on the transformer (rectifier), with 127 V, and it rotates the receiving cassette at the rate of 2 revolutions per minute, so that the rate of the movement of the tape is 2 mm per second.

The recording capacity of the autograph is 3–4 impulses per second. The paper tape on which the record is made requires no further processing.

(4) *Thermometer*. The temperatures are measured by the thermocouple and by any high-sensitivity calibrated galvanometer of standard make in our country.

(5) *Heat control in furnace* and in the test mineral is made effective by an ordinary autotransformer of the LATR type.

(6) *Rectifier* (Fig. 5), for conversion of the 127–220 V alternating current into a direct current at 250 V is required for the anode and grid circuits, as well as, at 6.3 V a.c., for feeding the filament wires of the tubes of the electronic amplifier.

(7) *Microphone,* for conversion of the sonic vibrations, originating at the instant of the decrepitation of a mineral, into electrical impulses. The simplified apparatus presupposes the use of the type DEM microphone.

All of the main parts of the apparatus were wired into the circuit through a terminal board (Fig. 6).

The operations were as follows:

A two-gram aliquot of the test mineral was ground to 0.25–0.5 mm and was placed in the sealed lower part of the quartz tube which was inserted into the thermofurnace. The thermocouple was set in direct proximity. As previously stated, the microphone was placed by the open end of the quartz tube.

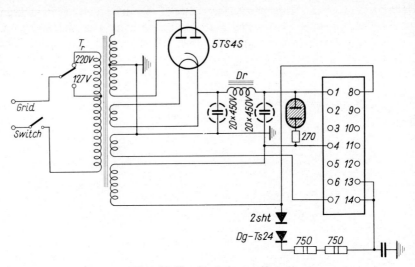

FIG. 5. Circuit of the rectifier.

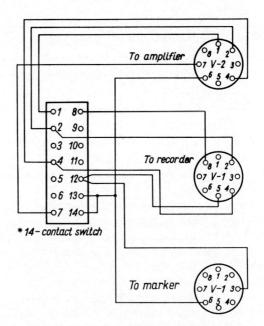

FIG. 6. Circuit showing connections of thermosonic recorder's main instruments.

Decrepitation of the mineral takes place on the application of heat. The accompanying sonic vibrations act on the membrane of the microphone and an electromotive force develops from the magnetic field at the microphone base. The electromotive force is magnified by the amplifier and transmitted to the control grid of the thyratron. On receiving the signal, the thyratron fires, the RP-7 relay acts and, through its contact, sends the current impulse to the wiring on one of the electromagnets of the autograph.

The electromagnet's keeper is pulled in and, with its pen, makes a mark on the tape, in the form of a thin vertical stroke. The number of ruptures corresponds to the number of the strokes on the tape, as long as the frequency of the ruptures does not exceed 4–5 per second. When the frequency becomes too high, the relay cannot keep pace with it and draws a solid horizontal line. The temperature is recorded every 20°C, by pressing the button on the face of the panel.

The thermofurnace must be heated uniformly, not faster than 20°C per minute.

The results obtained by the simplified thermosonic recorder with the electromagnetic autographic attachment (solid lines in Figs. 7 and 8) were verified by a concurrent logging of the decrepitation by the oscilloscope with a trailing attachment (dotted lines), as well as by visual determinations of homogenization temperatures of the inclusions, in the microthermochamber.

The test materials were samples of quartz from crystal-quartz-bearing pegmatites and quartz veins in which the sequence and the decreasing temperature of crystallization of the successive generations of quartz were clearly and definitely expressed. Samples of fluorite, calcite, and some other minerals were tested also.

Figures 7 and 8 are presented here as examples of the decrepitation logs by the electromagnetic autograph, writing on wax paper (solid lines), and by the high-quality oscilloscope, with a tracing attachment, writing on a photographic film (dotted lines).

The two upper sets of curves, Fig. 7,* represent the decrepitation temperatures of the early honeycomb quartz from the pegmatites of Volynia. This quartz contains a multitude of secondary inclusions which, in addition to the liquid, have also a very large gas phase. The inclusions

---

* The original always refers to the curves in Figs. 7 and 8 by number, e.g. "curves 1", "curves 2", etc., but without referring to the figures in which the curves are shown. Also, none of the curves in the figures are identified by numbers corresponding to those in the text (or by any numbers at all). Rather than annotate the curves in the already cluttered Figs. 7 and 8, I use the geographical names given in Figs. 7 and 8 (by the authors) and not the curve numbers, in order to harmonize the text with the illustrations [V.P.S.].

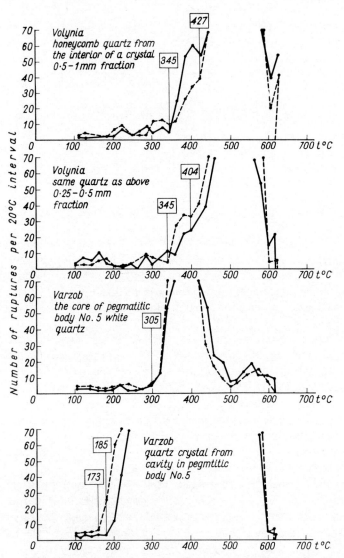

FIG. 7. Decrepitation curves for liquid inclusions, as given by the electro-magnetic autograph (solid line) and by the oscilloscope (dotted line).

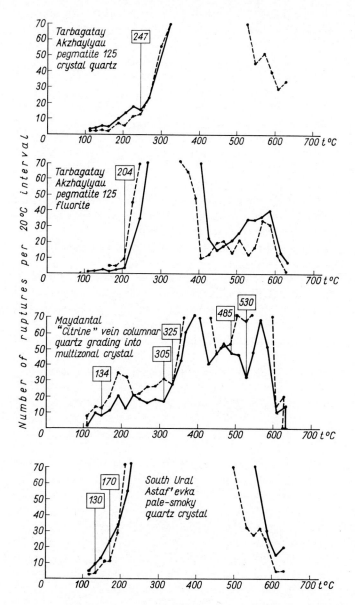

FIG. 8. Decrepitation curves for liquid inclusions, as given by the electromagnetic autograph (solid line) and by the oscilloscope (dotted line).

homogenize at 320–350°C. Such high temperatures of healing of fissures produced by the α–β-conversions of the quartz are definitely confirmed by the decrepitation tests. The top set of the curves, shows the decrepitation rate for inclusions in the 0.5–1.00 mm fraction and the next set of the curves, shows the rate for the 0.25–0.5 mm fraction of the same quartz (Fig. 7). The latter curves are smoother and clearer (comparisons of this kind were also made for many other samples). The rest of the tests were made on the 0.25–0.5 mm fraction giving the best results.

The two lower sets of curves, Fig. 7, represent the thermometric results on quartz from the pegmatites of Varzob, Pamir; the top set refers to the early white honeycomb quartz from the core of the pegmatites; the bottom one to the late pale-smoky quartz from the same pegmatites. The depositional sequence of the temperatures of these two varieties of quartz shows especially clearly in this comparison. The results obtained by the two different instruments are practically identical.

The top set of the curves, Fig. 8, represents the decrepitation temperatures of liquid inclusions in late generations of crystal quartz from a pegmatitic body; the next set down are the curves for a nearly colorless fluorite from the same pegmatitic body. The late quartz–fluorite depositional sequence is confirmed and also the readings by both instruments coincide exactly. The homogenization temperature of liquid inclusions in the Tarbagatay quartz and fluorite, by way of a check, was 180–190 and 160–180°C respectively.*

The next set of decrepitation curves, Fig. 8, refer to a multizonal quartz crystal from the high-temperature quartz–feldspar veins of Maydantal. This is the most highly involved case, when both of the instruments, logging the temperature through many stages of decrepitation of the liquid inclusions and through many growth stages of the quartz crystals, yielded entirely comparable results.

The bottom set of the decrepitation curves, Fig. 8, refer to liquid inclusions in a pale-smoky quartz from a cavity in vein No. 11, rich in crystal quartz, in Southern Ural. The decrepitation log by both instruments indicates a relatively low minimum temperature and a gradual decline from the peak, without pulsations. The homogenization temperatures of the same inclusions were also low.

One may see, by the decrepitation curves here shown, that the temperature log on wax paper, by the electromagnetic autograph, is a replicate of the oscilloscope's log on the photographic film, if the instrument is set up correctly, and the reliability and the scope of both of the instruments have the same value. Our curves confirm, in principle, the

---

* The corresponding decrepitation peaks, Fig. 8, are roughly at 247–540 and 204–420°C respectively; the quartz has also a small peak at ca. 210°C. *The minimum temperatures* are set by the authors at 204 and 247° [V.P.S.].

possibility of determining the temperatures of the formation of minerals by the decrepitation method. One needs presume that the simple and inexpensive set-up for an automatic thermosonic recorder suggested by us may be useful in promoting a widespread use of the method in the studies of minerals.

BIBLIOGRAPHY

1. DOLGOV, YU. A and L. D. RAYKHER, Avtomaticheskii termozvukoregistrator (dlya mineralogicheskikh issledovaniy). (The Automatic Thermosonic Recorder (for mineralogical investigations)). *Mineralog. sb. L'vov. geolog. obshch.* No. 7, 1953.
2. YERMAKOV, N. P., *Issledovaniya mineraloobrazuyushchikh rastvorov.* (Research in Mineral-forming Solutions.) Izd. Khar'kov. univ. 1950.
3. YERMAKOV, N. P., Metod rastreskivaniya v mineralogicheskoi termometrii. (The Decrepitation Method in Mineralogical Thermometry.) *Mineralog. sb. L'vov. geolog. obshch.* No. 4, 1950.
4. PEACH, P. A., A decrepitation geothermometer, *Am. Min.*, vol. 34, No. 5/6, 1949.
5. SCOTT, H. S., The decrepitation method applied to minerals with fluid inclusions, *Econ. Geol.* vol. 43, No. 8, 1948.

An Improved Thermochamber for the Analysis of Liquid Inclusions

V. A. KALYUZHNYI

SINCE Sorby's times [3, 4], in the course of the past century, the heating devices for microscopic observations of changes in the phase ratios of liquid inclusions had undergone a considerable evolution. Transmission of heat from its source to the test material was the principle of the design of such apparatus. The medium conveying the heat could be liquid, gaseous, or solid. The choice of the medium for heating the test material and the design of the heating unit itself must satisfy the following requirements: (a) the actual temperature of the inclusion must correspond to the temperature shown by the measuring device (a thermometer or a millivoltmeter); (b) there must be a provision for observations at high magnifications; (c) there must be a facility for attaining sufficiently high temperatures (up to 500–600°C). These requirements cannot be satisfied without assurances of a uniform heating of the test material at gradually increasing temperatures (or cooling at gradually falling temperatures). Hence good thermal insulation of the apparatus is particularly important.

The most exact results are obtained by heating the test materials in liquid media, with suitable precautions. However, the attainment of high temperatures is limited, in this case, by properties of the liquids employed. The highest attainable temperatures cannot be higher than 250–300°C.

The currently popular air-heated thermochambers have several advantages over the other types. Their main advantages include simplicity of construction, the possibility of obtaining temperatures up to 700°C, good visibility of the details of the test materials, ease of replacement of the test sections, and even the possibility of discovering new details in the test materials during the heating itself. However, the difficulties in assuring uniform heating of the test material and in maintaining a satisfactory thermal insulation lead to systematic errors in measurements of the temperatures. This was the reason for the change in the design of the old thermochamber [2]. The heating principle in the improved thermochamber is implemented by the transmission of heat through plates made of a heat-conducting metal. The heat is conveyed to the test material clamped between these plates.

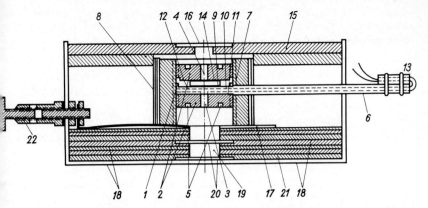

FIG. 1. The improved microthermochamber with contact-heating of the test section.

In Fig. 1, one may easily see that *21*, the body, *22*, the current supply, and *8*, the heating resistance, are analogous to these parts of Yermakov's thermochamber, but that the cylindrical inner part of the thermochamber is not the same. It consists of a cylinder made of metal (steel, aluminum, or bronze) whose inner surface has a thread and a thin supporting ring *1*. Two metallic plugs *2* are easily screwed into the top and the bottom of the cylinder. Each plug has a hole in its center, for lighting the test object *3* and for seeing it through the microscope *4*.

Each plug has two drilled holes *5* for a spanner wrench. The thermo-couple, encased in a two-hole porcelain tube *6*, is inserted through the orifice *7* whose diameter corresponds to the thickness of the porcelain insulator.

The inner part of the thermochamber is installed after the winding of the resistance unit *8* and setting the cylinder in place. The welded joint of the thermocouple *9*, rolled or filed down to 0.2–0.05 mm thickness, is inserted through the holes in the sides of the body and cylinder and is pressed against the glass disk *10* by the lower plug. A thin disk of mica *11* is inserted, as insulation, between the welded joint of the thermocouple, situated at the very rim of the hole, and the lower plug. A hole, of the same diameter as the hole in the plug, is cut through the center of the mica disk, for better visibility. In case the welded joint of the thermocouple is not thin enough, careless tightening of the lower plug may split the glass disk *10*. In order to avoid that, a layer of mica *12*, appropriately trimmed, is placed between the glass and the plug. The thickness of the mica must be the same as thickness of the welded joint of the thermocouple.

In such manner, the welded joint of the thermocouple will be held tight, in the same position, during all of the subsequent measurements of the temperature and will remain unaffected by changes of the test slides in the upper part of the working space of the chamber. In order to avoid transmission of twisting from changes in the thermochamber, [or] from the protruding outer parts of the thermocouple to its inner thin part, the free ends of the thermocouple are put through a short piece of porcelain tube *13*, attached to the insulator *6*. The test slide *4** is set upon the glass disk *10* with tweezers and is pressed gently against the disk by the upper plug. After that, the thermometric investigations are done in the usual way. The lid for the body of the thermochamber *15* was made of asbestos cardboard. Prior to that, the asbestos was lubricated with silica glue and ignited, by the thermochamber, together with *10*, the glass disk, set inside its bed. After such treatment, the asbestos lid would fit snugly into the upper end of the body and would not produce any dust or threads that could interfere with the determinations.

The asbestos insulation, even as in ordinary thermochambers, results in a more uniform heating of the chamber's interior, but, in our case, it is also intended to facilitate the use of long-focus microscope objectives

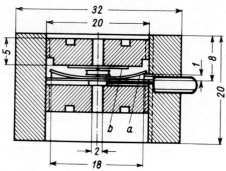

FIG. 2. The inner cylindrical part of the microthermochamber and the scheme of holding the test section during calibration of the thermocouple. Dimensions in mm.

When ordinary objectives are used, one must lower the height of the part of the chamber above the supporting ring *1* to 6–7 mm and use a thinner cardboard for making the asbestos disk *15*. For the thermal insulation, the mica plate *17* is placed in the lower part of the thermochamber, under the metallic cylinder, and layers of asbestos cardboard *18*, with hole *19* in their center covered by two slips of glass *20*. Water-cooling or air-cooling must be provided in order to protect the objective from heat and from premature deterioration [1]. A bronze cooler, built by us for that purpose, gave good results. The cooler was a bronze double layer ribbon fastened on the objective, with water circulating through its two holes.

---

* 14? [Ed.].

The asbestos lid has a special handle, thermally insulated. The lid is removed whenever the lower plug is unscrewed and the test section is replaced by another one.

The millivoltmeter is calibrated against the melting points of tin, lead, and zinc. For that purpose, as shown in Fig. 2, a rectangular plate *a*, 18 by 5 mm, is cut from a thin resilient sheet of mica. The short sides of the plate are rounded to fit the diameter of the plugs. The plate is set in the working space of the chamber, where it rests against the bulges of the ring *1* (Fig. 1). The metal, e.g. lead, is cut into thin shreds. One or two such shreds are placed in the center of the mica plate, opposite the hole in the lower plug. A small platelet, mica or glass, *14*, 2–2.5 mm thick, is place on top of the metal. One or two shreds of the metal are placed on top of the platelet, also opposite the hole in the lower plug. They are covered by a thin leaf of mica *b* (Fig. 2) and are pressed down by the upper plug.

Thus the metal employed in the calibration is held firmly in place, by the upper plug, while the mica plate *b* compensates, by its resilience, even the slight weakening of the clamp when the metal melts. The shred of the metal loses its shape and flows almost instantaneously, the moment the melting point is reached (the observations are done under the microscope). The millivoltmeter is marked, at that very moment, by the point corresponding to the melting point of the metal. As a rule, the metal on top of the quartz plate melts 1–2°C below the melting point of the metal under the plate. Consequently, the error in the temperature measurements due to deeper positions of the inclusions is not likely to exceed 1–2°C.

This method of calibration, with the welded joint of the thermocouple in a constant position, precludes accidental errors and discrepancies in the temperatures on top of the glass disk *10* and under that disk (Fig. 1). The total error in the temperature measurements, by our method, is not likely to be more than ±2°C (not counting errors in the millivoltmeter readings).

By way of control, we determined the homogenization temperatures of the same inclusions in a liquid medium (oil, whose temperature was measured by thermometer) and in the newly built thermochamber. The differences between the results did not exceed 2–3°C.

We made use of prepared sections and inclusions examined in 1951–1956 and of the laboratory notebooks of that period, in ascertaining errors in determinations of homogenization temperatures in thermochambers of the old design (air-heated). The most reliable of the analyses of the former years were compared with the best obtained in our thermochamber. We also made comparisons between homogenization temperatures of the same inclusions, as determined in the new thermochamber and in the thermochambers of the old design that are in use in the laboratories of the

University of L'vov. In such manner, we compared the results of approximately 60 analyses.

The investigations here reported lead us to the following conclusions:

(1) Homogenization temperatures obtained in air-heated ordinary thermochambers are always too low.

(2) The systematic errors in the determined homogenization temperatures, with the use of the air-heated thermochamber are explained by the following. The air space over the test section is poorly insulated from the colder air outside, because of the several holes in the thermochamber lid that are not tightly plugged. The cold outer air, as it penetrates through the cracks, lowers the temperature of the welded joint of the thermocouple, the size of which, by the way, is always appreciable. Only a small part of the thermocouple's surface touches the test section. The test section receives heat also from the surrounding air and from the mica (or glass) of the middle window of the thermochamber. The errors increase parallel to the increase in the surface of the soldered joint of the thermocouple which is not in contact with the test section, to the height to which the test-section-holder is raised toward the upper window, and to the temperature to which the test section is heated.

(3) The determined temperatures are, on the average, 30–40°C too low. If a chromel–copel or a chromel–alumel thermocouple is used, with a somewhat flattened hot-welded joint, 2 by 1.8 mm wide and 1.2 mm thick, the homogenization temperatures determined in the air-heated thermochamber will be 20–30°C below the actual temperatures, if the temperature of the test section is 100–200°C; if the temperature of the test section is 200–300°C the results will be too low by 40°C; they will be too low by 50–60°C, if the test section was heated to 300–400°C.

These corrections, by way of an approximation to the true temperatures, should be applied, with certain precautions, to the earlier thermometric determinations in which the air-heated thermochamber was employed.

BIBLIOGRAPHY

1. ANIKIN, I. N., Primeneniye mikroskopa dlya izucheniya vysokotemperaturnykh protsessov. (The Utilization of Microscope in Studies of High-temperature Processes.) *Zavodskaya Laboratoriya*, No. 7, 1956.
2. YERMAKOV, N. P., *Issledovaniya mineraloobrazuyushchikh rastvorov*. (Research in Mineral-forming Solutions.) Izd. Khar'kov. univ. 1950.
3. SORBY, H. C., On some Peculiarities in the Microscopical Structure of Crystals Applicable to the Determination of the Aqueous or Igneous Origin of Minerals and Rocks, *Phil. Mag.*, ser. 4, No. 15, 1857.
4. SORBY, H. C., On the Microscopic Structure of Crystals indicating the Origin of Minerals and Rocks. *Quart. J. Geol. Soc. (London)*, vol. 14, pt. I, pp. 453–500, 1858.

Thermometric Investigations of Vein Quartz and Crystal Quartz from Quartz Veins of the Dzhezkazgan-Ulutau District

S. N. Venediktov

In our studies of numerous ore-free monomineralic quartz veins of the Dzhezkazgan–Ulutau District, differing from each other in age, depositional environment, vein quartz structures, the occurrence of crystal quartz, and in other respects, we made a large number of thermometric determinations. The possible conclusions that may be derived from our findings make it necessary for us to consider, in brief, the results we obtained.

We used two methods in the thermometric analysis: (a) homogenization of gas–liquid inclusions and (b) decrepitation (rupture) of the inclusions. The first one was applied to crystal quartz and also to columnar and semitransparent drusy quartz; the second one was used for milky-white vein quartz in which the extremely small size of the inclusions made visual studies of the homogenization impossible.

The homogenization method is based on observing the homogenization of inclusions in thin polished sections of crystal quartz, on heating them gradually in a thermochamber. The thermochamber is set on the stage of a binocular lens or of a microscope. It needs no description here, since it was already described in detail by Yermakov [2], Zakharchenko [3], and by several other investigators. Thermometric studies by the decrepitation method were carried out at the Research Laboratory for Nonmetallic Mineral Raw Materials of the All-Union Geologic Institute (VSEGEI). Considerable aid in this project was accorded to the author by N. S. Lazarevich.

Up to recent times, the record of ruptures of the inclusions, brought about by heating vein quartz, crushed to a certain particle size, was made by ear (the acoustic method, first developed by G. Scott). Yermakov suggested an optical method, based on observation of the behavior of mineral grains in the thermochamber, as the grains shudder or change their positions when their inclusions explode. Yermakov, in describing the decrepitation method in his work, in detail, says correctly that "the subjectivity in ratings of the temperatures is still impermissibly high in this method, in comparison with the other methods" [2]. A substantial defect of the decrepitation method is the fact that it is "blind", inasmuch as it has no provision for a direct observation of the homogenization process in the inclusions.

These two features were the main reasons for the limited use of the decrepitation method in thermometric research. There is a hope that improvements in the procedures and the utilization of autographic instruments for logging the decrepitation will increase the popularity of the method in determining temperatures of mineral-forming solutions. Encouraging results along these lines were already obtained by Dolgov and Raykher who reported their studies of the decrepitation involving the use of an autographic instrument [1].

We also made use of a simplified self-recording device constructed at the VSEGEI by Zakharchenko, Lazarevich, and Moskalyuk.*

Most of our work was done with test materials crushed to 0.5 mm size. A finer grinding creates the danger of destruction of many of the larger inclusions. Trial runs with the 1 mm fraction and with lumps of quartz 2-4 mm in diameter showed that, in such materials, widespread rupturing of the inclusions begins at the same temperature as in the 0.5 mm fraction, but that the temperature range of the decrepitation maxima is broadened. A simple explanation is that the deep-lying inclusions rupture their walls only after a considerable heating over and above their homogenization temperatures. Every one of the experiments lasted for 15 to 20 min, that is, the temperature of the test material had to increase from 20-40 to 600°C in that time. The aliquots did not exceed 2 or 2.5 g, in order to assure uniform heating. Prolongation of the heating period to 30-50 min had no effect on the temperature of the inception of the main decrepitation of the inclusions, in comparison with the more rapid rates of application of heat.

The decrepitation log, as it appears on a developed photographic film, consists of lines whose frequency expresses the intensity of the process. The film with the temperature scale, graduated at 100 and 20° intervals, was calibrated at 5°C intervals, and the number of ruptures per 5°C was counted on the stage of a photo-magnifier. The counts were the basic data for drawing decrepitation curves (with temperature as the abscissa and the number of ruptured inclusions as the ordinate). The start of widespread ruptures of inclusions was not difficult to recognize, despite the high variation in the numbers of the ruptures per 5°C temperature interval and despite the extremely large numbers of ruptures at the peak of the decrepitation, so large that it was impossible to count all of them, in most of the samples. The start of the wave of widespread ruptures was indicated generally by 20-30 or 30-40 ruptures per 5°C increment of temperature.

---

* Described in this book of collected papers, pp. 593-603. Editor [N.P.Ye.].

We examined about fifty samples of quartz by the decrepitation method. The samples were from veins of different age and with different crystal structures. As shown by the researches of E. Ingerson, A. I. Ostrovskii and G. Kennedy, in the instance of low-temperature inclusions (up to 150°C), the homogenization temperature is very close to the true temperature of the mineral genesis, while, in the case of high-temperature inclusions, containing large quantities of dissolved mineral substances, appreciable corrections are required for determinations of the true temperatures; such corrections for concentrations of the included solutions and for high pressures at the time when the inclusions are formed are necessarily positive.

Samples of the vein quartz we examined generally contain inclusions whose ruptures occur above 300°C and even above 400°C. The value of the decrepitation method is by no means lowered by the impossibility of making well-founded corrections of the observed temperatures at which major decrepitation of the inclusions begins, temperatures that, to a first approximation, correspond to the minimum temperatures of mineral genesis. Determinations of the relative temperatures may have no lesser value than a knowledge of the true temperatures of mineral genesis, as a means of distinguishing some veins from some others or of delineating individual stages within the complex process of vein formation. From this point of view, our results are entirely satisfactory.

The highest temperatures for the start of major decrepitation of inclusions were obtained in the case of conformable veins, without any crystal quartz, in Precambrian schists and gneisses, veins that are composed of massive metamorphosed or "cast" quartz. These veins are the most ancient ones, by all evidence, and their Precambrian age is confirmed by the numerous pebbles of the metamorphosed vein quartz found in the conglomerates at the base of the Cambrian sediments, as well as their being cut by the crystal-quartz-bearing Variscian veins.

In five out of the six samples of the metamorphosed quartz examined by us, a very sharp decrepitation maximum was recorded at 520–550°C. Only in one sample was the maximum relatively weak, at 522°C. Four of the samples showed a second decrepitation maximum, perfectly definite, at 340–370°C, and coinciding with the decrepitation maximum for inclusions in the Variscian veins. Our observations in the field indicate superposition of a mineralization of a later age, probably Variscian, on the ancient veins. Even the appearance of crystal quartz in the ancient "cast" quartz veins is related to this late mineralization. In this particular case, the field data are fully confirmed by the results of the thermometric investigations. The Precambrian veins are easily distinguished from the Variscian by their decrepitation maximum at 520–550°C, as there is no decrepitation in the latter within this range of the temperature.

Thermometric studies of samples of the metamorphosed vein quartz from the conformable crumpled veins in the Lower Paleozoic rocks show that these veins resemble closely the Precambrian veins, in some respects, and the Variscian veins, in other respects, by their temperatures for the beginning of major decrepitation. Thus, out of the eight samples we examined, three displayed two decrepitation maxima each, the lower one at 365–375°C and the upper one at 510–570°C. The decrepitation curves of these veins are fully identical, in their character with the curves of the ancient Precambrian veins on which the Variscian mineralization has been imposed. Four of the samples showed only a single decrepitation maximum each, beginning at 365–397°C. This range of temperature corresponds to the start of major decrepitation of inclusions in the Variscian veins.

An exceptionally monotonous pattern of decrepitation of inclusions was observed in the analysis of fourteen samples from the Variscian veins composed of massive–granular and skeletal–columnar quartz. Every one of these samples showed only one peak of decrepitation beginning at 360–380°C. It is significant that the temperature range of the intensive explosions of the inclusions was relatively narrow; there was an abrupt decrease in the numbers of explosions, or else a complete cessation of explosions, at 400–425°C, in most of the samples. That was the difference between the samples of the Variscian veins we examined and the samples of the Precambrian and Paleozoic veins in which, as a rule, there is an extended temperature range for the incidence of major explosions of inclusions. The veins from which our fourteen samples were taken are situated at different distances from the intrusive bodies. Thus the quartz veins of Tamda, Zhaman–Kotr, and Nurman are rather far from the intrusions (15–25 km), while the veins of Kotr and Karabaytam are right next to them. We examined also samples from veins lying directly in the alaskite granites and in the gradodiorites. There is no relationship whatsoever, although it might be expected, in the sequence of temperatures of formation of minerals in the crystal-quartz-bearing Variscian veins and the various distances of these veins from the Late Caledonian intrusions. This fact confirms the absence of any genetic connection between the intrusions and the veins.

The thermometric studies of quartz from the zoned veins permit us to outline the different stages of their formation, as indicated by relationships between the different generations of quartz. The most typical examples of zoned veins are the quartz veins of Aktas I, Aktas II, and North Baykonur, situated in granodiorites. One always succeeds in finding the massive fine-grained metamorphosed quartz in them, the earliest one with respect to the other varieties of vein quartz. It is that particular quartz which happens to be characterized by the highest temperatures, in the range 410–438°C, at which massive decrepitation of the inclusions begins

Because of the accession of the next portion of hydrothermal solutions along the newly developed system of fissures, that quartz was subjected to a complete recrystallization and became the parent material of the coarsely granular quartz in which the maximum number of ruptures of the inclusions sets in at 350–380°C, the range corresponding to the rupture temperatures for inclusions in quartz of the Variscian veins.

The third stage in the formation of the veins, the time of development of the zones of columnar quartz, druse quartz, and "nests" of crystal quartz within the fragmentation zones, in re-opened fissures, and in networks of veins, begins after a drastic fall of temperatures of the mineral-forming solutions. Thus the homogenization of primary inclusions in the columnar transparent quartz of vein 3, Aktas I, takes place at 125–135°C (six measurements) and at 120–122°C (eight measurements), in the case of inclusions in basal parts of the crystals and druses. The corresponding homogenization temperatures of inclusions in the bases of crystals from the "nests" in the crystal quartz bearing veins of Aktas I and North Baykonur are 160–164 and 158–161°C (six measurements).

Approximately fifty specimens of crystal quartz from the Variscian veins were examined thermometrically, by the homogenization method. Also, more than 150 polished sections and spalls were examined visually, under the microscope. All of these materials, without exception, carried low-temperature liquid inclusions containing 5–15 per cent gas phase. Not a single one of the crystals we examined had any solid phases in its inclusions, so typical of high temperature inclusions with their high concentrations of dissolved salts.

The homogenization temperatures of inclusions in crystals from the Variscian veins situated in highly different rocks and at different distances from the Late Caledonian intrusions, including the veins in the intrusions themselves, are monotonous for primary inclusions: 120–140°C. The lower limit of homogenization temperatures of primary and primary–secondary liquid inclusions is within the range of 120–80°C (outer zones of the crystals). In all crystals for which these measurements were made, there was a gradual decrease in the homogenization temperatures from the central zone toward the periphery and the decrease would be as high as 20–40°C.

CONCLUSIONS

(1) Quartz veins of the Dzhezkazgan–Ulutau District were formed over a wide range of temperatures. The highest temperatures are indicated by the ancient veins whose age is Precambrian and Caledonian, on the basis of geologic evidence. The main bulk of quartz in these veins crystallized at temperatures exceeding 500°C, to a first approximation. The

Variscian mineralization, imposed on the ancient veins, has a definite expression in a second decrepitation peak, at 340–380°C which coincides with the crystallization temperature of quartz in the Variscian veins.

(2) Most of the Variscian veins were formed at 360–400°C. Considering the shallow depths at which these veins were formed (the maximum thickness of their Upper Devonian and Lower Carboniferous sedimentary overburden was 2000–2300 m), the pressure could be about 400–450 atm, at the time of the formation of the veins. According to Khitarov's experimental data [4] on stability of quartz and migrations of silica in hydrothermal environments, maximum change in the stability of quartz, under isobaric conditions, occurs in the 300–450°C range, up to the 500 atm isobar. One may readily see that the crystallization regime of the Variscian vein was very close to that type of the environment.

(3) Thermometric studies of vein quartz in zoned quartz veins make it possible to outline definitely the different stages of vein formation. Three such stages are recognizable in the most typical zoned veins in granodiorites. The first two of the stages, corresponding to the crystallization of the massive granular quartz, took place at 350–450°C, but the columnar quartz of the veins which forms the peripheral parts of the "nests" and of the rock crystal quartz was formed at 120–140°C in all types of the crystal-quartz-bearing Variscian veins.

(4) By comparing the results of thermometric studies of the vein quartz and of the crystal quartz, one may reach the conclusion that the latter crystallized within a very narrow range of temperature and from low-temperature hydrothermal solutions. The absence of gradual transitions in the crystallization temperatures of the vein quartz and of the crystals, but instead a radical difference between them, indicates that the main bulk of the crystal quartz, particularly in the economic crystal-quartz-bearing veins, was produced from an essentially fresh last portion of the hydrothermal solutions that entered the previously-formed veins through the zones of disturbances within the veins or through re-opened fissures. These weakly warmed hydrothermal solutions borrowed the bulk of their mineral load, primarily silica, from the host rocks, with the previously deposited massive granular quartz often functioning as a host rock. This supposition is confirmed by the appreciable alteration of the host rocks near the "nests" of the crystal quartz as well as in the columnar quartz zones.

(5) Further improvements in the methods of thermometric studies of vein quartz will be highly productive, for merely a knowledge of the relative temperatures of the formation of minerals helps us to distinguish one vein from another and permits us to outline different stages of mineral genesis within one and the same vein.

BIBLIOGRAPHY

1. DOLGOV, YU. A. and L. D. RAYKHER, Avtomaticheskii termozvukoregistrator. (The Automatic Thermosonic Recorder.) *Mineralog. sb. L'vov. geolog. obshch.* No. 3, 1949.
2. YERMAKOV, N. P., *Issledovaniya mineraloobrazuyushchikh rastvorov.* (Research in Mineral-forming Solutions.) Izd. Khar'k. univ. 1950.
3. ZAKHARCHENKO, A. I., *Mineraloobrazuyushchiye rastvory i genezis kvartsevykh zhil.* (Mineral-forming Solutions and the Origin of Quartz Veins.) Gosgeoltekhizdat, 1955.
4. KHITAROV, N. I., Experimental'naya kharakteristika ustoychivosti kvartsa i migratsii kremnezyoma v gidrotermal'nykh usloviyakh. (Experimental Characterization of Stability of Quartz and of Migration of Silica in Hydrothermal Environments.) *Tr. 4-go soveshchaniya po petrografii i mineralogii.* (Transactions of the Fourth Conference on Petrography and Mineralogy.) Izd. Akad. Nauk SSSR, pt. 2, 1953.

An Experiment in Studies of Liquid Inclusions in Iceland Spar from Deposits in the Siberian Platform

Ye. Ya. Kievlenko

Among the various types of deposits of Iceland spar, the calcite-bearing formations in effusive and hypabyssal rocks of the Siberian trap formations particularly have been attracting a great deal of interest. The widely known deposits in Iceland and in South Africa and, in our country, the East-Siberian deposits belong to that particular genetic group.

A large body of factual data has been accumulated, over many years, on such deposits, but their interpretations are frequently not very convincing even now, and are even mutually contradictory in regards to the conditions of origin of the deposits and to the many problems in the crystallization of calcite. Specifically, the nature of the mineral-forming solutions, a knowledge of which is indispensable for derivations of geologic premises of prospecting for new deposits as well as for the synthetic growth of Iceland spar, cannot be considered entirely clear, even up to the present time. The basic features of the solutions and the physico-chemical parameters of the mineral-forming environment must be determined, first and foremost, for practical purposes. A correct solution of these problems is scarcely possible, unless we take into account the objective experimental data obtained as the results of a comprehensive study of liquid inclusions in the calcite crystals.

It should be pointed out that the first determinations of the homogenization temperatures of liquid inclusions in Iceland spar from some of the East-Siberian sources were made by Yermakov [3] and, next, by Skropyshev [5], who had also attempted to ascertain the chemical composition of the inclusions by means of aqueous extracts of the calcite crystals.

Geologically the East-Siberian deposits of Iceland spar lie in the Lower Mesozoic Trap Rock Formation, occupying the central and the northwestern parts of the Siberian Platform [4]. The deposits are localized in breccia zones in tuff (the Ilempey type), in differentiated bodies of intrusive trap rocks (the Vilyuy type), in mandelsteins, i.e. amygdaloid sections of basalt flows, and in pillow lavas (the lower Tunguska type). The predominant mineralogic constituents of the calcite-bearing bodies are

[616]

sodium and sodium–calcium zeolites (natrolite, thomsonite, heulandite, stilbite, mordenite, and others), analcite, chalcedony, chlorites, hydromicas, montmorillonite, and occasionally sulfides (marcasite, pyrite). Large crystals of calcite of optical grade are formed, as a rule, during the last stage of the hydrothermal process, in cavities of magmatic or tectonic origin. Alteration of the host rocks may be occasionally intensive, involving analcitization and zeolitization of basic plagioclases as well as chloritization of monoclinic pyroxene and of volcanic glass.

Liquid inclusions are fairly common in Iceland spar and may attain the size of 0.5–1 cm³. Most of them are not wider than 1–2 mm. Accumulations of them are responsible for turbidity of the crystals.

Morphologically, we distinguish the faceted vacuoles (the so-called negative crystals) whose longer axis often coincides with the threefold symmetry axis of Iceland spar (Fig. 1), the rounded or half-rounded cavities (Fig. 2), and inclusions of bizarre shapes (Fig. 3). Skeletal structure of vacuole walls is observable in calcite from the Dzhekinda deposit.

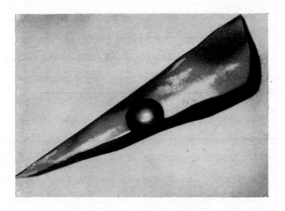

FIG. 1. Faceted liquid inclusion. Dzhekinda deposit. Magnification ×80.

Nearly all of the inclusions are two-phase at room temperature, with a gas bubble resulting from the cooling of the crystal and the contraction of the liquid. Only once did we find a three-phase inclusion, with a small crystal of halite, with liquid and gas, in a crystal from the Gonchak deposit (Fig. 4). Entirely liquid single-phase inclusions of cold-water solutions are found invariably in healed fissures and must be considered as secondary.

The liquid phase occupies generally 85–98 per cent of the total volume at 20°C, but anomalous liquid-gas phase ratios were observed in several instances. They may be due, at times, to the "stringing-out" of inclusions with unbalanced forms, but the main reason is a disturbance in their hermetic sealing. The perfect cleavage of calcite is conducive to such disturbances. As shown by Yermakov [3], the large size of the gas bubble,

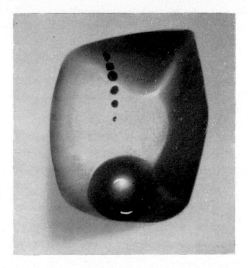

FIG. 2. Half-rounded isometric liquid inclusions. Shpat deposit.
Magnification ×56.

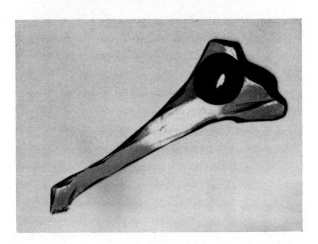

FIG. 3. Bulb-like, half-rounded inclusion. Dzhekinda deposit.
Magnification ×56.

in such cases, is the result of a leakage into fissures surrounding the inclusion and not of any contraction of the cooled liquid. As a rule, the disturbed ones are all large and their gas phase occupies up to 50 per cent of their volume.

Another specific reason for the anomalous size of the gas bubble is operative in inclusions contacting needles of mordenite which is also present in Iceland spar. As correctly stated by Skropyshev [5], a fraction of the water in such inclusions is taken up by the zeolite, which leads naturally to a decrease in the volume of the liquid phase.

The many available inclusions in calcite crystals from sources of various types were examined thermometrically (by N. I. Andrusov) and the largest ones of them were used for the chemical analysis of the included solutions.

FIG. 4. Three-phase disturbed inclusion with a small crystal of halite.
Gonchak deposit. Magnification × 56.

As known, the principle of thermodynamic studies of liquid inclusions is based on the supposition, which seems to be correct in the overwhelming majority of the cases, that particles of a homogeneous medium are captured by a crystallizing mineral. Consequently, the homogenization temperature of a two-phase inclusion permits us to define the lowest possible temperature at which the corresponding zone of the crystal could have grown. The data so obtained are closest to the true temperature of the mineral genesis when both the pressure and the temperature are relatively low. The latter is an entirely reasonable assumption for deposits of Iceland spar, on the general premises of geology.

In all, we examined more than one thousand crystals (split out, by cleavage) of calcite with liquid inclusions from which about two hundred and fifty test sections were prepared. Primary and pseudo-secondary inclusions (as in Yermakov's terminology) with normal gas–liquid phase ratios were selected for the experiments.

It should be pointed out that there are no special difficulties in identification of primary inclusions in Iceland spar, because they are found generally in growth zones or on compromise growth surfaces of the crystals [2]. Secondary inclusions, as a rule, are situated along cleavage planes or else along curved surfaces of conchoidal fractures.

The test sections were heated in a thermochamber of Yermakov's design, with the use of copper–constantan and chromel–copel thermocouples. A steam bath was employed for the larger inclusions with homogenization temperatures below 100°C. The rate of heating was determined empirically, depending on the inclusion size and thickness of the test section, and was about 10°C per quarter hour, on the average.

Every one of the inclusions homogenized in the liquid phase, with the exception of some obviously disturbed ones, with anomalously large gas bubbles, which would generally explode without having ever become homogeneous.

The determined homogenization temperatures of liquid inclusions are presented in Table 1. These temperatures are not very high, on the whole. They fluctuate between 40 and 157°C, corresponding to the degree of filling of vacuoles with the liquid (at 20°C) which is 83–98 per cent.

TABLE 1. HOMOGENIZATION TEMPERATURES AND COEFFICIENTS OF FILLING (at 20°C) OF LIQUID INCLUSIONS IN CRYSTALS OF ICELAND SPAR

No. in Sequence	Deposit	Deposit type	Homogenization temperature (°C)			Coefficient of filling with liquid at 20°C		
			Minimum	Maximum	Average	Minimum	Maximum	Average
1	Yangura-kta	Ilempey	43	117	72	0.90	0.97	0.95
2	Kuktule	Ilempey	40	42	40	0.97	0.98	0.98
3	Dzhekin-da	Vilyuy	94	153	110	0.84	0.93	0.91
4	Markhaya	Vilyuy	94	157	109	0.83	0.93	0.91
5	Gayn	Skarn	92	112	102	0.90	0.93	0.92
6	Shpat	Lower Tunguska	51	117	82	0.90	0.97	0.94
7	Gonchak	Lower Tunguska	50	139	66	0.85	0.97	0.96
8	Dzhezgli	Lower Tunguska	48	119	67	0.90	0.97	0.96

Comparisons of statistical curves (Fig. 5), with numbers of measurements and homogenization temperatures as the coordinates, demonstrate a satisfactory coincidence of the peaks for deposits of the same type: Yangurakta and Kuktule, 40–45°C; Dzhekinda and Markhaya, 105 and 112°C; Gonchak and Dzhezgli, 55–60°C, confirming by that very fact similarities in the conditions of their origin. The relatively wide range of homogenization temperatures of inclusions for a given deposit is to be explained by a progressive lowering of temperatures of the solutions in

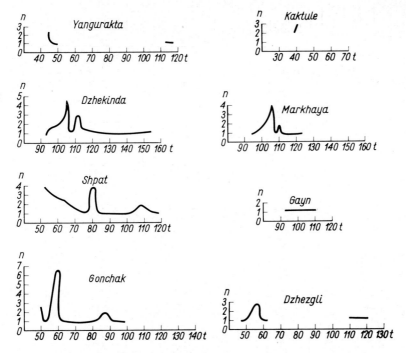

FIG. 5. Statistical curves of homogenization of liquid inclusions in crystals of Iceland spar from different deposits. t—temperature in °C; n—number of measurements.

which the crystals were growing. The occasional high temperatures, markedly different from the rest, may be related to disturbances in the sealing of isolated inclusions and may be omitted from consideration for that reason.

Figure 6 represents the relationship between the homogenization temperature and the coefficient of filling in a liquid inclusion at 20°C. That diagram makes it possible to determine the point of homogenization by the gas–liquid phase ratio at room temperature. A similar curve for distilled water lies somewhat above the inclusions' curve.

Thanks to the presence of large liquid inclusions, we had the opportunity to perform individual chemical analyses, having determined the composition and the true concentration of the included solution (Table 2; Ye. V. Rengarten, analyst). Extraction of liquid contents of the inclusions in Iceland spar and the microchemical determinations were done under the supervision of N. I. Khitarov, at the Laboratory of Magmatogenic Processes, Institute of Geochemistry and Analytical Chemistry, Academy of Sciences of the U.S.S.R., by the methods discussed by Khitarov et al. [6].

TABLE 2. CHEMICAL COMPOSITION OF LIQUID INCLUSIONS IN ICELAND SPAR FROM DEPOSITS IN THE SIBERIAN PLATFORM

Chemical constituents	Gonchak, specimen 1		Gonchak, specimen 2		Shpat, specimen 30		Nidym (section 2), specimen 3		Kuktule, specimen K-103		Yangurakta, specimen 82	
	mg	m-equiv.	mg	m-equiv.	mg	m-equiv.	mg	m-equiv.	mg	m-equiv.	mg	m-equiv.
HCO_3^-	0.19	0.003	not found	—	not found	—	not found	—	not found	—	not found	—
Cl^-	7.36	0.208	9.76	0.275	1.728	0.048	0.345	0.009	0.475	0.013	0.78	0.022
SO_4^{--}	not found	—	not found	—	not found	—	not found	—	not found	—	not found	—
Sum of anions	—	0.211	—	0.275	—	0.048	—	0.009	—	0.013	—	0.022
K^+	not found	—	not found	—	not found	—	not found	—	not found	—	not found	—
Na^+	0.72	0.030*	0.52	0.022	0.09	0.004	0.09	0.004	0.046	0.002	0.16	0.007
Mg^{++}	<0.0005	—	<0.0005	—	<0.0005	—	<0.0005	—	<0.0005	—	<0.0005	—
Ca^{++}	3.70	0.185	4.26	0.213	0.94	0.047	0.1	0.005	0.12	0.006	0.30	0.015
Sum of cations	—	0.215	—	0.235	—	0.051	—	0.009	—	0.008	—	0.022
$Ca(HCO_3)_2$	0.25	—	—	—	—	—	0.28	—	0.33	—	0.83	—
$CaCl_2$	9.93	—	11.82	—	2.60	—	0.23	—	0.12	—	0.41	—
$NaCl$	1.69	—	1.28	—	0.23	—	1.1	—	2.6	—	1.8	—
$Ca : Na$	6.1	—	8.1	—	10.4	—	—	—	—	—	—	—
Volume of vacuole, cm³	0.089	—	0.063	—	0.018	—	0.007	—	0.013	—	0.017	—
Total salts, g/l	136.3	—	230.0	—	158.0	—	74.0	—	47.0	—	72.0	—

* Should be 0.031 [Ed.].

Volumes of the vacuoles were determined from the weights of the solutions as well as by direct measurements of volumes of water required for filling the vacuoles with a micro-pipette. The calculations were corrected for solubility of calcite in water.

The analyses showed that the included solutions are highly concentrated (47–230 g/l) calcium and sodium chlorides whose ratio varies from 10.4:1 to 1.1:1. The lowest concentrations of salts were recorded in crystals from the Kuktule and the Yangurakta deposits (the Ilempey type) and the highest ones—from the Gonchak deposit (the Lower Tunguska type). The complete absence of SO_4^{--} is conspicuous, alongside the small quantities of HCO_3^- recorded only in one case.

Two large inclusions in Iceland spar from Gonchak were used for pH measurements of the solutions. The pH was 5.0–5.5, determined by using universal indicator.

An empirical diagram (Fig. 7), drawn by N. I. Khitarov and S. D. Malinin, of the PT relationship for pure water and a solution of salts corresponding to the average composition of the included solutions (aqueous

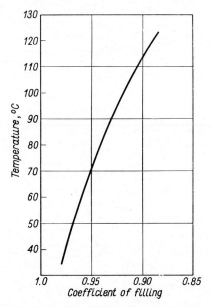

Fig. 6. Diagram of relationship between homogenization temperature and degree of filling at 20°C in liquid inclusions in Iceland spar from Siberian platform.

solutions of calcium and sodium chlorides, 70 g/l, at Ca:Na of 4:1) showed that, at low temperatures and at high coefficients of filling (80 per cent), thermodynamic properties of the two liquids are almost the same. The isochors in Fig. 7 begin to diverge appreciably only above 245°C. Consequently, the approximate pressure in vacuoles with liquid inclusions in calcite may be appraised, with sufficient accuracy, by means of the diagrams of state for pure water.

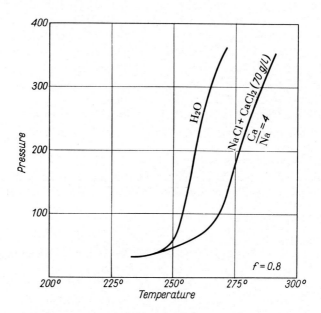

FIG. 7. *PT* diagram for NaCl+CaCl$_2$ solution in reference to pure water. (According to N. I. Khitarov and S. D. Malinin.)

According to Vukalovich [1], the pressure of saturated water vapor at the maximum specific volume, 1.208, in our case (the degree of filling 83 per cent; see Table 1), and at 230°C, equals 29 atm. If the specific volume decreases, the pressure will also decrease, so that at the average specific volume of 1.06 (degree of filling 94 per cent) and at 120°C, the pressure will be about 2.5 atm.

We may draw now several important conclusions regarding conditions of the formation of the Iceland spar deposits in the Siberian platform.

(1) In the last stage of the hydrothermal process, during the crystal growth of Iceland spar, the mineral-forming solutions were essentially multicomponent chloride solutions containing Ca^{++}, Na$^+$, HCO$_3^-$, CO$_2$ and practically devoid of SO$_4^{--}$ and of the heavy metal ions.

(2) The deposits were formed near the surface of the ground, at moderate pressures not over 30 atm. A gradual decrease of the pressure, down to the ordinary atmospheric one, was conducive to a quiet escape of CO$_2$ from the solutions and to the crystallization of calcite.

The Iceland spar was produced at low temperatures fluctuating, on the average, from 150 to 40°C. Also, the highest temperature of the main stage of the crystallization is a feature of the spar in deposits of the Vilyuy type (Dzhekinda, Markhaya); next, in the order of decreasing temperatures, follow the deposits in mandelsteins (Shpat), in pillow lavas (Gonchak), and in breccia zones in tuffs (Yangurakta, Kuktule).

BIBLIOGRAPHY

1. VUKALOVICH, M. P., *Termodinamicheskiye svoystva vody i vodyanogo para.* (Thermodynamic Properties of Water and Vapor.) Mashgiz, 1955.
2. GRIGOR'EV, D. P., K voprosu o razlichenii pervichnykh i vtorichnykh zhidkikh vklyucheniy v mineralakh. (On the Subject of Identification of Primary and Secondary Inclusions in Minerals.) *Mineralog. sb. L'vov. geolog. obshch.* No. 2, 1948.
3. YERMAKOV, N. P., *Issledovaniya mineraloobrazuyushchikh rastvorov.* (Research in Mineral-forming Solutions.) Izd. Khar'kov. univ. 1950.
4. KIEVLENKO, YE. YA. Osnovnyye tipy mestorozhdenii islandskogo shpata Sibirskoi platformy. (The Basic Types of Deposits of Iceland Spar in the Siberian Platform.) *Tr. VNIIP*, vol. 1, 1957.
5. SKROPYSHEV, A. V., Gazovo-zhidkiye vklyucheniya v kristallakh Islandskogo shpata (Gas–Liquid Inclusions in Crystals of Iceland Spar.) *Mineralog. sb. L'vov. geolog. obshch.* No. 11, 1957.
6. KHITAROV, N. I., YE. V. RENGARTEN and N. YE. LEBEDEVA. Khimicheskii sostav zhidkikh vklyucheniy Islandskogo shpata i voprosy ego genezisa. (Chemical Composition of Liquid Inclusions in Iceland Spar and the Problems of its Genesis.) *Geokhim.* No. 3, 1958.

On Inclusions of Solutions in Crystals of Tourmaline

M. M. SLIVKO

INTRODUCTORY REMARKS

STUDIES of residues of mineral-forming solutions in minerals have largely by-passed tourmaline and all we have, even now, is a few isolated inquiries into inclusions in crystals of that mineral. And yet, certain features of the growth of tourmaline crystals, so enigmatic at times, could be decoded by a detailed examination of inclusions in tourmaline, inasmuch as the two phenomena, the crystal growth and the inclusions therein, are most intimately interrelated.

The present communication presents the results on inclusions in crystals of polychromatic tourmaline from certain deposits in the Soviet Union (Central Ural and the Borshchovochnyi Kryazh) obtained as a part of the general exploration of tourmalines in these and other districts of the U.S.S.R.

Inclusions in tourmalines of these districts were dealt with in a few individual reports which, insofar as we know, exhaust the subject of inclusions in tourmaline for the entire territory of the Soviet Union. The earliest data on inclusions in tourmaline from the Borshchovochnyi Kryazh and from Central Ural are to be found in Yermakov's works [2], where some data on primary and secondary inclusions in polychromatic tourmalines are presented rather briefly and where it is emphasized that primary inclusions in tourmalines from Murzinka homogenize in the gas phase at 340–355°C. Secondary inclusions were found to be of the essentially-liquid kind, with homogenization in the liquid phase.

Our earlier paper [6] presents the results of our studies of inclusions in tourmalines of the Borshchovochnyi Kryazh. Primary inclusions in green and in pink zoned tourmalines are shown to homogenize at 272°C and 263–270°C respectively. We could find no inclusions that would homogenize in the gas phase. Later on, we undertook still more through investigations of inclusions in polychromatic tourmalines of the Borshchovochnyi Kryazh, with studies of certain particular moments in the formation and transformations of primary and secondary inclusions.

Information on the chrome* tourmalines of Central Ural may be found in Koltun's publication [4], who points out that primary inclusions in such

---

* "Khromovyi" meaning probably "colored". The primary meaning, "chromium", seems improbable in this case [V.P.S.].

tourmalines homogenize at 252–280°C, while inclusions homogenizing in the gaseous phase are entirely absent.

The foregoing citations exhaust the list of Soviet studies more or less pertinent to inclusions in tourmaline. Foreign publications on inclusions in tourmaline are even more scarce [11].

CLASSIFICATION OF INCLUSIONS AND CERTAIN FEATURES IN THEIR FORMATION

Liquid inclusions in tourmaline are a common phenomenon and some tourmaline crystals are full of them. We should point out that this fact is never taken into account in chemical and spectrographic analyses of tourmaline and particularly in the determinations of its specific gravity, although the great abundance of the inclusions must undoubtedly have an effect on the results. The astonishment of J. and O. Bradley [10] at variations in the loss on ignition of tourmaline is undoubtedly caused by variations in the quantity of inclusions. The problem is still open, however, and is in need of special supplementary studies.

Two-phase liquid inclusions are the most common ones in tourmaline. Their gaseous phase does not exceed 35 per cent of the vacuole's volume, except where there has been an obvious stringing out. Single-phase liquid inclusions are not typical of tourmaline and accordingly are rarely found. Multiphase inclusions are also scarce (liquid and solid phases; no gas

FIG. 1. Inclusions in liquid and solid phases without gas bubble. Borshcho-vochnyi Kryazh. 200×.

bubble) (Fig. 1), but multiphase inclusions of liquid–gas–solid phases, with as many as six solid phases, are widespread in tourmaline crystals, in Ural as well as in Borshchovochnyi Kryazh* (Fig. 2, *a* and *b*).

a

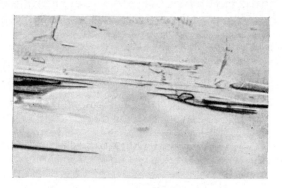

b

FIG. 2. Multiphase inclusions in tourmalines; *a*—from Borshchovochnyi Kryazh, 500×; *b*—from Central Ural, 60×.

A widely occurring captive mineral is particularly conspicuous among the solid phases. This mineral has the following characteristic features:

(a) A platy crystalline form, elongated and tending to become a hexagon in its cross-section.

---

* East of Lake Baykal [V.P.S.].

(b) An extremely easy solubility; the mineral dissolves rapidly when the section is heated to 35°C and does not recrystallize from the solution, at room temperature, for several months.

(c) Low indices of refraction; anisotropism [8].

These characteristics justify the classification of our mineral as a fluoborate of the alkali group, with a high degree of probability, an avogadrite–ferruchite [1], although additional studies are required for a definitive solution of the problem.

It should be noted that captive minerals, such as halite and sylvite, so common in inclusions in other minerals (quartz, topaz, etc.), were not encountered in the inclusions in polychromic tourmalines. Inclusions with liquid carbon dioxide in small quantities are extremely rare (a few isolated cases out of hundreds of thin sections examined). The same is observed also in inclusions in quartz crystals paragenetically associated with colored tourmalines, lepidolite, and albite [8].

In harmony with the genetic principle and in agreement with Yermakov's classification, primary, secondary, and pseudo-secondary inclusions were identified among the liquid inclusions in tourmalines.

Primary inclusions. Morphology and distribution of inclusions in a crystal depend on the manner in which the inclusions were formed. The most common process of formation of primary inclusions in tourmalines is related to the vicinal striations on prismatic faces of the crystals. The rapid deposition of tourmaline on the protruding vicinal ridges and the repression of the intermediate planes are conducive to a formation of vacuoles and the preservation of the mother liquor in them. The resulting inclusions are directly associated with the crystal's growth zones. In sections parallel to the threefold axis, their forms are cone-like, wedge-like, and, more rarely, tubular, but in sections perpendicular to the threefold axis they are shaped like droplets, with typical "tails" uniformly oriented, in a given inclusion group. The vacuole is not sealed after it is formed, in many instances. The delay in sealing results in a chainwork of inclusions (perpendicular to the threefold axis) showing constrictions and bulges. Such inclusions are flat; in longitudinal sections through the crystal their surfaces show clearly expressed striations.

This type is a variety of primary inclusions resulting from skeletal growth of the crystals [2].

In the instance of tourmaline, however, there are certain special elements of the growth, namely, the prismatic overgrowth [5, 8] that may form only on the monohedron face, in the course of the deposition of the substance. This type of growth, according to Matveyev [5], is explainable as a simultaneous and synchronous growth of thin fibers the net total of which become a fibrous crystal. Such crystals of tourmaline are widespread and common and their fibrous nature is easily recognized by their silky lustre.* The ideas of Matveyev are resonant echoes of Yerofeyev's theory [3] of the bunching of indivisibles based on crystallographic and crystal–optical studies of tourmalines. Without going into details of the mechanism of tourmaline crystal growth, we may point out that the growth of fibrous crystals may be regarded as an originally multinucleated growth. What is important to us is the fact that such growth leads to the formation of prodigious quantities of primary inclusions whose character and distribution depend significantly on the thickness of the indivisible components of the multiple crystal.

Tubular inclusions, whose length may be measured in centimeters, are formed, as a rule, in crystals composed of extremely thin fibers. Some of the tubes extend through the entire crystal and the long inclusions are often opened by transverse fissures.

Interesting groups of inclusions are formed when the individual components of a complex crystal are relatively large and their contact planes attain considerable dimensions, in the course of the simultaneous growth. One such group of inclusions is shown in Fig. 3 (the crystal grew from the bottom). The picture shows, first of all, the definite transverse zonation of the crystal, indicative of the crystal's growth only along the triple axis, and, next, the confinement of the inclusion groups to that zonation, although some individual inclusions pass over from one zone into the next one. Occasionally, instead of a large number of individual small inclusions, there is a formation of large flat inclusions with dentate or crested contours of their opposite sides corresponding to the two monohedra (see Fig. 3, the flat inclusion on the right).

It is particularly important to emphasize that, in the multi-nucleated growth of that kind, inclusions in the contact plane of the neighboring sub-individuals correspond to several periods of the crystal's growth and may contain mother liquors of different composition and of different states of aggregation, in the physico-chemical sense. This possibility must be taken into account in utilization of the inclusions for the purposes of mineral thermometric analysis.

The terminal growth zone is observed in some tourmaline crystals from Ural and from Borshchovochnyi Kryazh. This zone develops only on the monohedron, and a multitude of small embryonic crystals spring up at the very beginning of the zone's growth on top of the former face of the monohedron, whereupon the small crystals are covered by the overgrowth. The small crystals cause, in many instances, the development of tubular cavities that are plugged later, together with their liquid contents, or else [if vacant—V.P.S.] are left as hollow tubes emerging at the crystal's surface.

---

* A. Ye. Fersman made a report on varicolored tourmalines of the Borshchovochnyi Kryazh whose silky lustre resembles the chrysoberyls of Ceylon.

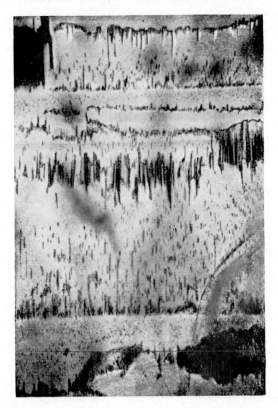

FIG. 3. Inclusions produced in the plane of contact between two different crystals of tourmaline. Borshchovochnyi Kryazh. 100×.

Inclusions and hollow tubes are especially common in small crystals inclined at a very small angle to the monohedron's plane [8]. Such inclusions are primary only in the terminal zone of the crystal.

Secondary and pseudo-secondary inclusions. The origins of these genetic types are related, in the main, to healing of fissures in the crystals, although there are also some other ways in which pseudo-secondary inclusions may be produced [2].

Transverse fissures or fissures practically in transverse positions are typical of tourmalines. Vertical fissures are relatively rare and are associated chiefly with splitting of a complex crystal into its individual components along the contact planes developed in the course of their simultaneous growth. The principal difference between pseudo-secondary and secondary inclusions is the fact that the former ones are produced from solutions in which the crystal is still growing, i.e. they are produced in fissures that do not outcrop at the crystal's surface, while the latter ones are produced from solutions alien to their host crystal. One detail needs to be pointed out here, a detail that must be taken into account in classifying a given inclusion either as a pseudo-secondary or a secondary one, in crystals whose growth can be traced chiefly or entirely in one single direction (tourmaline, beryl,* etc.). The healing of fissures in such crystals can proceed only at the expense of the solutions in which only the crystal's termination is still growing, in a practically or entirely complete absence of deposition of the cognate substance on the faces of the prismatic belt. For these reasons, the inclusions that are formed in the fissures have all the earmarks of secondary origin, formally, inasmuch as the healed transverse fissures traverse every one of the crystal's zones, including the outermost zone, while, in reality, the inclusions are pseudo-secondary, for the given crystal as a whole. This phenomenon was observed earlier by the author in his studies of inclusions in tourmalines from the Borshchovochnyi Kryazh [8].

When the solution enters the transverse fissures, different fissures are differently healed, depending on their width. If a fissure has an insignificant size, its healing generally is by way of a dendritic overgrowth. In places where a fissure is at its widest, the resulting vacuole begins to reorganize its form and to acquire the contours that are characteristic of the terminations of tourmaline crystals. Occasionally there develops, on the surfaces by which the inclusion is confined, a sculpture of the same type as on the pyramidal or the monohedral faces of the crystal. Inclusions that are formed in such manner develop highly involved contours, often with indications of stringing out, in the process of temperature decrease.

Wide transverse fissures (generally 0.5 mm across) are healed by means of a multinucleated overgrowth involving a formation of a fibrous veinlet, macroscopically conspicuous by its silky lustre against the general background of the crystal. There is a development of tubular inclusions, in such cases, even as in the instance of multi-nucleated growth.

As already stated, longitudinal fissures in tourmalines are produced by a splitting of the complex crystals. Such fissures are extremely fine, so that their healing produces flat inclusions with most highly varied contours and with a multitude of constrictions, conducive to stringing out and to the formation of inclusions with different gas–liquid phase ratios right next to each other. We must emphasize that it is difficult to distinguish between primary and secondary inclusions oriented along the triple axis of tourmaline crystals. Among the auxiliary criteria, in this connection,

---

* The so-called "settled" beryl crystals are well known, whose turbid lower part is crowned with a perfectly transparent head, without any indications of presence of the transparent zone on faces of the prism; this is evidence of the crystal's growth along the L_6 axis only.

one may use the relatively more simple form of primary inclusions and their better sustained positional orientation with respect to the main axis of the crystal.

ON UTILIZATION OF INCLUSIONS IN TOURMALINES IN MINERAL THERMOMETRIC ANALYSIS

Mineral thermometric analysis, based on determination of homogenization temperatures of inclusions, plays an important role in a wide variety of problems in mineral genesis (of individual minerals as well as of entire mineral deposits). Applications of that method in studies of polychromatic tourmalines had also yielded clear-cut results. Thus polychromatic tourmalines were deemed to be typical pneumatolytic minerals prior to the identification of the homogenization type of their primary inclusions. The very first studies had shown, however, that primary inclusions in tourmalines from Borshchovochnyi Kryazh homogenize in the liquid phase which is a direct proof of their hydrothermal origin. The same can be stated now with confidence in regards to tourmalines from Shaytagen (Central Ural) as well as in regards to tourmalines from the pegmatites of Black Hills, South Dakota, on the basis of Weis' [11] actual findings. It is a curious fact also that the average homogenization temperature of primary inclusions in polychromatic tourmalines varies within the 250–300°C range [8, 11]; only in some isolated cases do the inclusions homogenize at temperatures somewhat higher than 300°C, but this is an exception, not a rule.

In the consideration of possible utilization of inclusions in polychromatic tourmalines for the purpose of mineral thermometric analysis, we must pause at two important aspects of the selection of inclusions that would be suited for homogenization:

(a) The correct classification of any given inclusion or groups of inclusions as belonging to a definite genetic type;

(b) The problem of hermetic sealing of inclusions in tourmalines.

The intricate and multiform mechanism of the growth of tourmaline crystals leads to a variety of means by which the inclusions may be formed, as one may see from the foregoing discussion, in the case of primary as well as of pseudo-secondary and secondary inclusions. The quality of the research depends on the correctness of the identification of the genetic type of the inclusion. Consequently, this aspect of the subject merits a special attention in the thermometric analysis of tourmalines and one must find out, first of all, just how did the test crystal grow.

The problem of hermetic sealing of inclusions in tourmaline crystals is also an important one. Doubts arise, from the very start, as to the hermetic sealing of inclusions in fibrous ("bunched") crystals. Undoubtedly, not every one of the inclusions in such crystals meets the requirement of hermetic sealing, the prerequisite of suitability for homogenization. This too makes it necessary for the investigator to give careful attention to his experiments.

With this approach to the subject, of course, the studies of inclusions in tourmalines will yield positive results. And the conclusion in the abstract of Weis' paper in regards to the unsuitability of inclusions in tourmalines for homogenization is completely erroneous.*

BIBLIOGRAPHY

1. DANA, J. D. *et al.*, *Sistema mineralogii*. (System of Mineralogy.) Vol. I. Izd. Inost. Lit. 1953.
2. YERMAKOV, N. P., *Issledovaniya mineraloobrazuyushchikh rastvorov*. (Research in Mineral-forming Solutions.) Izd. Khar'kov. univ. 1950.
3. YEROFEYEV, M., Kristallograficheskiye i kristalloopticheskiye issledovaniya turmalinov. (Crystallographic and Crystal-optical Studies of Tourmalines.) *Zap. mineralog. obshch.* Pt. 6, pp. 81–342, 1871.
4. KOLTUN, L. I., Opyt geneticheskogo issledovaniya nekotorykh endogennykh mestorozhdenii po vklyucheniyam v mineralakh. (An Experiment in Genetic Investigations of Certain Endogenic Deposits in the Basis of Inclusions in Minerals.) Avtoreferat dissertatsii, 1953.
5. MATVEYEV, K. K., Iz nablyudenii nad mnogotsvetnymi turmalinami. (Some of the Observations on Polychromatic Tourmalines.) V knige:*Voprosy Geokhimii,mineralogii i petrografii*, pp. 82–88, Moscow–Leningrad, 1946.
6. SLIVKO, M. M., O polikhromnykh turmalinakh. (On the Subject of Polychromatic Tourmalines.) *Mineralog. sb. L'vov. geolog. obshch.* No. 6, 1952.
7. SLIVKO, M. M., Issledovaniye turmalinov nekotorykh mestorozhdenii SSSR. (Investigations of Tourmalines from Certain Deposits in the USSR.) Avtoreferat Dissertatsii, 1954.
8. SLIVKO, M. M., *Issledovaniye turmalinov nekotorykh mestorozhdenii SSSR.* (Investigations of Tourmalines from Certain Deposits in the USSR.) Izd. L'vov. univ. 1955.
9. FERSMAN, A. YE., *Ocherki po istorii kamnya.* (Essays in History of Stone.) Vol. I. Izd. Akad. Nauk SSSR, 1954.
10. BRADLEY, J. E. S. and OLIVE BRADLEY, Observations on Coloring of Pink and Green Tourmaline. *Mineralog. Mag.* vol. 30, No. 220, 1953.
11. WEIS, P. L., Fluid Inclusions in Minerals from Zoned. Pegmatites of the Black Hills, South Dakota. *Am. Mineral.* vol. 38, No. 7/8, 1953.

---

* In *Geologiya i geografiya*, Abstr., 1954, No. 3, Abstr. No. 2733. It should be noted, by the way, that no such conclusion is to be found in Weis' original paper.

Homogenization Temperatures of Inclusions in Crystal Quartz from the Ol'gino Deposit, the Far East

L. S. PUZANOV

THERMOMETRIC studies of crystal quartz from various sources of piezo-optical quartz acquired a broad momentum after the publication of the Yermakov's book *Research in mineral-forming solutions* [2].

Simplicity of the method of study, and the easy facility of making polished sections of quartz crystals, give us the opportunity for large-scale determinations of homogenization temperatures of included solutions in quartz and, by that very fact, for an objective approach to ascertaining the lower temperature boundaries and the temperature regime under which the given deposit had been formed.

Most of the thermometric data on inclusions in crystal quartz of hydrothermal origin indicate homogenization temperatures of 100–290°C [1, 2, 3]. There has developed an opinion, for that reason, that there can be no significant accumulations of crystal quartz that could meet industrial specifications, if the crystallization of quartz took place from high temperature solutions.

The Ol'gino [or Ol'ginskoye—V.P.S.] deposit of piezo-quartz in skarns was discovered not so long ago, in the Far East, and it has developed that its lower limit of temperature at which industrial grade crystal quartz has formed is higher than in the other crystal quartz districts.

The Ol'gino is associated with Upper Proterozoic sediments in the Aesop's Range (Khrebet Aezopa), the district of Verkhnyaya Bureyna, the Khabarovsk Territories ["Verkhnebureyinskii Rayon, Khabarovskii Kray"—V.P.S.]. The deposit's site is 3 to 4 km from the outcrops of some minor intrusions of porphyroid biotite granites of Post-Cretaceous age, with a gently sloping roof.

The Upper Proterozoic sediments consist of micaceous, quartz–micaceous, and carbonaceous–micaceous shales and arkosic sandstones with admixtures of carbonaceous materials. The rocks are folded into a large anticline, extending to the north-west. The anticline structure is complicated by minor folds on its aprons. The regional dip of the rocks, in the vicinity of the deposit, is 30 to 70° north-east.

A series of low-amplitude disturbances and intensely fissured zones, with *ca.* east–west orientations and steep angles of dip, is developed extensively in the area of the deposit. The post-magmatic solutions made their ascent through these disturbed zones; they produced amphibolite–pyroxene and garnet–pyroxene skarns in horizons of the arkosic carbonate sandstones. The skarns carry appreciable quantities of disseminated coarse flaky molybdenite, native bismuth, cassiterite, galena and sphalerite and have the shapes of lens-like bedded deposits. Crystal quartz veins, abundant in cavities, are also associated with the skarns. These veins do not pass the skarn boundaries, either on the strike or on the dip. There are numerous indications of wolframite, molybdenite, cassiterite, and polymetallic ores in the district.

The quartz-bearing cavities are filled mainly with tremolite, skarn fragments, clays of different colors, quartz rubble, calcite, and large quantities of crystal quartz ranging from fractions of one centimeter to 0.5 in length, with the prevailing length of 10–15 cm. The crystals have a typical obelisque habit and are characterized by their "shirts," up to 2–3 mm thick, composed of milky-white quartz, covering the entire crystal, or else two or three of the crystal's prismatic faces and the corresponding rhombohedral faces. Crystals without such shirts are far more rare.

Most of the quartz crystals have zoned structures, expressed by alternating colorless and smoky zones and an orderly distribution of solid inclusions of actinolite, tremolite, chlorite, and ore minerals.

Thirty sections were sawed out from the deposit's most typical crystals. These sections were oriented preferably along the optical axis; they were examined with care and were described as seen under the binocular. On the basis of the examinations of the sections, of associations of inclusions with elements of the crystal's growth, systems of fissures and of zones, it became possible to designate the following types of vacuoles containing different proportions of gas and liquid (no inclusions with solid phase could be found in the crystals):

(1) Faceted tubular inclusions, associated with the crystal's center, are distributed parallel to the prismatic face; maximum length up to 5 mm and the width of 0.25–0.5 mm; 70–80 per cent gas-filled. Solid inclusions are visible at the base of such vacuoles; the solid had settled from the solution onto the rhombohedron face at the time of the crystal's growth. The solid inclusions often function as starters of the vacuoles (Fig. 1).

(2) Faceted tubular inclusions with the width:length ratios of 1:3 or 1:4 (1 mm long, up to 0.3 mm wide), situated in the next zone of the crystal, closer to the periphery, as well as near the base, in some specimens. This type of vacuoles contains 50–60 per cent of the gas phase.

(3) Weakly faceted isometric vacuoles, 0.1–0.2 mm in size, with the gas phase occupying 30–40 per cent of the total volume, situated in the central parts of the crystals, in the healed fissure systems.

(4) Tubular vacuoles, weakly faceted, as a rule, in the zone penetrated with actinolite, closer to the crystal's central part. The length of these inclusions is within the range of tenths of a millimeter and their width is several hundredths of a millimeter; the width:length ratio is 1:5 or 1:6. The gas content is 75 per cent, by volume.

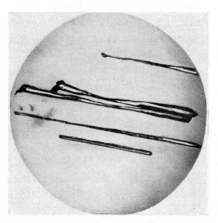

FIG. 1. Strongly elongated tubular inclusion. Solid inclusions are visible, as termination of vacuoles. 12×.

The same type of inclusions, but with 70 per cent gas phase, is found in the outer part of the zone. However, the same part also contains some rounded weakly faceted inclusions with a gas content of up to 50 per cent.

(5) Among the pseudo-secondary inclusions in healed fissures that pierce the different zones of the crystals, we note some weakly faceted vacuoles with different phase ratios: 30–40 per cent gas in the central section, but 10–5 per cent gas in the peripheral part. Shapes of the vacuoles tend to be more irregular, as one goes from the center to the periphery.

(6) Extremely small inclusions, irregularly shaped, chiefly liquid, are widespread in the milky-white shirts covering the faces of the crystal.

Homogenization of the inclusions at different phase ratios produced the following results:

The faceted inclusions, tubular and severely elongated, situated in central sections of crystals, containing 70–80 per cent gas, homogenize in the gas phase (type II) at 295–325°C.

Nearer to the peripheral parts of crystals, as far as the zone with the needles of actinolite, the gas content of the tubular vacuoles decreases down to 50 per cent and the homogenization temperature decreases from 320 down to 300°C. It is a matter of interest, that all 12 of the available inclusions, with about 60 per cent gas, homogenize in the liquid phase, as in type I. Errors in the measurements of the volumes are excluded, in this particular case, because the measurements were made in regular tubular inclusions.

The weakly faceted isometric vacuoles, under the actinolite zone, containing 30 and 40 per cent gas, homogenize as in type I, at 310 and 315°C respectively. These inclusions are secondary, with respect to the central part of the crystal, and their formation should be related to the fissures inside the crystal which were healed during the subsequent growth. Further accession of the solutions caused a partial etching of the crystal surfaces, followed by their regeneration and by deposition of quartz with actinolite on top of the zones of the crystals. Inclusions in that new zone also exhibit the trend: a progressive decrease in the gas content toward the periphery of the zone and a corresponding lowering of the homogenization temperatures.

The weakly faceted tubular inclusions in the zone penetrated with actinolite contain 75 per cent gaseous phase, if situated near the inner part of the crystal, and homogenize at 325°C. Inclusions situated closer to the periphery of the crystal have only 70 per cent of the gaseous phase and the homogenization temperature is 290°C. The homogenization temperature decreases down to 230°C, for inclusions with 30 per cent gas situated outside the actinolite zone, and next to the outer faces of the crystal the span of temperature was established at 280 and 260°C [*sic*].

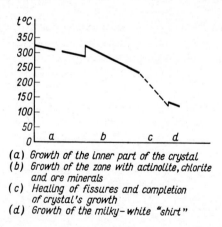

(*a*) Growth of the inner part of the crystal
(*b*) Growth of the zone with actinolite, chlorite and ore minerals
(*c*) Healing of fissures and completion of crystal's growth
(*d*) Growth of the milky-white "shirt"

FIG. 2. Diagram of temperature regime of solutions.

Pseudo-secondary inclusions of highly irregular and frequently branching shapes, containing 15 and 10 per cent gas, yield homogenization temperatures of 205 and 150°C respectively, while the inclusions with 5 per cent gas have homogenization temperatures of 115–120°C. Inclusions of this sort are responsible for a serious lowering of the industrial grade of the raw material. They are situated in healed fissures that do not touch the milky-white "shirt" of the crystal.

Inclusions in the milky-white shirt itself contain about 15 per cent gas and homogenize at 130°C, an indication of a second increase in the temperatures of the acceding solutions.

Thus the very last stages of the crystal quartz growth in the deposit at Ol'gino were distinguished by relatively high temperatures of the quartz-forming solutions, as compared with the other Russian sources of piezo-quartz. Variations in the temperature regime at Ol'gino are shown diagrammatically (Fig. 2). That figure records definitely the twice-repeated increase in the homogenization temperatures caused by accession of fresh portions of solutions after the tectonic movements.

Yermakov [2] made the first determinations of homogenization temperatures in inclusions of crystal quartz from a skarn belonging to an ore deposit in the Far East. The deposit's several generations of quartz gave the following homogenization temperatures:

Long prismatic formations: 300°C; dipyramidal forms: 100–130°C; zoned crystals: 300–140°C. Inclusions in quartz from the quartz–datolite rock homogenized at 320°C.

The figures just cited are very close to the homogenization temperatures of inclusions for the deposit at Ol'gino. This may be typical of quartz crystals associated with skarns.

It may be possible in the future, in all probability, to estimate the pressures at which the Ol'gino deposit of piezo-quartz was formed. The problem is highly involved, however, because of the relatively small difference in the homogenization temperatures of the inclusions whose gas content ranges from 80 to 50 per cent. This latter circumstance may be explained evidently by a drastic change in the pressure regime, at the time of the crystal growth, which, at this time, cannot be easily taken into account.

BIBLIOGRAPHY

1. ZAKHARCHENKO, A. I., *Mineraloobrazuyushchiye rastvory i genezis kvartsevykh zhil.* (Mineral-forming Solutions and Origin of Quartz Veins.) Gosgeoltekhizdat, 1955.
2. YERMAKOV, N. P., *Issledovaniya mineraloobrazuyushchikh rastvorov.* (Research in Mineral-forming Solutions). Izd. Khar'kov. univ. 1950.
3. KALYUZHNYI, V. A. and L. I. KOLTUN, O davleniyakh i temperaturakh pri obrazovanii mineralov nagol'nogo Kryazha. (On Pressures and Temperatures during Formation of Minerals of the Nagol'nyy Kryazh.) *Mineralog. sb. L'vov. geolog.* No. 7, 1953.

Thermometry and Composition of Liquid Inclusions in Crystal Quartz from Deposits in Dagestan Highlands

A. A. SHARKOV

DEPOSITS of crystal quartz in the highlands of Dagestan are in the oldest Middle and Upper Liassic sediments, severely dislocated and metamorphosed, extending as a belt in a north-westerly direction. This belt consists of thick sandy-shaly beds assembled in a large anticlinal fold running from south-east to north-west. The fold is complicated by numerous and chiefly conformable tectonic fractures along which there are dikes of diabase and numerous veins of quartz.

Sandstones, shales, and diabases are the host rocks of the quartz veins. However, the vast majority of the crystal quartz-bearing quartz veins are localized in quartz sandstones. Nests of crystal quartz are situated in the centers of the veins and in parts of the veins adjoining the marginal selvages.

Large quantities of inclusions of mineral-forming solutions, captured during the crystal growth, are present in the crystal quartz, as shown by microscopic examinations. The inclusions are chiefly liquid, but with different gas–liquid phase ratios. All of the inclusions homogenize in the liquid phase, and this is evidence of their hydrothermal origin.

Our thermometric studies were conducted by the homogenization method, in a thermochamber built by Yermakov [1], and set on the microscope stage. The homogenization temperatures were determined for inclusions in crystals extracted from quartz veins in sandstones, shales, and diabases. More than a hundred polished sections of these crystals, with liquid inclusions, were taken, in different orientations with respect to the crystallographic elements of the crystals.

Liquid inclusions are concentrated chiefly in the basal parts of the crystals and, to a lesser extent, in the crystals' terminations. Most of our reference measurements were made on primary inclusions spreading out, like a fan, from the center of crystal's growth or following the main axis, upwards as well as sidewise, at right angles to crystal faces, and in crystal growth zones. The inclusions have various shapes. The most common ones are negative crystals, well faceted (Fig. 1). Dimensions of the inclusions

[640]

are reckoned in tenths, hundredths, and thousandths of a millimeter; 0.5–1 mm sizes are rare. The gas phase constitutes 10–25 per cent of the volume, in multiphase inclusions, and up to 15 per cent in two-phase ones. It may be up to 40 per cent in extremely rare cases. The solid phases are represented by large number of captive minerals and associated ("sputnik") minerals. The former constitute generally 2–25 per cent, and even up to 50 per cent by volume.

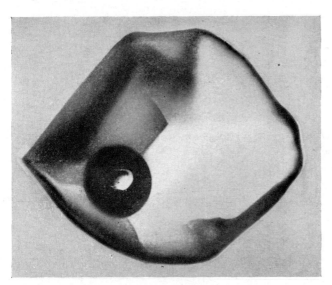

FIG. 1. Two-phase liquid inclusion shaped as negative crystal. 330×.

Characteristically, the associated minerals in multiphase inclusions do not dissolve even on heating to 300°C. Heating of the sections to still higher temperatures causes decrepitation of the inclusions followed by an intensive browning of the sections, which indicates the presence of large quantities of dissolved iron.

A large number of thermometric determinations on the crystals show that single-phase and multiphase inclusions homogenize, in the main, between 105 and 200°C (Table 1).

One may see in Table 1 a uniform lowering of temperatures of the solutions during the crystal growth. Only in some zoned crystals from the nests of the Ayshat–Kuli does one observe a radical increase in the solutions' temperature during the middle period of the crystallization.

A typical tri-zoned crystal was examined in detail. The crystal's inner zone, a dome-like termination, is the "hood of solution";* the central zone

* I.e. a more or less rounded crystal termination; the rounding was caused by a solvent action of some fluids [V.P.S.].

is a phantom, with its boundaries outlined by adhesions of chlorite; the outer zone is perfectly transparent. Gas bubbles in the liquid inclusions of the inner zone disappear at 160–150°C; inclusions in the central zone homogenize at 200–180°C; the gas bubbles in the outer zone's inclusions disappear at 170–160°C. Pseudo-secondary inclusions in healed fissures homogenize at 160–150°C (Fig. 2).

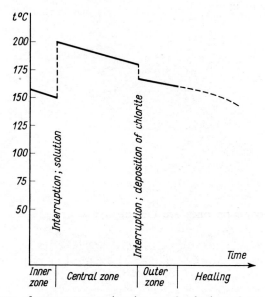

FIG. 2. Curve of temperature regime in growth of tri-zonal crystal quartz.

Figure 2 shows that crystallization of quartz from the solutions begins at temperatures corresponding to the homogenization at 160–150°C. After that, there is an accession of hotter fresh solutions which first dissolve some of the crystal and, next, deposit the crystal's central zone.

The crystal's central zone was forming at temperatures corresponding to the inclusions' homogenization temperatures of 200–180°C. That second stage of the crystal's growth was terminated by the deposition of chlorite, which enveloped the crystal as adhesions.

The transparent outer zone was produced and the fissures of the inner zones were healed during the third stage of the mineral genesis, at temperatures corresponding to the homogenization temperatures of 170–160°C.

The data obtained by us allow us to maintain that the formation of crystal quartz in the Ayshat–Kuli deposit was characterized by a pulsation in the accession of hydrothermal solutions involving occasionally a rise in the temperature.

TABLE 1. AVERAGE HOMOGENIZATION TEMPERATURES OF INCLUSIONS IN CRYSTALS, BY ZONES

Source [in Azerbaydzhan — V. P. S.]	Temperature (°C) zones			Number of crystals	Number of measurements
	inner	central	outer		
Inkhokori	150	145	145	3	16
Shayitil'	185	165	155	7	43
Il'yan-Khevi	187	170	135	5	30
Kemer	193	174	135	10	51
Balakuri	150	135	110	15	77
Gartel'	150	130	105	5	30
Nagornoye	170	150	145	6	30
Ayshat-Kuli	200	160	125	22	80
Dakki-Chay	140	130	120	4	10
Vel'ketil'	130	120	105	5	15

As many as three different captive minerals may be present in the primary liquid inclusions. At times, not every one of them can be identified.

The most common ones are the tangled-fiber aggregates of actinolite, consisting of very fine needle crystals, easily broken in the stormy effervescence of gas bubbles during the heterogenization. These aggregates were identified by us as byssolite. Inclusions resembling a hammer or a

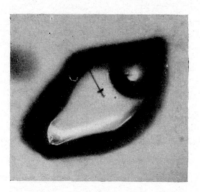

FIG. 3. Multiphase liquid inclusion. Sword-shaped captive minerals inside. 600×.

sword are more rarely found. Such inclusions are formed by needles of rutile and actinolite (Fig. 3). Crystals of halite and sylvite are still more rare; their faces are overgrown by an unidentified mineral, possibly a carbonate (Fig. 4).

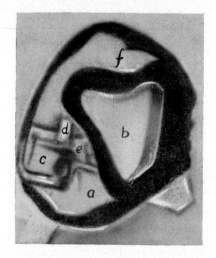

FIG. 4. Multiphase liquid inclusions.
a—aqueous liquid solution; *b*—gas; *c*—halite; *d*—sylvite; *e*—carbonate (?); *f*—unidentified mineral. 900×.

Development of the inclusions with actinolite and rutile took place before the beginning of crystal quartz growth and these minerals were captured later, together with liquid, in all probability. Presence of the accessory minerals is typical of inclusions homogenizing at the lower (110–150°C) as well as at the higher (150–200°C) temperatures.

Liquid carbon dioxide was found only in a few crystals from Ayshat–Kuli. It envelopes the gas bubbles (Fig. 5) and is transformed into gas at 30–31°C.

We extracted the solutions, in order to determine the chemical composition of the liquid inclusions. The extracts were filtered, evaporated, and subjected to microchemical analysis (T. I. Bashmakova, analyst, the All-Union Institute of Mineral Raw Material), in the instance of four specimens from different sections of the deposit (Table 2).

The pH of the extracted inclusions was found to be 7.6. The results here reported show that the liquid inclusions contain relatively dilute alkaline aqueous solutions. They carry insignificant quantities of mineral substances, chiefly chlorides, with the predominance of potassium over sodium.

There is an abundance of carbonates and appreciable quantities of sulfates are also present. The presence of fairly large quantities of dissolved silica is characteristic.

In the examination of the aqueous extracts, we also made confirmatory spectrographic analyses of the dry residues of the filtrates (Table 3).

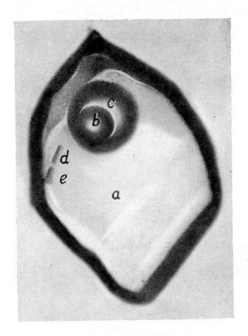

FIG. 5. Multiphase liquid inclusions.

a—aqueous liquid solution; *b*—gas; *c*—liquid carbon dioxide; *d* and *e*—unidentified mineral 500×

TABLE 2. MICROCHEMICAL ANALYSIS OF AQUEOUS EXTRACTS

Constituent	Specimen							
	166		119		180		284	
	mg/l	mg-equiv.	mg/l	mg-equiv.	mg/l	mg-equiv.	mg/l	mg-equiv.
Cl^-	61.98	1.75	17.72	0.56	20.78	0.58	12.77	0.36
$[HCO_3]^-$	17.08	0.28	12.2	0.20	14.64	0.24	20.74	0.34
$(SO_4)^{--}$	34.23	1.71	24.85	0.52	22.97	0.48	26.72	0.56
SiO_2	57.4	0.52	31.9	0.95	38.90	0.74	49.70	0.60
Ca^{++}	14.23	0.71	21.35	1.06	16.17	0.80	14.88	0.74
Mg^{++}	4.09	0.34	4.37	0.36	4.37	0.36	3.87	0.32
Na^+	25.01	1.08	3.91	0.17	5.90	0.26	2.99	0.13
K^+	9.62	1.13	6.52	0.64	6.69	0.62	7.67	0.67
Sum		6.52		4.46		4.08		3.72

The latter indicated large quantities of Si, Ca, Na, K in the solutions, with the characteristic preponderance of potassium over sodium. Al, Fe, Ni, Ti, Cu, Pb, Zn were found to be present almost invariably.

Proceeding from these findings, one may be led to believe that the formation of quartz veins and crystal quartz took place within a narrow

TABLE 3. SPECTROGRAPHIC ANALYSIS OF DRY RESIDUES OF FILTRATES (IN %)

Element	Specimen			
	166	119	180	284
Si	>1	>1	>1	>1
Al	—	0.01	0.01	0.001—0.01
Mg	0.01	0.001—0.01	0.01—0.1	0.01—0.1
Ca	0.1	1	1	1
Fe	0.001	0.001	0.001	0.001
Mn	0.001—0.01	0.001	0.001	0.001—0.01
Ni	0.01	0.001	0.001—0.01	0.01
Ti	0.001	0.001	—	0.001
Cu	0.001—0.01	0.01	0.001—0.01	0.001—0.01
Pb	0.01	0.001—0.01	0.001—0.01	0.01
Zn	0.001—0.01	0.01	0.001—0.01	0.01
Na	>1	1	0.1—1	0.1—1
K	>1	>1	>1	>1

range of the temperature, from weakly alkaline hydrothermal solutions. The overwhelming majority of the crystal quartz crystals was formed at gradually decreasing temperatures, disturbed, on occasions, by tectonic opening of fissures and by accessions of fresh solutions.

BIBLIOGRAPHY

1. YERMAKOV, N. P., *Issledovaniya mineraloobrazuyushchikh rastvorov.* (Research in Mineral-forming Solutions.) Izd. Khar'kov. univ. 1950.
2. ZAKHARCHENKO, A. I., *Mineraloobrazuyushchiye rastvory i genezis kvartsevykh zhil.* (Mineral-forming Solutions and Origin of Quartz Veins.) Gosgeoltekhizdat, 1955.

On the Subject of Variation in Physico-Chemical Factors of Equilibrium During Mineral Genesis in the Fluorite Deposit at Aurakhmat

G. G. GRUSHKIN

GENERAL INFORMATION

The deposit of Aurakhmat lies at the surface of a stratigraphic unconformity between massive limestones and overlying flinty shales, between the Lower and the Upper Tournais respectively. The shales, functioning as a screening lid, were responsible for a stagnant environment of the solutions at the time of the mineral genesis.

The principal structural components, within the boundary of the unconformity on which the structural control of the ore-deposition depended, are the axes of small folds of the second order with which the dome-like bulges of the eroded massive limestones are associated. Around these bulges of the tough massifs, there is a development of very small periclinal structures caused by enveloping of the limestone nuclei by the shales. The unidirectionally oriented pressure on the sides of the dome-like fold was conducive to the stratification of the massive limestones and shales, development of fragmentation zones between the formations, and development of fissures in the limestones.

These weakened and easily permeable zones became the sites of deposition of hydrothermal minerals (Fig. 1).

The second structural factor controlling the ore deposition is the Upper Palaeozoic overthrust, the Brichmullah, in the overriding portion of which the Aurakhmat deposit is situated. This overthrust was reactivated by the Alpine tectonics. Pyritization, quartizification, deposition of crested scalenohedral and prismatic calcite in small cavities of crusts, fully analogous to what is found in the deposit itself, has been discovered in fragments of breccias, in the plane of the main rift, which provides the basis for the view that the Brichmullah overthrust was the principal ore-conducting channel. Such is indeed the case with the mineralized rupture cutting the western apron of the structure (Fig. 1).

The site and the depositional environment of the ore body were determined by a combination of all of the structural-lithologic factors here described.

The deposit was formed at 2.5–3 km depth, if we take into account the reconstructed thickness of the eroded profile.

Sill-like intrusions of syenite–monzonites, of Vise and Namur age, are well developed in the district. According to Smol'yaninov [16], the syenite–monzonites contain up to 0.23 per cent F. We observed thin smears of

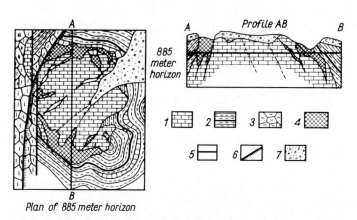

FIG. 1. Outline of geologic structure of the deposit at Aurakhmat.

1. Massive limestones; *2.* Flinty shales with limestone interlayers; *3.* Fragmented shales; *4.* The ore body; *5.* The ore channel; *6.* The Brichmullach (Brichmullinskii) overthrust (renewed in the Alpine time); *7.* River terrace gravels.

violet fluorite in fissures within these rocks and in the associated hornfelses. By analogy with other districts in the neighborhood, the age of the fluorite mineralization is either Upper Permian or Lower Triassic. Thus there is no detectable direct relation between the fluorite ores and the parent intrusions.

The principal minerals of the main ore body were deposited in the following sequence: fluorite, barite, sulfides, quartz, calcite. This sequence is ascertained by the sum-total of the [following] indications: intersections, envelopments, and replacements for every pair of the minerals. The main minerals, fluorite, quartz, and calcite, are represented by several generations. Five generations were identified, in the instance of fluorite: dark-violet (zoned); violet (zoned parallel to the cube and the dodecahedron faces); bluish transparent; greenish (zoned parallel to the cube and the octahedron faces); finally, pink fluorite. Quartz is represented by four generations: short columnar semi-transparent; crested transparent; needle–microcrystalline; hornfels-like. Calcite has also four generations: milky-white; brownish manganiferous–ferruginous (rhombohedron, scaleno-hedron, prism); coarsely crystalline semi-transparent (scalenohedron, complicated by groups of curving faces); short prismatic transparent.

RESULTS OF INVESTIGATION OF THE TEMPERATURE REGIME
IN THE FORMATION OF THE DEPOSIT

The principal results of measurements of the temperatures at which the main hypogene vein minerals of the deposit were formed are reported in the following pages. The measurements were made by the homogenization method for liquid inclusions, including the inevitable limitations of the accuracy inherent in the method itself. The three minerals composing up to 95 per cent of the total mass of ores in the deposit—fluorite, quartz, calcite were examined separately, by their generations. Special features of the temperature in the deposition of every one of the generations, the temperature limits, etc., were established by the investigation.

In all, we made 680 determinations of homogenization temperatures. Most of them were made on primary inclusions, on solutions captured by crystals during their growth; a smaller number is of a later origin; very few of the inclusions could be designated as of the solvent-action type [5]. The results are summarized in Table 1.

TABLE 1. SEPARATION SEQUENCES AND TEMPERATURES OF FORMATION OF THE PRINCIPAL HYPOGENE MINERALS

Generation of fluorite	Homogenization temperatures of inclusions (°C)		
	Primary	Pseudo-secondary, in healed fissures	Inclusions produced by solvent action
Dark-violet, zoned	149–147–144	149–147–142–138–133–131	142–122
Violet, zoned	180–172–168–164–151–147–133	184–168–160–151–149–147–144–133	206–200–192–188–172–158–150–115
Barely bluish, transparent	160–135–133–129	164–160–156–151–147–135	208–164–151–105
Greenish	210–205–190–156–151–147–140–133–131–113–105	188–156–151–147–145	233–210
Pink	—	121–119–115–101–90	—

The uniformity of homogenization temperatures of primary inclusions is conspicuous; the same applies to pseudo-secondary inclusions in healed fissures. The coincidence of the temperatures indicates that fissuring and healing of crystals are concurrent with their further growth, against the background of repeatedly occurring tectonic movements on which accessions of fresh portions of the solutions depend. Healing of inner parts of a crystal is synchronous with the crystallization of its outer layers and with the corresponding development of pseudo-secondary or primary–secondary inclusions [6]. The temperature difference between the solution (233–105°C) and the crystallization (210–105°C) of fluorite indicates that solution of fluorite is caused not by a change in the temperature (which is the same as the crystallization temperature), but by a change in composition of the dissolved salts and in concentration of the solutions during the fluoride and the silica stages of the process resulting from an in-flow of a solution with a different composition.

Out of the four generations of quartz, we were able to examine only two thermometrically, the short columnar semi-transparent and the crested transparent ones. The other two varieties of quartz, the needle–microcrystalline and the hornfels-like, contained no gas–liquid inclusions.

TABLE 2. TEST RESULTS ON THE TWO FIRST GENERATIONS OF QUARTZ BASED ON 450 MEASUREMENTS

Generation of quartz	Homogenization temperatures of inclusions (°C)	
	Primary	Secondary, in healed fissures
Quartz I, short–columnar, semi-transparent	Center of crystal: 219 Middle of crystal: 196 Margin of crystal: 193	192 168, 144 138, 129
Quartz II, crested, transparent	144	—

It follows from the data in Table 2 that quartz of the first generation was crystallizing at gradually falling temperatures.

Pseudo-secondary inclusions in quartz I were formed at 192–129°C, with the upper limit corresponding to the crystallization of the outer layers of the first-generation quartz (193°C). This means that both fissuring and fissure-healing in quartz of the first generation began after its crystal growth was complete. Quartz of the second generation was formed at 144°C, i.e. at the temperature of the fissure-healing in quartz of the first generation. This circumstance provides a sufficient measure of probability for us to assume that, at 138–129°C, during the healing of quartz I, the crystallization of quartz of the third and the fourth generations was taking place, while crested quartz of the second generation crystallized at 168°C.

There are few inclusions in calcite of the second and the third generations. In all, about thirty measurements could be made. The results showed that the second and the third generations crystallized at 98–78°C and 81–66°C.

In constructing the diagram of homogenization temperatures, we made positional correlations of inclusions for crystals of different generations.

In the homogenization of primary inclusions situated in planes parallel to faces of the crystal, we determined the mean values for every such plane. Next, in order to obtain the spatial scale, we measured the distances from the planes to the outer faces of the crystal. The abscissa in Fig. 2

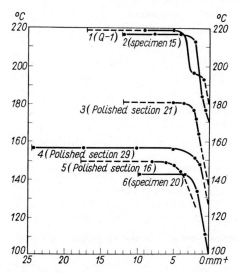

FIG. 2. Curves of temperatures during growth of crystals of quartz (*1* and *2*), fluorite (*3–6*) from Aurakhmat (*1, 3, 4, 5*) and from Chatmazar (*2* and *6*)*.

* Abbreviations "obr." (obrazets, specimen?) and "shl." (shlif, polished section? thin section?) are not explained in the original. "Shl." particularly may be an abbreviation covering a multitude of terms. Since the same curves represent several minerals (namely, *1* and *2*) and since the collective fluorite curves (*3–6*) do not include all of the breakdown (*1, 3, 4, 5*) and (*2* and *6*), much is left to the reader's imagination in the absence of explanations in the original text [V.P.S.].
† Abscissa: distance from the face of the crystal [V.P.S.].

shows distances from the plane of inclusions to the outer face of the crystal; the ordinate shows the corresponding homogenization temperatures. The dotted lines are the hypothetical course of the temperature, in parts of the curves for which no measurements were made. The left ends of the curves refer to the centers of the corresponding crystals.

The diagram shows that the temperature of crystallization of quartz and fluorite from two different deposits remained practically the same, from the moment of nucleation to nearly the end of the crystal's growth, and the sudden plunge downward, occurred only right before the end of the crystal's growth. The amplitude of the fall is as high as 40–50°C. In the short columnar quartz crystal from Aurakhmat, the falling temperature curve is complicated by an intervening step. Because of that, the transparent central part of the crystal became enveloped in a turbid shirt, 2–3 mm thick and brim-full of inclusions.

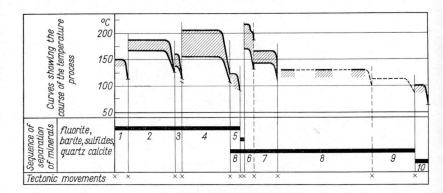

FIG. 3. Sequence of separation and temperatures of formation of hypogene minerals from Aurakhmat.

1. Dark-violet zoned fluorite; *2.* Violet zoned fluorite; *3.* Bluish transparent fluorite; *4.* Greenish fluorite; *5.* Pink fluorite; *6.* Columnar quartz; *7.* Comb quartz; *8.* Finely crystalline needle quartz; *9.* Hornfelsic quartz; *10.* Calcite (rhombohedron→scalenohedron→prism).

Figure 3 represents the paragenetic pattern of the sequence of separation of the minerals and the course of the temperature regime for every stage of the ore-forming process. The following may be seen in that diagram:

(1) The ore-forming process took place, in the beginning, against a background of a general rise in the temperature followed by a general and gradual decrease in the temperature.

(2) The upper and the lower limits of the temperature are suggested for the series of the minerals; the range within these limits tends to widen, on the whole, on approach to the point of flexure, where the rise of the temperature ceases and its fall begins.

(3) The ore-forming process is not continuous; its course is subdivided into several successive stages; the intervals between the stages are expressed either by a succession of a mineral by another one or by a succession of generations of the mineral. In the majority of the generations, separated from each other by the interruptions, the moment of the succession co-incides with the moment of manifestation of tectonic movements within the mineralized zone.

(4) The correction, added to the determined homogenization temperatures of inclusions in fluorite, with the aid of Lemmlein's and Klevtsov's diagram [12], is 16, 27, and 33°C, for the dark violet, the violet, and the greenish fluorite respectively.

COMPOSITION OF SALTS AND CONCENTRATION OF SOLUTIONS

A layer of fluorite, 2 cm thick and weighing 2 or 3 kg, was the test material, isolated on the basis of the thermometric measurements and morphologic indications. A part of this sample was pulverized, for its extraction, and a part was used for the determination of total water contained in the inclusions. The extracted solution was analyzed microchemically (Table 3).

TABLE 3. RESULTS OF QUANTITATIVE MICROCHEMICAL DETERMINATIONS OF ANIONS AND CATIONS RECALCULATED AS PROBABLE SALTS, IN PERCENTAGES

Salts	Fluorite		
	Dark violet	Violet	Greenish
KCl	4.987	0.616	0.369
NaCl	4.560	6.515	0.415
NaF	1.045	0.357	0.338
$CaCl_2$	1.283	0.376	—
$MgCl_2$	—	1.265	—
$Ca(HCO_3)_2$	—	0.762	3.046
$NaHCO_3$	—	—	1.523
Sum	11.875	9.891	5.691
pH	7.0	7.3	7.6

Salts in the fluorite-forming solutions, as one may see from the results, undergo an orderly change in their composition, from stage to stage of the process, grading from the alkali chlorides and fluorides into sodium and calcium bicarbonates. The change is accompanied by an increase in alkalinity of the solutions. The trend is determined mainly by an external influence; the replacement of limestones by the fluorides and the accompanying liberation of appreciable quantities of calcium and CO_2. The liberated calcium is bound partly with fluoride and partly with bicarbonate. The increase in the dissolved calcium bicarbonate affects the pH of the solution, so that the originally neutral pH becomes weakly alkaline. The crystallization of fluorite is accompanied by a continuous decrease in the total dissolved salts. The falling concentrations of sodium fluoride and the concurrently rising concentrations of the bicarbonate are especially characteristic.

Uklonskii [17, 18] and Smol'yaninov [16, pp. 44 and 94] believe that the mineral genesis at the Aurakhmat took place by the following pattern:

$$3CaCO_3 + H_2SiF_6 = 3CaF_2 + SiO_2 + 3CO_2 + H_2O.$$

This equation indicates a simultaneous crystallization of quartz and fluorite, so that three parts of limestone are replaced by three molecules of fluorite plus one of silica. Such speculations are not supported, however, by the chemical analysis of the gas–liquid inclusions [4]. The presence of NaF,

$Ca(HCO_3)_2$, and $NaHCO_3$ was demonstrated among the salts in the inclusions in fluorite. We are proposing therefore the following reaction pattern for the fluoride stage:

$$CaCO_3 + 2NaF + CO_2 + H_2O = CaF_2 + 2NaHCO_3,$$

or

$$2NaF + Ca(HCO_3)_2 = 2CaF_2 + 2NaHCO_3.$$

It was not possible to examine the composition of the liquid inclusions of the silica stage of the process. Taking into account the presence of the alkalies and reasoning from Khitarov's experimental data [19], as well as from the data of other investigators and from Betekhtin's theoretical generalizations [1], we take the following reaction of transfer and deposition of silica, as the basic pattern:

$$x\,Na_2O \cdot y\,SiO_2 + 2HCl = y\,SiO_2 + 2NaCl + x\,H_2O.$$

According to this reaction, sodium silicate decomposes, on lowering of the temperature, and silica is liberated.

Transfer and deposition of fluorine [as fluorite], as it follows from the data here cited, occurs mainly with the participation of fluorides and alkalies, while transfer and deposition of silica is accomplished with the aid of chlorides and alkalies whose successions, in time and in composition of the abyssal solutions, may be the principal factor controlling deposition of the principal minerals of our deposit: fluorite first; quartz next.

The concept of the succession of stages in the ore-forming process is particularly important because of its cardinal value for our understanding of relationships in the spatial distribution of the economic mineralization in the deposits.

The latter statement needs to be qualified, as it does not exclude the possibility of a simultaneous deposition of fluorite and quartz, for example, in the short period intervening between the chloride–fluoride succession when fluorite and quartz are deposited at the same time (Fig. 3).

CHANGES IN THE pH DURING THE ORE-FORMING PROCESS

We already mentioned the determinations of pH of the natural solutions in the inclusions, as a part of our examination of gas–liquid inclusions in the series of generations of fluorite [4]. The pH levels for the dark violet (the earliest), the violet, and the greenish fluorite are 7.0, 7.3, and 7.6 respectively. This statement may be supplemented by the following indirect data. According to our investigations [3], the deposition of greenish fluorite, during the very last moments of growth of the outer layer of the substance, is accompanied by adhesions of kaolinite, identified chemically, by the immersion method, thermographically, and by the X-ray method.

According to the experimental findings [14, 20, 21], kaolinite is reproduced, at low temperatures, only from weakly acid or acid solutions. The fluorite layer with the adhesions of kaolinite crystallized at a low temperature, 105°C, so that one may believe that the kaolinite in question was laid down in a weakly acid environment [3]. The pink fluorite (crystallization temperature 121–90°C), which came down after the greenish fluorite, produced the following sequence of layers in the crusted ores (in mm): 5 pink fluorite; 5 barite rose; 2 pink fluorite; 3 barite rose; 7 yellow iron–magnesium calcite; 2 sugary pink fluorite; 10 semitransparent calcite [4]. As we know, barite also requires acid or weakly acid media for its precipitation.

The examination of the sequence of separation of minerals (kaolinite, barite) here performed allows us to maintain that the weakly alkaline environment of the fluorine stage of the ore-forming process was succeeded by a weakly acid environment, in the very end of the stage, after the deposition of fluorite, while the deposition of sphalerite and galena, cementing the barite fragments and filling fine fissures in the barite, is an indication of a still another shift in the pH, from acid to alkaline. It is established therefore, both by direct examination of the solutions and by indirect conclusions based on the paragenesis of the minerals, that the ore-depositional process was accompanied by fluctuations of the pH level of the solution in the vicinity of neutrality.

The cause of the variations depends on changes in the concentration of active oxygen whose zone of penetration, as we know, extends to 3 km depth, and still deeper. Variations in the pH during the ore-forming process, related to variations in the concentration of oxygen in ore-forming solution, justify the assumption, in harmony with Betekhtin's concepts [1], of a close paragenetic relationship between barite and sulfides and of the possibility of appearance, under favorable conditions, of polymetallic sulfides in quartz–barite–fluorite veins, as exemplified by the fluorite–barite–polymetallic deposit of Naugarzan and by others.

PRESSURES IN THE ORE-FORMING PROCESS

For every one of the three generations of fluorite here examined, we calculated the pressures at which the given generation of fluorite was being laid down [2]. It was essential, for such calculations, to calculate first the mean homogenization temperature of the inclusions, for every generation, on the basis of a large number of measurements, and the average volume of the gas phase in inclusions, in comparison to the inclusions' total volume. The results of these studies are reported in Table 4.

TABLE 4. DETERMINATION OF MEAN HOMOGENIZATION TEMPERATURES OF INCLUSIONS

Generation of fluorite	Number of measurements	Mean homogenization temperature (°C)	Per cent gaseous phase as of total volume of inclusions	Calculated pressure atm
Dark violet	258	149	2.734	240
Violet	484	180	2.074	425
Greenish	240	205	2.144	620

The methods of calculation were simple. It was established that, if we consider the volume increment of the inclusion's cavity, in view of the volume-expansion coefficient of the mineral, on heating from 20°C to the homogenization temperature, and the volume-expansion of the inclusion's liquid phase for the same limits of the temperature, the filling of the entire cavity of the inclusion with its liquid phase must occur at a temperature appreciably below the homogenization temperature, because of the large volume-expansion coefficient of the liquid. Consequently, as the inclusion is being heated to its homogenization temperature, there is a build up of pressure by which the volume of the liquid is compressed so that it equals the constant volume of the inclusion. The difference between the observed and the calculated homogenization point times the volume-expansion coefficient of the liquid, within the temperature range here considered, allows us to find that particular supplementary volume which must be compressed, in order to maintain the constant volume of the inclusion [sic]. Results of the calculations are shown in Table 4.

The magnitudes of the calculated pressures, very approximate as they are (reliability of the order of 10 per cent), are indicative nevertheless that, in the process of the mineral genesis, there may be considerable variations in the pressure at one and the same depth below the surface of the ground. In our example, the range of variation is 240–625 atm. This experimental finding invalidates the well-known concept of Lindgren as to a direct relationship between temperature, pressure, and depth of the deposition, a concept he employed as the basic principle in the genetic classification of hydrothermal ore deposits.

The most probable depth of formation of the deposit here discussed, with respect to the present surface of the ground, is 2.5–3 km, judging by the reconstruction of the profile. The pressure of water column, for 2.5 km depth, is 250 atm, and the static pressure of the overburden is 625 atm. If we compare our calculated results, 240–620 atm pressures, with these figures, we find that the limits of the calculated pressures coincide with the limits indicated by the pressures of the water column and the overburden, at a depth of 2.5 km. It is still very difficult to say whether relationships of this sort will determine the limits of the pressure variations also in other instances, particularly the pressure minima. As to the upper limit of pressure, one may reasonably assume that it is not likely to exceed the pressure of the overburden, since, were it not so, the system's internal pressure would exceed the external one and would have to be discharged accordingly by means of explosions, mechanical disturbances along the ore channels, or by seepages through the rock. Judging from the first results of our calculations, the pressure, as well as the temperature, may serve as a criterion of the depositional depth of the ore only if we know their upper and lower limits, while measurement of either alone would yield merely a rather relative datum. Consequently, we must strive to calculate the pressures for every stage of the ore-forming process, insofar as possible, in our examinations of ore deposits.

The pressure figures here obtained make it possible to calculate the pressure and the temperature differences between the first and second, and the second and third generations of fluorite: 31°C, 185 atm and 25°C, 195 atm respectively, or 6 atm per 1°C and 8 atm per 1°C respectively. If the pressure increment is reckoned at 6 atmospheres per every degree of heat produced by accessions of hotter fresh portions of the abyssal hydrothermal fluids, inasmuch as $P = f(T)$, the supplementary increment of 2 atm per °C, in the instance of the later generations of fluorite, may be explained only by an increase in bicarbonates and CO_2 in the solutions, the result of a progressive replacement of the host, the limestone, by fluorite, even as it is indicated definitely by the chemical composition of the included solutions (Table 3).

ON THE SUBJECT OF VARIATIONS IN THE PHYSICO-CHEMICAL FACTORS OF EQUILIBRIUM IN THE COURSE OF THE ORE-FORMING PROCESS

Genetic earmarks of any natural system find their expression in its primary physico-chemical factors of equilibrium (temperature, pressure, concentration, salinity, etc.) which are interdependent.

The process of formation of the Aurakhmat fluorite deposit is subdivided into several successive levels (stages) punctuated by interruptions. The stages are represented either by a mineral succeeding another one or by a succession of generations of one and the same mineral. Succession of the stages of the ore-forming process is accompanied by tectonic movements, so that, in the succession of generations of fluorite, there are variations in temperature, saline constituents and their concentrations, pH of the solutions and pressure, as well as in colors and shapes of the crystals.

Inasmuch as the deposit here described is associated with a regional rift, one may reasonably assume that tectonic movements were affecting both the mineral genesis and the discontinuities in the ore-forming process.

This influence was an expression of the high-tension tectonism of that major disturbance which had assured the delivery of the ore-forming accessions from the deep sources of mineralization to the site of the deposition of the ore. The association of renewals of the ore-deposition with tectonic movements is typical of ore deposits of the type here discussed.

Our particular case is a clear-cut confirmation of Smirnov's pulsation hypothesis [15], inasmuch as every successive stage in the ore deposition is characterized by an accession of a qualitatively different ore-forming solution at the site of the deposit.

It may be assumed, proceeding from the analysis of the temperature curve of the ore-forming process, that movements of the ore-bearing solutions were not a continuous flow, but proceeded by stages, slowing down and dying out toward the end of every stage in the accessions of hydrothermal fluids, in every case, punctuated by tectonic movements as the signs of an impending new pulsation.

Considering the data here reported, as well as the fact that the crystallization of minerals belonging to different generations was accompanied by a downward plunge of temperature, at the moment of completion of the mineral's growth, a plunge of the order of magnitude of 40°C, whereby the given stage of the process would be terminated abruptly, we may assume that the formation of the minerals was taking place in environments where the stages were marked off rather definitely. These stages were related apparently to a tectonic as well as a crystallizational "sealing off" of different parts of the deposit.*

Poyarkov and Korolev [13] arrived at the same conclusion, on the basis of purely geologic sequential relationships, while Lemmlein and Osadchev [11] had described an Alpine vein in which the presence of colored quartz, in the bottom of a large druse cavity, was ascribed to the extremely slow convection currents in the mineral-forming solution by which the vein's cavity was filled, i.e. to an environment that could arise only in a relatively confined system.

Yermakov [6] had found that relative temperature fluctuations during the growth of large crystals of optical fluorite, in one and the same vug, did not exceed 2 or 4°C, i.e. that the crystals were growing at a nearly constant temperature, which could be the case only if the vug was relatively well confined. It is this very kind of confinement of different stages

---

* This is probably the explanation of the fact that the ore-holding structures are chiefly systems of feathered ("operyayushchiye") fissures and fragmentation zones of the second and the third orders in which the periodic sealing off of the ores was better favored than it would be in some regional large ore-conducting ruptures, where continuous movements and a free flow of the solutions do not create the environment that would be conducive to retention of the solutions and deposition of the minerals.

of the ore-forming process that we have in mind in discussing the deposit at Aurakhmat.

All of this stands in complete harmony with the existing concepts of hydrothermal deposits, in the sense of open systems. They are open only to the extent of providing the opportunity for the development of a series of relatively confined stages of the process. The resulting pattern of discontinuities (pulsations) is expressed in the curve of falling temperatures (Fig. 3), in the sequence of the stages of a highly retarded circulation of the solutions, in the changing of composition of the solutions, in every new stage of the process, involving a disruption of the confinement by tectonic forces at the inception of every new stage.

It appears to us that the proposed form of paragenetic diagrams (Fig. 3) may have a value in classification, for our understanding of fundamental distinctions of open hydrothermal systems, as against natural systems of other genetic types. The temperature regime of the ore-forming process, related to certain moments in the tectonic movements inside the mineralized zone, is expressed by a discontinuous curve of temperatures. The deposition of minerals is renewed with every tectonic movement of the sequence, and so is the composition of the solutions. This phenomenon occurs against the background of a general rise in the temperatures and proceeds against the background of a gradual decrease in the temperatures. In this case, the frequent upsets in the physico-chemical equilibrium are reflected in the wide variety of hydrothermal formations, the products of a fractional distillation.

Korzhinskii [7, 8, 9, 10] devoted a series of papers to elaborations of problems in the physico-chemical analysis of a metasomatic zonation in the near-vein metamorphism and to the Phase Rule in open systems with entirely mobile components. The results presented in our article, on our studies of variations in the physico-chemical factors of the equilibrium, during the ore-forming process, allow us to pose the problem of applying Korzhinskii's physico-chemical constructions in the analysis of actual mineral deposits and of zones of the near-vein hydrothermal metamorphism.

While we believe, with Korzhinskii, that the filling of vein bodies with minerals and the near-vein alterations of the host rocks constitute a single and indivisible process, we are obliged inevitably to assume that the qualitative changes in the composition of ore-forming solutions, the kind that Korzhinskii neglects in his papers here cited, may bring about different alteration in the hanging wall (zonations), not at all as the result of the interactions between the rock and the original single solution, in the course of its infiltrational seepage into the fissure's walls, the way Korzhinskii assumes in his equations.

The procedures of Korzhinskii's physico-chemical analysis, as he himself emphasizes, has been developed for a relatively confined system and, for that reason, may be suited for ordinary hydrothermal veins only in the analysis of some single stage in their formation, provided it can be proved that this stage does not involve a superimposition of processes that are chemically different and are also different in the time. Before one may go ahead with Korzhinskii's analysis of veins, the decision requires a knowledge of what particular types of alteration in the hanging wall are related to qualitative changes in composition of the solutions, in time, and what others are caused by the phenomena of the infiltrational metasomatic zonation. If not, the qualitatively irreversible evolution of the ore-forming process, in time and space, may be replaced by a scheme of a purely spatial evolution.

BIBLIOGRAPHY

1. BETEKHTIN, A. G., Gridrotermal'nyye rastvory, ikh priroda i protsessy rudoobrazo-vaniya. (Hydrothermal Solutions, their Nature, and the Ore-forming Processes.) Sb. *Osnovnyye problemy v uchenii o magmatogennykh rudnykh mestorozhdeniyakh.* (Basic Problems in the Theory of Magmatogenic Ore Deposits.) Izd. Akad. Nauk SSSR, 1953.
2. GRUSHKIN, G. G., Gazovo-zhidkiye vklyucheniya kak mineralogicheskii manometr. (Gas–Liquid Inclusions as a Mineralogical Manometer.) *Zap. vseross. mineralog. obshch.* pt. 82, No. 2, 1953.
3. GRUSHKIN, G. G., Geneticheskoye znacheniye "prisypok" v mineralakh. (Genetic Significance of "Adhesions" in Minerals.) *Mineralog. sb. L'vov. geolog. obshch.* No. 7, 1954.
4. GRUSHKIN, G. G. and P. L. PRIKHOD'KO, Ob izmenenii khimicheskogo sostava, kontsentratsii i pH gazovo-zhidkikh vklyucheniy v ryade posledovatel'nykh gene-ratsii fluorita. (On the Subject of Variations in Chemical Composition, Concentration, and pH of Gas–Liquid Inclusions in a Series of Successive Generations of Fluorite.) *Zap. vseross. mineralog. obshch.* pt. 81, No. 2, 1952.
5. GRUSHKIN, G. G. and I. G. KHEL'VAS, Geneticheskiye tipy zhidkikh vklyucheniy i temperatury ikh obrazovaniya vo flyuoritakh. (Genetic Types of Liquid Inclusions and Temperature of their Formation in Fluorites.) *Tr. inst. geolog. Akad. Nauk UzSSR,* 6, 1951.
6. YERMAKOV, N. P., *Issledovaniya mineraloobrazuyushchikh rastvorov.* (Research in Mineral-forming Solutions.) Izd. Khar'kov. univ. 1950.
7. KORZHINSKII, D. S., Metasomaticheskaya zonal'nost' pri okolotreshchinnom meta-morfizme i zhily. (Metasomatic Zonations in Metamorphism next-to-fissures in relation to veins.) *Zap. vseross. mineralog. obshch.* pt. 75, No. 4, 1946.
8. KORZHINSKII, D. S., Otkrytyye sistemy s vpolne podvizhnymi komponentami i pravilo faz. (Open Systems with Entirely Mobile Components and the Phase Rule.) *Izv. Akad. Nauk SSSR, ser. geolog.* No. 2, 1949.
9. KORZHINSKII, D. S., Infil'tratsionnaya metasomaticheskaya zonal'nost' i obrazo-vaniye zhil. (Infiltrational Metasomatic Zonations and the Development of Veins.) *Izv. Akad. Nauk SSSR, ser. geolog.* No. 6, 1951.
10. KORZHINSKII, D. S., Ocherk metasomaticheskikh protsessov. (An Essay in Meta-somatic Processes.) Sb. *Osnovnyye problemy v uchenii o magmatogennykh rudnykh mestorozhdeniyakh.* Izd. Akad. Nauk SSSR, 1953.
11. LEMMLEIN, G. G. and B. YA. OSADCHEV, Vertikal'noye raspredeleniye v zhile bes-tsvetnykh i dymchatykh kristallov kvartsa. (Vertical Distribution of Colorless and Smoky Quartz Crystals in a Vein.) *Dokl. Akad. Nauk SSSR,* vol. 50, 1945.

12. LEMMLEIN, G. G. and P. V. KLEVTSOV, Sootnosheniye termodinamicheskikh parametrov P–T–V dlya vody i 30 per cent vodnykh rastvorov NaCl. (Relationships of the P–T–V Thermodynamic Parameters for Water and for 30 per cent Aqueous Solutions of NaCl.) *Zap. vsesoyuzn. mineralog. obshch.* pt. 85, No. 4, 1956.

13. POYARKOV, V. E. and A. V. KOROLEV, Nekotoryye osobennosti treshchinnykh zhil i voprosy ikh glubinnykh poiskov. (Certain Characteristic Features of Veins in Fissures and Problems in Prospecting for them in Depths.) *Zap. Uzbek. Otdela vseross. obshch.* No. 4, 1953.

14. SEDLETSKII, I. D., *Kolloidno–dispersnaya mineralogiya.* (Colloidal–Dispersed Mineralogy.) Izd. Akad. Nauk SSSR, 1945.

15. SMIRNOV, S. S., K voprosu o zonal'nosti rudnykh mestorozhdenii. (On the Subject of Zonations in Ore Deposits.) *Izv. Akad. Nauk SSSR, ser. geolog.* No. 6, 1937.

16. SMOL'YANINOV, N. A., Flyuoritovyye mestorozhdeniya Srednei Azii. (Fluorite Deposits of Central Asia.) *Tr. Tadzhiksko-Pamirskoi expeditsii,* 1935.

17. UKLONSKII, A. S., Materialy dlya mineralogii Turkestana. Brichmullinskoye mestorozhdeniye plavikovogo shpata. (Data for Mineralogy of Turkestan. The Brichmullah Deposit of Fluorspar.) *Tr. Turkestan. nauch. obshch.* vol. I, 1923.

18. UKLONSKII, A. S., Ekskursiya v Chimgan i Aurakhmat. (Excursion to Chimgan and Aurakhmat.) *Tr. III vseross. geolog. s'yezda,* 2, 1928.

19. KHITAROV, N. I., Experimental'naya kharakteristika ustoychivosti kvartsa i migratsii kremnezyoma v gidrotermal'nykh usloviyakh. (Empirical Characterization of Stability of Quartz and of Migration of Silica in Hydrothermal Environments.) *Tr. 4-go soveshch. po experimental. mineralog. i petrograf.* Izd. Akad. Nauk SSSR, 2, 1953.

20. MOREY, G. W. and E. INGERSON, The Pneumatolytic and Hydrothermal Alteration and Synthesis of Silicates, *Econ. Geol.* vol. 37, suppl. to No. 5, 1937.

21. NOLL, W., Die Mineralbildung von System SiO_2-Al_2O_3-H_2O. *Neues Jahrb. f. Mineral.* Bd. 70, 1935.

Special Features of the Origin of the Lebedinoye Gold-Ore Deposit Ascertained on the Basis of Inclusions in Minerals

L. I. KOLTUN

Two principal types of ore deposits are typical of the Lebedinoye: (a) metasomatic deposits; (b) vein bodies. In addition, disseminated ores in magmatic rocks (syenites, syenite–porphyries, and others), and in skarn zones, are recognized although neither one of them has any practical value.

Metasomatic ore deposits are bedded bodies associated with dolomites of the Cambrian sedimentary complex. Their dimensions vary both areally and vertically and depend on intensity of solution action, on their composition, state of aggregation, temperature, and, to an appreciable extent, on the character of the host rocks, their porosity, fissuring, bedding, etc. As noted by Fastalovich and Petrovskaya [3], most of the metasomatic deposits have lenticular shapes and are elongated in a north-easterly direction, in correspondence with the orientation of the tectonic zones.

The metasomatic ore deposits are composed of ankerite with abundant disseminated pyrite. The pyrite may amount, in places, up to one quarter of the total ore and generally consists of irregular grains.

Thin and weak veinlets of pyrite, chalcopyrite, sphalerite, gold, and other minerals are found in the continuous bodies of ankerite.

The vein ore bodies consist chiefly of quartz veins, with varying quantities of ore minerals, quartz–hematite veins, some thin calcitic, dolomitic, and ankeritic veins, mainly in the Cambrian sedimentary beds, and fairly large quantities of sulfides.

Fastalovich and Petrovskaya recognize four paragenetic associations of minerals at the Lebedinoye: (a) pyrite–ankerite (in metasomatic deposits); (b) quartz–pyrite (in vein ore bodies), with rod-like quartz composing 80–90 per cent of the total mass of the vein; (c) quartz–polymetallic, represented by quartz, pyrite, pyrrhotite, sphalerite, galena–bismuthite [bismuthinite?], chalcopyrite, tetrahedrite, and bornite; (d) hematite—with hematite, scaly mica, and quartz.

These mineral associations are listed in the sequence of their separation. Quartz, the basic vein mineral, is present in all of them, but its morphologic features are different in every one of the associations.

[662]

Bilibin [1] related the mineralization to hydrothermal manifestations, while recognizing two types of formations in the deposit: (a) the zones of silicified limestones; (b) the quartz veins and metasomatic deposits.

The ore-forming process in the deposit was characterized more fully by Fastalovich and Petrovskaya.

In their opinion, the magma of the post-Jurassic intrusions was the source of the mineralizing solutions, as proved by spatial relationships between the ore veins and the syenite–porphyry massifs.

The ore-forming process is subdivided into a series of stages separated from each other by tectonic movements within the mineralized zone:

(1) The stage of pyrite–ankerite aggregate and of the early pyrite disseminated in syenite porphyries.

(2) The stage of rod-like quartz and of the metasomatic replacement of limestones by a chalcedony-like aggregate.

(3) The stage of granular quartz and of the bulk of the sulfides.

(4) The gold stage.

We examined inclusions of mineral-forming solutions in all transparent and semitransparent minerals.

Inclusions in minerals from the metasomatic ore deposits were examined ahead of the rest, i.e. inclusions in ankerite and in the chalcedony-like quartz. After that, we examined inclusions in minerals of the vein bodies: quartz, fluorite, calcite, sphalerite, ankerite, and dolomite.

Ankerite is widespread and abundant in the deposit. It constitutes about 30 per cent of the ore mass in the metasomatic deposits and is the earliest mineral.

Inclusions of mother liquors in ankerite were examined in order to determine the state of aggregation and the lowest temperatures which could bring about the replacement of dolomite by ankerite.

All of the inclusions in ankerite were found to be of the liquid two-phase type, homogenizing as in type I (in the liquid phase). The homogenization temperatures varied over a wide range. Thus inclusions found in the finely crystalline ankerite, in one of the deposits, homogenize at 360, 305, and 275°C. Homogenization temperatures of 260, 248, and 232°C are also typical of the specimens from the central part of the deposit. Inclusions in specimens from other parts of the deposit homogenize at 375–232°C.

In one of the specimens of pyrite–ankerite aggregate, at the contact with a non-replaced limestone, a thin tapering veinlet was found whose margins consisted of finely crystalline yellowish ankerite. The veinlet's center was filled with very small cubical crystals of pyrite.

Such veins develop, it appears, as the result of a deposition of pyrite and ankerite in small vacant fissures or in porous sections of the limestone.

The ankerite crystals in such veins contain large quantities of two-phase liquid inclusions. One of the crystals has a clear expression of two growth zones: a gray inner one, with a multitude of very small liquid inclusions, and an outer one, transparent, with few inclusions. Inclusions in the inner zone are situated parallel to the growth zone of the crystal; they homogenize in the liquid phase at 375–346°C. In addition, we also find there inclusions with homogenization temperatures of 340–328°C which are secondary to the inner zone, but pseudo-secondary with respect to the outer zone. The inclusions in the outer zone homogenize at 342–325°C; their elongated sides run parallel to the crystal's faces. Thus, judging from the homogenization temperatures of primary inclusions in the ankerite crystals, as well as from inclusions in the grains of ankerite, one may form an opinion as to the lowest temperatures at which the massive ankerite bodies were produced, with a fair degree of reliability.

The main replacement of the dolomitized limestones by ankerite took place at 375–325°C, as a result of activities of the hydrothermal solutions.

Liquid inclusions with homogenization temperatures of 300–232°C are late, with respect to the bulk of the ankerite.

Chalcedony-like quartz is well developed in the dolomitized and oolitic limestones, but is rarer in ankerite and in the other rocks.

The distribution of its grains is irregular. They cement the rock, in places, but are found only as isolated patches elsewhere. The grains are irregularly shaped, although rhombohedral pseudomorphs after ankerite and dolomite are fairly common.

According to Fastalovich and Petrovskaya, this quartz is analogous to the rod-like vein quartz which is widespread in sedimentary rocks and particularly in intrusive rocks of the deposit here described.

A small quantity of various inclusions is observable under the microscope in thin sections of the chalcedony-like quartz. Among them, the following kinds are distinguished; two-phase, liquid, complex, with liquid carbon dioxide; tri-phase, with a solid phase, but without liquid carbon dioxide.

Primary and secondary inclusions are not easily differentiated, because of the absence of faces on the quartz. However, if we consider that essentially-gaseous inclusions, homogenizing as in type II, are found only in this variety of quartz in the deposit, we may confidently ascribe to them a primary origin. Homogenization temperatures of the essentially-gaseous inclusions vary over the range 410–340°C.

Homogenization temperatures of liquid inclusions vary a great deal: 348, 340, 329, 324, 309, 291, 272, 258, 248, 244, 230, 202, 174, 149, 142°C; they are expressions of the subsequent stages of the mineral genesis.

Most of these liquid inclusions have undoubtedly a secondary origin, but it is possible that some of them are primary, especially the ones with high homogenization temperatures.

The tri-phase inclusions (with a solid phase) homogenize at 206, 204, 190, 187°C and their solid phase disappears ahead of the gas bubble. They are secondary, in all probability.

Judging from the inclusions of mineral-forming solutions, the chalcedony-like quartz was produced by a metasomatic replacement of the carbonate rocks caused by some initially gaseous solutions. The replacement process continued also through the hydrothermal stage.

Rod-like quartz fills the veins in syenites and syenite–porphyries, and more rarely in the Cambrian sedimentary rocks and the Archaean granites. Among the post-magmatic formations, it stands next to ankerite in quantitative prominence, and is later in origin than the ankerite.

Five kilometers to the south-east from the deposit, the rod-like quartz veins in the syenite–porphyries are associated with fluorite, so that the vein margins are filled with quartz and the vein centers with fluorite.

The rod-like quartz crystals are full of inclusions. Fastalovich and Petrovskaya pointed out that it contains inclusions of a dust-like substance, as well as liquid inclusions, and the distribution of both of them is not uniform, but banded and zones. The interior of the crystals is generally inclusion-free; the outer zone, on the contrary, overflows with inclusions.

Four markedly different varieties of inclusions were discovered on examination of thin sections of the quartz; multiphase, with a large number of solid phases; multiphase, with a small number of solid phases; two-phase, liquid; complex, with carbon dioxide.

Two-phase liquid inclusions and inclusions with carbon dioxide are more abundant than the rest. The primary inclusions are clearly distinguishable from the secondary ones and are in fixed association with growth zones of the quartz. The multiphase inclusions with either a large or small number of solid phases are obviously primary. The former ones are found only in the interior of crystals; the latter in the intermediate and outer zones. The primary inclusions in the surficial zones of some crystals are also of the two-phase liquid type.

Let us consider now individually the inclusion varieties that homogenize as in type I (in the liquid phase).

In the multiphase inclusions with large quantities of solid phases, the latter constitute 30–45 per cent of the total volume; the gas phase varies from 18 to 26 per cent; the volume of the liquid phase depends on the volume of the solids.

The solid phases, i.e. the captive minerals [2], have various shapes. Hexagonal, octagonal, or ovoid transparent crystals are the most common ones. Characteristically, several such crystals, right next to each other or in different corners of the vacuole, are found in one and the same inclusion. Cubelets, apparently of NaCl and KCl, are found, also brownish and yellowish, elongated ones, and some pale or brownish granular aggregations of captive minerals.

It is of interest that octagonal and hexagonal captive minerals, typical of this inclusion group, are also found as solid inclusions of the "associates" in crystals of the quartz. They are found in the same zones where the multiphase inclusions with their captive analogues are also present.

On heating, the cubelets are the first ones to dissolve; the octagons and the hexagons are the next ones; after they are dissolved, the gas bubble disappears also.

The brownish granular aggregate of the minerals is the last one to pass into solution, at 360–490°C, although, on occasions, its complete solution is not attained and the inclusion explodes.

The multiphase inclusions with a low content of solid phases are typical of the intermediate and the outer zones of the crystals of the rod-like quartz, as well as of a certain fraction of fluorite crystals, as we shall see later. Similar inclusions were found also in grains of the chalcedony-like quartz.

On heating in the thermochamber, the homogenization of such is smooth in its course. The hexagonal and the octagonal crystals disappear first; the rest of the solid phase vanishes simultaneously with the gas bubble. A complete homogenization takes place at 300–255°C.

The two-phase liquid inclusions are obviously secondary, in the majority of the cases. They occur as chainworks in healed fissures. Characteristically, many of them are shaped like negative crystals, while some others are tubular.

The complex inclusions with carbon dioxide are secondary, judging from their positions in the crystals. Their phase ratios vary, even in one and the same fissure.

On heating, these inclusions explode at different temperatures, from 80 to 320°C. Inclusions in which the liquid carbon dioxide is low, not over 5 or 10 per cent by volume, homogenize at 230–180°C.

The available data indicate that the rod-like quartz was formed from hydrothermal solutions whose original concentrations were high, as evidenced by the multiphase inclusions. Both the concentrations and the temperatures of the solutions were decreasing somewhat during the deposition of the quartz. The process was concluded by the activities of relatively dilute solutions at 225–160°C.

Thus the presumptions of Fastalovich and Petrovskaya, to the effect that the chalcedony-like quartz may be correlated with the rod-like quartz, were not confirmed. The metasomatic replacement of calcite, dolomite, and ankerite by the chalcedony-like quartz was made effective by the action of hot gaseous solutions. Deposition of the rod-like quartz in vacant fissures and further replacement of the carbonate rocks took place from liquid solutions, the successors to the pneumatolytic ones.

Fluorite grows directly on top of the smoky ferrugenous rod-like quartz. It is relatively poor in inclusions; it was possible, nevertheless, to trace the temperature regime of the solutions by examining a large number of fluorite specimens. The small crystals of fluorite, at their contact with the quartz, are 3–5 mm across. Crystal size increases with distance from the contact, so that, in the centers of the veins, they are as large as 2–2.5 cm in diameter.

Primary inclusions in fluorite were differentiated into two groups: multiphase (with solid phases) and two-phase liquid. Secondary inclusions were two-phase liquid and single-phase liquid ones.

In thin sections of fluorite we examined, taken directly from the fluorite–quartz contact, only the (primary) multiphase inclusions could be found, with homogenization temperatures of 290–220°C. At a greater distance from the contact similar inclusions homogenize at 250–185°C, and carry only a single solid phase, a hexagonal captive crystal.

No multiphase inclusions could be found in the central parts of the veins, where primary inclusions are of the two-phase liquid type, with homogenization temperature of 200–120°C.

Pseudo-secondary and secondary two-phase liquid and single-phase liquid inclusions are widespread and common. The two-phase pseudo-secondary inclusions homogenize within a wide range: 200–50°C.

One may presume that the fluorite formed simultaneously with the deposition of the rod-like quartz, at 290–160°C, and still lower.

The multiphase inclusions with solid phases are indications of the high concentration of the original solutions.

The early crystals of fluorite were formed synchronously with the deposition of the rod-like quartz and, for that reason, both of these minerals contain some inclusions whose solid phases and homogenization temperatures are analogous. However, the crystallization of fluorite continued even after the growth of the rod-like quartz crystals had ceased. The evidence for that is the two-phase liquid inclusions homogenizing at 180–50°C, the temperatures of the latest and cooled solutions participating in the healing of fissures and in the mineral genesis.

Granular quartz was deposited after the rod-like quartz and the fluorite. This quartz is associated with pyrite, pyrrhotite, chalcopyrite, and also with tetrahedrite and bornite. Milky-white or, occasionally, grayish calcite is found together with the granular quartz, in many places. The presence of the calcite is especially characteristic of veins situated in the pre-Cambrian carbonate rocks.

Veins filled by granular quartz are generally weak and have a multitude of branches. They cut through the veins of columnar quartz at an angle or, more rarely, are imposed on the columnar quartz veins, with the formation of a breccia-like fragmented mass of quartz and sulfides.

Finely crystallized transparent quartz, in association with pyrite, chalcopyrite, and other sulfides, in the ankeritic deposits, may be correlated with the granular quartz.

The granular quartz is full of inclusions none of which are larger than 0.001–0.01 mm. Their shapes are rounded, ovoid, or irregular.

Two-phase liquid inclusions and complex inclusions with carbon dioxide are conspicuous among the rest.

The liquid inclusions homogenize at 280–80°C and the ones with homogenization temperatures below 140°C are obviously secondary.

All inclusions with carbon dioxide are undoubtedly of a secondary origin and their phase ratios are not the same.

It follows therefore that granular quartz was produced apparently within the range of relative temperatures of 280–140°C.

Insofar as granular quartz is almost invariably associated with sulfides, it becomes possible to find the temperatures at which the sulfides were formed. We succeeded in direct examinations of inclusions only in sphalerite, but not in the other sulfides. According to the earlier investigations, and also to ours, the crystallization of sphalerite took place after the formation of pyrite II and of pyrrhotite.

Sphalerite (var. cleiophane) is not as widespread as pyrite, galena, and other sulfides. It fills small cavities in the granular quartz or else occurs as a dissemination in the same quartz, as fine irregularly shaped grains closely associated with galena and, more rarely, with pyrite and chalcopyrite. We examined thoroughly only two of the specimens and made seventeen determinations of the homogenization temperature in them.

Even that number of measurements was sufficient for a general outline of the range of temperatures wherein the sphalerite formed.

The primary inclusions in sphalerite are rounded, ovoid, weakly elongated; they homogenize at 192–136°C. The secondary inclusions are irregular, angular, and with a multitude of constrictions; they homogenize at 120–90°C.

The granular quartz was produced at a minimum temperature of 280–140°C, while sphalerite was precipitated from solutions at a minimum temperature of 192–136°C, judging from the liquid inclusions. Inasmuch as pyrite and pyrrhotite were precipitated ahead of sphalerite, as shown from the examination of polished sections, the minimum temperature of their formation must be somewhat above 192°C.

The minerals that followed sphalerite, chalcopyrite, galena, tetrahedrite, bornite, and others, were separating while the sphalerite's fissures and fissures in the granular quartz were being healed, at still lower temperatures: 130–120–90–70°C.

In such manner, on the basis of inclusions in granular quartz and in sphalerite, and knowing the sequence of separation of individual sulfides, we are able to outline, however tentatively, the temperature regime for most of the minerals belonging to that stage of the mineralization (Table 1).

TABLE 1. OUTLINE OF SEQUENCE OF SEPARATIONS OF MINERALS AND OF THE TEMPERATURE REGIME OF THE SOLUTIONS DURING THE STAGE OF THE GRANULAR QUARTZ AND THE SULFIDES

Stage	Sequence of separation of principal minerals	Temperature of solutions, by inclusions (°C)								
		270	240	210	180	150	120	90	60	30
Granular quartz with sulfides	Quartz (granular)									
	Pyrite II									
	Pyrrhotite									
	Sphalerite									
	Galena									
	Chalcopyrite									
	Tetrahedrite									
	Gold									
	Bornite									

Tectonic movements within the mineralized zone took place after the deposition of the granular quartz. These movements opened new channels for the circulating solutions from which hematite and some quartz and mica were deposited.

According to Fastalovich and Petrovskaya, the quartz–hematite veins cut through the formations belonging to the preceding stages of the mineralization. Specifically, small veins of hematite cut across the metasomatic ankeritic bodies and are cross-cutting also with respect to the veins of columnar quartz and quartz–sulfide.

The quantities of quartz are insignificant in comparison with hematite. The quartz is found in the selvages of the hematite veins and, very rarely, as well-faceted small crystals in cavities inside the hematite veins.

Primary inclusions in quartz from the selvages of the veins homogenize at 305–245°C; while primary inclusions in quartz from the vein cavities homogenize at 175°–140°C.

Homogenization temperatures of secondary inclusions in quartz from the selvages are about the same as those of the primary inclusions in the finely crystalline quartz from the vein cavities. The range of the former ones is 180–140°C and of the latter ones 175–140°C.

It is evident that the healing of early fissures in the granular quartz involving the formation of secondary inclusions in these fissures and of the fine quartz crystals in the vein cavities were interdependent, in the process of formation of the quartz–hematite veins.

Consequently, the finely crystalline quartz is epigenetic, with respect to hematite, and is later than hematite. It may be synchronous with calcite of the last stage of mineralization, judging from the homogenization temperatures of its inclusions.

Calcite-filled veins are found only within the boundaries of the Cambrian sediments consisting of carbonate rocks; limestones, dolomitized limestones, and dolomites. Dolomite and barite, as well as pyrite, sphalerite, galena, chalcopyrite, and other minerals were deposited together with the calcite.

The ore minerals are concentrated mainly in the selvages of the veins or, more rarely, in cores of the veins. The following sequence of separation was established, in polished sections: pyrite, tetrahedrite, sphalerite, chalcopyrite, galena.

Galena, sphalerite, and tetrahedrite are absent in some of the veins, but pyrite and chalcopyrite are always present, at least in small quantities.

Two-phase liquid inclusions, homogenizing as in type I, were noted in every sample of the calcite, together with some single-phase liquid inclusions.

There are two clearly defined groups of inclusions in calcite, based on shape, which are typical also of *dolomite*. The first group consists of inclusions with smooth rounded contours and with oval or slightly elongated shapes; the second group's inclusions are flattened and their contours are sharp and angular. Inclusions in the second group are secondary and pseudo-secondary.

The primary inclusions homogenize at 165 to 60–55°C. The secondary inclusions are of the single-phase liquid type, in the majority of the cases. The same refers to the dolomite.

Thus, judging from inclusions of mineral-forming solutions, both calcite and dolomite, together with the co-deposited sulfides, belong to the low-temperature hydrothermal formations.

On a consideration of the thermometric data on inclusions in the minerals of the deposit, it becomes evident that the ore-forming process took place against a background of variations both in the temperatures and in the concentrations of the solutions.

The following successive stages of mineralization in the deposit (Table 2) are definitely outlined by the data of geologic–mineralogic and thermometric investigations. Each stage is separated from the preceding one by tectonic movements within the mineralized zone resulting in fragmentation of the previously formed ore veins. At the same time, there were changes in the migration paths of the solutions and development of new fissures that were subsequently filled by minerals of younger age.

The deposit's mineral genesis is connected mainly with hydrothermal activities. Pneumatolysis is evident but weak, identified only in the chalcedonic quartz stage superimposed metasomatically on the pyrite–ankeritic ore deposits.

Curiously, the pneumatolysis showing in the chalcedonic quartz stage developed not at the start of the ore-forming process, the way it generally is in the formation of complex polygenic deposits, but after the pyrite–ankerite deposits were already formed, during intensive tectonic movements.

The hydrothermal period of mineralization, in time, may be divided accordingly into two stages: the early and the late ones.

The early hydrothermal stage is expressed by single phase, the ankerite–pyrite. The replacement of the dolomitized limestones and the formation of massive bodies of pyrite–ankerite were taking place under the influence of highly ferruginous hydrothermal solutions whose relative temperature was falling from 375 to 325°C.

After that, there was a rise in the temperature of the solutions, with an appreciable lowering of the pressure caused by a re-opening of the old tectonic fissures and by formations of the new ones. As the result, there was a short-term change in the state of aggregation of the mineral-forming solutions. The gaseous silica-bearing solutions caused the replacement of ankeritic ore bodies by chalcedony-like quartz.

The late hydrothermal stage is divided into four parts by the intervening new tectonic movements within the mineralized zone. These subordinate stages, different in temperature and in the composition of the solutions, are: (1) columnar quartz with fluorite; (2) granular quartz with sulfides; (3) hematite; (4) calcite and dolomite.

The bulk of the sulfides and gold were deposited during the granular quartz stage. We must remark here that the preceding investigators [3] recognized the deposition of gold as an independent stage, in the wake of the deposition of sulfides and hematite, using the occurrence of gold in all of the mineral complexes as their evidence.

Indeed, gold was present, in some quantity, in pyrite–ankerite, quartz–fluorite, quartz–sulfide, quartz–hematite, and in other associations, where its distribution was highly non-uniform.

In our view, there was no gold stage, as such, and gold was deposited in all stages of the hydrothermal process, in various quantities.

The irregular distribution of gold in different veins and different parts of the deposit, its accumulation in some places and its dispersion elsewhere, may be explained by the intersections and the accumulations of the veins of different age belonging to different stages of the mineralization, by local superimpositions of the mineralization processes, and by the isolated character of the mineralization in the other fissures and veins.

The connection of the deposit here discussed with derivatives of the post-Jurassic syenitic intrusions was proved by several investigators (Yu. A. Bilibin, A. I. Fastalovich, and others) and stands beyond doubt at this time. However, the source of the ore-bearing solutions, the active magmatic hearth, lay far deeper than the intrusive bodies that outcrop now at the ground's surface and is unrelated directly either to the mineralization or to the portion traversed of the ore-bearing veins.

This fact is sustained by the examination of inclusions in different minerals from different parts of the deposit and at different distances from the intrusive bodies. The homogenization temperatures of inclusions in minerals representing definite stages of the mineral genesis are characteristically constant for the entire area of the deposit, regardless of composition of the host rocks or of proximity of the intrusives. No abrupt or even gradual changes in the temperature, in relation to distance from the intrusives, could be observed.

BIBLIOGRAPHY

1. BILIBIN, YU. A., *Petrografiya Aldana* (*posleyurskiye intruzii*). (Petrography of Aldan. Post-Jurassic Intrusives.) Izd. Akad. Nauk SSSR, 1941.
2. YERMAKOV, N. P., *Issledovaniya mineraloobrazuyushchikh rastvorov.* (Research in Mineral-forming Solutions.) Izd. Khar'kov. univ. 1950.
3. FASTALOVICH, A. I. and N. V. PETROVSKAYA, Kharakter orudeneniya lebedinogo zolotorudnogo mestorozhdeniya. (The Character of Mineralization in the Lebedinoye Gold Ore Deposit.) *Sovet. geolog.* No. 2/3, 1940.

Certain Features of the Origin of the Kara-Oba Deposit Discovered with the Aid of Microthermometric Analysis

I. V. Banshchikova

Vein formations in the rare metal deposit at Kara-Oba, Central Kazakhstan, are highly variable in the character of their mineralization, morphology, and structural positions. They are divided into several groups, in accordance with stages and phases of their development, as visualized by geologists who had previously examined the deposit. O. A. Sinev's genetic classification, accepted for that deposit, is as follows:

(1) Quartz–topaz veins;
(2) High-temperature quartz veins;
   (a) quartz–cassiterite veins;
   (b) quartz–molybdenite veins;
   (c) quartz–wolframite veins with cassiterite, molybdenite, and bismuth minerals;
(3) Medium–temperature quartz–wolframite veins with sulfides;
(4) Low-temperature quartz veins;
(5) Quartz–fluorite veins and lenses;
(6) Albite veinlets.

In addition, among the high-temperature quartz–wolframite veins, there are six recognized groups filling the fissure systems with different orientations. Sinev believes that their development was discontinuous, in time, although his determinations of the age relationships are entirely tentative.

Definitions of the principal stages of the formation of the deposit, excepting the denial of the independent genetic significance of the quartz–topaz veins, do not result in controversies among geologists, but, when it comes to subdivisions of the high-temperature vein-forming process into sub-stages, different geologists do it differently. We have in mind here chiefly the group of high-temperature tungsten-bearing veins and the so-called quartz–cassiterite veins that differ from the tungsten veins by their higher content of cassiterite. The differences of opinions may be explained only by the absence of reliable criteria for a more detailed classification.

The microthermometric method, already so useful in a series of complicated problems of the origin of endogenic deposits, gives us the opportunity to obtain objective data for differentiation between sub-stages of the mineralization.

This article is a report on microthermometric investigations of topaz crystals from three groups of veins belonging to the high-temperature stage of vein-formation: the quartz–cassiterite group (veins Nos. 88, 87, and others), and two groups of quartz–wolframite veins (veins Nos. 21, 26 and 1, 10). We had no specimens of topaz from the other groups of the quartz–wolframite veins that would suit the purpose.

Three groups of inclusions were recognized in the topaz crystals we examined: fluid two-phase, gaseous, and complex (with carbon dioxide).

The fluid two-phase (gas–liquid) inclusions of mineral-forming solutions are the most abundant ones of all. They differ among themselves morphologically and in their phase ratios, but are definitely classifiable by their genetic positions in crystals. The most common ones are tubular and irregularly shaped forms of primary liquid inclusions in different growth zones of the crystal. Their liquid–gas phase ratios vary, depending on their homogenization temperatures which are within the range of 302–261°C. Pseudo-secondary inclusions are also fairly common, within the same range of homogenization, but only in fissures piercing the corresponding inner zones of the crystal. Flat or irregularly shaped complex vacuoles in cleavage planes (001) are far rarer. These latter inclusions homogenize characteristically at 342–305°C and 240–220°C. Such temperatures are found also for inclusions in healed fissures running out of the fractured zones of the crystals.

The gaseous inclusions contain about 36 per cent liquid phase and homogenize at 282–285°C, with an inversion point 32–35°C below the homogenization temperature.

The complex inclusions with carbon dioxide contain 31 to 41 per cent liquid phase and homogenize at 278° and 298°C, also with an inversion point, but 20–40°C below the homogenization temperature.

Orderly relationships in the distribution of inclusions in crystals may be discussed more conveniently by individual groups, separately. We must make a reservation now, namely, that, for various reasons (destruction of inner parts of the crystals or absence of inclusions in them), the innermost parts of the crystals can be characterized here only for the quartz–cassiterite group of veins. Thus we may characterize most fully the growth of topaz crystals only in that particular group of veins.

The group of cassiterite veins (Nos. 88, 87). The inner parts of the crystals from vein 88 contain liquid two-phase inclusions homogenizing at 305°C. As one proceeds from the interior to the periphery of the crystals, the homogenization temperatures decrease uniformly, from zone to zone, down to 275°C. All of the inclusions homogenize as in type I (in the liquid phase), as shown by curves 2–4 (Fig. 1).

Complex inclusions, with carbon dioxide, and containing 41 per cent liquid are found in the growth zone not far below the surface of the

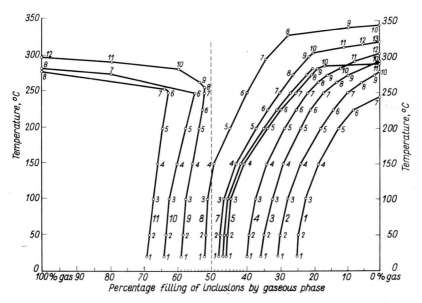

FIG. 1. Homogenization types of inclusions of mineral-forming media in topaz from wolframite veins of the Kara-Oba deposit.

crystals. These inclusions homogenize at 299°C, as in type II, sub-type 2, in the gas phase, with the inversion point, as characterized by curve 9. Gaseous pseudo-secondary inclusions are also there, with 36 per cent liquid, alongside the complex inclusions with carbon dioxide and 41 or 31 per cent liquid. These inclusions homogenize also with an inversion point, at 282, 290, and 278°C respectively and the course of their homogenization is represented by curves 10 and 11.

Small irregularly shaped liquid inclusions homogenizing at 250°C are encountered near the surface of the crystals, alongside liquid inclusions in fissures originating in the crystals' interior, and flat irregular inclusions in the crystals' cleavage planes, with homogenization temperatures of 250, 239, 230°C. These homogenize as in type I, as illustrated by curve 1.

Group I of wolframite veins (veins 26, 21, and others). No inclusions could be found in the central parts of the topaz crystals from veins 26.

The middle zones of the crystals contain liquid two-phase inclusions whose homogenization temperatures decrease gradually and uniformly toward the periphery, from 287° to 270°C. Their homogenization is as in type I and is represented by curve *4*.

The exterior part of the crystals contains a zone of two-phase fluid inclusions with 46–48 per cent gas. These inclusions homogenize in the liquid phase, with an inversion point, as in type II, sub-type 3, with a critical point at 290–292°C, as represented by curves *5* and *6*. The restoration of the phase boundary in these inclusions, on cooling, involves boiling. Fluid two-phase inclusions in healed fissures originating in the outermost zones are found throughout the crystals, and so are the irregular inclusions in the cleavage planes whose homogenization temperatures are 258–250°C or 237–222°C. Curve *1* represents the homogenization of all of these inclusions.

Group II of wolframite veins (vein Nos. 1, 10, and others). In this case, we examined inclusions mainly in the outer zones of the crystals. The growth zones contain fluid two-phase inclusions whose homogenization temperatures decrease gradually from 268 to 261°C [toward the periphery? —V.P.S.]. The homogenization is as in type I and is characterized by curve *3* and comparable curves in the same field of the diagram.

There are no inclusions in growth zones near the surface of the crystals, but elsewhere, on cleavage planes, there is an abundance of inclusion groups consisting of small to relatively large elongated individuals with 46–52 per cent gas. They homogenize in the liquid phase, at 342–320°C, with an inversion point, as shown in curves *7* and *8* [*sic*]. It was discovered, in a thin section of one crystal, that tubular inclusions, with the same phase ratio, homogenizing at 330°C, can be tracked along the fissure which begins not very far from the crystal's outer growth zone, but does not run through that zone. Consequently, these inclusions are genetically pseudo-secondary and are representative of one of the last growth zones of the crystal. Also, one may find some irregularly shaped liquid inclusions in healed fissures whose homogenization is at 239°C, type I.

The presence of sufficient numbers of growth zones in the crystals, characterized appropriately by the inclusions, enables us not only to offer a general outline of the topaz-producing environment but also to obtain diagrams of the temperature regime of the solutions during the crystal growth for all of the vein groups we examined. The homogenization curves, the expressions of the homogenization process in different inclusion groups, make it possible to recognize the participation, in the formation of topaz, of solutions in different states of aggregation.

As shown by the microthermometric investigations, the temperature regime of the solutions was similar for all three of the high-temperature vein groups we examined (Fig. 2).

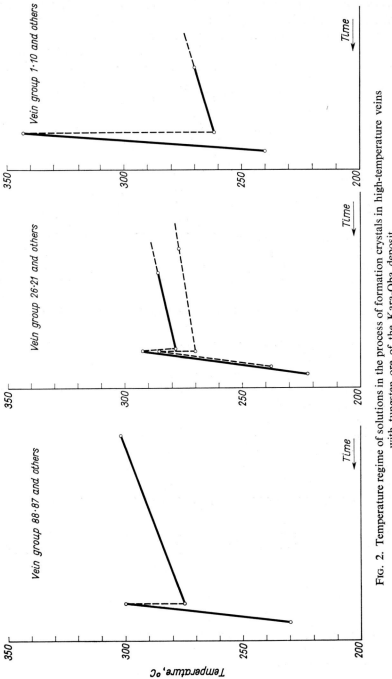

Fig. 2. Temperature regime of solutions in the process of formation crystals in high-temperature veins with tungsten ore of the Kara-Oba deposit.

Growth of the inner parts of the topaz crystals took place from hydrothermal solutions of various densities and minimum temperatures of about 305–300°C (uncorrected for pressure during the mineral genesis), while the temperature of the solutions was falling uniformly down to 270–262°C. The outer growth zones, with their gaseous and highest-temperature liquid inclusions, belong to the late superimposed stage of repeated pneumatolysis brought about by an opening of the channels produced by new tectonic movements.

As shown by the homogenization curves, the outer zones of the crystals were formed both from low-density fluids (up to 69 per cent gas at room temperature), with a relatively high content of carbon dioxide (the south-eastern section of the deposit) and from aqueous solutions (45–52 per cent gas), in the deposit's northern and central sections. Temperature of the gaseous solutions cannot be determined exactly from homogenization temperatures of gaseous inclusions in the outer zones. The lowest temperatures of the aqueous solutions involved in the repeated pneumatolysis, in certain definite section [of the crystals or of the deposit?—V.P.S.], were within the range of 342–285°C. The topaz-forming stage, in the repeated pneumatolysis, was of short duration, as evidenced by the small quantity of mineral substance in the thin outer zones of the crystals. The gaseous solutions of the repeated pneumatolytic stage, indicative of an abrupt decrease of pressure and of the accompanying renewal of fissuring of the crystals, were rapidly cooled and transformed into liquid aqueous solutions.

We may conclude accordingly that topaz crystals in the veins we examined were produced in two stages, from solutions that differed in state of aggregation: (1) in an early substage of the hydrothermal stage (about 305–260°C) and (2) in a late substage of the repeated pneumatolysis (about 350°C). That second stage was shorter than the first and was more variable; it was succeeded by a late hydrothermal substage.

This odd but a highly typical regime of the solutions during the growth of the earliest vein-filling minerals provides the answer to the problem of the age relationships within the crystals and is indicative of the synchronism and the uniformity of the conditions in which the various groups of wolframite and so-called cassiterite veins formed. The latter may be regarded now merely as a cassiterite-enriched variety of wolframite vein.

Inclusions of Solution at the Boundary between the Seed and the Overgrowing Layers in Synthetic Quartz Crystals

V. Ye. Khadzhi and G. M. Safronov

In the determinations of quality of synthetic quartz crystals, we often run into various defects grouped in the crystals' inner zones, chiefly along the boundary between the seed and its quartz overgrowth and also in the adjoining layers. Heterogeneity of the crystal in these areas is disturbed for the following reasons:

(1) Settling of foreign impurities on the surface of the seed, at the beginning of the growth, and their subsequent preservation as solid and liquid inclusions.

(2) Development of inclusions of the mother liquor in the seed or in its outer zone.

(3) Physical differences between the seed's substance and the substance of the overgrowing zones.

The present article is a discussion of the conditions of development and of morphologic–genetic features of liquid inclusions in the seed. They are fairly common in synthetic quartz. A satisfactory joining of the growth, with the seed-overgrowth transition invisible to the naked eye, is relatively rare. The seed is a defective zone almost invariably, and must be discarded in the final processing of the crystals.

The group of inclusions of mother liquor here discussed differs from all other varieties of liquid inclusions by its morphologic features and the mutual orientation and positions of the inclusions in the crystal. Cavities with solution and gas phase may be elongated–tubular, tubular, club-shaped, capillary, acicular, and other shapes elongated in some particular direction. The vacuoles are always sunken completely into the seed and their sharply pointed thin ends are directed inwards in the crystal. All of the vacuoles are sealed practically at the same time, so that their bulging upper ends are situated in the same plane. The gas phase, in the bulging parts of the vacuoles, lies at the seed's surface level. The length of the vacuoles ranges from hundredths to 0.5 mm. Spindle-shaped and drop-shaped cavities are preponderant, 0.1–0.3 mm in length. The coefficient of filling of vacuoles with liquid phase is constant and corresponds to the autoclave's filling coefficient before the experiment. Liquid phase occupies generally 80 per cent of the volume of the cavity, and the gas phase the remaining 20 per cent.

The short axes of the tubular vacuoles are oriented parallel to each other and form a certain definite angle with the surface of the seed. This angle varies within a wide range and depends on the orientation of the cut surface of the seed plate. In crystals grown on seeds parallel to the base, the vacuoles are elongated at right angles to the surface which separates the seed and the overgrown substance.

Topography of the seed's surface is reproduced in some crystals, by development of a large number of tubular vacuoles during the initial stage of the crystal's growth.

Cases were observed in which the capillary cavities of inclusions pierce the entire seed, right through, and yet most of the inclusions are to be found on the periphery of the seed. The vacuoles may inter-connect, on one side of the seed, to form cavities of bizarre outlines. In places, the spindle-shaped vacuoles enter the seed so deeply that they coalesce with vacuoles on the seed's opposite side. V-shaped and X-shaped cavities may be produced, under such conditions, with a common gas phase. The coalesced vacuoles may be symmetrical, on occasions. Their connecting channel becomes constricted, in the middle part of their common cavity (Fig. 1). The gas phase may migrate into one of the coalesced vacuoles,

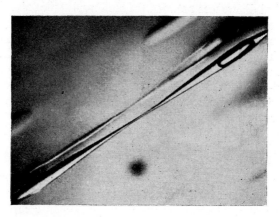

FIG. 1. Inclusion of solution in two-spindle-shaped vacuoles connected by a narrow channel in the axial part of the seed. The gas phase lies in the right part of the vacuole. 120×.

although it has been also noted that it stays in the two opposite ends of the vacuole despite the connecting channel. The stringing out phenomena were observed, involving a breakdown of the fine connecting channels into a chainwork of microscopic cavities.

The tubular vacuoles are produced early in the crystallization cycle. Cone-like pits appear on the seed's surface, as the result of the solvent action of the solution in the process of its saturation. The form of these pits depends on orientation of the cut surface of the seed, the degree of homogeneity of the crystal's substance, and the deviation of the etching. With the entry of the supersaturated solution into the growth zone, a deposition of crystalline substance begins on the etched seed. The cones produced by the solvent action are narrowed, but their depth remains unchanged. The pits and the capillary channels are rapidly overgrown at the relatively slow rates of crystal growth and the mother liquor is sealed in.

If, in etching of the seed, there is a development of holes through the seed, there is also a formation of vacuoles of the kind shown in Fig. 2*.

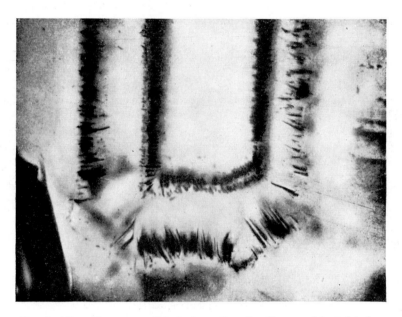

FIG. 2. Alternating zones of inclusions of mother liquor originated before completion of the crystal's growth. 80×.

Large openings in the seed are overgrown slowly, even under the optimum conditions of crystallization, and they leave behind, in the overgrowing layers, flattened wedging-out trigonal cavities with the solution which occasionally have no time to be sealed and are left outcropping on the crystal's surface in the form of holes or trigonal channels.

---

* Fig. 1? [Ed.].

Repeated supplementary growth of synthetic quartz crystals produces alternating zones with inclusions in the crystal's interior. Thickness of these individual zones depends on duration of the etching prior to the resumption of the growth in the next cycle in the sequence. Figure 2 shows a transverse section of a crystal which was placed in the autoclave three times in succession, as a seed. The depth of the solvent action was insignificant, in the instance of the first two short-term cycles, as registered by the relatively small size of the drop-shaped vacuoles. On the third occasion, however, the needle-shaped vacuoles penetrated the seed to much greater depths. One may plainly see the orderly orientation of the capillaries in the pyramidal growth on different planes.

In studying the character of the solvent action on different grades of quartz, one cannot help observing the fact that seeds prepared from natural and from synthetic crystals behave differently under the impact of the aggressive alkaline medium. All other things being the same, seeds

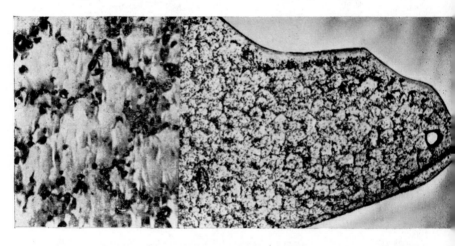

FIG. 3. The seed (left) subjected to selective etching along boundaries of the cone growth accessory to the surface of the base; 2×. On the right: a part of the seed's surface. 40×.

made of synthetic quartz are generally etched more severely than seeds made of natural quartz. Defect-free monocrystalline plates of natural quartz are least susceptible to etching. In case of the appearance of any fissures, twin crystals, inclusions, or other sites of weakness in the seed, it is such weakened areas that are dissolved ahead of the rest. The etched sections are particularly favorable for the nucleation of vacuoles. They are easily recognized among the rest of the tubular cavities of the etched zone by their association with certain definite orientations coinciding with the fissure planes and with the positions of twin surface. Solution of the seeds may be so intensive, on occasions, that the seeds fall off their frames to the bottom of the autoclave.

Very odd etching figures were discovered on seeds made from synthetic quartz crystals cut parallel to the surface of the base. Figure 3, a photograph of an etched seed (the cycle was interrupted), shows an abundance of solution figures whose dense network covers the entire surface, excepting its narrow marginal zones. Distribution of the cones produced by the solvent on the seed's surface resembles, in its general features, the orientation of inclusions in the "honeycomb" quartz from pegmatites of the Volynian deposits of piezo-quartz, with only one difference, namely, that, in the former case, the network is two-dimensional, while in the latter one we have in mind the cellular skeleton produced by the clustering of gaseous inclusions. By examining the seed's surface at high magnifications, we may see that most of the funnel-shaped pits left by the solvent are partially faceted. The through-going holes in the seed acquire hexagonal contours. Their edges run parallel to the faces of the hexagonal prism.

The orderly etching of seeds made of synthetic quartz has the following explanation. As already proved, the overgrowth pyramid on the (0001) surface which occupies the bulk of the crystal's volume consists of a large number of accessory cone overgrowths in sub-parallel orientation [1]. Under certain physico-chemical conditions, there is deposition of an admixture on the crystal's surface which is preserved in the "parasitic" pyramids of growth. Dimensions, shapes, and distribution of the areas with that adsorbed impurity (admixture) depend on the structure of the crystal's surface. Consequently, the defective sections in the pyramid on the base, high in impurities, are more abundant chiefly in the accessory cones of the overgrowth. Solution of the seed preceding the growth of the crystal is irregular in its course.

Experiments with the etching of synthetic quartz by HF and observations on crystal growth on seeds made of synthetic crystals had shown that the zones high in impurities are the first ones to pass into solution. In the solution of seeds, cut parallel to (0001), the solvent diffuses through the channels running deep into the crystal, as radial bundles, whose direction coincides with positions of the aforesaid cones in the pyramidal overgrowth of the base. Regeneration of such seeds is accompanied by a development of numerous club-shaped vacuoles of mother liquor spreading out like fans, like bundles—"bushes," along the boundary between the seed and the overgrowing crystal. An example of the radial orientation of cavities containing the solution is given in Fig. 4.

In the preparation of seeds from one and the same crystal, parallel to the base, positions of the vacuoles, with respect to the surface of the seed, will depend on the distance between the cut surface and the seed. The network of etching figures on the seed should grow more dense as it

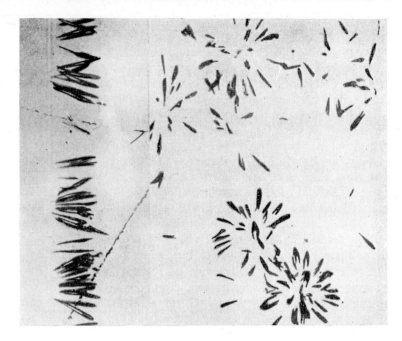

FIG. 4. Radial distribution of vacuoles in seed prepared from a synthetic quartz crystal.

a—the photograph's plane parallel to the face of the hexagonal prism; 120×. *b*—the photograph's plane parallel to the surface of the base; 120×.

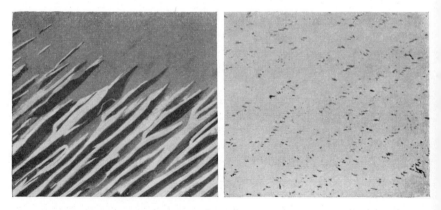

FIG. 5. Left: surficial sculpturing of the crystal grown on the "oblique cut surface" of the seed, in the face zone of the negative rhombohedron; 32×. Right: the orderly distribution of inclusions along the seed's surface in the same crystal; 20×.

progresses from the outer zones of the crystal toward its inner zones. The areas of relatively homogeneous pyramids grown on the faces of the positive and the negative rhombohedra are dissolved gradually, from the surface (Fig. 5), and, while overgrowing the seed, contain no inclusions of solution.

The other example, just as convincing, in support of the theses here presented, is the mutually parallel distribution of the vacuoles in crystals grown on seeds that were set at small angles with the face of the negative rhombohedron (oblique sections) in the zone of the negative rhombohedron. The elongated form of the "parasitic pyramids", the collectors of impurities produced by regeneration of the ribbed surface of the "slanted cut-sections", serves to define merely a general orientation of the series in which the groups of vacuoles are arranged. Within the range of a given series in the given plane there are occasional insignificant deviations (10–20°) of the long axes of the vacuoles involving coalescence of the cavities.

The data here reported indicate that the orderly orientation of the channels produced by the solution of the crystalline substance, as recorded by positions of the vacuoles with mother liquor, helps us in the refinements of certain details in the internal morphology of synthetic quartz crystals.

BIBLIOGRAPHY

1. SAFRONOV G. M. and V. YE. KHADZHI, Termometricheskiye issledovaniya zhidkikh vklyuchenii v iskusstvennom kvartse. (Thermometric Studies of Liquid Inclusions in Synthetic Quartz.) *Trudy VNIIP*, vol. I, pp. 57–61, 1957.

In Reference to Hermetic Sealing of Liquid Inclusions

V. A. KALYUZHNYI

EVERY one of the basic premises of the homogenization method rests on the assumption, one way or the other, of a complete imperviousness of the crystal's substance to liquids and gases, both in thermodynamic environments of the earth's crust and in the artificial restoration of the homogeneous state of inclusions by heat. A question arises naturally in regards to the security of the hermetic sealing of inclusions, particularly in regards to permeability of the crystal to liquid and gaseous solutions, as influenced by temperature and by pressure gradients. Such problems were discussed in the past chiefly on the basis of visual observations [1]. Some new experimental data were published recently in confirmation of the imperviousness of crystals [5] as well as in opposition to this idea [7]. We undertook therefore certain experiments, in order to test the hermetic character of inclusions.

As a rule, hydrothermal crystallization takes place at high temperatures and pressures both of which are gradually decreasing, so that the distribution of primary inclusions, from the center to the periphery of the crystal, almost invariably corresponds to the normal sequence of temperatures, from high to low. Consequently, the degree of filling of inclusions at the base and in the center of the crystal must be lower than in inclusions near the faces of the crystal. This orderly trend in the degree of filling, from the center to the periphery, must be disturbed, if we assume the possibility of migration of solutions. In reality, however, the latter is practically never the case.

Single-phase liquid inclusions are often preserved in the outer zones of the crystal terminations, despite the fact that the crystals remained in open vugs or miarolitic cavities for millions of years [1]. Moreover, the fluid contents of inclusions are already at appreciable pressures even at room temperatures. For example, when two-phase gas–liquid inclusions in morion from Volynia were opened at 25°C, in glycerine, the volume increased a hundred times [2], i.e. an internal pressure as high as 100 atm was indicated. Inclusions with liquid carbon dioxide, practically 100 per cent full, are fairly common in the outer zones of crystals. Pressures inside such inclusions should be appreciable indeed. However, these inclusions retained their original pressure and the degree of filling notwithstanding the immensely long period of their existence. Facts of this sort constitute evidence, it appears, of the imperviousness of crystal structures of minerals such as quartz, topaz, calcite, fluorite, and others, in the environment of the earth's crust.

Experimental studies of the permeability of crystals are rather scarce. There is a lot more data on the behavior of different solid substances at extremely high pressure gradients. It is known, for example, that glass and fused quartz become permeable to water, alcohol, and ether at room temperature, at pressures in excess of 15,000 atm [6].

The homogenization temperature, so sensitive to any change in the over-all specific volume of the contents of a vacuole, serves as the index of penetration of liquid through a crystal into the inclusion (or out of it). There are two lines of approach, in this connection.

(1) An appreciable excess of pressure inside the inclusion, as compared with the external pressure, is developed by overheating of the inclusion liquids (overheating, in the sense of heating above the homogenization temperature). In the case of migration of the solution out of the inclusion, the homogenization temperature in a re-run test should increase somewhat, as the result of an increase in the specific volume of the liquid at the given temperature.

(2) Conversely, by placing a crystal with liquid inclusions in an autoclave and by creating a high external (with respect to the crystal) pressure of water in the autoclave, it is possible to stimulate penetration of water into the crystal, from the outside, causing a decrease in the inclusion's specific volume and, consequently, also a decrease in homogenization temperature. These experiments must last a long time, so as to approximate natural conditions.

The first line of approach, however, may not always give us a clear-cut answer to the problem. The point is that the homogenization temperature may be raised not only by a migration of solution through the crystal structure. The same effect may be produced by a development of fine fissures next to the vacuole and by a squeezing of the included solution into such fissures [1, 3]. This is particularly typical of crystals with a perfect cleavage. The only incontrovertible proof of ineffectiveness of the factors here considered would be a constancy of the homogenization temperature before and after the experiment. Experiments in the autoclave are far superior to the former kind, as their results are far more reliable, because the inclusions so treated fail by any means to attain their homogenization temperatures, not to speak of their ever being overheated.

The earliest data on migration of water through crystalline quartz were published by Skinner [7]. The inclusions were kept in the thermo-chamber for 3, 20, and 110 hr at 122, 128, and 121°C respectively, or

17–34°C higher than the homogenization temperatures would become filled with the liquid phase, after the experiment, at temperatures 12–15°C higher than the original homogenization temperatures. According to the author, this is the result of leakage of solution from the inclusions.

In the autoclave experiments, liquid inclusions in quartz, after the 24- and the 60-hour treatments at 70°C and 600 and 850 bars, yielded homogenization temperatures 15–16°C lower than the original ones (Table 1).

TABLE 1

Diameter of vacuole maximum millimeters	Homogenization temperature before experiment (°C)	Pressure in autoclave (bars)	Duration of experiment (hr)	Homogenization temperature after experiment (°C)	Difference between homogenization temperature (°C)
1.25	90			81	9
1.20	108			92	16
1.00	109			94	15
1.00	101			86	15
0.75	107	850	60	90	17
0.75	97			81	16
0.75	93			83	10
0.50	97			85	12
0.40	101			87	14
0.25	106			99	7
1.20	110			102	8
1.00	111			106	5
0.75	96	600	24	91	5
0.75	95			90	5
0.40	108			102	6
0.30	108			100	8

According to the author, that was the result of a penetration of water from the outside, through the quartz crystal into the inclusions.

In a paper by Richter and Ingerson [5], published one year later, the authors report the results on heating and prolonged storage of inclusions in a thermochamber 20, 25, and 30°C above their homogenization temperature. After experiments lasting for 3–6 hr, the inclusions showed the same homogenization temperatures as they did before and consequently had retained their original degree of filling. In their argument with Skinner, the authors maintain also that it is impossible, under ordinary geologic conditions, to attain an appreciable difference in the pressures inside the inclusions and outside the crystal, in a vug.

We attempted a repetition of Skinner's experiments, in view of the controversial character of his findings. We used a thermochamber of a new design, involving a contact-heating of the test material in conjunction with the MRShchPr-54 millivoltmeter, for measuring homogenization temperatures. The apparatus permits an accuracy of ± 1 or 2°C in the measurements.

When multiphase inclusions in topaz are opened in glycerine, the initial volume of their gas bubble increases tens of times. This is an indication of their considerable internal pressure, at room temperature, caused by their gaseous consituents. Two such inclusions, in one and the same field of the microscope (Fig. 1), were kept at 365–380°C for 23 days.

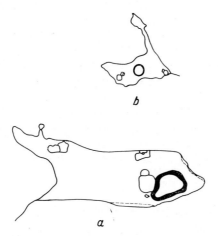

b

a

FIG. 1. Multiphase inclusions in topaz from Volynia. 150×.

The larger one of the two (*a*) showed a homogenization temperature of 382°C, for its liquid phase* in the first hours of heating. This temperature remained unchanged during the first two weeks, whereupon it rose 4 or 5°C and stayed at that same level for the remaining 9 days of the experiment. No changes in the form of the vacuole could be detected.

The second inclusion (*b*) is about three-quarters the size of the first one. It homogenized at 342°C, in the liquid phase, at the beginning of the experiment. Since the second inclusion was kept at the homogenization temperature of the first one during the experiment, it was kept superheated by 25–40°C throughout. The inclusion's internal pressure was probably several times as high as the pressure calculated from the *PT* relationship, under such conditions, as, for example, in the instance of 30 per cent NaCl: 480 atm [4]. However, the inclusion's homogenization temperature remained constant, 342 ± 1°C, throughout the 23 days of the experiment, despite its disequilibrium. The inclusion's form had remained also unchanged.

---

* I.e. solid phases still persisted? [Ed.]

We used the apparatus of the Laboratory of Mineral Fuels, the Institute of Geology of Economic Minerals, Academy of Sciences of the Ukrainian SSR, in our studies of the hermetic character of inclusions, as influenced by external pressures. The desired water pressure against the test material containing inclusions was attained by heating an autoclave nearly 100 per cent filled with water. The seal of the autoclave, operating on the principle of uncompensated area, was cooled by flowing water, assuring thereby a completely hermetic sealing of the apparatus. The pressure was measured by a Bourdon spring gauge.

It developed, as the result of our studies, that there was no change in the original degree of filling of the inclusions in any of the quartz test materials placed in the autoclave and kept there for 90 hours at 150–160°C and 830–880 kg/cm² pressure. There was no change in the homogenization temperatures before and after the experiment. This constitutes evidence of the imperviousness of quartz, under the experimental conditions (Table 2).

We believe that Skinner's erroneous data resulted from inexact measurements of the homogenization temperatures. Judging by the design of

TABLE 2

Inclusion No.	Name and type of deposit	Homogenization temperature before experiment (°C)	Temperature (°C)	Pressure kg/cm²	Duration (hr)	Homogenization of temperature after experiment (°C)
1	Bristenstock (the Alps); crystal quartz	190				190
2		191				191
3	Synthetic quartz	305				305
4		250	150–160	830–880	90	250
5	Pegmatite (Volynia); morion	245				245
6		234				234
7		231				231

the heating stage he employed, his findings were influenced very appreciably by the low external temperature affecting the upper layers of the silicate* liquid (used for heating the quartz sections) and affecting also the thermocouple contacts, on account of the large cooling surface of the glass well intended for microscopic observations.

The data here reported may be taken as proof of the imperviousness of most minerals to water. Zeolites are an exception, since their structures

---

* Silicone [Ed.].

are characterized by open passages through which molecules of foreign substances may easily move. The sealing of inclusions may be considered unreliable if they are situated on compromise growth surfaces, on twin planes, etc., i.e. in positions where the orientation of the crystal structure is disturbed and the portions making the structure do not entirely mesh. That problem, however, requires a special investigation. The experimental data we obtained also may be considered insufficient. In order to dispose of any doubts as to the imperviousness of crystal structures, it would be desirable, in addition to theoretical premises based on the orderly relationships of crystal bonds in the structure, to perform analogous experiments with a large number of minerals, under conditions closely approximating the hydrothermal and pneumatolytic environments of mineral genesis.

BIBLIOGRAPHY

1. YERMAKOV, N. P., *Issledovaniya mineraloobrazuyushchikh rastvorov*. (Research in Mineral-forming Solutions.) Izd. Khar'kov. univ. 1950.
2. KALYUZHNYI, V. A., Zhidkiye vklyucheniya v mineralakh kak geologicheskii barometr. (Liquid Inclusions in Minerals as a Geological Barometer.) *Mineralog. sb. L'vov. geolog. obshch.* No. 9, 1955.
3. LEMMLEIN, G. G. and M. O. KLIYA, Izmeneniya zhidkikh vklyuchenii pod vliyaniyem vremennogo peregreva kristalla. (Changes in Liquid Inclusions under Influence of Temporary Overheating of Crystal.) *Dokl. Akad. Nauk SSSR*, vol. 94, No. 2, 1954.
4. LEMMLEIN, G. G. and P. V. KLEVTSOV, Sootnosheniya termodinamicheskikh parametrov P–T–V dlya vody i 30%-kh vodnykh rastvorov NaCl. (Relationships of the P–T–V Thermodynamic Parameters for Water and for 30 per cent Aqueous Solutions of NaCl.) *Zap. vsesoyuz. mineralog. obshch.* pt. 85, No. 4, 1956.
5. RICHTER, D. H. and E. INGERSON, Some Consideration Regarding Liquid Inclusions as Geologic Thermometers. *Econ. Geol.* vol. 49, No. 7, 1954.
6. POULTER, T. C. and R. O. WILSON, The Permeability of Glass and Fused Quartz to Ether, Alcohol, and Water at High Pressure, *Phys. Rev.* ser. 2, vol. 40, 1932.
7. SKINNER, B. J., Some Considerations Regarding Liquid Inclusions as Geologic Thermometers, *Econ. Geol.* vol. 48, No. 7, 1953.

Investigations of Chemical Composition of Inclusions in Fluorite by the Ultra-micromethod

I. N. Maslova

WE MADE use of ultra-microchemical analysis for the first time, in place of the formerly employed spectrographic method and the method of aqueous extracts, in the investigation of the chemical composition of inclusions in minerals. The ultra-microchemical method is based on the analytical principles of micro-analysis, but differs from the latter in its techniques that permit determinations of extremely small quantities of substance (1 γ)* in extremely small aliquots of the solution (1 λ).*

The main instrument employed in the method is a biological microscope with micromanipulators (see Figure) by means of which most of the pieces of the apparatus can be transposed. The basic operations are carried out on the microscope stage. Liquid transfer is done by means of the so-called piston attachment which consists of a piston and a micropipette. The reaction vessels are cone-shaped capillaries.

The ultra-micromethod [1, 2] is suited for direct determinations of chemical composition of the liquid phase itself. Our first experiments were conducted with liquid inclusions in fluorite from the chamber [vuggy?] pegmatites of the Kermet–Tas deposit.†

Thinnest tubular inclusions, oriented at right angles to crystal faces, are preponderant in the peripheral zones of the fluorite crystal. Some larger inclusions (hundredths to tenths of one millimeter) and—rarely—macro-inclusions several millimeters large are found closer to the crystal's center, in the colorless fluorite.

It was the larger inclusions, closer to the crystal's center and not the tubular inclusions in the peripheral zone that were examined in the present study. The liquid phase of the test inclusions occupies 90–96 per cent of the volume and the gas phase, conversely, 10–4 per cent. Such liquid inclusions were opened, on the microscope stage, by squeezing with two lenses (flat–convex and flat–concave) that could be pressed together or

---

* 1 microgram and 1 microliter respectively [V.P.S.].

† The fluorites with liquid inclusions of microscopic size were placed at our disposal by N. P. Yermakov.

drawn apart (see Figure). Slavyanskii's method of opening gas bubbles in glass [5] was the basis of our procedure. The procedure required preparation of thin sections of the test material about 1 mm thick with an area of 2–4 mm². The prepared section moves freely in the microscope field of vision and an inclusion surrounded by the smallest possible quantity of the host mineral is easily opened. In case the inclusion's diameter is

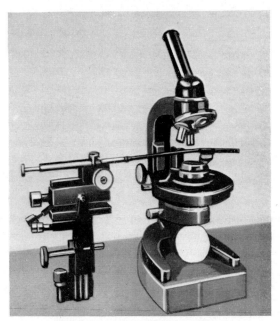

Microscope with micromanipulators.

tenths of one millimeter, the fissure caused by squeezing runs generally right through the inclusion which makes it easy to extract the solution. Sections with inclusions hundredths of one millimeter in diameter are split into several small pieces, on squeezing, and the extraction of their liquid is rendered more difficult accordingly. The solution is extracted by washing the opened vacuole with twice-distilled water (with the aid of the piston attachment). Several inclusions need be opened in order to obtain the test solution of the desired concentration and volume (0.001–0.01 mm³). The desired concentration is determined empirically; it depends on quantities of the constituents present in the solution (sixteen to thirty-two sections would have to be opened).

The test solutions we obtained were examined by the ultra-micro-chemical techniques based on diagnostic reactions. Qualitatively, large quantities of Na^+, K^+, Cl^- were indicated in the solutions, together with smaller quantities of Ca^{++} and F^-.

In addition to the chemical composition of the solutions in microscopic inclusions, the solutes were determined qualitatively in inclusions 5 mm long and 2 mm wide. The liquid and the gas phases occupy 69 per cent and 31 per cent respectively of their volume. 0.03 mm³ of the solution was extracted for analysis from a macro-inclusion which was opened by a drill 1 mm in diameter. Qualitative analysis of the extracted solution showed presence of Na^+, K^+, Ca^{++}, Cl^-, F^- and absence of Mg^{++}, Al^{+++}, Fe^{+++}, SO_4^{--}, CO_3^{--}, PO_4^{---}; the solution had a pH of 4. The concentrations of Na^+, K^+, Cl^- were proved to be large alongside small concentrations of Ca^{++} and traces of F^-. Semiquantitative relations between the determined ions were rated as follows:

$$Cl^{1-} > F^{1-}$$
$$Na^{1+} > K^{1-}$$
$$K^{1+} > Ca^{2+} \,.$$

The hypothetical chemical combinations are: NaF, NaCl, KCl, $CaCl_2$. It is known [3] that strong acids (HF, HCl, H_2S, CO_2) may be present in the gas phase. The acid reaction of our test solution may be due to the presence of such acids. The effect of CO_2 of the concentration of hydrogen ions in gas–liquid inclusions was proved experimentally by Kalyuzhnyi [4].

The chemical composition of liquid inclusions in fluorite from the same source was determined at the All-Union Institute of Geology (A. I. Zakharchenko's oral communication) by the method of aqueous extracts. He detected Na^+, K^+, Cl^-, F^-. The qualitative ionic relations were found to be the following: there is nearly one and one half times as much Cl^- as F^-; $Ca^{++} > (Na^+ + K^+)$. The hypothetical composition as salts (mg per 100 g sample*) is: 0.1 KCl; 4.2 NaCl; 5.2 CaF_2; 0.4 $MgCl_2$; 1.4 $CaCl_2$.

Comparisons of our results with Zakharchenko's data showed nearly complete agreement as to the chemical composition of the solutions, but a discrepancy as to the quantitative proportions of the detected ions.

BIBLIOGRAPHY

1. ALIMARIN, I. P. and M. N. PETRIKOVA, Ul'tramikroanaliz. (Ultra-microanalysis.) *Priroda*, No. 1, 1955.
2. BENEDETTI-PIKHLER, A., *Tekhnika neorganicheskogo analiza*. (Techniques of Inorganic Microanalysis.) Izd. Inostr. Lit. 1951.
3. YERMAKOV, N. P., *Issledovaniya mineraloobrazuyushchikh rastvorov*. (Research in Mineral-forming Solutions.), Izd. Khar'kov. univ. 1950.
4. KALYUZHNYI, V. A., K rezul'tatam opredeleniya pH zhidkikh vklyucheniy. (In Reference to the Results of Determinations of the pH of Liquid Inclusions.) *Geokhim.* No. 1, 1957.
5. SLAVYANSKI, V. T., Metod analiza gaza v puzyr'kakh diametrom 'men'she 0.2 mm. (Method of Analysis of Gas in Bubbles Smaller than 0.2 mm in Diameter.) *Steklo i keramika*, No. 11, 1953.

---

* Presumably of solid—Ed.

Brief Communications

Xenogenic and Artificial Liquid Inclusions in Synthetic Quartz

G. M. SAFRONOV

A PECULIAR group of xenogenic inclusions of bituminous substances has been encountered in synthetic quartz. Such inclusions were concentrated in elongated cavities over the seed and chiefly on one side of the crystal. Three phases could be seen in these inclusions at room temperature: gas (20–29 per cent, and more); mother liquor (0–5–15 per cent); a pale-brown bituminous substance (up to 60–80 per cent) resembling thick butter in its consistency.

The inclusion's shape was pear-like or cone-like (Fig. 1).

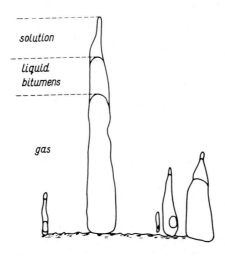

FIG. 1. Shapes of xenogenic inclusions in synthetic quartz.

The cone bases sit on top of the seed. The elongation of the inclusions coincides with the direction of the L_3 axis, in crystals grown on seeds cut parallel to the base.

The length of inclusions may be up to 1–2 mm. The cavity wedges out gradually in the constricted parts of inclusions where the mother liquor is situated. One may see occasionally, in the expanse of cavities of such large three-phase inclusions, a chainwork of fine capillaries with two-phase inclusions in which the liquid phase is represented by the quartz-forming solution or by the bituminous substance.

Some of the inclusions contain very small particles of solid phase floating in the bituminous substance that tend to accumulate in the upper section of the cavity. In such cases, the gas phase is to be found invariably in the viscous bituminous substance where it is segregated in two or three gas bubbles.

Some of the entirely xenogenic inclusions are devoid of the mother liquor, but are very high in the gas phase, occupying more than 80 per cent of the inclusion's volume; the balance of 20 per cent consists of liquid petroleum products.

A peculiar emulsion is produced, on rising temperatures, by bitumens that were added intentionally to the quartz-forming solution. These bitumens adhere to the seed's surface, as a multitude of small droplets, in the beginning of the cycle.

The small droplets are preserved as such or together with the quartz-forming solution by the relatively rapidly growing crystal. Vacuole dimensions and shapes of the xenogenic inclusions indicate that the original diameter of the adhering bituminous droplet was growing progressively smaller in the course of its sealing off. The original diameter is shortened progressively by the overgrowing layers, while the crystal's face boundary advances, and a cone-shaped inclusion is the result. By considering the dependence of surface tension on temperature, one might expect that the droplets of liquid petroleum substances would spread on the seed surface as a thin film. A film of that sort would block the crystal's surface and would seriously impede its growth. In reality, however, the droplets of petroleum remain dispersed on the (0001) plane of the growing crystal and are found as groups only in certain definite sections of the plane.

Development of the isolated inclusion cavities containing petroleum substances depends apparently on thermodynamic conditions in the autoclave, on concentration of the solution, and on the rate of advance of the crystal's surface during its growth.

Constrictions and thinned sections of the vacuoles are produced when the crystal's growth is at its fastest, while the bulging sections correspond to retardation of growth. Zones of skeletal growth often contain inclusions of petroleum substances together with two-phase inclusions of the crystal-growing solution.

Orientation of the vacuoles is controlled initially by morphology of the micro-relief of the seed and of the growing crystal's faces. The character of their surface pre-determines the sites of formation of the capillaries while the front of the growing crystal face is moving outwards. By virtue of their positions on the (0001) plane, xenogenic inclusions constitute boundaries between the growth stages.

Most of the sporadically occurring inclusions originate commonly in places where the homogeneity of the crystal surface has been disturbed. Among the proofs of that fact is the presence of fairly large (up to 2 mm, on the long axis) flattened xenogenic inclusions between sub-individuals of the inherited Dauphiné twin in the overgrown layer of quartz.

Complex xenogenic inclusions are often succeeded by two-phase inclusions of mother liquor with normal gas–liquid phase ratios, at increasing distances from the seed surface, in the rapidly growing layers of quartz. Their gas–liquid ratios correspond to the degree of filling of the autoclave (Fig. 2).

FIG. 2. Relationship between complex xenogenic and ordinary two-phase inclusions. Surface of the seed is showing in the bottom of the photograph.

Crystals and isolated blocks of crystalline quartz with ultrasonically drilled openings were placed in the autoclave alongside the ordinary seeds. Depending on the rate of growth of the quartz crystal faces, there was also an overgrowth of the cylindrical cavity, concurrently, and a gradual narrowing of the cavity because of the deposition of SiO_2 on its walls. The overgrowth was not uniform. The thickness of the layer of synthetic quartz was increasing on the walls of the cavity in proximity to the outer boundary of the crystal, bathed by the solution. There was no such deposition of SiO_2 in the deep part of the cavity where even the scratch marks and the furrows left by the drill were preserved. This is an indication of a relatively weak diffusion of the concentrated solution into cavities of small dimensions.

In order to produce large-volume artificial inclusions of this kind in quartz crystals and in seeds we drilled holes at right angles to the (0001), (01$\bar{1}$1), (10$\bar{1}$1), and (1120) planes. In the latter case, it was necessary to polish the crystal edge between the two adjoining faces of the hexagonal prism. Later on, such sections of the crystal had undergone regeneration.

The end of the hole facing in the "plus" direction of the crystal's X-axis would be overgrown first. After that the opposite hole would be overgrown also.

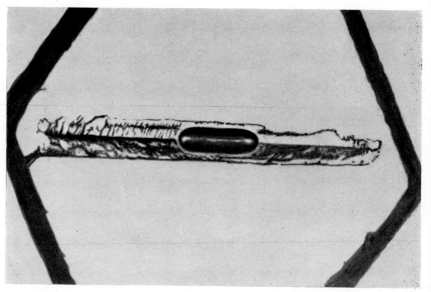

FIG. 3. Vacuoles of a synthetic inclusion with ribbed sculpture of the walls.

The vacuole cross-section would become a rhomb (Fig. 3) during the period of time required for sealing of the inclusion. The micro-relief of the vacuole's walls, with its many ledges and pits, merits our attention. The surface boundaries of individual ledges run parallel to the faces of the hexagonal prism.

The gas–liquid phase ratio corresponded to the degree of filling of the autoclave.

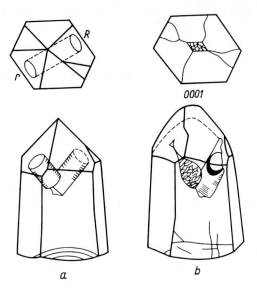

Fig. 4. Overgrowth over channels drilled in quartz crystals: *a*—before the experiment; *b*—after the end of the experiment.

The drilled channels perpendicular to the (0111) and the (1011) faces (Fig. 4) were being overgrown while a gradual narrowing of the cylindrical cavity was taking place. The cavity was assuming the form of a simplified trihedron; the opening on the plane of the small rhombohedron was being overgrown most rapidly. It should be pointed out that, as a result of the rapid growth of the (01$\bar{1}$1) and the (10$\bar{1}$1) faces, injured by the drill, a surface of the form (0001) appeared on the crystal (Fig. 4*b*). That surface appeared as the result of a change in the shape of both artificial and natural crystals, a function of the ratio of the linear velocities of growth of the faces.

The channels drilled at right angles to the (0001) plane acquire a trigonal cross-section regeneration, but are not fully overgrown until the (0001) plane is displaced by the rhombohedra.

In case of a defective seed, the channel parallel to the L_3 axis may be overgrown even earlier.

Inclusions represented in Fig. 4 contained, in addition to the gas and the solution, about 10 per cent of petroleum-like substances and 25 per cent of solid greenish-gray particles (possibly asbestos) brought into the cavities by the solution. Curiously, the bulk of the solid phase in the cavity was in the channel under the (01$\bar{1}$1) face, i.e. in the part of the inclusion that was first covered over.

As the result of our first experiments, we succeeded in producing tour large inclusions, up to 1 cm³ in size, none of which was entirely sealed. The drilled channel's hole on the face of the crystal became coated with a white silicate. Deposition of colloidal silica was not observed in any of the vacuoles of the artificial inclusions after withdrawal and cooling of the crystals.

We made no attempt at a homogenization of these inclusions by heat, because of the thinness of their quartz overgrowth and because the prepared test sections were fragile.

It should be pointed out that production of large-volume inclusions in synthetic quartz crystals presents a definite interest not only in mineralogical thermometry, but also in the research on composition of the media and in ascertaining the pH in different periods of the synthetic process and in different sections of the crystallizer.

Further experiments along these lines show us the extent of similarities and differences in composition of the crystal-forming solution and of its specimens captured and locked in artificial inclusions.

Some Data on Thermometry of Optical Fluorite from the Magadan Territory

V. P. PODGORNOVA

THE test materials here examined were fragments of crystals 4–6 cm in diameter. Most of the crystals are colorless; pale-blue, greenish, and occasionally lilac hues are rare.

The crystals are of cubic habit. The surface of their outer faces is dull, even, or of a blocky structure. Every one of the surfaces exposed by fracture has a curved structure.

The fluorite here described contains chiefly liquid inclusions. Dust-like inclusions and inclusions of platy white crystals (not larger than 1 mm) are relatively rare. Inclusions of sulfides and tourmaline may be found occasionally.

All we know about the geologic structure of the deposit from which the specimens were sent to us is that its fluorite is associated with the thick parts of the quartz–fluorite veins and with vug-like accumulations in brecciated zones of stanniferous skarns. The latter contain also pyroxene, garnet, quartz, calcite, sulfides of iron, zinc, and copper, cassiterite, and other minerals.

In all, we examined 145 inclusions and made 540 experiments with heating these inclusions in the thermochamber.

The outlines of primary liquid inclusions are generally irregular, showing occasionally very fine and even hair-like branching; in the latter case, they look like spiders. Such inclusions are occasionally grouped in different zones or else are associated with the solid inclusions. More often, their distribution in the crystals is far from uniform; groups in one place and individuals in others.

We considered the isolated inclusions and the groups of inclusions separately. The groups were associated with healed fissures.

In one of the crystal fragments, we were able to recognize five growth zones, with inclusions as the criteria. One side of the fragment had preserved a part of the roof-tile structure of the surface of the crystal. The width of the identified growth zones ranged from 0.5 to 1.5–2 cm. As shown in Table 1, the homogenization temperatures of the two-phase inclusions fluctuated within a 10°C range.

[701]

The homogenization temperatures of primary two-phase inclusions in other fragments of fluorite varied from 126 to 251°C.

We proved that homogenization temperatures of these inclusions increase somewhat, in repeated heating, after every repeated test, particularly in the range above 130–140°C, whereupon further repetitions cease to affect the homogenization temperature. There was a solution of inclusion walls during the heating; the system comes to complete equilibrium with the confining solid phase which corresponds to the moment when the inclusion was finally sealed.

The increase in the homogenization temperature was caused by a slight and visually unnoticeable increase in the volume of the vacoule, back to its original size. The visible gas–liquid phase ratio remained unchanged, before and after heating experiments, so that the phenomenon could not be ascribed to decrepitation of the crystal.

TABLE 1

Growth zones center to periphery	Inclusion Nos. and temperatures of disappearance of their gas bubble (°C)	Remarks
First	I. 129	
Second	I. 134; II. 138, III. 129; IV. 122	
Third	I. 138; II. 132; III. 139	
Fourth	I. 132; II. 134; III. 129; IV. 136; V. 136; VI. 134	Inclusions II and III are associated with the scaly mineral
Fifth	I. 129; II. 134	

In one of the specimens we found a group of liquid inclusions with a solid phase consisting of very small and thin stars. The gas bubble in these inclusions began to increase at 70°C; while the size of the stellar solid inclusions not merely failed to grow smaller, but, on the contrary, showed an increase in size of some of their rays. The phenomenon is related either to the absence of hermetic sealing, on account of the star-shaped mineral, or else to a reaction between that mineral's substance with the solution involving an uptake of water and a formation of a hydrate.

In the fluorite we examined, one finds occasionally some inclusions with a solid phase in the shape of colorless or pale-brownish small crystals that dissolve at 60°C, in one case, and at 64°C, in the second one. Further increase in the temperature results in the explosion of these inclusions, at 124 and 122°C, while the gas bubble is far from gone. The second inclusion was heated to 60°C, and not to a complete disappearance of the solid phase, whereupon it was cooled again to 22°C. The captive mineral then began again to increase, while assuming a different shape and a deeper brown color.

Some relatively scarce liquid inclusions originated in an association with scaly or platy solid inclusions. Their gas bubble vanishes at 160–170°C. Inclusions associated with the youngest fissures homogenized within the following ranges of temperature: 126–132, 138–143, and 144–167°C. These inclusions, associated with the youngest fissures, have smooth contours, in the vast majority of cases, and are occasionally round or egg-shaped. They are invariably flattened, to some extent, in the direction perpendicular to the plane of the fissure.

The nearly identical homogenization temperatures of the primary two-phase inclusions, from the center to the periphery of the crystal, may be ascribed to a relatively constant temperature of crystal growth (or, at least, of the growth of the majority of the crystals).

The two-phase inclusions in healed fissures, the ones that have the most symmetrical shapes, show the same homogenization temperatures as most of the primary inclusions in the crystal's growth zones.

The monothermal (or nearly so) environment of fluorite crystal growth discovered in the deposit is a favorable indication in assessing the deposit as a potential source of crystal raw materials, according to Yermakov.

A Typical Case of Expressions of Primary
and Secondary Inclusions in Quartz

V. F. LESNYAK

WE HAD the opportunity to observe the most characteristic expressions of primary and secondary inclusions in zoned crystals of quartz of magmatic origin that had suffered the subsequent action of hydrothermal solutions.

Crystals of igneous quartz in which we studied the inclusions are phenocrysts in acidic effusive rocks of the Caucasus (vicinity of Tbilisi). They are bi-pyramidal crystals with only a very weak development of prismatic faces (Fig. 1). Their size is 2–3 mm to 2.5 cm in length and up

FIG. 1. Bi-pyramidal crystal of quartz from effusives of Transcaucasia. 3×.

to 2.3 cm in the transverse section. The large yellowish-gray crystals are generally transparent, in very thin sections; the small ones have a dull colorless surface and are made transparent by polishing. A longitudinal section (along the main axis) of one of the transparent quartz crystals shows a clear zonation; the four growth zones are particularly clear; each one of them consists, in turn, of narrower zones that the delineated only by the positions of their abundant inclusions of mineral-forming medium.

In the zoned cut through the crystal represented in Fig. 2, as well as in the other similar sections, three families of inclusions are clearly distinguished: (a) inclusions of a solidified fused substance; (b) multiphase inclusions of highly concentrated liquid solutions; (c) two-phase liquid inclusions of dilute liquid solutions.

(1) The inclusions of a solidified fused substance (glass) serve to establish the boundaries of the crystal's growth. They are undoubtedly primary and they represent the physico-chemical conditions in which the

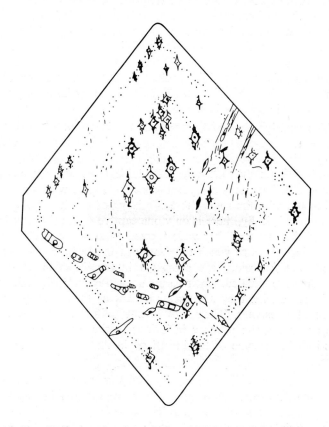

FIG. 2. Longitudinal section through pyramidal crystal of quartz with primary inclusions in growth zones.

mineral was formed and under which it grew. A special morphologic feature of these inclusions is the negative form of their host crystal they assumed, so that all of them, from the largest to the smallest, display an orderly orientation, namely the long and the short axes of the host crystal (Fig. 2). This phenomenon is rarely observed and we do not know of any of the descriptions in the literature. In case this orderly relationship is a constant one (this needs verification by other test materials), the included

negative crystals may serve as reliable diagnostic indications in determinations of the crystallographic axes in mineral fragments.

Presence of fine fissures and of extremely small gas bubbles surrounding the inclusions like haloes are typical features of the solidified inclusions in the quartz here described.

The inclusions described by us here were produced by the capture of
droplets of the melted substance (the mineral-forming medium) by the
growing crystal faces. Moreover, the clear-cut zonation of the crystals is
indicative of certain variations in the conditions of their growth from the
melted substance. There was no formation of primary–secondary or of
secondary inclusions of solidified glass, it appears, because of a high
viscosity of the melt and of obstructions to its entry into the phenocrysts
along microscopic fissures in the latter.

(2) The multiphase liquid inclusions are localized in healed fissures
that often traverse the crystal's growth zones; such inclusions are definitely
secondary (Fig. 2). They differ strikingly from the previously described
solidified inclusions by their morphologic features and by composition.
They are typical inclusions of hydrothermal solutions, with the contraction
gas bubble and with the solid phase consisting of captive crystals of cubic
form. Characteristically, there is only one captive crystal in each inclusion,
evidence of the fact that they were formed from one and the same solution, in all inclusions of which the family of the inclusions in question is
composed. The inclusions are elongated in the direction of the fissure
in which they are situated. Their forms are tetragonal, trigonal, and trap-
ezoidal in places, i.e. they are not as equant as the (primary) inclusions
of the fused substance. Their size is not uniform, but not as widely
variable as among the primary inclusions in the crystal's growth zones.
The gas bubble in some of the inclusions in that group is in vibrational
movement.

(3) The two-phase liquid inclusions of low-temperature solutions are
still later than the multiphase ones. They are situated in healed fissures
intersecting the fissures with the multiphase inclusions; they have elongated
forms with pointed edges (Fig. 2). Their gas phase is appreciably smaller,
by volume, than the gas phase of the multiphase inclusions.

In such manner, in the section through the crystal of igneous quartz,
we observe a clear-cut and definite expression of the primary and the
secondary natures of the inclusions, the reflections of the different physico-
chemical environments in which they were formed. The primary inclusions
were formed in the magmatic stage of the crystal growth; the secondary
ones (multiphase and two-phase) were formed in the later hydrothermal
stage, after the formation of the host rocks of the crystals.

In such manner, in the example here discussed, we encounter the
genetic representatives of inclusions in their most typical expressions.

The solutions by which the liquid inclusions were produced had nothing to do with the growth of the quartz crystals containing these inclusions, so that the inclusions are secondary indeed. It becomes a different matter entirely, when it comes to healing of fissures in crystal quartz and in other minerals growing in a free space. In such circumstances, with very rare exceptions, the fissures are healed by solutions that bathe the crystals and simultaneously deposit the outer zones of the same crystals, up to and including the outermost thinnest layer. Some investigators unfortunately refer to such inclusions as secondary, up to the present time, despite the fact that they are definitely identified as primary–secondary or pseudo-secondary in the Soviet literature.

The basic difference between such inclusions and the secondary inclusions just described is so important for the genetic use of relics of mineral-forming media in crystals that any further confusion of the concepts of secondary and pseudo-secondary inclusions appears to be entirely impermissible.

Index to Plates

Index

OTHER TITLES IN THE SERIES OF
MONOGRAPHS IN EARTH SCIENCES